Recent Studies in Avian Biology

Recent Studies in

AVIAN BIOLOGY

edited by ALBERT WOLFSON

contributors

DAVID E. DAVIS

L. V. DOMM

JOHN T. EMLEN, JR.

DONALD S. FARNER

HARVEY I. FISHER

HERBERT FRIEDMANN

DONALD R. GRIFFIN

CARLTON M. HERMAN

JOSEPH J. HICKEY

GEORGE H. LOWERY, JR.

ALDEN H. MILLER

ROBERT J. NEWMAN

ALEXANDER WETMORE

Published under the sponsorship of the American Ornithologists' Union

UNIVERSITY OF ILLINOIS PRESS, URBANA, 1955

Library of Congress Catalog Card No. 54–12306

PREFACE

In the fall of 1947, Hoyes Lloyd, then President of the American Ornithologists' Union, appointed the following Committee on Research: Donald S. Farner, Herbert Friedmann, S. Charles Kendeigh, Ernst Mayr, Alden H. Miller, Mrs. Margaret M. Nice, Josselyn Van Tyne, and Albert Wolfson (Chairman). The most ambitious and significant part of the program which the Committee adopted in the spring of 1948 was the preparation of a book on recent research in ornithology. As originally conceived, the book was to consist of articles in those fields of ornithology in which substantial contributions had been made within recent years, with each article written by an active investigator.

There were two objectives in mind when the plan for the book was proposed. The first was to stimulate further research in ornithology. It was hoped to accomplish this by review and evaluation of recent data and concepts, by demonstration of our ignorance of important facts, and by the definition of basic problems. The second objective was to provide biologists in other fields with a convenient and authoritative source of the contributions of ornithological research to broader biological fields, such as systematics, evolution, anatomy, behavior, etc.

The Committee selected the fields to be represented and in the fall of 1949 invited the participation of the individuals who are the present authors. However, not all of the fields originally selected by the Committee are included in the present volume. Topics were assigned, but each author was free to define the scope of his article, bearing in mind the objectives of the book as a whole. Each article is an independent unit in itself, but the subjects are clearly interrelated. Some articles are complementary and discuss aspects of one field. For example, chapters 1 and 2 are concerned with systematics and evolution; chapters 6, 7, and 8 deal with separate problems of bird migration—orientation, annual stimulus, and nocturnal migration.

The dual aims of the book imposed a difficult task on the authors. In addition, each author had his own particular problems because of differences in the nature of the topics and the status and methods of the fields being reviewed.

An attempt was made to achieve uniformity in general organization and in matters of usage and of style. However, with a large group of collaborators and a wide range of subjects, it soon became evident that some variation was inevitable. Preparation of the articles began in 1950. The first manuscripts were completed early in 1952, the last ones early in 1955.

A book of this kind is by its very nature a cooperative project, and many persons have helped to make its publication possible. It is a great pleasure for me to acknowledge their contributions and assistance and to state my indebtedness to them. Josselyn Van Tyne and Robert W. Storer read many of the manuscripts and the following persons read the manuscripts of the chapters indicated: chapter 1—Herbert Friedmann; chapter 2—Dean Amadon, William J. Beecher, Ernst Mayr, Alden H. Miller, Frank A. Pitelka; chapter 3—Hildegarde Howard, Alden H. Miller; chapter 4—William J. Beecher, Andrew J. Berger; chapter 6—William J. Beecher; chapter 8— Josselyn Van Tyne; chapter 9— S. Charles Kendeigh, Mrs. Margaret M. Nice; chapter 10— Howard L. Hamilton; chapter 11—Paul L. Errington, Frank A. Pitelka; chapter 12—Charles H. Blake, Edward S. Deevey, Jr., G. E. Hutchinson; chapter 13—A. L. Nelson, E. E. Wehr, and other members of the staff of the Patuxent Research Refuge. Persons who read the manuscripts for chapters 5 and 7 are acknowledged in those chapters. Additional acknowledgments are given in the text. The many helpful suggestions and criticisms which were received have resulted in the improvement of the book.

Josselyn Van Tyne read galley proofs and page proofs; Alden H. Miller read galley proofs; Robert W. Storer read galley proofs of the first five chapters. Their careful reading of the proofs was extremely valuable in innumerable ways. I am particularly indebted to them for their editorial skill and for giving their time so generously.

Donald D. Jackson, editor of the University of Illinois Press, demonstrated unusual patience in attending to numerous details of design and manufacture. His efforts are much appreciated. Harvey Fisher graciously consented to index the volume.

Finally, I wish to express my gratitude and indebtedness to the members of the Committee on Research for their cooperation and help in getting the program underway, to the authors for their patience and the immense amount of work and thought which they put into their articles, and to Josselyn Van Tyne for continual encouragement and for his tireless efforts in helping with the book at all stages.

ALBERT WOLFSON

May 15, 1955
Evanston, Illinois

LIST OF CONTRIBUTORS

DAVID E. DAVIS
Associate Professor, Division of Vertebrate Ecology, School of Hygiene and Public Health, Johns Hopkins University, Baltimore 5, Maryland

L. V. DOMM
Professor of Anatomy, Stritch School of Medicine, Loyola University, Chicago, Illinois

JOHN T. EMLEN, JR.
Professor of Zoology and Chairman of the Department of Zoology, University of Wisconsin, Madison 6, Wisconsin

DONALD S. FARNER
Professor of Zoophysiology, State College of Washington, Pullman, Washington

HARVEY I. FISHER
Professor of Zoology and Chairman of the Department of Zoology, Southern Illinois University, Carbondale, Illinois

HERBERT FRIEDMANN
Curator, Division of Birds, United States National Museum, Smithsonian Institution, Washington 25, D. C.

DONALD R. GRIFFIN
Professor of Zoology, Biology Laboratories, Harvard University, Cambridge 38, Massachusetts

CARLTON M. HERMAN
Wildlife Pathologist, Patuxent Research Refuge, United States Fish and Wildlife Service, Laurel, Maryland

JOSEPH J. HICKEY
Associate Professor, Department of Forestry and Wildlife Management, University of Wisconsin, Madison 6, Wisconsin

GEORGE H. LOWERY, JR.
Professor of Zoology and Director of the Museum of Zoology, Louisiana State University, Baton Rouge, Louisiana

ALDEN H. MILLER
Professor of Zoology and Director of the Museum of Vertebrate Zoology, University of California, Berkeley 4, California

ROBERT J. NEWMAN
Assistant Curator, Museum of Zoology, Louisiana State University, Baton Rouge, Louisiana

ALEXANDER WETMORE
Research Associate, Smithsonian Institution, Washington 25, D. C.

CONTENTS

chapter 1

CONCEPTS AND PROBLEMS OF AVIAN SYSTEMATICS IN RELATION TO EVOLUTIONARY PROCESSES . . . Alden H. Miller

The original purpose of the study of systematics was to develop an orderly assemblage of facts about the kinds of animals and plants and where they occur on the earth so that the array of organic life could be adequately comprehended. Devices for organizing the facts in order to reveal certain natural relations were early instituted and were largely crystallized in the Linnaean system of binary nomenclature. This basic objective of systematics still holds today and is just as valid and essential an undertaking as it was in Linnaeus' time. But in avian systematics the gathering of the simpler data on the discrete kinds of birds proceeded rapidly and advanced to a stage by the end of the last century wherein essentially all the valid species had been discovered in Eurasia and North America and the prospects for finding more were very limited even in the less well known areas of the tropics and the southern continents.

The Darwinian era of evolutionary interest set a new focus for interpretation in avian systematics. Efforts to arrange species and groups in a classification that would reflect their evolutionary history were soon made. The revived efforts in this direction of the present day which utilize our improved store of data have been reviewed in the chapter on classification by Herbert Friedmann. But even more directly related to Darwin's own thinking was the concern avian systematists began to show for the method of origin of species as reflected by the facts gathered in their taxonomic work. The stirring of interpretative effort is illustrated by Coues' statement of 1872 (p. 142) made thirteen years after the appearance of *The Origin of Species* where, in reference to the several members of the genus *Junco,* he remarked: "All these forms of the genus, in fact, seem to be nascent species, still unstable in character; but the modification of the *Junco* stock has passed the merely varietal stage." To be sure, even in pre-Darwinian time some writers were commenting on the derivation of species within groups from pre-existing forms, although without connotations which modern students would derive from such statements.

THE BIOLOGIC SPECIES CONCEPT

Passing over many of the halting and diversionary steps in the history of interpretative systematics (see Stresemann's able review, 1951) and of the dis-

Manuscript received January 1, 1953.

cussion of the nature of the species unit, we note that it was possible in ornithology to arrive quite early at a biologic species concept. This began to take form about the turn of the century. The concept is one which emphasizes in species the attainment of a stage where free transfer of genetic material can no longer take place between related forms as a consequence of one or several isolating mechanisms, working singly or in combination, and not because of geographic separation alone. This contrasts with the morphologic species concept which rests on the degree and completeness of structural differentiation.

To illustrate the early attainment of the essentials of the biologic concept in ornithology, attention is directed to Grinnell's analysis of the Chestnut-backed Chickadees, *Parus rufescens,* in 1904. Although his treatment of them was advanced for the period, it is not suggested that he was alone in his species concept at that time. In this paper Grinnell conceived of the species *rufescens* derived from an ancestral and very similar species *hudsonicus.* Ecologic and adaptational differences along with slight but constant morphological contrast argued for this specific separation. The later-proved sympatry of these two species in British Columbia has substantiated the biologic distinction sensed by Grinnell. At the same time he joined as races of *rufescens* other forms of considerable morphologic contrast that exist in isolated areas on the California coast because of their evident biologic similarity and presumed incomplete reproductive isolation. Moreover, although Grinnell made this study at a time when Mendelian genetics was in its infancy, his discussion of interbreeding and the possible transfer of characteristics by dispersal and crossing was remarkably consonant with the later explicit knowledge that has developed about these topics. Also, as implied, his interpretation was phylogenetic and distinctly Darwinian in slant.

The way was therefore open through the decades of the present century for the application of a biologic species concept in birds. This was especially true because of the rich and well-worked taxonomic data already available, because the ranges of birds could be traced readily by observation and collecting, and because nesting and mating behavior and reactions between species could be watched in great detail. That a biologic species concept was in process of taking hold was understood only by certain ornithologists; others that were using it hardly were aware of a shift in emphasis of a formal type from a strictly morphological approach, for inevitably we must continue to use morphological evidence along with, if not of necessity in lieu of, the desirable data of a general biological nature. Crystallizing the distinction and labeling the kinds of species concepts has largely come about through the general reviews of Dobzhansky (1937) and Mayr (1942), which have made the issues plain.

Ideally the biological species status is demonstrated by the sympatric test, that is, by the occurrence together of close relatives in nature without interbreeding. But at least three types of situations arise in which biologic distinction is difficult to determine or define when sympatry is absent or is contradictory.

The first and perhaps most perplexing of these situations is that in which a series of forms shows insular distribution either on true islands or on ecologic islands of continental areas. Here a natural test of physiologic or behavioristic isolating mechanisms cannot be observed. The interpretive taxonomist is forced to guess whether or not two entities would interbreed if the geographic-ecologic barrier were removed. It is not satisfactory to decide this issue solely on the basis of interbreeding responses in captivity where the very important behavioral or ethological barriers may either be artificially lowered or accentuated. Acute comparative observations of behavioral detail and of the ecology of the separate populations can provide clues suggestive of a biologic barrier, but such evidence cannot be fully counted on. In practice, the person dealing with such an array seldom has well-documented observational evidence on similarities or differences and resorts to the degree and completeness of morphologic distinctions in order to reach a decision, estimating whether or not the distinction is as great as that known in sympatric species pairs in similar kinds of birds. Since morphologic distinctions by no means correlate closely with the biologic criteria, the taxonomist in effect partly or entirely returns to a morphologic species concept. Or perhaps better, he holds an ideal biologic concept, follows it if he can, but in large measure for practical reasons falls back on the morphologic evidence. This must prove particularly galling for some who espouse with extreme vigor the biologic criteria and yet have to resort to the morphologic concept they seem almost to despise. Some wise words have been written in this regard by Stresemann (1936:157): "Whoever uses trinomials in a modern way [this refers essentially to use of a biologic and geographic species concept], will have to be gifted not only with knowledge, but also with tact and last but not least with *moderation.* It is sometimes more misleading than helpful to rank very widely different forms as subspecies, only on account of obvious affinity to some geographic representative. No fast line can be drawn here. . . . Whoever wants to hold to firm rules, should give up taxonomic work. Nature is too disorderly for such a man."

Comparative observations of the biology of allopatric forms have been undertaken recently in a critical effort to weigh species status. The differences in ecology in the morphologically very similar species of dowitchers (*Limnodromus*)—one showing preference and adaptation for fresh-water marshes and shores, the other showing preference for salt-water areas—brought out by Pitelka (1950) are important and constitute the kind of attack needed in coping with the biologic concept in allopatric forms. This is true whether or not a person concludes that the differences shown in this instance are great enough to satisfy his mind that a biologic species distinction exists. Similarly, but with opposite conclusions on species status resulting, Pitelka (1951) has closely compared the insular Scrub Jay, *Aphelocoma coerulescens,* of Santa Cruz Island, California, with mainland relatives in respect to behavior and ecology, and has not found sufficient differences to suggest that it would not interbreed with those relatives should they become sympatric. The fundamental distinctions in locomotion, song, call notes, social behavior, and utilization of cover of *Junco phaeonotus* and *Junco caniceps* led me some time ago (1941) to maintain these closely adjacent allopatric, noninterbreeding forms as distinct species although the coloration of their plumage, but not that of their soft parts, was only moderately differentiated.

The second type of situation where sympatric proof of species status is lacking is that where two forms are in contact and do engage in limited interbreeding in a zone of junction. *A priori* we may expect to find situations in these junctions ranging from sporadic crossings once in a hundred or several thousand matings, as indeed may take place even in sympatric species (sympatric hybrids) such as *Anas acuta* and *Anas platyrhynchos,* to percentages of interbreeding running up to 100 per cent. What amount of gene flow between the two entities shall we seize upon as most significant in negating species status? Are we not forced to admit that any one amount is arbitrary and to recognize that the significant aspect of this situation is the gradation of stages as a demonstration of evolutionary state and process?

The amount of interbreeding in contact zones has been considered as an index of the biologic divergence attained (see Sibley, 1950). This matter has lately received considerable attention, which it rightly deserves. Again, the opportunity to observe mated pairs and to collect them as mates is an attack on the problem fortunately open to the ornithologist. Mating preference, pairing procedure, viability of young from cross matings, and success of F_1 individuals in their own reproduction are subjects that can be pursued. The interbreeding of "near species" of Yellow-bellied Sapsuckers, *Sphyrapicus varius,* has been investigated in this way in part by Howell (1952), and two forms of Tufted Titmice, *Parus bicolor,* similarly have been studied in the contact zones by K. L. Dixon (1955).

To illustrate the gamut of interbreeding percentages, at least in general by listing proportions of hybrids (fertility known or inferred) to parental types, we may cite the following contact areas:

Hybrids 0-5 per cent

Pipilo ocai and *Pipilo erythrophthalmus* on Cerro San Felipe in Oaxaca, Mexico; no hybrids in 64 samples (Sibley, 1950).

Lophortyx gambeli and *Lophortyx californica* at east bases of San Jacinto and San Bernardino mountains, California; 1 hybrid in 44 samples (A. H. Miller, MS).

Hybrids 5-20 per cent

Junco oreganus and *Junco aikeni* in drainage of Big Horn Valley and vicinity in southern Montana; 5 hybrids in 73 samples (A. H. Miller, MS).

Pipilo ocai and *Pipilo erythrophthalmus* on Mount Orizaba, Mexico; 19 hybrids in 117 samples (Sibley, 1950).

Sphyrapicus "varius" ruber and *Sphyrapicus "varius" nuchalis* in vicinity of Kersely, British Columbia; 4 hybrid adults among 30 or more parental types (Howell, 1952).

Hybrids 20-50 per cent

Junco hyemalis and *Junco oreganus* in Yellowhead Pass area and adjoining eastern piedmont, Alberta; 9 hybrids (hybrid history in recent generations inferred) out of 44 samples (reinterpreted from Miller, 1941).

Terpsiphone rufiventer and *Terpsiphone viridis* in Entebbe-Mabira area, Uganda, Africa; 7 hybrids out of 26 samples (Chapin, 1948).

Sphyrapicus "varius" daggetti and *Sphyrapicus "varius" nuchalis* in Crowder Flat area, Modoc County, California; 20 hybrids among 42 individuals (Howell, 1952).

Hybrids 50-70 per cent

Junco oreganus mearnsi and *Junco oreganus montanus* in center of contact zone (Alturas Lake, Cape Horn) in central Idaho; 17 "hybrids" or mixed-character birds out of 24 samples (Miller, 1941).

When the last stage of mixture cited is involved, the form of junction should doubtless be interpreted as one of complete freedom of interbreeding, for in this instance the seven parental-type birds could be regarded as segregates from the crossings. Their exact proportion will of course depend on the manner of inheritance and number of independent differentiating characters, particularly whether or not the characters are unifactoral or multifactoral. Higher percentages of hybrids or mixed-character birds up to 100 would reflect largely a multifactoral inheritance. In any event, weak barriers to interbreeding or lesser defects in viability and fertility of hybrids would under such circumstances be impossible to detect except through experimental procedures.

The third situation in which sympatric evidence is indecisive or inadequate is that in which race chains form, exhibiting normal racial intergradation along the chain but at certain terminal or subterminal points showing two end forms capable of sympatric existence. This interesting condition has been especially brought out by Rensch (1933:32) and by Mayr (1942). There seem to be no instances of it on the North American continent alone among birds, although other vertebrate groups demonstrate it there. In the larger Eurasian area and in the complex island archipelagoes of the Pacific a number of instances are known among birds. A good example is that of *Phylloscopus trochiloides* in Asia worked out by Ticehurst (1938).

These overlapping chains are not actually so difficult to deal with as the first two situations where sympatry is lacking. They have been properly treated of late as single species by setting aside the sympatric condition of the terminal points under these special circumstances in favor of the compelling evidence that there is no reproductive isolation along the connecting links of the whole chain.

The evolutionary significance of these chains is very great, for they show how readily species status at the ends can evolve from a racial stage—how racial differences are compounded or extended, so to speak, to end in reproductive isolation. It is of course easy to see how the dropping of links in such chains through extinction would quickly convert the group into two separate polytypic species. The fuller exploration of these chains, and the related situations in double invasions, with comparative analysis of behavioral and other possible isolating devices in the field should prove very rewarding in the future.

A more involved situation related to that in overlapping chains and entailing variable amounts of interbreeding is that in which two polytypic species once probably fairly well isolated biologically and spatially come into contact and even into sympatry. Such is the situation in the red-eyed towhees of Mexico, analyzed by Sibley (1950) and already partly reviewed (p. 4), and apparently in the weaver finches *Passer domesticus* and *Passer hispaniolensis* in North Africa (Meise, 1936). In a sense these complexes are like the single overlapping race chains in that they show that the member races or populations have attained different degrees of reproductive isolation, but in this case following a period of separate existence as related polytypic species. As we have already seen, these degrees of isolation range from noncrossing, through limited crossing, to free crossing (Cerro Viejo population in the towhees). The species concepts, biological and morphological, run into particular trouble in complexes of this kind, but the difficulties in applying them need not be unduly magnified, for again the important matter is the demonstration these cases afford of stages in the attainment of the species level which are here undergoing a series of natural tests. Also the degree of importance of introgressive hybridization in the modification of partial biological isolates can be assessed.

THE GEOGRAPHIC PRINCIPLE IN SPECIATION

The realization that most if not all species arise from minor variations and races that are geographically spaced and differentiated had its roots in the avian taxonomic work of the last half of the nineteenth century. The wide occurrence of this process in other vertebrates and in most other sexually reproducing animals has come to be recognized more slowly, and only in the last two decades has it been given real emphasis (Rensch, 1933; Mayr, 1942, 1947). The progress of American ornithology in this regard was distinctly pioneering in character. Ridgway, J. A. Allen, and Coues in the 1870's and 1880's built on Baird's earlier appreciation and exposition of geographic variation. Much of this development is attributable to what was then rightly considered mass collecting and to the building of large museum series representative of many geographic areas on the continent of North America. Confronted with this evidence for geographic variation, Baird and his followers began to break away from the idea of fixity of type and a kind of elementary statistical approach was begun. This was true whether or not these Americans were fully in accord with Darwin. J. A. Allen (1871) for example was distinctly Lamarckian in his interpretation of geographic variation and did not apparently accept or was not impressed by Darwinian selection: doubtless the influence of Agassiz was here reflected.

In Europe this important matter of geographic variation, a corollary and great substantiation of Darwinism, was suppressed by most avian taxonomists in spite of the acceptance and support of the Darwinian views by many European zoologists. This is surprising because European workers had brought out, even before J. A. Allen, several of the general ecologic rules of geographic variation. Hartert and Seebohm (see Stresemann, 1951) sought determinedly, with ultimate success, to gain acceptance in Europe of the American ornithological approach and the trinomialism that signalized it, and Hartert in particular broke away from the tendency residual in some American taxonomists up to and beyond the end of the century to adhere strictly to extant intergradation as a necessary requirement in relating two geographically complementary forms as subspecies. This, however, was achieved independently among the American ornithologists as shown in the case cited of *Parus rufescens* (p. 2) as handled by Grinnell and by workers such as Oberholser and Chapman. Hartert (1891) made it especially clear that geographically complementary forms, even if not in contact, might best be considered subspecies, if differentiated in lesser degree, in order to show their natural affinities. In this he seems to have formulated the principles of geographic systematics more soundly than Kleinschmidt to whom these views are widely attributed in connection with his Formenkreis doctrine (1900, 1926). The latter had inherent in it the unfortunate postulate of independent origin of each species or Formenkreis, and the geographic principle of linking complementary forms as races, partly as a consequence, was unwisely applied in an extreme way by Kleinschmidt. Rensch later (1929, 1934) recast the principle and set a terminology of geographic Rassenkreise and Artenkreise (polytypic species and superspecies of Mayr, 1942) which was divorced from the unreasonable aspects of Kleinschmidt's views, thereby reaffirming the geographic principle both of race formation and of species derivation from races.

But these views of Rensch had actually long been held by Hartert and many American workers even though not so fully elaborated by them. In short, such an understanding of geographic speciation was an everyday matter for working avian taxonomists in many centers, and perhaps partly because of this they did not fully exploit its theoretical implications for students of evolution in general. They perhaps were deterred in part, too, by the real, although unnecessary, gap in the thinking on evolutionary lines of the geneticists and naturalist-taxonomists of the period before 1930. The new systematics as conceived and reviewed by Dobzhansky (1937), Huxley (1942), Mayr (1942), and others has at last made it plain that the prior advances in taxonomy, with avian systematics playing an important part, had established the geographic principle of speciation.

Is indeed all speciation in birds mediated through geographic isolation or spacing? Mayr (1942, 1947) and Miller (1941, 1951) have held that it is and that any ecologic speciation or origin of races and species while the populations or forms are sympatric is out of the question. Even the situations that at first inspection seem most likely to represent ecologic speciation have proved to be instances of geographic spacing on a small scale. Such were the findings of Marshall (1948) on Song Sparrows differentiated in ecologically dissimilar marsh and upland areas in the San Francisco Bay region; and in the Galapagos finches a probable history of like kind has been suggested by Lack (1947) for the currently sympatric, ecologically partly differentiated species of Darwin finches. In concluding that all speciation goes through this geographic process in birds and is not therefore purely ecologic, we of course recognize that the ecologic differentials of the separate geographic areas are very important. Thus probably most geographic variation is also ecologic in the sense that any two areas where two races or species may form are rarely if ever identical ecologically. The kind of ecologic speciation that seems ruled out is sympatric ecologic differentiation, for it is almost inconceivable in birds that a local ecologic differential could become so effective as gradually to isolate two entities that are in contact. Either a most rigorous selection in two adjoining ecologic strata must be envisioned, of an order quite beyond our experience in birds, or a sudden appearance of a major mutation disrupting the processes involved in interbreeding must take place. Neither of these conditions is theoretically impossible, although the establishment of a suddenly differentiated, fully viable isolate from one or a few pairs that simultaneously gained expression of the same critical mutations (presumably by combination of pre-existing recessives) is statistically nearly impossible and ecologically most unlikely.

Goldschmidt (1952) continues to hold much hope for sympatric speciation by saltation. I see no need rigorously to exclude such a possibility, but at the same time it should be pointed out that there is not a single instance in a group of birds well worked out systematically and whose variations are interpreted in the light of population genetics where such a saltatory process seems likely to have occurred. Contrarily, group after group demonstrates the development of both species and races gradually and only through the permissive isolation of geographic spacing. It is important to recognize that the preponderance of evidence indicates the geographic process and that this is the main truth of avian speciation even if we choose not to close our thinking to consideration of occasional other processes—processes that are undemonstrated in birds to date and are indeed unconvincingly shown in most other animal groups.

The recognition of polymorphism or major mutational color types by Stresemann (1926) and others does not presuppose sympatric isolation of the striking variants concerned. Rather, if such morphologic saltations lead to reasonably constant new types, they do so by gradual replacement in a panmictic population, the new mutant taking over a particular geographic area from the pre-existing type, not by developing in sympatric isolation. A later invasion of territory after reproductive isolation has arisen under geographic separation may then lead to sympatry of the contrasting types.

DEMONSTRATION OF SPECIATION

The geographic process in the origin of subspecies is readily accepted by Goldschmidt, who indeed has contributed greatly to its elucidation in moths (1934). Geographic variation occurs in a great majority of bird species, and this lesser evolution is certainly not now denied in general by any group of evolutionists even if the factors contributing to it (selection pressure, mutation pressure, population size, and dispersal rate) are variously weighted by the different workers. It is the elevation of races to the species status—the attainment by the races of reproductive isolation—which is less universally acknowledged by zoologists, although here again ornithological systematists have seen so many examples of it in their material that most of them tend to accept this step as quite normal.

The proportion of species that are passing from a stage of geographic isolation as races to one of reproductively isolated species at any one time should be expected to be small. Once a species has passed the final stages of reproductive isolation, it may have a very long geologic history as a species entity. The unstable period while reproductive isolation is being acquired, even though we think of this as a gradual, multiphase process, is still but a short segment of the geologic history of the particular phyletic line.

The demonstration of the process of gradual attainment of reproductive isolation from a stratum of geographic races need not become involved with the issue of an arbitrary line drawn to denote when species status has been reached. The review (p. 4) of the degrees of interbreeding of forms in geographic contact should make this clear. The gradation of conditions, and the very uncertainty of species status in some groups, demonstrates the critical stages achieved along the line of progress to the unquestioned species. Such is true of the genus *Junco* where the disagreement as to how many forms have attained species status (Miller, 1941; Mayr, 1942) has little importance because within the array of essentially allopatric entities, the end point of full species status has been reached, as is generally acknowledged, in such types as *J. phaeonotus* versus *J. caniceps,* and *J. vulcani* versus *J. alticola,* whether or not the degree of reproductive isolation is sufficient in the eyes of some persons to rate *J. hyemalis, J. oreganus, and J. aikeni* (p. 5), as species. Along the line from normal racial status to normal species status in *Junco* are at least six distinct types or levels, some of them nascent species or semi-species with partly effective reproductive isolation: *oreganus* versus *shufeldti* (normal races); *mearnsi* versus *montanus; caniceps* versus *mearnsi; cismontanus* versus *montanus; aikeni* versus *mearnsi; caniceps* versus *phaeonotus* (normal species).

Between *Pipilo erythrophthalmus* and *Pipilo ocai* (Sibley, 1950), as already mentioned, there are four different degrees of reproductive isolation, one of them apparently full isolation. The forms are regarded as secondarily in junction, as is probably largely true also in *Junco,* and they demonstrate thereby the variable degrees of reproductive isolation attained. The fact that they are not beyond hybridization, under some circumstances free hybridization (Cerro Viejo group), indicates the transitional condition these species are in.

Mayr and Gilliard (1952) in their analysis of two types of honeyeater in New Guinea, the Black-bills and Wattle-birds, have found an extensive secondary hybridization between them, although the presumed adaptations of the birds for their respective high and low zonal levels holds in check to a degree the free spread of hybrids and the introgression of characters. These types have not progressed far toward species level although morphologically they could easily be regarded as species. But in the same group is a geographic isolate, *Melidectes leucostephes,* a Wattle-bird, which though not actually proved to be reproductively isolated has presumably differentiated in this way, as well as strongly morphologically, and is regarded as a separate species.

Pipilo fuscus and *Pipilo aberti* (Davis, 1951) are two species that are to a limited degree sympatric and are fully isolated reproductively wherever they are in contact. That *aberti,* the derived form, has arrived at full species level there can be no doubt and thus no transition can be demonstarted. However its prior history as a geographic race of *fuscus,* although never provable in an absolute sense, is indicated in strongest fashion by the nature of its morphological resemblance and the highly probable ecologic-geographic history of its habitat and of that of its close relative.

A similar situation obtains in the narrowly sympatric *Dendrocopos nuttallii* and its presumed ancestor *Dendrocopos scalaris* (Miller 1951). The two are fully isolated reproductively now but are closely similar morphologically and biologically and appear to have been racial types in the past, *nuttallii* as a coastal geographic race of the widespread *scalaris* of the deserts and arid Southwest.

In the Darwin finches of the Galapagos archipelago, the evident history of two sympatric species, *Camarhynchus psittacula* and *C. pauper,* on Charles Island is that of geographic races formerly on separate islands of the group, like races of the first species that now exist. A subsequent reinvasion of

Charles by one of the forms apparently occurred after reproductive isolation had been achieved (Lack, 1947) as proved by the sympatry and lack of evidence of crossing there at the present time. Amadon (1950) has outlined a similar history of *Loxops parva* and of *Phaeornis palmeri* of Kauai Island in the Hawaiian archipelago, each now at the species level living sympatrically with near relatives, but each with a rather evident prior status as a geographic race of an ancestral species. The subsequent and double invasion procedures in archipelagoes have indeed afforded a number of such rather clear histories (see Mayr, 1942) of the elevation of races to the species level.

A warning may be sounded with respect to one facet of the interpretation of borderline stages in the origin of species. This relates to the assumption that junctions of forms showing partial interbreeding are secondary contacts. Likewise certain instances of free interbreeding or intergrading are classed as secondary in contrast with others in which contact is assumed never to have been lost and which hence are classed as primary. How actually can we marshal facts to support classification of contacts as primary and secondary? Can the nature of the hybrids be used? Many persons have used such evidence, although probably without much justification. The signs of segregation and independent assortment of characters in the crossings and the concomitant increased variability in the junction zone has lead to the conclusion by some that the meeting is secondary, whereas actually such phenomena, as is well known, depend merely on the presence of unifactoral independently assorting genetic control—a type of control that might occur, as in various sorts of polymorphism, whether or not the populations had ever been out of contact. On the other hand, the involvement of a large number of characters in a single hybrid zone, whether they are unifactoral or multifactoral, does argue for a secondary contact, as such a large number of factors probably would not have arisen to differentiate the types on either side of the junction if the populations had not been fully isolated for a time. Moreover, the greater the number of characters involved, the more likely it is that some will arise of the rarer unifactoral type which gives the so-called hybrid appearance (Miller, 1949). Still the nature of the hybrid group merely indicates probability and does not constitute proof.

A second line of evidence comes from the history of the distributional patterns of the types concerned. It is seen that the two kinds occupy different areas now that are judged from geologic and paleobotanical, and floristic and faunistic evidence to have been shut off from one another previously, as by an uninhabitable glaciated area. In some instances such a history, although never absolutely provable, is highly probable. In other instances the course of history is just a guess, particularly on the point that there was no residual section of contact. Yet one assumption about history coupled with another involving the kinds and numbers of characteristics of the hybrid birds is allowed to support the positive designation of contacts as primary or secondary, and I fear on occasion a measure of circular reasoning enters and this classification is then used in other connections to support the notion of the separate biogeographic history of the areas concerned.

Especially when interbreeding is relatively free is it difficult to be sure that the contact is primary or secondary. Particular gene constellations, significantly compatible as combinations and of good adaptive value, may have arisen in adjoining geographic areas to set off rather sharply the corresponding races, even though the thread of contact, if only weak and filterlike, was never broken. The intergrading or hybridizing and the variability in this remaining or somewhat augmented contact may have the "appearance" of secondary junction, and the history of the race areas may suggestively support the idea. Yet here might be a primary contact that is becoming attenuated and that perhaps ultimately will reach the point of breaking. Contrarily, two forms well separated geographically but rather slightly differentiated, especially by characters exhibiting blending, may through subsequent joining interbreed and grade finely with no local increase in the index of variability. Such a cline would pass for a primary contact, I fear, though of course it is not.

We can, then, only part of the time be on fairly sure ground in classifying contacts as primary and secondary. The distinction is theoretically of much interest, but the application of it in many instances is dubious and should not be lightly undertaken.

MECHANICS OF RACIAL EVOLUTION

Although the acceptance of the widespread occurrence of geographic races is general, the means by which these important initial stages are attained still offer almost unlimited avenues of investigation in birds. How is the segregation of individuals bearing distinctive hereditary features into populations and races achieved? How do the individual variants of any particular kind become increased out of proportion to others and grouped in particular areas as the predominant or even the exclusive type there? The answer would appear to lie largely in the selective process, in the adaptive or preadaptive value of particular traits or of favorably balanced combinations of genes and traits (Wright, 1951). Although ornithology is in no particularly advantageous position to assess the operation of natural selection, and the topic will not be especially reviewed here, it is a distinctly favorable field for investigating the organization of populations in which the segregation and increase of attributes must take place, the structure of the population having much to do with the way in which selection pressure operates (Wright, *op. cit.,* and preceding works).

Population size is an essential matter in calculating how genes can become spread and fixed either by natural selection or by chance fixation as a result of inbreeding. But mere determination of numbers of breeding birds of a

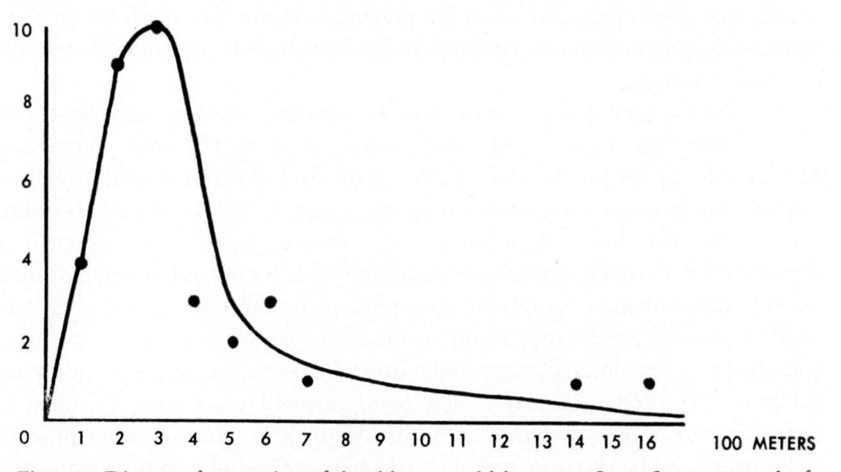

Fig. 1. Distance from point of hatching at which young Song Sparrows settle for breeding. Ordinate, number of individuals; abscissa, distance in hundreds of meters, with class interval of one hundred meters (1 = 50 to 150 meters).

species per acre, or in the aggregate for a race or a part of the range of a race, is not at all sufficient for purposes of estimating these evolutionary possibilities. We must get at the matter of genetic transmission within the population and this means knowledge of mate constancy, speed of reproduction, dispersal of young from point of origin in terms of numbers of other individuals of the species with which it may make genetic contact, and the effect of local barriers, "road blocks," or filters that channel, or impede, the free flow of genes within the population.

A great deal of general information is at hand on these topics, but there are only a few species of birds for which the data are more than fragmentary and even in these the gathering of population data was conducted without realization of the potential importance of the study for evolutionary investigations. Accordingly some easily obtained and pertinent facts were let slip from grasp. This commentary does not detract from the value and merit of such studies in relation to other objectives the workers had in mind.

The Song Sparrow, *Melospiza melodia,* is a species in which the liaison of population study and systematics has been especially pursued. From Nice's (1937) work on this species it was found possible (Miller, 1947) to estimate the distance to which young Song Sparrows most often disperse and the number of other Song Sparrows with which they may be thrown and might have equal chance of interbreeding (see Fig. 1). Such a group of birds within which there is free interbreeding in the span of one generation is designated in population genetics as the effective breeding unit and it is the basis for the interesting mathematical estimates of evolutionary changes developed by Haldane, Fisher, and Sewall Wright. This free interbreeding, or panmixia, is actually not an attribute that is simply present or absent, but it grades off from perfect freedom to reduced freedom in accordance with distance, if not also with other factors.

From Nice's data it was found that the effective breeding unit lies in an area of about 400 meters' radius and consists of about 150 adult individuals. At least this applies for the type of Song Sparrow population that she analyzed in Ohio which is not completely or strictly resident. With effective breeding units of this size, local differentiation of a random type can be expected, or is possible, if it is not masked or counterdirected by natural selection. Such random differentiation, unrelated to environmental factors, is in effect the result of isolation by distance within a continuous population. The differentiation, however, becomes obvious only over distances ten or more times the radius of the effective breeding unit area; it could occur over distances of three or more miles, therefore. In this theoretical, random differentiation, such changes as occurred in one type of character would not be followed or paralleled by other independently inherited characters unless together they formed a more harmonious gene combination. On the other hand, if observed differentiation correlated with environment and formed clines, it would point to the ascendency of natural selection in the process—the molding of the clines by this agent.

The knowledge of the systematics of Song Sparrows on the Pacific Coast of North America prior to Marshall's work (1948) was considerable by ordinary standards and it served to reflect random fixation or differentiation in some degree. The nonadaptive, erratic characterization of the races on certain of the channel islands off southern California seemed then, and still does, explicable in this way. For example, the birds of Santa Rosa and Santa Cruz Islands and the distant San Clemente Island are essentially the same. But the Song Sparrows of small intervening Santa Barbara Island are modified, inexplicably in terms of selection or island history, in the direction of extreme grayness and small size. The birds of San Miguel Island, not far from Santa Rosa, differ unpredictably, being small somewhat like those of distant Santa Barbara Island and somewhat gray, but in a different manner than those of Santa Barbara.

On the mainland we seemed also to see local random fluctuations, less sharply defined, yet entailing some characters not obviously adaptive. However, in the mainland populations something additional to random fixation was evident, with some measure of adaptive coloration coming to notice as though this coloration were superimposed on, or built out of, the more local random type of differentiation by the directive forces of natural selection. This latter seems particularly true of the pale, desert Song Sparrow, *saltonis*.

When Marshall returned to an analysis, more exhaustive than hitherto, of the Song Sparrows of the San Francisco Bay region, he found a gradient system in the characters which correlates with geography and environment, and thus is not random, but which does not offer any clues as to the guiding selective action. Whatever the selective forces may be, Marshall perhaps has minimized the possible aid in the origin of the differentiation afforded by prior minor random fluctuations. If such random differentiations existed, as seems likely from the potentiality he has shown in the Southampton Bay group, they would give selection a better "hand hold" for action, a form of intergroup selection (Wright, 1951), than would mere individual variation. In other words, selection may work more quickly by favoring a local group whose considerable proportion of beneficial attributes or combinations of traits is acquired partly by chance than by picking out slowly the occasional slightly favorable individual variants scattered in a large population of less well endowed individuals. Also a pool of heterozygosity in such a species that is enhanced by intergroup exchange of genes from local random differentiations would be a favorable substrate for selective action and origin of particularly compatible gene constellations.

The combination of attack on the problems of evolutionary processes in Song Sparrows has been fruitful to some considerable degree. Through good fortune as well as the general advance of ornithological knowledge we had available in connection with the same species an excellent population study and a most instructive set of local variations in characters and ecology. These combinations need not be matters of chance in the future, for we can select working material carefully on the basis of taxonomic experience for its potentiality in revealing evolutionary processes and, on the basis of our ample knowledge of bird behavior and ecology, for susceptibility for co-ordinated population analysis. In this direction lies a significant future for advanced avian systematists. A similar focus is also healthful for future population work which can all too easily lapse into purposeless counting and marking.

AN ASSESSMENT OF CERTAIN METHODS AND SITUATIONS IN ORNITHOLOGY IN RELATION TO THE STUDY OF SPECIATION

Some Inherent Advantages of Ornithological Material

Many of the favorable aspects of ornithology as a source of data pertinent to evolutionary inquiry have been touched on in preceding pages. No full cataloguing of these will be undertaken here. The points that merit special review are:

(1) Ability in ornithology to observe behavior in the wild and thus to see responses to environment and particularly to the barriers and discontinuities of the environment important in the processes of geographic differentiation.

(2) Ability to observe reactions toward closely related forms and toward members of their own kind on the part of free-living organisms in respect to competition, species recognition, and mate recognition.

(3) Ability to ascertain differentials in reproductive rate and population density as measures of success in different environments by procedures of watching, counting, and marking.

(4) Possibility of observing mortality in relation to environmental conditions and thus obtaining indication of the operation of factors of natural selection; this area of inquiry has been only rather weakly developed for birds to date.

(5) Ability, because of the prevalence of pair bonds persistent during a breeding season, to observe types and numbers of cross-matings in hybrid areas and to follow the reproductive success of such matings.

(6) Ability to analyze both in wild birds and in captives the process of pair formation and courtship in order to detect partial or complete isolating mechanisms of a behavioral type, which in birds often evolve into effective species barriers in the wild before genetic sterility barriers arise.

(7) Ability through observation and marking to determine many aspects of population structure such as turnover, mate constancy, and dispersal of young and adults.

(8) Ability to preserve taxonomic study specimens for indefinite periods, without, in most instances, any complicating deterioration, as samples of populations showing all external aspects of structure and color.

(9) Ability through the museum preservation of skins of different age classes and by reason of the complex, yet fairly well ordered systems of feather replacement to make age determinations of samples and thus to ascertain age composition of populations; in this way we may refine knowledge of racial differentiation which might otherwise be confused because of the variable mixture of age classes.

(10) Ability to use a large proportion of the available specimens for quantitative geographic comparisons of dimensions because of the attainment at an early age of definitive proportions in most groups of birds.

Items 1 through 7 in the foregoing review are based essentially on the simple but important circumstance that most birds are diurnal and are fairly large conspicuous organisms that can be watched under natural conditions. Moreover, the amateur interest in such observable organisms can be enlisted, adapted, and to a degree directed to contribute much information usable in evolutionary studies. Indeed the development of adequate taxonomic materials (points 8 to 10) and of museum facilities has also been supported by amateurs and it should continue to be greatly enhanced by them.

Some Weaknesses and Defects of the Ornithological Material and Approach, with Certain Suggestions for Remedying Them

(1) No wild bird type has proved adaptable for large-scale breeding experiments to ascertain the genetics of characters involved in evolution. In

general, even among domestic birds, reproductive rate is low and attainment of breeding condition is delayed to a degree that genetic studies are not feasible on the scale known for some insects, fishes, and even rodents. The relatively large cages required for birds, the complicated psychological reactions to captivity, and food problems present practical obstacles. However, the tremendous expenditure of effort and money in maintenance of captives by aviculturalists could in greater degree than at present be diverted from the purely esthetic goal to planned and carefully controlled experimental crossing. If trained geneticists could work with avicultural enthusiasts, some very important genetic information bearing on speciation would be derived. Most technical biologists do not have the time nor the expensive facilities for such work, nor are they generally justified in seeking research grants for it when the yield in results will be at slow rate. But the layouts developed and already supported by aviculturalists, through other motivation, could be adequate if their interests were modified sufficiently to support wholeheartedly the technical aspects of the breeding experiments.

(2) In spite of the great advances made in assembling in research museums large series of specimens essential to the analysis of geographic differentiation and speciation, the number of usable specimens is still relatively small compared with the massive collections available in some groups of insects and small fishes. This is of course due partly to the fairly large size of many kinds of birds which places great demand on museum space, but also it results from the time required in collecting and particularly in preparing a good, fully usable, permanent study specimen. The constant effort to provide adequate museum space and to encourage the collecting of large and significant series by all persons having any interest in birds must be continued. The urge to restrain collecting as a conservation measure which is alarmingly widespread is quite unrealistic in terms of what is now known of the principles of carrying capacity and reproductive potential related to wild populations. Such restriction has sensible applicability to only a few threatened species. Yet efforts to restrain collecting, supported also in considerable degree by the sentimentalism of persons uninformed or unsympathetic to scientific groups, continue and they must be corrected if the maximum contribution of ornithology to evolution and general biological understanding is to be realized.

(3) Although museum specimens properly prepared and cared for in insect-proof and light-proof containers are relatively stable reference materials, much more so than those for most groups of animals, there is nevertheless some slight alteration to be expected from the oxidation of pigments, especially of certain of the melanins. A few species are especially susceptible to this "foxing" process. Whether this deterioration is enhanced by certain temperature conditions or by certain fumigants, or by preservatives used in preparation, is little known and such topics badly need careful long-range investigation. Certainly the use of borax in this connection is dangerous, and at least enough

is known about its tendency to alter colors of hair and feathers to indicate its absolute avoidance in preparing specimens, contrary to the recommendations still made in several manuals on technique. But whatever practices may be found in need of correction in order to avoid or minimize color alterations, the analyst of taxonomic material must constantly be on the alert to detect such color changes in his material, much more than he has been in the past, and correspondingly to rule out differential effects that are not based on the genetic attributes of the organisms.

(4) The lack of application of statistical procedures in analyzing racial and other differentiation persists in ornithology to a considerable degree. Lack of actual use of statistics as well as thinking in these terms is attributable partly to tradition, the following of the lead of earlier taxonomists, and partly to the influence of the work of a considerable number of amateurs whose opportunities for understanding the values and uses of statistics are in general restricted. The contributions of such amateurs who work into the more technical aspects of ornithology is not to be decried, but efforts should be made to educate them. The determination of the statistical reliability of differences seen in specimens by one test or another, of varying degrees of formality, is most essential for developing a sound analysis of differentiation and dependable systematics. Much more effort needs to be directed toward checking the reliability of differentiations already reported, using a statistical sense, than in the search for new racial differentations. As examples of the proper awareness of these matters, see Amadon (1949) and Dickinson (1952).

(5) A further defect of ornithological work of the past, not inherent to the field, and indeed matched by the taxonomic practices in a number of other groups, is the formal description as races of extremely minor entities either real or often apparently unreal biologically. This seems attributable to some degree to a pernicious aspect of nomenclatural procedure, namely the association of the name of the describer with a new name created, and to the natural pleasure derived from the discovery of new entities. These two motivations, which cannot be or should not be done away with, nonetheless should be held in check by the influence of a body of opinion developed in a more understanding group of workers. There still occur descriptions of races of birds based on features attributable to age, foxing, chance contaminants in the feathers, and methods of preparation of a particular collector, and on statistically unreliable differences and extremely tenuous even if valid differences. Although the damage done by untrained and unwise systematists engaging in such practices is not irreparable—their proposals can always be synonymized—the distraction they cause in the taxonomic arena and the diversion of the time of the more discerning analyst and reviser in straightening out the picture and in sifting false claims impedes progress in the biological interpretation of the material.

Other Suggestions for Improvement

There was recently published by Van Tyne (1952) an excellent statement of practices and principles in collecting for taxonomic work on birds which gives many points to be observed in assembling material. It is designed to insure more data associated with each specimen and to indicate practices to be avoided so as to reduce error in taxonomic studies. The statement should be carefully reviewed and its recommendations heeded by all future collectors.

Although Van Tyne properly urges the recording of a maximum of data on the specimen label, it must be realized that there are practical limits to this and that co-ordinated notebook records, referring to the specimen clearly and preferably by specific number, should also be made which will be accessible not just to the collector but to all who will use his collections in the future.

The integration of taxonomic studies with general evolutionary inquiry along the several lines suggested in this review seem to point toward a conversion, already partly accomplished, from the period of collection building by the professional collector and trader to that of collecting by the biological investigators themselves. A sample of specimens of a particular population incorporated in a museum if taken by the investigator of the problem they contribute to, with personally recorded data on labels and in notebooks and representing the direction in the field toward the selection of the most significant animals and information, is worth one hundred fold a like number of specimens obtained from a commercial collector even though the latter supplies standard minimal data with reasonable accuracy. However, the biological investigator must be willing to learn and patiently to apply the techniques for making good permanent taxonomic specimens.

The acquisition of specimens from remote areas on a general or mass-collecting basis will and doubtless should be continued by museums. However, whenever possible, research institutes will do best to invest in the field work of the investigator himself who will pursue a focused program of collecting with prime or principal emphasis on the taxonomic, evolutionary, or other biological study which he is pursuing. The specimens obtained may be somewhat less numerous than would be obtained by a collector per se but they will be vastly more significant. Moreover the money invested in building collections will also be invested in the experience of the research man, and many intangible as well as specific values will accrue. More particularly, if a man who is analyzing a group to trace in it evolutionary history and to observe signs of processes be supported to conduct his own field operations, he can alter his attack from day to day on the ground as new facts disclose themselves. We do not want to depend on museum-bound theorists and interpreters who are not in touch with the living organism in its natural setting. Ornithology is a field science in large measure and much of its strength, including its contributions to the new systematics, lies in this fact.

Bibliography

ALLEN, J. A.

1871. On the mammals and winter birds of east Florida, with an examination of certain assumed specific characters in birds, etc. Bull. Mus. Comp. Zool., 2:161-450.

AMADON, D.

1949. The seventy-five per cent rule for subspecies. Condor, 51:250-258.

1950. The Hawaiian honeycreepers (Aves, Drepaniidae). Bull. Amer. Mus. Nat. Hist., 95:157-262.

CHAPIN, J. C.

1948. Variation and hybridization among the paradise flycatchers of Africa. Evolution, 2:111-126.

COUES, E.

1872. Key to North American birds. Naturalists' Agency, Salem, 361 pp.

DAVIS, J.

1951. The distribution and variation of the Brown Towhees. Univ. Calif. Publ. Zool., 52:1-120.

DICKINSON, J. C., JR.

1952. Geographic variation in the Red-eyed Towhee of the eastern United States. Bull. Mus. Comp. Zool., 107:273-352.

DIXON, K. L.

1955. Ecological analysis of the interbreeding of Crested Titmice in Texas. Univ. Calif. Publ. Zool. In press.

DOBZHANSKY, T.

1937. Genetics and the origin of species. Columbia University Press, New York, xvi + 364 pp.

GOLDSCHMIDT, R.

1934. Lymantria. Bibliographica Genetica, 11:1-186.

1952. Evolution, as viewed by one geneticist. Amer. Scientist, 40:84-98, 135.

GRINNELL, J.

1904. The origin and distribution of the Chestnut-backed Chickadee. Auk, 21:364-382.

HARTERT, E.

1891. *Fide* Stresemann, 1951:260.

HOWELL, T. R.

1952. Natural history and differentiation in the Yellow-bellied Sapsucker. Condor, 54:237-282.

HUXLEY, J.

1942. Evolution, the modern synthesis. Harper and Bros., New York and London, 645 pp.

KLEINSCHMIDT, O.

1900. Arten oder Formenkreise? Jour. Ornithol., 48:134-139.

1926. Das Formenkreislehre und das Weltwerden des Lebens. Gebauer-Schwetschke, Halle-S., x + 188 pp.

LACK, D.

1947. Darwin's finches. Cambridge University Press, x + 208 pp.

MARSHALL, J. T., JR.

1948. Ecologic races of Song Sparrows in the San Francisco Bay region. Part II. Geographic variation. Condor, 50:233-256.

MAYR, E.

1942. Systematics and the origin of species. Columbia University Press, New York, xiv + 334 pp.

1947. Ecologic factors in speciation. Evolution, 1:263-288.

MAYR, E., and E. T. GILLIARD

1952. Altitudinal hybridization in New Guinea honeyeaters. Condor, 54:325-337.

MEISE, W.

1936. Zur Systematik und Verbreitungsgeschichte der Haus- und Weidensperlinge, *Passer domesticus* (L.) und *hispaniolensis* (T.). Jour. Ornithol., 84: 631-372.

MILLER, A. H.

1941. Speciation in the avian genus *Junco.* Univ. Calif. Publ. Zool., 44:173-434.

1947. Panmixia and population size with respect to birds. Evolution, 1:186-190.

1949. Some concepts of hybridization and intergradation in wild populations of birds. Auk, 66:338-342.

1951. An analysis of the distribution of the birds of California. Univ. Calif. Publ. Zool., 50:531-644.

NICE, M. M.

1937. Studies in the life history of the Song Sparrow. I. A population study of the Song Sparrow. Trans. Linn. Soc. N.Y., 4:vi + 247 pp.

PITELKA, F. A.

1950. Geographic variation and the species problem in the shorebird genus *Limnodromus.* Univ. Calif. Publ. Zool., 50:1-108.

1951. Speciation and ecologic distribution in the jays of the genus *Aphelocoma.* Univ. Calif. Publ. Zool., 50:195-464.

RENSCH, B.

1929. Das Princip geographischer Rassenkreise und das Problem der Artbildung. Gebrüder Borntraeger, Berlin, 206 pp.

1933. Zoologische Systematik und Artbildungsproblem. Verh. Deutsch. Zool. Gesellsch., Zool. Anz., suppl. bd., 6:19-83.

1934. Kurze Anweisung für Zoologisch-Systematische Studien. Akademische Verlag., Leipzig, 116 pp.

SIBLEY, C. G.

1950. Species formation in the Red-eyed Towhees of Mexico. Univ. Calif. Publ. Zool., 50:109-194.

STRESEMANN, E.

1926. Uebersicht über die "Mutationsstudien" I—XXIV und ihre wichtigsten Ergebnisse. Jour. Ornithol., 74:377-385.

1936. The formenkreis-theory. Auk, 53:150-158.

1951. Die Entwicklung der Ornithologie von Aristoteles bis zum Gegenwart. F. W. Peters, Berlin, xv + 431 pp.

TICEHURST, C. B.

1938. A systematic review of the genus *Phylloscopus.* Brit. Mus., London, viii + 193 pp.

VAN TYNE, J.

1952. Principles and practices in collecting and taxonomic work. Auk, 69:27-33.

WRIGHT, S.

1951. Fisher and Ford on "the Sewall Wright effect." Amer. Scientist, 39:452-458, 479.

chapter 2

RECENT REVISIONS IN CLASSIFICATION AND THEIR BIOLOGICAL SIGNIFICANCE . . . Herbert Friedmann

While from a purely philosophical approach macroevolution may be merely an extrapolation and only the cumulative results of long ages of microevolution, its essential elements and aspects are less readily accessible to the interpretive methods and paraphernalia of the biologist than are those incipient stages currently studied as speciation phenomena. The latter often are still in, or show unmistakable marks of, the evolutionary arena in which they have been but recently involved. The higher categories, on the contrary, have lost many of these revealing signs and have become comparatively stable and therefore present fewer openings for the evolutionary investigator to probe into their past history. It follows, then, that recent attempts to rearrange the higher categories of avian classification are apt not to show as much in the way of fresh concepts of biological significance as to reflect the impetus of such new thoughts on the reviser's methods and results. The zoologist, working with recent (i.e., living) species, should be alert to, and cannot help but be influenced by, other types of research on living creatures or parts thereof, especially by the experimental approach to biological processes and phenomena. But, as Simpson has recently pointed out (1944:97-98), the differentiation between families, orders, and classes " . . . is almost unnoted by the experimentalist, or if he does think of it, he is inclined to dismiss it as inaccessible for profitable study. It is, for instance, surprising to a paleontologist to open an elaborate memoir on the origin of higher categories . . . and to find that the higher categories in question are subgenera, at the highest possible evaluation. . . ."

For the purposes of the present paper, revisionary studies may be divided into three groups—attempts to revise the general classification of the class Aves as a whole, revisions of the classification within higher categories such as families, and revisions of polytypic species or of single genera of considerable scope, with, of course, any necessary consideration of closely allied genera. On the whole, it appears that often the purpose behind a revision of the forms of a species or the contents of a genus has been very different from that underlying the alteration of previous systems of classifying the included members of a family or of the avian system generally. The originating

Manuscript received October 1, 1953.

cause in the study of smaller groups frequently, if not usually, has been a sense of the need to "straighten out" the groups in order to facilitate the identification of specimens. In the studies of higher categories and of the entire class the purpose has not been connected with specimen identification but with clarifying relationships. It is also true that as one progresses from the revisionary review of the closely knit group of the species or genus to the larger scale of the family and eventually of the entire class, the amount of verifiable, detailed information and the opportunity for making meaningful comparisons decrease as the gaps in the evidence increase. The student of a compact group, such as *Cisticola* or *Phylloscopus* or *Eremophila* or *Limnodromus* or *Junco,* usually is able to know his material more completely and more intimately than the investigator of larger, more inclusive, higher categories. We, therefore, may expect not only different approaches but also different degrees of definiteness in the conclusions in various types of revisionary studies.

REVISIONS OF THE ENTIRE AVIAN SYSTEM

Systematic ornithologists are aware of the fact that the members of the class Aves have been divided into considerably more families in relation to the total number of species, on relatively slighter anatomical characters, than any other class of vertebrates. It is understandable, therefore, that a tendency has arisen to unite families where possible, to reduce the disproportionately large number of them and to bring the classification of birds more into harmony with that of other groups. Examples of this tendency in relatively recent years are the merging of the Turdidae, Muscicapidae, and Sylviidae into one family; the proposed division of the Coerebidae, putting one part in the Parulidae and the other part in the Thraupidae; the proposed placing of the Chamaeidae in the Timaliidae; the merging of the Anhingidae with the Phalacrocoracidae, the Tetraonidae and Numididae with the Phasianidae, the Phoeniculidae with the Upupidae, etc. This has, in turn, given rise to a certain amount of opposition, due in part, it is true, to mental inertia (which is, of course, no argument and should be dismissed from consideration) and in part to a philosophically valid argument, the gist of which is as follows. Birds are more completely known, on a world-wide basis, both in their forms and their habits than any other group of animals, and to revise the classification of the best known to conform with that of the less well known seems less sound than to use the best known group as a standard and to attempt to bring the systematics of the other groups into closer accord with that of the birds. On the other side of the picture we have the indisputable fact that the classification of birds has grown out of a multitude of studies of taxonomic discontinuities of a low systematic order, and that the result reflects what Simpson (1944:97-98) has called the myopic outlook produced by too much concentration on small differences. Furthermore, until recently, by far the greatest bulk of the work was done on geographical fragments of the world's bird population, all too often without regard to the remaining and related fragments existing in other geographical areas.

If the higher categories, the orders and families, have any meaning (and that they do, or should, is generally agreed), they are branches, of varying sizes, on a phylogenetic tree. To assume, as some have done, that there is no intrinsic reality in these higher categories is to forget that historical sequences and relationships are realities even though their definition be expressed in less precise terms than those of current species. Their reality is of a different nature, not measurable directly in terms of size and weight, but yet detectable physically by conformity of structural characters, and therefore, even though lacking in definite limits, of a type of reality akin to that of current species. I use the expression "type of reality" deliberately as there are other kinds of reality. Ideas have reality even though they may be devoid of independent or concrete existence; their effect in human history probably outweighs that of most physical realities. Any science worthy of the name is a system of ideas based on verifiable factual data and not merely an orderly and documented collection of facts by themselves.

To get back to the branches of the phylogenetic tree—to the higher categories—a survey of recent revisionary studies indicates that the chief result has been an attempt to reduce their number, to make the ornithic tree simpler, more of a noble tree with fewer but more generous branches. However much this may or may not please us esthetically is beside the point. We should not have in mind anything but a desire to reconstruct the tree as best we can, not to make of it a handsomer specimen, according to some subjective notion of handsomeness, or to prove or disprove a theory. Some among present bird taxonomists who would wield the pruning shears on the poor old phylogenetic tree with the greatest determination are not necessarily unaffected by some such inclinations, although they would reject them if directly aware of them. The fact that, as they themselves put it, they want to make the classification of the birds conform more to that of other parts of the animal kingdom suggests a touch of the pruning gardener's approach, a desire to "tame" or to regulate the wild growth pattern of the individual trees to form a nicer arrangement and to approximate a closer agreement between them.

There is a danger in pursuing the comparison of the phylogenetic tree and a real tree too far; the former is a reconstructed, ideated affair made of branches reaching backwards until they meet, and valid pruning of it is a matter of correcting earlier errors and of applying fuller knowledge to the bases rather than the tips of the branches, whereas the latter is a whole, integrated growth, the pruning of which is deliberately planned towards a desired result and affects chiefly the tips of the branches and not their bases. At the same time it should be kept in mind that just as different species of trees have quite dissimilar growth patterns, there is no reason for assuming that phylogenetic trees should be less variable. If the difference in the degree of structural distinctness in, let us say the orders of mammals or reptiles on the one hand, and of birds on the other, means anything, it means that the phylogenetic trees of the first two show a different growth pattern from that of the third. This should not be disturbing to the zoologist, and there is no real need to attempt to bring them into a common pattern of greater similarity. On the other hand, it cannot be denied that, were it possible to do so without violating the data, it would be advantageous to students of the subject to arrive at a classification in which categories of equal rank in different groups were equally well marked.

There is still another point to be considered in this discussion; the birds may be, in fact many zoologists would say they are, not a class comparable to the mammals or reptiles, but a subdivision of the reptilian stock, of the Sauropsida of many authors. Even so, there is no reason to expect the growth pattern of that part of the sauropsidan "tree" that comprises the birds to approximate the reptilian section in the number, size, and spread of its branches.

As Miller has pointed out (1949:84-88), the fact that the higher categories may have no effective delineation does not imply that the differentiation they represent has proceeded at a constant pace from one level to another. The evidence, and it must be admitted that practically all the evidence of taxonomy is no more than circumstantial, indicates that some major terminal differentiations developed slowly, others more rapidly. Simpson has attempted to distinguish two modes—a quantum and a phyletic mode of evolution—but Miller finds the two types may intergrade to the extent that no modality is distinguishable.

It so happens that there have been published recently two independent outlines of avian classification, one by Mayr and Amadon (1951) and one by Wetmore (1951), the former dealing with recent birds only, the latter treating of fossil as well as recent forms. In both cases the authors have studied much material and data, and the differences in their results reflect differences in points of view rather than in factual information. In order to make the two systems more directly comparable we may delete from Wetmore's classification 7 orders and 42 families known only from fossil material. This leaves a total, according to Wetmore's list, of 27 orders and 171 families of living birds, while Mayr and Amadon have listed 28 orders and 134 families. As far as the orders are concerned, the only difference is that the flamingos have been kept as a separate order by Mayr and Amadon, while Wetmore has considered them a suborder of the Ciconiiformes. There is, thus, a heartening agreement here, which indicates that the classification of birds to orders seems to have reached a fairly stable position. While there is some difference in the sequential position given to some of these orders on the two lists, this is relatively inconsequential as no linear recording can, in the nature of things, be correct. As Mayr and Amadon have stated, the relationship of avian orders is a problem that will probably never be wholly solvable as their connections are lost in an unrecorded antiquity, and their present analysis is rendered obscure because of much evolutionary convergence. "One point that is frequently overlooked is that all living birds are exceedingly specialized in different directions and that this specialization had its beginning in the remote past. . . . " Mayr and Amadon have made no serious study of non-passerine ordinal classification and therefore made no attempt to alter the arrangement in Wetmore's earlier list. Were they to do so, it is possible that the present apparent agreement might be affected.

The classification of birds to families, however, shows far less agreement. Thus, in the perching birds, the terminal order in both lists, we have the same birds included, but in one list they have been grouped in fifty families, while in the other, sixty-nine families have been used for them. However, fifteen of the nineteen extra families recognized by Wetmore have been listed as valid sub-families by Mayr and Amadon, which nearly equalizes the two systems. When one considers the degree to which the personal equation affects the distinction between what constitutes a family and what a subfamily of passerine birds, there is really less important difference here than might seem at first glance. On the whole, Mayr and Amadon have given greater weight to similarities than to differences between groups of birds and have tended to base their ideas of phylogenetic relationship on total resemblance or similarity whereas Wetmore has generally emphasized dissimilarities more than resemblances and evaluated morphological characters as to generic, familial, or ordinal status. Neither list refers to the suggestion put forth by Lowe (1946) that the piciform birds and the passerine groups should be merged in one order, and that their differences are of only subordinal value.

There is, however, a more important disagreement than that of the number of recognized families and subfamilies. The two lists differ widely in the relationships between the families of passerine birds, as far as such matters are expressible in a chronological list. Wetmore's listing ends with the Fringillidae, which family is twelfth from the end according to Mayr and Amadon, who, in turn have considered the terminal family to be the birds of paradise (fifty-ninth from that position in Wetmore's list!). The arguments for their choice of the terminal group are as follows. Mayr and Amadon have on their side the conclusions of W. K. Parker, MacGillivray, Sharpe, Newton, and the majority of check-lists and reference works. They have supported their views by citing Portmann's studies (1947), and have considered that " . . . *Corvus* ranks above other birds in brain development. As Dr. J. P. Chapin has pointed out to us, however, were similar attention given to certain icterids, sturnids, ploceids, and perhaps others, they might prove just as 'advanced.' Nevertheless we have thought it best to follow the school that would terminate the oscinine series with the Corvidae and allied families." Wetmore has placed the Fringillidae at the end because " . . . this group is the modern expression of a main core or stem that through the earlier Tertiary periods has given rise to more specialized assemblages that we now recognize as distinct families. . . . Attempts to arrange the avian families with the Corvidae and their allies in the terminal positions . . . because of supposed more advanced development of the brain appear to me quite uncertain. . . ."

If there is, as seems to be the case, room for such divergent judgments among well-informed specialists, what is the biologist who is not an avian specialist to gather from the data of passerine classification? It must be realized that the main value of a system of classification is its usefulness and dependability to the nonspecialist; the taxonomic expert in the group does not need it to guide him; he knows, or should know, what species and other categories he is dealing with, and it is chiefly when he attempts to annotate large segments of his material or to extract generalizations from it that the systematist has occasion to express his data against a framework of presumed phylogenetic relationships. Systems of classification with their co-ordinated zoogeographic data are useful to the evolutionist, as distinguished from the group specialist. But to accept either of the two lists discussed above as basic data from which to draw further deductions is to invite difficulties. Obviously both cannot be correct; actually both, as their authors would freely admit, are tentative approximations to an over-all descriptive statement and have points of weakness as well as of strength. Mayr and Amadon have the following to say of the suborder Oscines. "The difficulty in finding good anatomical characters that besets the avian taxonomist at every level is particularly acute in this suborder. As a group song birds are the most advanced, successful, and apparently latest to evolve of the entire Class Aves. They have developed an infinite variety of types, and many annectant and intermediate forms are still in existence. The 'phylogenetic tree' of the group, if it could be drawn accurately, would probably resemble a great flat-topped 'umbrella' tree."

The uncertainty of relative placement of particular groups in the total system is further reflected in Mayr and Vaurie's summary of evolution in the drongos (1948), based on the latter's exhaustive study (1949) of the family as a whole. They have written, " . . . It is characteristic of the present status of bird taxonomy that the relationship of species and subspecies within the family can be worked out down to the most elaborate details, while it is as yet impossible to give a clear cut diagnosis for the family as a whole, or to state its nearest relatives. . . . Since the family seems devoid of any diagnostic character, it appears probable that it may have to be reduced to the rank of a subfamily, but it is not even known as yet of what family. Although the correct placing of the family in relation to the other families of song birds is so far impossible, there is no difficulty in recognizing any member of this family as a drongo. The Dicruridae are a compact and very characteristic group of species. . . ." This frank statement about one of the most completely surveyed passerine groups reveals the highly speculative nature of any taxonomic system.

Since the above discussion was written, Beecher (1953) has brought out still another attempt to reconstruct the phylogeny of the families of passerine birds. His conclusions have been based primarily on personal investigation of the jaw musculature, but he has also considered the other characters used by earlier workers. Inasmuch as he has made but little attempt to list the families in linear sequence, it is somewhat difficult to compare his conclusions directly with those of the two lists discussed above. Beecher has broken from both in many details; thus, he has derived the seed-cracking groups independently from fruit and insect-eaters at several points, with the result that what had been considered subfamilies of the Fringillidae and Ploceidae have been presented as offshoots of quite separate and divergent stocks with subsequent superficial convergence. Some of his other conclusions, such as the derivation of the swallows (Hirundinidae) and the starlings (Sturnidae) as side issues along the line of evolution of the thrushes (Turdidae) from the warbler-flycatcher assemblage (Sylviidae-Muscicapidae), and of the weaverbirds (Ploceidae) and honey-eaters (Meliphagidae) from the grass warblers (Cisticolinae) may seem difficult to support unless one is willing to accept jaw musculature as the main guiding criterion.

In general, Beecher has assumed that food-niche specialization played a dominant role in passerine evolution, and further he has assumed that characters of simpler structure are reliably primitive. He has divided the whole order Passeres into two main groups on the basis of a constant but simple difference in the pattern of the jaw muscles. In each of these sections he then has arranged the component groups in a series " . . . of increasing general complexity as they become adapted to the fruit-, nectar-, and seed-niches provided by the evolution of flowering plants. . . ." It is thought, however, that the evolution of flowering plants came into full array as we know them today by the end of the Cretaceous, considerably earlier than the efflorescence of the various passerine bird families, so this supposed chronology of feeding adaptations is open to question and probably was not necessarily as rigidly imposed on passerine phylogeny as a study of the jaw muscles alone might seem to indicate. Beecher's study is illuminating and thought-provoking, but his conclusions, like those of any other investigator, have to be measured against the totality of all the factors and characters involved in the course of phylogenetic differentiation.

So far we have been discussing only a few of the differences in the passerine portion of the two lists; numerous other examples from the same order, or from other orders, might be cited, but they would add nothing further to the discussion. The fact remains that any proposed arrangement of bird families is open to question at many points. That such classifications are not provable things does not, however, mean that they have no value or usefulness. If they had no use other than as a frame of reference to which to attach otherwise isolated fragments of knowledge, they would be useful, but they could not be looked upon as having any inherent significance. However, these systems have always been advanced by their proposers as representing "natural" arrangements, meaning, of course, that, from the available information, they were looked upon as approximating the relationships and descent of the groups they contained. This is still the case, but the picture is complicated by the fact that enough is now known to allow students of the subject with diverse points of view to arrange and to rearrange the data in more ways than one and to support their results with no inconsiderable array of evidence. Certainly the information available today on the habits, plumages, structures, and distribution of birds of all parts of the world is far greater than even two decades ago, but there is still no correspondingly greater uniformity of opinion concerning the passerine families and concerning the apparent locus of original bifurcation of familial branches on the phylogenetic tree of other orders as well.

The picture has a more reassuring aspect, and it is this side of it that is more important than the one described above. For several decades, roughly from 1890 to 1925 there was rather little interest in classification of higher categories of birds, and the earlier systems were followed uncritically as methods of convenience. In his brief survey of American ornithological literature from 1883 to 1933, Stone (1933) has not even listed classification as such as a topic, and his account of publications dealing with bird anatomy shows how little the data of morphology were being oriented towards questions of phylogeny and classification. In the past twenty-five years there has been a great rekindling of interest in avian morphology, as all museum curators in charge of extensive collections of alcoholic material are aware, and a good percentage of these investigations has been definitely slanted towards questions of phylogeny and relationship. It seems likely that a corpus of data will become available that may enable investigators to settle many of the present points of disagreement. But it seems inevitable, almost inherent in the material, that the taxonomy of the higher categories will always fall short of being ideal, wholly reliable data in the strict sense of the term.

REVISIONS OF INDIVIDUAL FAMILIES

Although there is much uncertainty as to the degree of relationship between families of birds, there is less difference of opinion among informed specialists as to what species belong in each family. It is paradoxical, but yet a true situation, that many of these families seem in every way like natural, acceptable categories but yet defy attempts at accurate and trenchantly delimiting description. There are still a few birds whose family allocation remains doubtful, but such cases are quite small in number, especially when compared with the vast majority that seem "obviously" members of the families in which they are placed. The problem, then, in revising the classification of the contents of a single family is usually (except in the passerine groups) a matter, not of deciding what to include and what to exclude, but of trying to determine evolutionary trends within the family and to arrange the genera and species accordingly. This point of view constitutes the important change from the older approach where the classifier often looked about for characters of convenience around which the species could be grouped. Inasmuch as most such studies were carried out on museum (i.e., dead) material, and inasmuch as at the time little was known of the birds in life, the old method was not unjustified in its day, but there is no point in continuing it merely because it was once the best that could be worked out.

That all such characters are variable within and beyond the limits of the families in which they have been used reveals their limitations and emphasizes the need for a large number of characters of different types—structural, ethological, developmental, and distributional—on which to formulate a satisfactory arrangement of the species considered to form such a group. Probably few bird families have ever been reviewed with as ample material as was the case with Vaurie's (1949) study of the drongos (Dicruridae). This family contains some twenty species, or an even hundred species and subspecies, grouped in two genera. Of the hundred forms, all but three were available to the reviser, and the total bulk of material was large—about thirty-six hundred specimens, mostly with good data. It seems safe to assume that the systematic evaluation of the drongos is in fairly definitive shape; future changes, if any, are apt to be minor. This study has revealed that the characters of the more specialized species, such as elongated or curled rectrices, tail rackets, frontal crests, and feather gloss have all developed independently in different parts of the family, and that every one of these characters in all the included species varies geographically, often with an observable correlation between degree of distinctness and degree of isolation, and in relation to environmental factors such as temperature and humidity. There seem to have been only a few discernible evolutionary trends within this small, compact assemblage.

A much larger, more widespread and more diversified family that has been recently reclassified is that comprising the ducks, geese, and swans (Anatidae). Delacour and Mayr (1945) have emphasized the great age of the family as indicated by the large number of aberrant and primitive genera but have pointed out that these genera do not mean that evolution has come to a standstill in the family. ". . . Many genera, particularly *Branta, Anser, Tadorna, Anas,* and *Aythya,* present convincing evidence of active speciation. Incipient speciation is evidenced by the occurrence of about 25 forms which, though we consider them subspecies, are sufficiently distinct to be listed as full species by other recent authors; nearly completed speciation is evidenced by the occurrence of at least 10 superspecies. . . ."

Distributional problems in this family are very numerous and highly diversified. Thus, some species, such as the Mallard (*Anas platyrhynchos*), Gadwall (*Anas strepera*), Pintail (*Anas acuta*), Fulvous Tree Duck (*Dendrocygna bicolor*), and White-faced Tree Duck (*Dendrocygna viduata*) have enormous, even discontinuous, ranges, while others are extremely restricted geographically. Examples of the latter group are Salvadori's Duck (*Salvadorina waigiuensis*), Spectacled Eider (*Arctonetta fischeri*), Cape Shoveller (*Spatula capensis*), Hawaiian Goose (*Nesochen sandvicensis*), Pink-headed Duck (*Rhodonessa caryophyllacea*), and the New Zealand Mountain Duck (*Hymenolaimus malacorhynchus*), to mention but a few. Other types of distributional problems are raised by the presence of endemic races of mainland species in remote oceanic islands. In other words, as contrasted with the drongos, the duck family presents a much greater number of problems the solutions to which should be reflected in its classification. In this group, fortunately many observational data on living birds were available not only from the field but also from the aviary, a fact which permitted a many-faceted approach and which helped to correct many errors in earlier systems. It is not the purpose of this paper to point out specific changes in classifications, and not all of the changes proposed in the case of the Anatidae have met with unqualified acceptance, but this particular study may well become a model for subsequent attempts. Not only have the usual type of morphological characters been utilized, such as the scalation of the tarsi, but the plumage pattern of the downy chicks, the presence or absence of a double annual molt, general relative body proportions, posture, mode of pair-formation, display, nesting habits, food, and feeding habits have all been brought to bear on the arrangement of these birds. " . . . To be satisfactory and reliable, any system must be based on the greatest possible number of known characters, and an overvaluation of a few primarily functional characters has led to great confusion in the taxonomy of the Anatidae. . . ."

It has long been a recognized principle of sound taxonomic procedure that only such morphological characters as seemed to be little or not at all affected by function and adaptation should be used, characters that thus became looked upon as phylogenetically conservative. Herein lies at once the strength and the weakness of a study such as this one on the ducks. When a consideration of one group of characters leads to a classification at variance with the picture presented by a given morphological character or set of characters, the latter are apt to be dismissed as adaptive and hence unreliable. On the other hand if they all agree, these same characters are paraded as additional argument and proof for the proposed system, even though their function remains the same. Yes means yes, but no does not mean no. In bolstering the argument for the taxonomic significance of habits it is stated that " . . . habits and behavior are deeply rooted and are usually the product of very ancient evolution . . .", but when structures associated with differences in habits are dismissed as "adaptive" or "functional," these ethological connections suddenly seem to lose much of their force. And yet these apparent contradictions are not necessarily as serious as they might seem; the evaluation of each set of characters in any group can only be arrived at by careful consideration in connection with related and unrelated characters in the same or related groups. There is no hard and fast rule of universal applicability. A character may seem to be phylogenetically stable and reliable in one group and not in another. A character that seems eminently functional and adaptive is not without value either, if for no other reason than that it emphasizes the distinctness of the difference in the habits it is correlated with in the group. If the habits are as deep-rooted in the ancient past as is assumed, then correlated structures may also have a significant antiquity. The revision of the classification of the *Anatidae* has been presented with a commendable variety of supporting evidence, and this is its chief significance. It is disconcerting however, after being lead along from one change to another, each with suggestive reasons, to be told at the end of the study that "in every respect except the inventory of the species, the family is still insufficiently known. . . . The internal anatomy of ducks is a completely neglected field. . . . The biology of the ducks is even less known than their morphology." And the ducks are a relatively well-known family!

A simpler case, illustrating the inadequacy of the earlier attempts at classification based on a few minor external structural characters, such as the shape of the tail, the tarsal feathering, the form of the nostrils, etc., is that of the swallows (Hirundinidae). Here (Mayr and Bond, 1943) the altered arrangement was due largely to a growing knowledge of the swallows as living creatures, and not only as museum corpses, and a recognition of the fact that many of the species that look very similar in the museum trays are widely divergent in life in their nesting habits, flight, and voices.

A recent revision of the Hawaiian honeycreepers (Drepanididae), is of more than usual interest (Amadon, 1950). Famous as a small group showing a degree of adaptive radiation otherwise unparalleled in any single avian family, these birds had been previously classified, chiefly on bill characters, into some eighteen genera, most of them monotypic. Now this unwieldy splitting has been reduced by half, and, even so, five of the nine genera contain but a single species apiece. The apparently primitive, least specialized species are considered as perhaps most like some of the American Coerebidae, but the anatomical characters involved are so slight that one cannot rule out of consideration the possibility of their derivation from any of the thin-billed American groups of nine-primaried song birds, such as the Parulidae or the Thraupidae. The high degree of adaptive radiation is interpreted as a result of the fact that " . . . competition among similar sympatric species places a selective premium upon divergence; if suitable empty ecological niches are available adaptive radiation may result. If they are not, one or the other of two such competing species will be exterminated, or both may survive by rigid specialization for only slightly different ecological niches. In major adaptive changes the intermediate steps will as a rule not be well adapted for either the old or new ecological niches. Hence, such transitions are usually abrupt. These principles are admirably illustrated by the genus *Hemignathus.* On geologically recent, isolated archipelagos adaptive radiation is now in progress; on continents evolution is usually in the later, more stabilized stages of minor adaptations and specializations. . . . " In the Hawaiian honeycreepers the general course of speciation was probably not different from that in other families and involved populations that were cut off from each other on different islands. However, there was a great deal of subsequent moving about and overlapping of species with the result that on a large island such as Hawaii no fewer than fifteen species occurred. " . . . In some species inter-island stragglers are so frequent that differentiation does not occur or is held at the racial level. The more isolated islands receive fewer stragglers, and as a result endemism is very pronounced. The large islands have a more varied ecology than do the smaller ones. This is reflected in a richer avifauna, apparently because many species are able to survive on the larger islands by utilizing ecological niches absent on the smaller ones. . . . "

Comparable to the review of the Hawaiian honeycreepers, in that it too is primarily a study of the over-all biology of the group and not merely a rearranging of its members, is Lack's study of the Galapagos finches (Geospizinae), now generally known, as a side result of this work (Lack, 1945; 1947), as Darwin's finches. Like the honeycreepers of the Hawaiian archipelago, these finches also inhabit a group of oceanic islands and show remarkable, but less spectacular, adaptive radiation in bill form. In the older literature on these birds there is much confusion and disagreement, due largely to the unusual nature of the variations presented by them as compared with the more usual variations of continental forms. On large land masses passerine birds of closely allied forms often vary in plumage color and pattern and in size, but are usually fairly similar in shape and form of the bill and other structural characters. In Darwin's finches, on the contrary, closely related species usually differ markedly in the bill and little, if at all, in plumage; actually the plumage differences that do occur are chiefly of generic significance. Furthermore, the variability in some of these birds is much greater than in ordinary birds. For example, the variation in the bill of *Geospiza fortis* is so great that the extremes were formerly classified as two or even three different species. Extensive collections and field observations were needed to demonstrate that all were really a single exceptionally variable species. Had but a single example of each extreme been known, systematists might well have placed them in separate genera. Here again there were secondary shiftings and movings about, so on some of the islands all but two or three of the fourteen species were found; no one island had less than three species on it. As Lack has pointed out, " . . . related species differ so much in beak that, were they mainland birds, they would unhesitatingly be placed in different genera. But in other respects, including plumage, they are often very similar, indicating close relationship. . . . On oceanic islands the land birds are at an earlier stage of evolution than on the continents. On the continents the divergence into finches, warblers, tits and woodpeckers obviously took place in a much more distant past than the corresponding divergence among Darwin's finches in the Galapagos. . . . " The general interpretive results of this study, made on the life histories of the living birds as well as the characters preserved in museum specimens, are as follows. Island races of the same species reveal great variability, the range of this variation running from slight average size differences to very striking ones. On the whole there is a correlation between the degree of difference and the degree of isolation involved. While some of these divergencies appear to be adaptive, others are not obviously to be looked upon in this way. New species come into being when forms that originated geographically isolated from each other later meet and yet remain distinct. When two such related species meet, there is usually keen competition, and survival of both depends on a secondary ecological isolation, which gives selective value to specializations and hence favors adaptive radiation.

Other recent revisions of special families have been characterized more by the fact that their proposers have had much more complete museum material (geographically and systematically) than was previously available, rather than by any intensive and extensive personal familiarity with the birds in life or any particularly noteworthy new biological data on them. Among families so treated, with varying degrees of conviction, may be mentioned the Corvidae (Amadon, 1944), the Sturnidae (Amadon, 1943), the Pycnonotidae (Delacour, 1943a), the Nectariniidae (Delacour, 1944), the Timaliidae (Delacour, 1946), the Bombycillidae (Arvey, 1951), the Asiatic Alaudidae (Vaurie, 1951), Dicaeidae (Mayr and Amadon, 1947), and the subfamily Estrildinae of the family Ploceidae (Delacour, 1943b). These revisions present no biologically significant conclusions, as such, but by arranging the species and genera concerned, in keeping with present knowledge, make it easier for them to be used in biological studies. A point that may be worth mentioning here, and that is brought out in the study of the Corvidae, is the fact that while behavior may often be of systematic value, it has to be used just as cautiously as any other kind of character. Thus, the three species of jays of the genus *Aphelocoma* are very similar morphologically, except for variation in the relative length of wing and tail, but differ greatly in their eggs, voices, and in their gregarious or solitary manner of living. Even subspecies of the same species differ markedly in temperament.

The chief trend in all these revisions of the contents of bird families has been to reduce the number of genera and to rearrange such genera as are kept in a less arbitrary, more "natural" way. There is, and probably always will be, difference of opinion among specialists as to the limits of individual genera and as to their exact relationships, but the trend is nevertheless apparent even though at times partly obscured.

Changes in concepts of the relationships of families of birds in the past two or three decades are not so much the result of any novel ideas or the sources of new ideas, but are mainly the reflection of fuller information than was available earlier. Within such a complex group as the passerine birds there is still no agreement as to the "best" or the most "natural" sequence in which to list the included families. Within the confines of individual families, increasingly more complete knowledge of the habits of birds of all parts of the world (and hence of exotic relatives of familiar species) has made it evident that a system of classification based wholly on structural characters, often minor ones at that, is not always natural. The present efflorescence of revisionary studies is the expression of a growing conviction that this fund of knowledge has become sufficiently large and extensive to call for its inclusion in formulating systematic conclusions. Others of these studies have been undertaken primarily to discover and to describe the trends of evolutionary differentiation in discrete groups, so as to build up a mass of comparative data on this important but generally elusive subject; and still others have had the more modest but still useful aim of surveying critically the included forms, in order to provide a sounder basis for the recognition of genera, species, and races involved and for the interpretation of the distribution of the group in light of the known geological history of the areas inhabited.

REVISIONS OF SINGLE GENERA OR OF POLYTYPIC SPECIES

Since much of the material contained in revisionary surveys of single genera or of polytypic species is discussed in the preceding chapter, the account here will emphasize those aspects that bear most directly on classification. By and large, it may be said that recent studies of these smaller avian categories fall into one or the other of two types. Some of them, such as the detailed and elaborate monographs on the warblers of the genus *Phylloscopus* (Ticehurst, 1938) or *Cisticola* (Lynes, 1930), are enormously useful to the museum systematist, but in spite of their real value and the amount of new information they present, they are of relatively little philosophical interest because their authors were concerned only with disentangling and straightening out difficult taxonomic and nomenclatural problems in order to know how to distinguish and to identify the species and races involved and how to apply the existing names available for them. Other studies were not occasioned primarily by the embarrassment of difficult material in need of elucidation, but by biological questions, the solutions of which were attempted on genera or species that promised to be adaptable for the purpose. In these studies the resulting revisions are really only incidental products of the work itself. Among these, and their number is rapidly growing, may be mentioned reports on the forms of the genus *Junco* (Miller, 1941), *Limnodromus* (Pitelka, 1950), *Pipilo* (Sibley, 1950; Davis, 1951), *Otocoris* [*Eremophila*] (Behle, 1942), *Dendrocopos* (Voous, 1947), *Icterus* (Beecher, 1950), *Lanius* (Olivier, 1944), and *Aphelocoma* (Pitelka, 1951).

Although Lyne's work on the warblers of the genus *Cisticola,* a large and most difficult group, is purely a systematic treatise (including life history data in its approach) and therefore makes no attempt to pose any particular theoretical problems, and consequently attempts to solve none, it is a study of such unusual proportions that it contains much material of broad interest. As the author modestly put it, his " . . . first objective has never been more than to make these birds known alive or dead, and to give them their 'correct' names, in order that they may be discussed, studied and enjoyed without getting into a maze of ambiguity over the names. . . . That other matter of wider influence in its bearing on other groups of birds and problems of general biology should have arisen in pursuit of the main objective is only natural, and out of this category, that relating to the perennial *mode* of dress (plumage) and its relation to sexual activity is certainly worthy of development and application to other groups of birds. . . . " This illustrates the point; the study was undertaken to clarify the status and validity of the species and subspecies already in the literature; that data of broader interest came out of it is due to the author's perspicacity in recognizing points of general significance beyond his immediate task. Quite possibly the discovery and description of a highly involved plumage situation is the one single result of greatest biological significance in the monograph. The term "mode," not previously employed in ornithological literature, is " . . . coined to express what cannot be called a habit, for whatever may be its cause, its existence can only be perceived through the effect on the organism"; nor is it "well called 'sequence of plumages', because that term really applies only to what is contained in the *mode.*"

The perennial mode "is practically confined to that belt of the African continent contained between the parallels of Lat. 8° north and south of the Equator anything outside of which is very exceptional. . . ." Some idea of the complexity of the situation, and a condition which made museum determination of specimens previously very difficult and uncertain, may be sensed from the fact that "the majority of species inhabiting this equatorial belt range continuously, not only right through it from north to south, but also on beyond it to where the seasonal *mode* is the only one, so naturally there can be nothing like precise geographical boundaries between the two *modes,* and the obvious corollary is that fairly large border zones exist where something else happens; that is so, and what happens there is that some individuals have the seasonal and some the perennial *mode,* which is precisely what happens on a smaller scale inside the belt itself; in other words, the individualism which characterizes in high degree the transition from one *mode* to the other in the border zones is often found in varying and lesser degree within the equatorial belt. . . ." If this study of *Cisticola* produced no other result than the elucidation of a wholly new aspect of plumages and molts in birds it would still be a significant work. Numerous other genera of smaller size and less complexity have also been revised in recent years, but we have room here only to discuss a few of those studies that show the changed approach that is making systematics once again a field of general biological interest and significance.

The sparrows of the genus *Junco* were studied, not primarily from a taxonomic or a nomenclatural angle, but for the evidence they reveal concerning the evolution of the various plumage characters developed in different parts of the group, " . . . to make a thorough analysis of races and species as they occur in nature in order to determine the degree of unity of each, and to trace differentiation from individual variants through successive stages of group differentiation to the species. . . . " While not nearly as large, in the number of included forms, as *Cisticola, Junco* is still not a small genus, and its species and races present a fair number of discrete characters for study and appraisal. The opposite extreme is shown in the shorebird genus *Limnodromus,* comprising only two closely similar species, one with three races, the other with none. In this case the study was focused on their small morphological and ecological discontinuities primarily as indicators of the course of adaptation and differentiation in the past history of the group. Although differing only in slight characters, chiefly relative proportions, two groups in the genus have become differentiated to the species level, *L. scolopaceus* characterized by its relatively long bill, long legs, and short wings, and *L. griseus* characterized by relatively short bill, short legs, and long wings. Prior to this work they were assumed to be races of one species, but now we find that the two are ecologically as well as morphologically distinct, *scolopaceus* being a fresh-water bird and *griseus* a form of brackish areas. As Pitelka has told us in the opening paragraph of his paper, " . . . evidence on morphological and ecological discontinuities between closely related species and on variational trends forecasting discontinuities within species now constitutes, for higher vertebrates at least, the best data we have on the course of adaptation and species formation. . . . At the same time that such studies elucidate species relationships, they serve to localize areas where critical problems of species ecology can be investigated and where available data on historical geology can be brought to bear on questions of phylogenetic history. Thus, detailed analyses of morphological variation and distributional relations in these species groups serve not only to provide a picture of evolutionary radiation in them, but simultaneously to orient us with reference to basic questions of ecology and faunistics. . . . "

In his study of the variations of the Horned Larks, *Eremophila alpestris,* of western North America (21 subspecies!), Behle (1942) has found not only great geographical variation but unusual individual variability and sexual and age dimorphism. An attempt was made to correlate the racial characters with physiographic features of their ranges as a means of furthering knowledge of the environmental factors involved in the process of racial differentiation. Some of the subspecies were found to be more stable, others less so; some to be wide-ranging and locally variable, others more restricted and more homogeneous, and often with sizeable intermediate populations characterized by intermediate geographic differentiation. Unlike some investigators of other groups, Behle has considered isolation to have been an aid, but not more than an aid, in the formation of subspecies.

Another aspect of recent approaches to systematic data may be illustrated by Voous's attempt to determine whether historical influences upon distribution and differentiation could be detected in the present distribution and classification of the woodpeckers of the genus *Dendrocopos* (Voous, 1947). To this end there were sought out cases of parallelism in the distribution of a small number of other birds as well (*Garrulus glandarius,* for example) in the recent and former distribution of the Arcto-Tertiary forest vegetation, and in geological (late Tertiary and post-Tertiary) occurrences. The genus is a large one, containing some thirty-five species with many races, and is shown to be divisible into six groups. These include a number of species which are not only closely related systematically, but which also show apparent geographical relations, the latter being discernible in the recent distribution of the members of the group. The author has found that while the genus has a wide range, its absence from Madagascar, southern Africa, tropical South America, Papua, and Australia suggests a relatively recent dispersal from southeastern Asia, which he considers to have been its geographic locus of origin. The six groups within the genus show no geographic relations between them, although taxonomic relations are obvious. The recent distribution of the holarctic species of the genus seems to have been greatly affected by the glacial periods, and the results of important movements of whole populations in the interglacial and postglacial periods are considered to be detectable in the recent distribution of these forms. In other words, in this study we have an attempt, and not unsuccessful, to reconstruct the geographic displacements and infiltration of a genus during its whole history—another aspect of the tendency to consider the present picture as a result of, and hence as a clue to, the geographical and phylogenetical history that led up to it, and not merely as a descriptive fact in itself.

A somewhat different approach to the study of past distributional data in connection with present results is to be seen in a most revealing study of the Red-eyed Towhees of Mexico (Sibley, 1950). Two species, *Pipilo erythrophthalmus* and *P. ocai* of the central Mexican highlands, attracted attention because of the numerous specimens that turned up showing various degrees of intermediacy between these otherwise well-differentiated, strongly marked species, and the whole problem was studied along the lines of attempting to evaluate the results of what seemed to be subsequent, or secondary, contacts between differentiated populations that seemed to have reached the stage of at least partial physiological isolation. As Sibley has expressed it, " . . . such secondary contacts are the proving grounds for testing the degree of isolation which has been attained in the dynamic process of species formation. If complete physiological isolation has been attained, the two forms will live as sympatric species and continue to diverge, although existing side by side. If the degree of separation attained by the time the secondary junction is established is not sufficient to maintain isolation, the result will be hybridization. . . . " Sibley's results indicate clearly that there were no less than four secondary contacts between the two groups, apparently dating from different times and from different degrees of specific stability. Thus, in Oaxaca the two groups exist sympatrically without interbreeding; on Mount Orizaba the situation is similar but with occasional hybridization between them, but from Jalisco to southern Hidalgo the population is highly variable and largely of hybrid nature. Out of a series of seventy-seven specimens, no two were alike, due to the various recombinations of *erythrophthalmus* and *ocai* characters.

A study such as this not only helps to explain what would otherwise remain puzzling specimens but gives a reliable clue as to the relative age of the species involved in different portions of their present range. The towhees provide informing glimpses into the process of species formation that are no longer possible to get from many other groups of birds.

These few studies must suffice for our survey; the chief impetus behind many of the recent revisions of avian classification has been to investigate the nature of the categories from the subspecific level up to the ordinal one, and to arrange the information about birds in a form, and against a frame of reference, where it may be used more effectively as an important part of the biological evidence bearing on major theoretical problems, in line, where possible, with the results emanating from the laboratories of the geneticists and physiologists. The studies of compact, lower categories, such as single genera and polytypic species, are generally based on fuller data and have the advantage over those dealing with families and orders in that they are more directly susceptible to the application of recent findings in other biological fields. The compartmentalized division of the biological sciences may have been necessary to allow for the growth of each compartment, but the time has now come when it is profitable to attempt to co-ordinate the data and the ideas of several of these specialities. That this is being done by taxonomists and by a few geneticists is one of the significant trends in current biology. That it is largely the work of systematists (including, of course, the paleontologists) has done much to offset the criticism often leveled at the taxonomist by specialists in other biological fields and has done much to reassert the fundamental place in biological work that the old classical field of systematics used to occupy. There is no denying the fact that the data of taxonomy are not provable in the sense that experimental results may be and that in careful analysis these data are more informed opinions than ascertained facts, but yet their total picture has the ring of truth to it, and this essential rightness is being demonstrated again by the fact that it can and does incorporate the new data of genetics without real difficulty. The obstacle was chiefly an outmoded concept of the nature of systematic units, and this, especially with the broadened concept of the species as the basic element of the categories above it, is no longer a bar to further progress. Avian taxonomists, working with a body of data more complete than is available to any other group of specialists, have been able to take a leading part in this work, a work that should become increasingly convincing as the numerous deficiencies, exposed in the process, are studied and remedied.

Some twenty years ago one of the "old fashioned" systematists (Rothschild, 1932) wrote that "although the systematist is primarily concerned with the organisms as produced by Nature, and not with the creative forces which have evolved them, his researches extend to so many different species that he is bound to collect evidence bearing on those forces and their working. There are, in fact, many questions which can only be answered with the help of extensive systematic collections. . . ." In the whole complex of biological sciences, the results of laboratory experiments give important data and help to build up certain parts of the picture; as systematic and ecological "natural history" data become more and more complete it becomes not only possible but incumbent upon the taxonomist to apply them to these experimental data, and vice versa, and to see whether they "fit" or whether they need alteration. Hence the taxonomist becomes, as his field of data becomes more completely known and documented, a vital link in the process of making understandable the facts of the world of living things.

Bibliography

AMADON, D.

1943. The genera of starlings and their relationships. Amer. Mus. Novit. No. 1247, 16 pp.

1944. The genera of Corvidae and their relationships. Amer. Mus. Novit. No. 1251, 21 pp.

1950. The Hawaiian honeycreepers (Aves, Drepaniidae). Bull. Amer. Mus. Nat. Hist., 95:157-262.

ARVEY, M. D.

1951. Phylogeny of the waxwings and allied birds. Univ. Kansas Publ. Mus. Nat. Hist., 3:473-530.

BEECHER, W. J.

1950. Convergent evolution in the American orioles. Wilson Bull., 62:51-86.

1951. Convergence in the Coerebidae. Wilson Bull., 63:274-346.

1953. A phylogeny of the Oscines. Auk, 70:270-333.

BEHLE, W. H.

1942. Distribution and variation of the Horned Larks (*Otocoris alpestris*) of western North America. Univ. Calif. Publ. Zool., 46:205-316.

DAVIS, J.

1951. The distribution and variation of the Brown Towhees. Univ. Calif. Publ. Zool., 52:1-120.

DELACOUR, J.

1943a. A review of the genera and species of the family Pycnonotidae (bulbuls). Zoologica, 28:17-28.

1943b. A revision of the subfamily Estrildinae of the family Ploceidae. Zoologica, 28:69-86.

1944. A revision of the family Nectariniidae (sunbirds). Zoologica, 29:17-38.

1946. Les timaliinés. L'Oiseaux, 16:7-36.

DELACOUR, J., and E. MAYR

1945. The family Anatidae. Wilson Bull., 57:3-55.

LACK, D.

1945. The Galapagos finches. Occasional Papers Calif. Acad. Sci. No. 21, 151 pp.

1947. Darwin's finches. Cambridge University Press, x + 208 pp.

LOWE, P. R.

1946. On the systematic position of the woodpeckers (*Pici*), honey-guides (*Indicator*), hoopoes and others. Ibis, 88:103-127.

LYNES, H.

1930. Review of the genus *Cisticola.* Ibis, 12th ser., vol. 6, suppl. no., vii + 673 pp.

MAYR, E.

1942. Systematics and the origin of species. Columbia University Press, New York, xiv + 334 pp.

MAYR, E., and D. AMADON

1947. A review of the Dicaeidae. Amer. Mus. Novit. No. 1360:32 pp.

1951. A classification of recent birds. Amer. Mus. Novit. No. 1496:42 pp.

MAYR, E., and J. BOND

1943. Notes on the generic classification of the swallows, Hirundinidae. Ibis, 85:334-341.

MAYR, E., and C. VAURIE

1948. Evolution in the family Dicruridae (birds). Evolution, 2:238-265.

MILLER, A. H.

1941. Speciation in the avian genus *Junco.* Univ. Calif. Publ. Zool., 44:173-434.

1949. Some ecologic and morphologic considerations in the evolution of higher taxonomic categories. In Ornithologie als Biologische Wissenschaft. Carl Winter, Heidelberg, pp. 84-88.

OLIVIER, G.

1944. Monographie des pies-grièches du genre Lanius. Lecerf, Rouen, 326 pp.

PITELKA, F. A.

1950. Geographic variation and the species problem in the shore-bird genus *Limnodromus.* Univ. Calif. Publ. Zool., 50:1-108.

1951. Speciation and ecologic distribution in the jays of the genus *Aphelocoma.* Univ. Calif. Publ. Zool., 50:195-464.

PORTMANN, A.

1947. Etudes sur la cérébralisation chez les oiseaux, II. Alauda, 15:1-15.

ROTHSCHILD, W.

1932. The pioneer work of the systematist. Nature, 130:529-531.

SIBLEY, C. G.

1950. Species formation in the Red-eyed Towhees of Mexico. Univ. Calif. Publ. Zool., 50:109-194.

SIMPSON, G. G.

1944. Tempo and mode in evolution. Columbia University Press, New York, xviii + 237 pp.

STONE, W.

1933. American ornithological literature, 1883-1933. In Fifty years' progress in American ornithology, 1883-1933. American Ornithologists' Union, pp. 29-50.

TICEHURST, C. B.

1938. A systematic review of the genus *Phylloscopus.* Brit. Mus., London, viii + 193 pp.

VAURIE, C.

1949. A review of the bird family Dicruridae. Bull. Amer. Mus. Nat. Hist., 93:203-342.

1951. A study of Asiatic larks. Bull. Amer. Mus. Nat. Hist., 97:437-526.

VOOUS, K. H.

1947. On the history of the distribution of the genus *Dendrocopos.* Limosa, 20:1-142.

WETMORE, A.

1951. A revised classification for the birds of the world. Smiths. Misc. Coll., 117, No. 4, 22 pp.

chapter 3

PALEONTOLOGY . . . Alexander Wetmore

Increase in our knowledge of the paths of avian evolution through the record of fossils comes slowly but steadily in the form of specimens, obtained in most part as casual finds during search for other vertebrates, and to a lesser degree from examination of earlier records. The latter, in particular, in the past two decades has been of value, not only for the better understanding of relationship of species that have been described, but also for correction of identifications made by early investigators who were handicapped in their studies by the small amount of skeletal material of modern birds available to them.

NUMBER OF FOSSIL SPECIES KNOWN

The great *Handbuch der Palaeornithologie* by Kálmán Lambrecht, published in 1933, gives a complete résumé of knowledge in the field to the end of 1932. The present writer (1952) recently has assembled the list of fossil birds described since the appearance of Lambrecht's work to the end of 1949 for presentation before the Tenth International Ornithological Congress in Uppsala, Sweden, in June, 1950. This is, in part, the basis for the discussion in the following pages. The list of fossil species recorded in the two sources mentioned includes 787 forms, the majority of which come from the latter half of the Tertiary period. The series begins with the earliest flying feathered creatures of the Jurassic, 150,000,000 years ago, and extends to kinds that have become extinct in Recent time, some of which were known to primitive prehistoric man. Relative to the revisionary work on the species named or identified by early workers there may be noted the considerable collections of skeletons of modern birds added in recent years to the extensive materials in the U.S. National Museum, and the growing collections now found in the Museum of Vertebrate Zoology at Berkeley, in the University of California at Los Angeles, and in the museums of the universities of Kansas, Michigan, Cornell, and elsewhere.

In brief summary, the recent finds in the field of avian paleontology have served to clarify and extend our knowledge but have not given any completely new concepts relative to the avian group. Birds as a class must have

Manuscript received May 1, 1954.

attained their present general form toward the end of the Cretaceous, since in Eocene and Oligocene time we find examples of the flying, swimming, and running types with which we are familiar today. Novelties have consisted of variations in size from what we consider standard for our living species, adaptations to specialized habit in groups of conservative type in the modern world, and occasional kinds that give a clue to ancient relationships between forms that seem widely separated when only the living birds are considered.

From this general survey of this field of ornithological knowledge, it seems strange that more has not been learned of the bird life of Cretaceous time, particularly in North America, in view of the extended search for fossils in beds of this period. In the main the early kinds of birds that must have existed then have left scant traces, as after seventy-five years our principal knowledge centers in two types, the aquatic *Hesperornis* and its allies, and the volant *Ichthyornis* and its associates. The second greatest gap in our present information relates to the passeriform group, which is the most abundant today, but is represented by few fossils that are older than the Pleistocene.

In the following discussion comments are arranged more or less in systematic order to facilitate their presentation.

THE MOST ANCIENT AMERICAN BIRDS

Marsh in his original studies of the Odontognathae gave figures of the brain in *Hesperornis* and *Ichthyornis,* presumed to be based on endocranial casts, that showed a reptilian form decidedly different from that of modern birds in the lesser development of cerebrum and cerebellum when viewed from above, with the optic lobes visible instead of being hidden. Tilly Edinger (1951) in a recent study has found, however, that Marsh's figures are reconstructions and could not have been made from actual casts. Further, the casts that can be made from Marsh's fossil specimens demonstrate a definitely avian brain, with no indication of specific reptilian characters. This finding, based on careful study, denies, therefore, the long accepted belief in the primitive brain development of these two ancient birds.

Gregory (1952) has produced even more startling information relative to the skull of *Ichthyornis.* After a detailed study of all of Marsh's material he has found that the lower jaws attributed to *Ichthyornis* resemble the jaws of the reptilian mosasaurs in all their details. Further, these jaws are too large to match the slender elements of other parts of the skeleton, and there is no indication of articulation with the main part of the skull. Gregory has pointed out too that the fragments identified as from the upper jaw of *Ichthyornis* are also of doubtful interpretation. He has concluded that "the toothed jaws attributed to *Ichthyornis* are not those of a bird but belong to a small mosasaur," the latter being a swimming reptile. We are left uncertain, therefore, as to whether this group of birds possessed teeth.

When the early penguins were fully committed to an aquatic life so that it was no longer necessary or desirable for them to fly in air, they were freed from any formula of restriction of body bulk in relation to wing and tail spread that governs in the flying bird. The buoyant support given by water made aquatic flying with reduced wing surface practicable and allowed the development of the cushion of blubber over the body desirable for continued existence in the coldest waters. Abundant aquatic food also promoted growth in size, and change to a heavier, more compact form, while at the same time the feathered body cover became stiffened and more extensive, the neck thickened, and the legs shortened—developments which are favorable to conservation of body heat, and, through streamlining, to greater efficiency in submersed movement. In considering these facts one must be brought more firmly to the conclusion that the penguins are the most specialized of our living birds in the sense that they have departed far from the standard form adapted for flight that has controlled the development of other groups.

The adaptation of body form in these birds is an interesting parallel to the increase in size and change in proportions found in the wholly aquatic cetacean group among mammals. Penguins, however, unlike the whales and their allies, seem to have been able to live in semitropical areas only where cold water currents have been available for feeding grounds.

One of the more important papers on fossil penguins in the period with which we are concerned is that of George Gaylord Simpson (1946), a clear and admirably presented synopsis of literature, with much additional information from fossil material collected by the author in Patagonia. As a result, in the family Spheniscidae Simpson has recognized five subfamilies, one of which includes all of the living genera. The modern birds seem to have no close lineal association with any of the four fossil groups, but present in a manner a combination of the characters found in the fossil Paraptenodytinae and Palaeospheniscinae. It is probable that the direct ancestors of the modern group were present in early Miocene, but with such limited distribution that no fossils have yet been found. The fossil species known are quite distinct, and all come from the present southern hemisphere range of the living members of the family. The largest was believed to have been about 5 feet in height and to have weighed more than 200 pounds. In contrast, according to Murphy (1936), the Emperor Penguin, the largest living species, stands from 3½ to 3¾ feet tall and weighs from 57 to 94 pounds.

The origin of penguins from flying ancestors is convincingly evident from Simpson's clear presentation. Only from the wing of a volant type could the highly specialized flipper of the penguin have been developed. The terrestrial proto-penguins that some earlier students have postulated as penguin ancestors have no support in the fossil record, and the indication is that the true penguin was developed directly from some flying group with habits like those of the diving petrels (Pelecanoididae) that fly both in air and beneath the surface of the water. Penguins remain as one of our most specialized groups of birds, but at the same time they appear to have descended from common avian ancestry and not independently from another line arising from the reptiles, as some investigators have supposed.

The fossil family Cladornithidae proposed by Ameghino for his genera *Cruschedula* and *Cladornis* from Oligocene deposits in Patagonia was supposed, in part, to support the theory of early penguinlike birds of terrestrial habit. According to Simpson, however, this family should not be included in the Sphenisciformes. The present writer (1951: 2-3, 15) has placed this group tentatively in the Pelecaniformes.

The question of the origin of the ostrichlike birds and their allies, the rheas, cassowaries, and emus, has been another subject of considerable dispute between those who believe that these modern flightless birds have descended from a line that has always been flightless and those who hold that the flightless condition is a degeneration developed when the original flying stock became wholly terrestrial. Schaub (1941) has described an interesting fossil, *Eleutherornis helveticus,* that gives useful information on this subject. The bird in question, represented by a fragmentary pelvis found in the Bohnerz formation of the Eocene near Egerkingen, Switzerland, was a species somewhat smaller than the living Rhea, *Rhea americana,* and in general similar to the ostrich. However, the cross-section of the lower end of the vertebral column, and the position of this relative to the acetabulum, are definitely similar to the condition found in the higher groups of carinate, as opposed to ratite, form. There may be here, therefore, in this ancient fossil valuable, though fragmentary, evidence that these running types came in fact from flying ancestors. The writer (1951: 3, 14) has placed this bird in the distinct family Eleutherornithidae in the order Struthioniformes.

THE MOAS

The moas of New Zealand, first made known to science by Sir Richard Owen in 1840, have been the subject of many investigations, with the description of numerous forms. More recent finds of extensive material have stimulated Archey (1941) to prepare a concise review that has included a survey of older material with coverage of the newer finds, giving a clearer view of these strange, flightless birds. Earlier attempts at a classification based on size and proportions of the leg bones have been replaced by a more logical scheme where the genera are distinguished by the form of the skull, sternum, and pelvis, added to the form and proportionate length of the three main bones of the leg. On this basis Archey has divided the known moas among two families, the Dinornithidae, with one genus and six species, and the Anomalopterygidae, the shorter and stouter forms, of which there are five genera and fourteen species.

Archey believes that the moas are most closely allied to the kiwis, and that these two, while widely separated, are perhaps closer to the rheas than to other groups. While many moas were destroyed by natural causes at the end of a Pleistocene period of glaciation, the final extermination came through the agency of man some time after the arrival of the earliest Polynesians, who are supposed to have reached New Zealand several generations before the great Maori migration of A.D. 1350.

Archey's studies of large series of bones found together in apparently contemporaneous cave deposits have indicated a considerable individual variation in length and heaviness of femur, tibia, and metatarsus, so that wide limits of difference in dimension in the lower limb are evident in the same species. Formerly this variation led to much confusion and uncertainty in identification. The tallest individuals found in the genus *Dinornis* are believed to have been not more than ten feet in height, as against earlier statements that they stood twelve feet or more.

In addition to the skeleton there are interesting details of other kinds. Feathers of moas found in caves and other deposits have been of loose construction without barbicels. The aftershaft, when present, is about one half the length of the feather. Some feathers are rufous with a darker central area and a light-colored tip, some are brown at the base with a white tip, and some reddish brown with a darker brown shaft stripe. Egg shells of three types have been found in fair abundance, with a few complete or nearly complete specimens. Perfect examples range in size from 120 × 91 mm. (attributed to *Eurapteryx curtus*) to 201 × 138 mm. (*Pachyornis elephantopus*) and 253 × 178 mm. (*Dinornis robustus*). The shell is thin when compared to that of the egg of the ostrich or of the extinct *Aepyornis*, with smooth surface, and many pores, which are small and circular, or larger and slit-like. Most of the egg shells are cream color, though pale green fragments have been found. Tracheal rings show variation in form, and in some instances a loop in the trachea is apparent. (One may speculate as to whether this was a sexual character, as in the genus *Ortalis* of the Cracidae, or whether it was found in both male and female.)

The oldest record of moas is of leg bones described by Hutton from deposits of the latter part of the Tertiary, either Upper Miocene or Lower Pliocene, at Timaru. Remains have been found also in Nukumaru beds of Middle Pliocene age. Large numbers of bones and occasional footprints have been located throughout the Pleistocene. The various groups seem to have been differentiated in the latter part of the Tertiary and to have persisted well through the Pleistocene into the Recent, through considerable changes in climate, in spite of the limited land area available, which, however, at the maximum glaciation was only partially covered by ice. The well-documented data now available make the moas one of the better known groups among the fossil forms.

PETRELS, FLAMINGOS, AND THE GOOSE TRIBE

Among the procellariiform birds, fossil remains of shearwaters are fairly common, so that several species are recorded from Miocene and Pleistocene beds. The first report of a true petrel (except for bones of living species) is that of *Oceanodroma hubbsi,* named by Loye Miller (1951), from the Middle Miocene of Capistrano Beach, Orange County, California. The skeleton indicates a bird resembling the Ashy Petrel, *Oceanodroma homochroa,* but somewhat larger and more robust in form. Dr. Miller points out that the true petrels are ocean-ranging species whose bodies at death seem to sink in the sea, since it is rare to find a dead one washed up on a beach. The present fossil comes from a shale and mudstone deposit that was laid down in deep water. The Miocene species therefore may be assumed to have been as pelagic in habit as its modern relatives. The specimen is particularly significant not only as a record for this particular group of species but as indication that the present form of these birds is one of far-reaching antiquity.

The family Phoenicopteridae, for the long-legged, long-necked flamingos, allied to the ducks and geese and to the storks, has a known history in Europe from the Lower Miocene (Aquitanian) deposits of France. Four species of the peculiar genus *Paloelodus* have been named by Milne-Edwards from these beds. Another, *Phoenicopterus croizeti,* from the same age, is placed in the same genus with the more widely distributed species of our living birds. Other European fossils, somewhat tentatively placed in this suborder, are still older.

In North America a Pleistocene flamingo, *Phoenicopterus copei,* from Fossil Lake, Oregon, has long been known. More recently, Alden Miller (1944) has named another flamingo, *Megapaloelodus connectens,* from South Dakota, allied to *Paloelodus* of similar age in France, and thus has recorded this ancient group in North America. Loye Miller (1950) has identified a specimen from the Barstow syncline of the Upper Miocene, near Barstow, California, as a further record of *Megapaloelodus connectens,* thus extending the range assigned to this species both in geologic time and geographically. In the living genus, *Phoenicopterus floridanus,* allied to our modern species, has been named by Brodkorb (1953) from the Middle Pliocene of Polk County, Florida, and *Phoenicopterus stocki,* of pygmy size, has been described by Loye Miller (1944) from the Rincón Pliocene of Chihuahua in northern Mexico. The records are of importance in the history of the family.

An extinct goose, *Geochen rhuax* Wetmore (1943), described from bones of prehistoric age, found in a bed of ash beneath an ancient lava flow on the island of Hawaii, adds an unexpected species to the avifauna of the oceanic islands of the central Pacific region. The extinct form is completely different from the well-known Nene, or Hawaiian Goose, *Nesochen sandvicensis,* from the same island, being much larger in size and more similar to the Cape Barren Goose, *Cereopsis novaehollandiae,* of Australia than to any other living species of the family. It is interesting that, as a member of the subfamily Cereopsinae of the Anatidae, *Geochen* also is near *Cnemiornis calcitrans,* the great extinct species of New Zealand. Apparently this style of bird was formerly widespread in the Pacific area, where it has continued into historic time only in Australia.

In the fossil history of the ducks, geese, and swans another interesting find is *Paranyroca magna* A. H. Miller and L. V. Compton (1939) from the Lower Miocene of Bennett County, South Dakota. This had the size of a swan, and was much specialized for swimming and diving. Its peculiarities are such that it is placed in a distinct family, the Paranyrocidae, which in the compressed form of the metatarsus parallels the diving ducks (subfamily Aythyinae), but is distinct from them in the form of the metatarsal head which is more like that found in the screamers (suborder Anhimae).

A TERRESTRIAL VULTURE

While discoveries of fossil birds regularly reveal new species, most of these are more or less closely similar to kinds that are living today. Only rarely does one appear that is completely strange. In this latter group is found *Neocathartes grallator* (Wetmore), an American vulture named in 1944 from the upper Washakie beds of the Eocene of Wyoming. The find on which this species is based is notable also in having the skull, leg bones, and wing bones preserved, since most fossil birds are represented by single elements.

Neocathartes was about as long in body as a King Vulture, *Sarcoramphus papa,* but of more slender form. The leg bones were long and strong, with well-developed toes, differing decidedly from any others in the vulture group. The wings correspondingly are reduced; thus they demonstrate the anomaly of a species of limited flight in birds that otherwise are marked especially by flying and soaring ability. The neck of *Neocathartes* was strong and muscular, and from the depressed lines marking the surface of the cranium it is probable that the head was bare of feathers. We find represented then a cursorial vulture that, while able to fly, evidently was mainly terrestrial, and one that apparently stood in the same relation to the species of the Cathartidae that the Secretary-bird, *Sagittarius serpentarius,* does to the true hawks and eagles. It thus presents an entirely new type among the members of the carrion-feeding group to which it belongs, and it is placed in the classification in a superfamily apart from other American vultures. On the whole it is one of the strangest and most interesting fossils that it has been my fortune to study and describe.

THE LARGEST FLYING BIRD

The California Condor is so much a bird of the West that it has been no great surprise to find fossil remains in the caves and asphalt deposits of California. Through more recent discoveries the range of the condors during the Pleistocene has been found to have extended across to Florida and south to Nuevo León in northeastern Mexico. Fisher (1947) has identified all fossil material from western North America, formerly considered to be of the living species *Gymnogyps californianus,* as the somewhat larger, extinct *Gymnogyps amplus* L. H. Miller. The still larger extinct species *Teratornis merriami,* named originally from California, likewise has been found in the Pleistocene of Florida and Nuevo León. And, in deposits, probably of Pleistocene age, in Smith Creek Cave, east-central Nevada, Howard (1952) recently has found the wrist bone of a huge bird, *Teratornis incredibilis,* that seemingly dwarfed the previously known species *T. merriami* in the same proportion that Merriam's Teratorn towered over the condors of its day. The single bone of *incredibilis* is so characteristic in form that its relationship is without question. It represents the largest flying bird that has been known—with a calculated wing spread of 16 to 17 feet—so we may hope for further finds to give us more details as to its form.

In connection with these reports, as further indications of the former range (or possible range) of the great birds of this group, I recall condor bones found in Recent deposits in caves in Nevada, New Mexico, and the Chisos Mountains, Texas, as well as the stories of the Blackfoot Indians about a huge bird, larger than any other known, that they saw from time to time up to half a century or more ago along the eastern foothills of the Rockies in Montana and Alberta (Schaeffer, 1951).

ANCIENT CRANE-LIKE BIRDS

In the order Gruiformes, recent discoveries have given the family of the limpkins, the Aramidae, a long and diversified record in the Tertiary period. The living species, *Aramus guarauna,* is evidently ancient, though the only fossil record for it is from Pleistocene beds in Florida. In the Middle Miocene of Sioux County, Nebraska, we find *Aramornis longurio* Wetmore (1926), known from the lower end of a metatarsus, differing from the living bird in more slender legs and in different shape of the trochlea that form the support for the toes. From the Brule beds of the Oligocene we have *Gnotornis aramiellus* Wetmore (1942), which is peculiar in being a limpkin but only about one-third as large as the other species known. It differs also in the form of the humerus. And finally, also from the Brule beds of the Oligocene, we find *Badistornis aramus* Wetmore (1940), which is generally similar in the metatarsus to the living species, but shows definite approach to the cranes, thus indicating the ancient connection between the Aramidae and the Gruidae that allies them in the order Gruiformes. *Badistornis* appears rather definitely ancestral to *Aramus,* while *Aramornis* seems more a specialized offshoot that became extinct while the true limpkin line continued to Recent time.

The genus *Bathornis* Wetmore was described in 1927 from Oligocene deposits, being based on the lower part of a metatarsus. In recent years abundant material of the group has been found, so that four species now have been recognized, all from Oligocene beds. The trochleae of the metatarsus bear a general resemblance to the thick-knees, and the first species described, *Bathornis veredus,* was placed in a separate subfamily under the Oedicnemidae. Excavations of the Museum of Comparative Zoology in deposits near Torrington, Wyoming (Wetmore, 1933), brought to light an abundance of bones of this genus, sufficient to give a clearer idea of its relationships, so that now the group is recognized as a distinct family, the Bathornithidae, allied to the living cariamas of South America. The species of *Bathornis* were not as long-legged as the cariamas, and evidently had greater powers of flight. They were apparently ground inhabitants that must have been common, possibly even gregarious, from the indication of the abundant remains at Torrington. The outcrop here at the time the first finds were made was estimated to be half a mile long and from one to three feet thick. Bird bones in this average six to the cubic foot, the greater part being those of *Bathornis.* The abundance is greater than that found to date in any group of North America birds in the Tertiary, being equalled only by the quantities of bones found in the asphalt beds of the California Pleistocene. Remains of the four species of *Bathornis* described to date have been found in Colorado, Wyoming, Nebraska, and South Dakota. They constitute an element in our avifauna that has completely disappeared.

A FLIGHTLESS AUK

In the fossil record of the auks, auklets, and murres one of the anomalies has been the flightless *Mancalla californiensis* named by Lucas (1901) more than fifty years ago from a broken humerus found during the digging of a tunnel in the city of Los Angeles. While originally supposed to come from Miocene deposits it is known now to be of Pliocene age. A little over thirty years later Loye Miller (1933) recorded a second fragmentary humerus of *Mancalla* from Pliocene beds near San Diego. Material has accumulated to the extent that recently Miller and Howard (1949) have been able to present a detailed study that covers the major parts of the skeleton, making *Mancalla* one of the best reported birds of Pliocene time. This study shifts *Pliolunda diegense,* another species named by Miller (1937), also to the genus *Mancalla,* where it is marked mainly by smaller size. It now becomes *Mancalla diegense* (L. H. Miller).

The statement of Lucas that *Mancalla californiensis* was flightless has been completely verified, the bird having been highly specialized for an aquatic life, with the wings functional but considerably modified for effective use in progression in water. Correlated with this condition of flightlessness in the air, the legs were somewhat better developed than is the case in the ordinary species of the auk group. In the modifications of the wing-bones *Mancalla* shows many convergent resemblances to penguins, as does the flightless Great Auk, *Pinguinus impennis.* It is most interesting that two groups of flightless birds of this general form have developed among the auks on the coasts of North America, the two species of *Mancalla* on the Pacific and the Great Auk on the Atlantic. The latter, while remembered mainly through the record of its destruction at the hands of early voyagers, is known also from Pleistocene caves at Gibraltar and in southern Italy. It is assumed as certain therefore that the Great Auk was present during Pliocene time, so both it and *Mancalla* were living then as contemporaries. Miller and Howard, in calling attention to numerous convergent resemblances between *Mancalla* and penguins, postulated for the former a line of evolution parallel to that of all other auks, and through this they at first were inclined to recognize a distinct family, the Mancallidae. Later, Howard and the present writer in a more detailed comparison between *Mancalla* and the somewhat less aberrant Great Auk agreed that it would be better to list it in a separate subfamily, the Mancallinae.

FOSSIL PERCHING BIRDS

Newer information relative to the Passeriformes has come principally from the Pleistocene asphalt deposits of California, where bones of thirty-six living species have been identified, ranging from Horned Larks (*Eremophila alpestris*), Cliff Swallows (*Petrochelidon pyrrhonota*), ravens, and shrikes to Chipping (*Spizella passerina*) and Fox (*Passerella iliaca*) sparrows. We have some additional information on extinct species in this group through the recent studies of A. H. Miller (1947), who has named *Pandanaris convexa* from Rancho La Brea, an icterid, with a curious, even curvature of the culmen, that seems related to living cowbirds and blackbirds. *Pyelorhamphus molothroides* A. H. Miller (1932) is another member of the blackbird family found in a Pleistocene cave deposit in New Mexico. This is allied to the living cowbirds, but is of somewhat different type. The age of this species probably is Pleistocene, though possibly it is from the older centuries of Recent time. *Pipilo angelensis* Dawson (1948), another recent discovery at Rancho La Brea, is a towhee that is large in size compared to the living species of that region and differs from the large *Pipilo ocai* of Mexico (Dawson, 1950) in conformation of the upper mandible.

A DESERT FOSSIL BED

One of the early abundant finds of fossil bones of birds was made at Fossil Lake in the desert area of eastern Oregon, the site being discovered in 1876 by Governor Whiteaker of Oregon. Thomas Condon and Charles H. Sternberg worked here in 1877, and E. D. Cope visited the locality in 1879. A number of collections have been made, and the bird material obtained has been the most diversified in species for any locality in North America, except that from the brea pits of California. Papers by Cope and R. W. Shufeldt have named new forms and listed others still living, so the site has figured extensively in our records. Dr. Hildegarde Howard (1946) has assembled the approximately 2,500 bird bones available in the various collections for a careful check on the earlier identifications and has made numerous corrections through more extensive, modern knowledge of the subject. Among sixty-six forms now definitely recognized, sixteen are extinct. The age in the Pleistocene is believed to be about equivalent to that of the Rancho La Brea beds in California.

In the case of the large grebe and the coot of the Fossil Lake deposits, Dr. Howard has found that differences from the living forms are evident but are of such a nature that she has suggested recognizing the fossils as distinct but under trinomial names in connection with the specific name of the living bird to which they are allied, viz., *Aechmophorus occidentalis lucasi* for the grebe, and *Fulica americana minor* for the coot. In this sense the subspecific relationship would be that of the chronocline as proposed by George Gaylord Simpson, representing close connection through geologic time, rather than in the usual contemporaneous sense where we deal with geographic space. This proposal, in the manner in which it is formalized, introduces a new concept in systematic ornithology that undoubtedly will be apparent in other cases where sufficient prehistoric osteological material becomes available. In fact it is suggested now in a few other cases that concern the Pleistocene. In formal classification such names dealing with related sequence through consecutive periods of geologic time will need to be differentiated from the ordinary usage of trinomials to indicate allied races that are in existence contemporaneously.

Another important general article by Hildegarde Howard (1950) has presented an interesting summary of the geologic history of the avian orders based on the fossil species that have been described. This has covered an extensive survey of the literature, as well as Dr. Howard's personal studies.

In conclusion, attention should be drawn to two reports by Lambrecht (1935) from the Middle Eocene of Germany, in which the enthusiasm of the scientist may have gone beyond the facts. *Geiseloceros robustus* is placed in the family Bucerotidae, which if valid, would extend the range of the hornbills from their present territory in Africa and southeastern Asia to north-central Europe in Eocene time. The specimen on which this determination is based includes ribs, furcula, scapula, and wing bones, the family determination being made on the metacarpus and the ulna. While superficially the metacarpus resembles that of a hornbill, the ulna agrees only in heavy size. The bones, from the illustrations and description, seem to be considerably distorted, so the family allocation appears to require more careful check.

Eocathartes robustus Lambrecht, a supposed Eocene condor, described in the same paper (Lambrecht, 1935), is a second report of a species of the cathartid group in Europe. The specimen is better preserved than the hornbill, but from the description and the figures, does not indicate clearly that it is a form of this group of vultures, today found only in the western hemisphere. It would be desirable to check this further when there is opportunity, as well as to re-examine also *Plesiocathartes europaeus* named by Gaillard from beds of Lower Oligocene or Upper Eocene age in France, the other example of a supposed cathartid vulture in western Europe.

Bibliography

ARCHEY, G.

1941. The moa, a study of the Dinornithiformes. Bull. Auckland Inst. Mus. No. 1:1-119.

BRODKORB, P.

1953. A Pliocene flamingo from Florida. Chicago Acad. Sci. Nat. Hist. Misc., 124:1-4.

DAWSON, W. R.

1948. Records of fringillids from the Pleistocene of Rancho La Brea. Condor, 50:57-63.

1950. A comparison of *Pipilo ocai* and the fossil *Pipilo angelensis.* Condor, 52: 88.

EDINGER, T.

1951. The brains of the Odontognathae. Evolution, 5:6-24.

FISHER, H. I.

1947. The skeletons of Recent and fossil *Gymnogyps.* Pacific Science, 1:227-236.

GREGORY, J. T.

1952. The jaws of the Cretaceous toothed birds, *Ichthyornis* and *Hesperornis.* Condor, 54:73-88.

HOWARD, H.

1946. A review of the Pleistocene birds of Fossil Lake, Oregon. Carnegie Inst. Wash., Publ. 551:141-195.

1950. Fossil evidence of avian evolution. Ibis, 92:1-21.

1952. The prehistoric avifauna of Smith Creek Cave, Nevada, with a description of a new gigantic raptor. Bull. So. Calif. Acad. Sci., 51:50-54.

LAMBRECHT, K.

1933. Handbuch der Palaeornithologie. Gebrüder Borntraeger, Berlin, xx + 1024 pp.

1935. Drei neue Vogelformen aus dem Lutétian des Geiseltales. Nova Acta Leopoldina, Abh. Kaiserl. Leop.-Carolin. Deutschen Akad. Naturf., new ser., 3:361-367.

LOWE, P. R.

1933. On the primitive characters of the penguins, and their bearing on the phylogeny of birds. Proc. Zool. Soc. London, Pt. 2, 1933:483-538.

LUCAS, F. A.

1901. A flightless auk, *Mancalla californiensis,* from the Miocene of California. Proc. U.S. Nat. Mus., 24:133-134.

MILLER, A. H.

1932. An extinct icterid from Shelter Cave, New Mexico. Auk, 49:38-41.

1944. An avifauna from the Lower Miocene of South Dakota. Univ. Calif. Publ. Bull. Dept. Geol. Sci., 27:85-100.

1947. A new genus of icterid from Rancho La Brea. Condor, 49:22-24.

MILLER, A. H., and L. V. COMPTON

1939. Two fossil birds from the Lower Miocene of South Dakota. Condor, 41:153-156.

MILLER, L.

1933. The Lucas Auk of California. Condor, 35:34-35.

1937. An extinct puffin from the Pliocene of San Diego, California. Trans. San Diego Soc. Nat. Hist., 8:375-378.

1944. A Pliocene flamingo from Mexico. Wilson Bull., 56:77-82.

1950. A Miocene flamingo from California. Condor, 52:69-73.

1951. A Miocene petrel from California. Condor, 53:78-80.

MILLER, L., and I. DE MAY

1942. The fossil birds of California, an avifauna and bibliography with annotations. Univ. Calif. Publ. Zool., 47:47-142.

MILLER, L., and H. HOWARD

1949. The flightless Pliocene bird *Mancalla.* Carnegie Inst. Wash., Publ. 584: 201-228.

MURPHY, R. C.

1936. Oceanic birds of South America. American Museum of Natural History, New York, vol. 1, xxii + 640 pp.

SCHAEFFER, C. E.

1951. Was the California Condor known to the Blackfoot Indians? Jour. Wash. Acad. Sci., 41:181-191.

SCHAUB, S.

1941. Ein Ratitenbecken aus dem Bohnerz von Egerkingen. Ecl. Geol. Helvetiae, 33:274-284.

SIMPSON, G. G.

1946. Fossil penguins. Amer. Mus. Nat. Hist. Bull., 87:1-99.

WETMORE, A.

1926. Descriptions of additional fossil birds from the Miocene of Nebraska. Amer. Mus. Nov., No. 211, 3 pp.

1933. Bird remains from the Oligocene deposits of Torrington, Wyoming. Bull. Mus. Comp. Zool., 75:297-311.

1940. Fossil bird remains from Tertiary deposits in the United States. Jour. Morph., 66:30-34.

1942. Two new fossil birds from the Oligocene of South Dakota. Smiths. Misc. Coll., 101, No. 14, 6 pp.

1943. An extinct goose from the island of Hawaii. Condor, 45:146-148.

1944. A new terrestrial vulture from the Upper Eocene deposits of Wyoming. Ann. Carnegie Mus., 30:57-69.

1951. A revised classification for the birds of the world. Smiths. Misc. Coll., 117, No. 4, 22 pp.

1952. Recent additions to our knowledge of prehistoric birds. Proc. Tenth Internat. Ornithol. Cong., pp. 51-74.

chapter 4

AVIAN ANATOMY, 1925-1950, AND SOME SUGGESTED PROBLEMS . . . Harvey I. Fisher

The "modern" trend in biological sciences seems all too often to imply that "anatomy as such" may be overlooked in the evolution of the "better and more accepted" avenues of approach to biological problems. The synthesizers of current evolutionary thought frequently ignore many aspects of anatomy. They may pay lip-service to the field by saying that certain anatomical work needs to be done, and then go ahead with detailed phylogenies on the basis of easily observed external features. Thus the internal morphology, which embraces a host of distinctive traits, particularly for major taxonomic categories, may be virtually ignored.

Geneticists forget sometimes that the phenotypes of the organisms with which they work are anatomical features, as well as the visible expressions of the organism's genotype. In one sense, these workers are dealing with experimental anatomy. By changing the internal structure—the genotype—by gene mutations, recombinations, removal, etc., they are affecting the apparent structure. Their work on the variants is impossible until the usual or "normal" appearance, structure, or behavior is known; this norm can only be established through the medium of detailed descriptive and comparative anatomy. The study of the inheritance of skeletal dimensions in the domestic fowl by Maw (1935) is a good example of the use of gross avian anatomy in genetics. See also Quisenberry, Roberts, and Card (1941).

The result of this tendency to overlook the potential contribution of internal anatomy has led to some unfortunate events, at least in the field of ornithology. There are instances of complex studies of the plumages, life habits, evolution, and origin of a species, with almost no anatomical data. Occasionally we later find that the bird has been placed in the wrong genus or family, and perhaps even the family is misplaced. There have been taxonomic revisions upon taxonomic revisions of genera and species, oftentimes without reference to morphological features other than the external ones.

The fossil record of birds is very scanty. How, for example, is it possible to identify and allocate correctly fossil bones without detailed knowledge of either their fossil or Recent relatives? We must know the degree of variation,

Manuscript received June 5, 1952.

quantitative and qualitative, of all comparative material. Only in this way are comparisons or allocations valid.

The current phylogenetic tree of the class Aves is largely a bush because of the absence of Mesozoic remains. This segment of the evolution of birds must probably remain a question until more fossils are brought to light, but we can perhaps untangle some of the smaller twigs. To do this we must know more about the modern forms. Information concerning habitat, social organization, behavior, anatomy, etc. must be obtained, but present-day attributes of a species must be judiciously handled in any discussion of evolutionary sequences or relationships.

This trend of "disfavor" for things morphological is evidenced not only by the attitude of the modern writers, but by the decline in the number of anatomical research studies and compendia produced in the last fifty years. Anatomy, at least as far as ornithology is concerned, reached its zenith in the latter part of the nineteenth century and was climaxed by the studies of such men as Gadow, Garrod, and Fürbringer. Monographic studies since 1900 on any aspect of avian anatomy are few and far between. The highly valuable general treatise on birds by Stresemann (1927-1934) and the anatomy section by Benoit of the recent volume (vol. 15, 1950) of *Traité de Zoologie* (edited by Pierre-P. Grassé) are exceptions, although they cannot be considered strictly as research monographs. There was no mention of anatomy in *Fifty Years' Progress of American Ornithology 1883-1933,* which the American Ornithologists' Union published in 1933.

There is little question that the role of anatomy may have been overemphasized during the last century, sometimes to the exclusion of other pertinent information, and that decisions made on anatomical bases alone were often incomplete or even in error. The pendulum has, however, swung too far in the opposite direction.

OBJECTIVES OF THIS REVIEW

The purposes here are to review briefly some of the contributions anatomy has made to the science of ornithology in the last quarter-century, to point out some problems which need anatomical study, to suggest avenues of approach, and to present a bibliography of some of the morphological papers of this period. With regard to this last objective it must be noted that more emphasis has been placed on the inclusion of papers illustrating lines of future, fruitful research than on inclusion of all papers on avian anatomy. The latter would be impossible in the limited space available, but an attempt has been made to include most of the more significant contributions.

There are various ways to approach the study of anatomy. The classical one is descriptive or a straightforward detailing of the observed structure of an organ, a region of the body, or the entire animal. This is a useful means of "getting into the record" information that can be used by other workers.

This type of study, however, is usually not as interesting, or perhaps as productive, as the comparative descriptive aspect which may be superimposed. The comparative study of structures must of necessity involve their study and description, but it goes much further in allowing the worker to present analyses of relationships and of differences in function. The latter study of the correlation of structure and function, adaptive or functional anatomy, leads to the intensely interesting field of the interdependence of form, function, and environment, and often to the origin and relationships of different taxonomic categories.

An attempt was made first to discuss these approaches in anatomy in separate sections of this review. This soon broke down because of the interdigitation of the fields. Hence, the papers mentioned are now arranged around organ systems or problems in ornithology; this leads to some crisscrossing of discussion and to an arbitrary choosing of matters to be emphasized. The anatomy of fossils is discussed by Alexander Wetmore in another chapter, and I have not included the microscopic phase of anatomy.

ACKNOWLEDGMENTS

The following persons have read the manuscript in detail and have offered valuable suggestions: William J. Beecher, Andrew J. Berger, Harold C. Hanson, and Robert W. Storer. My sincere thanks go to them.

WEIGHTS AND OTHER DESCRIPTIVE ASPECTS

The simple matter of recording weights of birds has not received adequate attention. As long ago as 1922 Heinroth wrote a comprehensive and thought-provoking article on the relation of body weights, egg weights, and periods of incubation. Huxley (1927), in discussing the relation of egg and body weights, largely in relation to Heinroth's work, concluded that each group of birds shows a definite characteristic curve of its own, and that egg weight is only a function of body size in a group whose members are within a definite size range. This aspect of body weight needs further study, for the detailed experimental work on domestic fowl is inconclusive (see Quisenberry, Roberts, and Card, 1941:117-118, for a review). Rensch (1931) studied the ratio of weight of heart to weight of body and noted that the ratio may increase up to 20 per cent with an increase of only 1,500 feet in altitude and a drop of only 3 degrees C. in mean annual temperature. Moreau's criticism (1944b) of this work of Rensch includes points applicable to many papers in avian anatomy and taxonomy—the series was probably inadequate; specimens from the two levels were not comparable on age, sex, or physiological bases; and there was insufficient statistical treatment. Moreau (1944a) provided some information indicating that Palearctic forms may be lighter in weight in their winter quarters than on the breeding grounds. He also noted that some species are apparently heavier at higher altitudes—supporting Bergmann's hypothesis.

In 1938, Hutt and Ball studied the relation between body weight and number of feathers per unit of body surface and found that the number of feathers per unit of surface increases as body weight decreases. Zedlitz (1926) discussed body weight in migratory versus resident birds, but the data are too few for conclusions. Wolfson (1945) studied experimentally the seasonal deposition of fat and body weights in Oregon Juncos, *Junco oreganus*. He found increases in body weight, as a result of the accumulation of fat, just prior to migration. The variation in weight in his migrant birds was up to 19 per cent. Seasonal fluctuations in the weights of petrels and penguins were noted by Richdale (1947). Stewart (1937) published one of the more extensive listings of the weights of various species, and Bellrose and Hawkins (1947) recorded weights of ducks in Illinois. Fiora (1933 and 1934) listed weights of birds, and Wetherbee (1934) gave weights of live birds. It is probable that most of our accurate and valuable data on bird weights must come from such live material.

Baldwin and Kendeigh (1938) noted that weights of an individual may vary 12 per cent during the day, and Heinroth (1922) found a seasonal variation up to 40 per cent on either side of the mean weight. Linsdale (1928:312), Nice (1938), and Baldwin and Kendeigh *(op. cit.)* have indicated many of the variables affecting weights of birds. Rensch recently (1950) noted some salient possibilities in relation to sex and body weight. Edinger (1942) correlated body size and size of pituitary in Recent and fossil ratites and suggested that pituitary disturbances might have been responsible for the large body size usually found in this "group."

It is thus evident that before we may use weights in any major degree in taxonomy, as Amadon (1943a) has suggested, we must have great series of weights for populations of the same species under varying conditions of life. Miller (1941:255) has, however, demonstrated that in breeding male Oregon Juncos, taken over a six-week period, the coefficient of variability of weight was 5.2, a figure not at all out of line with expected variation in zoological samples. The suggestion of Amadon was that weight is a good index to general body size, and that weight may be used as a less variable factor to which other, more variable, aspects may be compared in taxonomic work. The suggestion needs additional investigation, for Miller (1941) has shown in several races of juncos that wing and tail length are poorly correlated with weight and that sometimes a reverse correlation is present. Amadon (1943b) has further suggested that in some groups body weights may be calculated from egg weights, with an accuracy up to 95 per cent.

The point of interest is that weight may be used in these different ways and that its use should be aided by increased collection and publication of these data. Competent field collectors now add this information to the original label prepared in the field.

Related to this need for more recorded weights on entire birds is the need for weights of single organs and the correlation of weight with various environmental conditions and with functions. Latimer (1927b) on the Domestic Turkey *(Meleagris),* Schneider and Dunn (1924) on the White Leghorn Chicken *(Gallus),* and Latimer and Wager (1941) have approached this in their studies of correlation and variability in several organ systems. Engels (1938a), working with the American Coot *(Fulica americana),* had sufficient material to show something of the degree of variation in the bones of a species and in sexual dimorphism, as well as proportions between bones.

Rensch's work (1931) on the geographical variation in size of internal organs (heart, stomach, intestines) and in number of eggs laid, although inconclusive, suggests many avenues for further productive research.

Descriptive studies of a certain organ or organ system of a single species, such as those of Baudouin (1936) on the osteology of the Cormorant, *Phalacrocorax carbo,* and of Larson (1930) on the Road-runner, *Geococcyx californianus,* are valuable bases for future comparative work and, if sufficiently detailed, they show the inherent variability and thus are of use in taxonomic and evolutionary studies. Linsdale's study (1928) of the variation in the bones of the Fox Sparrow, *Passerella iliaca,* is one of the most detailed analyses. He found individual variation to be slight as compared to geographic variation, and showed that most bony elements in this species varied in size geographically. Fisher (1947) showed that variability in the bones of Recent and fossil forms of the California Condor, *Gymnogyps californianus,* was essentially the same and that the Pleistocene form differs only in size from the modern California Condor. Hildegarde Howard (1947b) established the presence of much the same situation in the Black Vultures *(Coragyps atratus)* and the Golden Eagle *(Aquila chrysaëtos).* Riddle (1928) found seasonal and sexual differences in weights of liver and spleen; Hartman (1946) gave weights of adrenal and thyroid glands; and Schwartz (1949) studied, inconclusively, the relative weights of heart and liver. Assuming that weight and use of an organ are related, much might be learned of gross differential function by such studies.

Fred Glenny (1942-1945) has published numerous papers[1] on the arterial system of birds, particularly the carotid area. These are chiefly descriptive and as yet limited in scope. Nonetheless, such studies, preferably performed on a comparative basis, will provide fundamental information from the viewpoint of taxonomy, evolution, and function.

Pterylography has not been emphasized recently; perhaps no more than twenty detailed research papers have appeared. Most of these are related to taxonomy and will be discussed in that section. For information on most species

[1] In this and in similar instances in which a series of papers on a single topic have been published by an individual, the titles listed in the bibliography may represent only a small part of the total number. They have been selected for breadth of interest and variety of source of publication.

we must resort to papers published about fifty years ago, and the search is often disappointing, for much is unstudied. The problems of the origin and evolution of feathers, and trends in evolution, are not satisfactorily solved.

RESPIRATORY SYSTEM

The structure of the respiratory system, including the lungs and air sacs, is still only incompletely known, even in the few birds which have been investigated. Without knowledge of the detailed structure, the manner in which the system functions will remain largely hypothetical. What morphological information is available is, for the most part, concerned with a half-dozen species of ducks, pigeons, and domestic chickens. Functional studies are similarly limited, although this complex system is one of the outstanding avian characteristics.

In 1924 Brandes reviewed the past work and presented his interpretation of structure and regulation—postulating valves to control air flow and direction, as did Vos (1937). Krogh (1941) and Zeuthen (1942) pointed out that the presence of valves had not ever been demonstrated, and the latter does not think valves are necessary, if the parabronchial muscles could control the flow. There may be independent control of the flow to the air sacs, but to my knowledge it has not been checked, although experimental work in pressure chambers should be informative.

Most research on respiration has centered around the analysis of gases in the various parts of the system. From this the workers have attempted to infer something of structure and function. Dotterweich (1933, 1936), Walter (1934), Scharnke (1934), and Plantefol and Scharnke (1934) used this approach. Vos (1935) using dissection, vital dyes, X-rays, and paraffin molds concluded that the valves (still undemonstrated) between the mesobronchus and the vestibulum were closed at expiration and open on inspiration, but the problem remains unsolved. Scharnke's paper of 1938 has a detailed analysis of gaseous contents, which is closely tied in to the morphology and function. Incidentally, his work shows the great danger in generalizing on the basis of scanty information on a few species—the systems in the duck and pigeon differ considerably, and the differences are not clearly related to the diving habits of the ducks. Scholander (1940) came to the conclusion, after rather extensive experiments, that forms are adapted for diving not by structural differences so much as by physiological features. The oxygen stores of divers may be somewhat greater, but not enough to permit full-scale oxygen consumption for a long period; he thinks the divers are relatively insensitive to the carbon dioxide in the inspired air and that they possess a differential vascular control which keeps the central nervous system and the heart well supplied and forces other organs (muscles for example) to operate anaerobically. Scholander demonstrated the insensitivity, but the other factors mentioned need further work. A comparative anatomical study on the systems in several species of ducks of varying diving habits would be very productive and would provide a foundation for interpretation of adaptations in the diving forms. Dehner (1946) has developed an apparatus for measuring the respiratory volume of large birds; it is a modified oxygen-dilution setup which could be used advantageously in this comparative work on diving birds.

The relationship between locomotion and respiration is still unknown. There must be some sort of control to prevent overventilation when the bird is in flight or even moving rapidly on land. Whether this is a joint structural and neural control or only the latter is not known. Zeuthen (1942) has suggested that perhaps the upper limit of the speed of locomotion is determined by the maximum safe rate of heat loss. As Krogh (1941) has indicated, breathing is apparently synchronized with flight; but how? Some workers feel that inspiration occurs on the upstroke of the wing; others say it is simultaneous with the downstroke. And Fraenkel (1934) is not sure there is any relation to wing movements in *Fringilla coelebs.* He thinks there may be in the pigeon.

Richardson (1939) has suggested that the well-developed subcutaneous air sacs in the Brown Pelican, *Pelecanus occidentalis,* may be adaptations to cushion the impact when this species dives into water from a height. Comparative studies on other "high-diving" and related, but not diving, forms would be of interest.

It is generally agreed that many parts of the bird's body are penetrated by ramifications of the air sacs. Injections of paraffin, Wood's alloy, and other metals, followed by dissection or maceration, have made it possible to determine some of these in some species. One finds only scattered bits of information; try, for example, to find information on the diverticula of the thoracic sacs. What of the possible pneumatization of the head? Bremer (1940) studied the cephalic air spaces, but made no note of the connections, if any, between these and the air sacs.

PRODUCTION OF SOUND

Sounds made by birds, as an integral part of their behavior, originate in several ways. The winnowing or drumming of the snipe (Carr-Lewty, 1943), the whistle produced by the tail of a hummingbird, and the clacking of the upper and lower mandibles are well-known sounds resulting from specialized structures. Our discussion of sounds will be limited to those coming from the trachea.

The general pattern of the syrinx has been established for many species. Knowledge of intraspecific and interspecific variation in structure is, however, very scanty. Köditz (1925) made a comprehensive comparative study, describing in great detail the number of muscles—their attachments, relative sizes, and the nerves innervating them—as well as all other parts of the syrinx. Rüppell (1933) wrote an exhaustive treatise on the physiology and structure of the vocal sounds of birds, based on comparative morphological and experimental work. His refinements of the theory that vocalization is the result of the vibration of membranes of various lengths and that pitch depends upon diameter and length of tubes involved still stand. He noted, however, that variation from species to species should be expected.

Few workers have published anything relative to these views. The studies of Alden H. Miller (particularly 1934, 1935, and 1947) furnish one of the few examples of comparative study within a natural taxonomic group. He noted in owls that the syrinx was smaller in females, but found no qualitative differences between the sexes, or oftentimes between species, to account for differences in calls. The pitch of the main note or hoot is determined in large part by the diameter of the air passages which determines the length of the vibrating membranes. Size of air passage varies with body size. Since no structural differences were found between the sexes or species (except in *Tyto,* which adds another bit of information justifying the separation of the Tytonidae from the Strigidae) nervous control must be the major factor in the production of various calls. The findings of Appel (1929) for the Brown Leghorn Chicken also indicate neural control. He found no sexual dimorphism, and ovariotomized females crowed, with no apparent change in the syrinx. Appel's work is at variance with Myer's (1917) on *Gallus domesticus,* variety unspecified. Myer verified the fact that air sacs are necessary for normal sound. It may be that selection in these domestic fowl, while not for quality of voice, has adventitiously produced changes in the syrinx.

It is well known that the males of most species of ducks possess well-developed syringes and, oftentimes, special enlargements of the trachea anterior to the syrinx. Females show lesser development of the syrinx and are not known to have any tracheal bulb. Yet, the females of some species are reported to have louder voices than the males. In geese there is usually no sexual difference in structure (Canada Geese, *Branta canadensis,* for example), but some observers can detect differences in voice.

Gullion has recently (1950) correlated sexual differences in the voice of the American Coot with differences in structure of the syrinx. It is apparent that comparative studies of a great many different species must be made before we can speak with confidence regarding voice production in the class Aves.

In passing, it should be pointed out that the function as resonating chambers of the air sacs, trachea, chambers in the head, and other cavities is usually assumed, although the exact pattern for each species may not be known. Detailed functional study of this region may turn up many interesting situations, as for example that found by Gross (1928) in the Heath Hen, *Tympanuchus cupido.* In this species the vocal sac or resonating chamber is simply the enlarged cephalic end of the esophagus and is connected to the respiratory system only through the pharynx. It functions only on inflation with air which comes from the respiratory system, and not with air coming directly from the outside.

ANATOMY AND TAXONOMY

It is obviously impossible here to note all the papers in which comparative anatomy has been used as an aid in showing relationships. The main function of this section is to indicate ways in which morphology has been used, to point out what appear to be fallacies and inadequacies, and to suggest additional taxonomic problems needing anatomical study.

No review of this subject would be complete without discussion of the work of Percy Lowe. Space permits consideration only of his studies on two major "groups"—the waders and the ratites—within the twenty-five year period being considered. Lowe early (1926 and before) placed too much emphasis, it seems to me, on one or two characters (quadrate and nasal glands) in his vast revisions of the shorebirds. True, he made use of other features but too often they were arranged around the groups set up by him on the basis of a few structures. The quadrate is at best a difficult bone to study and is definitely a part of the jaw apparatus; the latter structural relationship means that the quadrate probably varies "in tune with" the bones of the jaw and ear region, with the muscles, and indeed with the whole ecology of the food-getting mechanism. Likewise, the nasal glands are closely integrated in their structure and physiology with external conditions. Other studies of the waders by Lowe (1931a, 1931b, and 1933a) also seem to emphasize too much certain features subject to "easy" change or ones that perhaps were carried along as part of a single adaptive mechanism in a morphogenetic field. We cannot judge the validity of many of his taxonomic conclusions, for little new evidence has been found; the "wading birds" are still one of the most troublesome groups, anatomically and taxonomically.

In 1928, 1933b, and 1942, Lowe emphasized the "primitiveness" of the ratites and postulated that the Struthiones and penguins came from the same ancestral stock, the Struthiones representing a cursorial line and the penguins a line adapted for swimming. Gregory (1935) and Murphy (*in* Gregory, *op. cit.*) disputed the primitiveness of the ratites, as have other workers. Gregory noted that no evidence was at hand to show that the "paleognathous" palate is truly primitive. Both Lowe and Gregory assumed the existence of a single paleognathous type of palate and relied heavily on this single feature. It remained for McDowell (1948) and Hofer (1949), working independently, to show that the "paleognathous" palate was in reality several different types. Again, although many other anatomical features were discussed, there was overemphasis on a single character, and one that may very well have been related to the herbivorous habits of most of the forms (*Apteryx* excepted). Edinger (1942) introduced the interesting hypothesis that many of the characteristics of the ratites (size, flightlessness, plumage) may be the result of pituitary disturbances, rather than representing any sort of primitive or advanced feature.

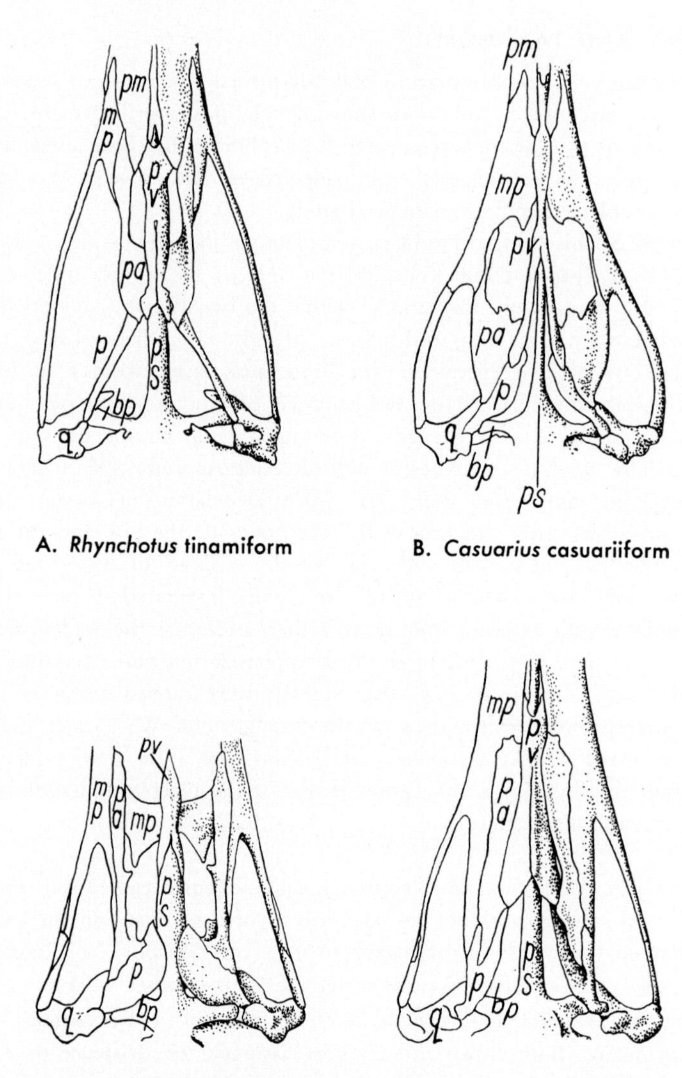

Fig. 1. The diversity of the "palaeognathous" palate as observed in ventral view. Four "types" may be observed. After McDowell (1948).

Sushkin (1927) relied heavily on the markings of the horny sheath of the palatal surface in his work on the weaverbirds. Although this characteristic would seem to be, in part at least, adaptive, he has shown the apparent validity of this feature by the use of many other characteristics.

This suggested criticism of some of the work of Lowe and others should not be interpolated to mean that adaptive modifications are not useful in taxonomy, particularly at the higher levels. It is evident that the forms in a major group may show the same adaptive features. We recognize classes, orders, families and oftentimes genera on this basis, but we do not now place all birds showing a similar adaptation, say one for food-getting, in the same order (hawks and owls, for example). Other characteristics, not now plainly adaptive but which in their origin were probably adaptive or carried along genetically with adaptive structures, are used. If we agree that "key adjustments" (adaptations) as used by Miller (1949:84) are responsible for the origin of higher categories, we must expect that adjustments will often show up as evident adaptations, or preadaptations, at the specific or racial level. The difficulty is in recognizing them for what they are. Often we must see the "result" at the generic or familial level and then work back to the next lower category to realize the significance of a certain structural entity. (See Miller, 1949, and Engels, 1940, for further discussion of the role of adaptations in taxonomy.)

The point of difference in opinion as to the use of adaptive features in classification at the generic, specific, and racial levels thus should not be one of whether or not to use them; it should center around the way in which they are used! "Lumping" is not an answer; this simply covers up, nomenclatorially at least, these demonstrable differences. Nor is the answer to choose one feature and use it to the exclusion of other characteristics.

Beecher (1950:83), in connection with his study of the American orioles, has suggested that "numerous . . . cases of inter-generic convergence and especially parallelism may occur in passerine birds." In the orioles he feels there is an apparent convergence of two genera; this view is based on a study of the jaw apparatus and the plumage. In the light of his statement about parallelism it would seem particularly important to investigate more fully other phases of the biology, before building too formal a view of the phylogenetic relationships. Further, it may well be true that " . . . most adaptive modifications producing new passerine lines have been primarily dietary" (page 52). These seem to be distinguishing features as we look at the present-day representatives of the passerines, but I am unable to cite other detailed studies verifying this, and it seems unwise to depend too much on these differentiations in studying interfamilial relationships and to derive one modern group from another modern group.

Although such studies as those by Engels (1940), Richardson (1942), and Beecher *(op. cit.)* are valuable for the evidence they present, they must be integrated with many other studies of distribution, of habitat, and of behavior, in arriving at even tentative conclusions as to the relationships of forms for which the fossil record is so incomplete.

The work of McDowell (1948) and of Hofer (1949) has re-established the view of Max Fürbringer, who in 1888 decided the ratites were not a uniform group, basing his conclusions on a detailed study of the skeleton, muscles, and nerves of the limbs, as well as of the fossil record. Even with the evidence of these two recent papers we still do not know the relations of the ratite birds to other groups. Craigie in several papers (1928-1941) used the cerebral cortex in attempting to show relationships. Detailed studies of neognath palates are needed, to be used along with studies of other aspects of the birds, but perhaps the answer is to be found primarily in the unknown fossils. McDowell's suggestion of neoteny as the reason for the "primitive" appearance of the ratites should be further studied in other groups.

Hofer (1945) noted that the characteristics of the tinamous, often used to show their connection to the ratites, might result from secondary adaptations and hence not be primitive at all. In 1949, however, while noting the diversity of the "paleognathous" palate, Hofer thought a common or uniform ancestral type for the ratites might be permitted, and that the tinamous were perhaps close to this type.

Böhm's study (1930) of *Balaeneiceps rex* is an example of the use in taxonomy of detailed work on the skeleton. Kattinger (1929) made an excellent study of intraspecific variation—sex, individual, and racial—in the avian skeleton. The work is mostly qualitative, and the little quantitative analysis there is is inadequate, but many points mentioned would provide fruitful areas of further research. Koch (1927) attempted to use the structure of the ovary taxonomically; although it is not convincing, the paper is provocative and the subject would bear further studies. Gorham and Ivy (1938), in a survey of the occurrence of the gall bladder in vertebrate animals, concluded that this structure might be of taxonomic value. All carnivorous birds thus far investigated have a gall bladder. Herbivorous or insectivorous forms may or may not possess this structure; its presence in one of the species may indicate a closer relationship to a carnivorous form. But in no order of birds (as the orders are now constituted) is the gall bladder invariably absent in all species.

Edinger, whose work of 1942 has been mentioned previously, has suggested that pituitary disturbances could account for certain characteristics of the ratites. Detailed studies of the relation between pituitary size and function and other structures would be valuable. Most studies of the pituitary in birds have emphasized its relation to reproduction and to other glands, and not the overall end result of variations in pituitary functions on plumage, egg size, differential effect on the bony parts, posture, and a host of other traits. Turkewitsch (1936) attacked taxonomic problems on the basis of the structure of the bony labyrinths. Little research along this line has been accomplished lately.

Fisher used pterylosis (1943), structure of the skull (1944), and the bones and muscles of the appendages (1946) to verify the existence of two distinct subgroups within the family Cathartidae, the New World vultures. Compton (1938) demonstrated features in the pterylosis of the Falconiformes which supported the classification within the order and also showed that *Pandion* was closely related to the cathartids; the modifications of the Osprey are largely adaptations for plunging and immersion in water. Wetmore (1936) studied the number of contour feathers in passerine and allied birds in one of the few papers of its kind; Hutt and Ball's (1938) is the only other study of this kind with which I am familiar. Hudson (1948), using only the muscles of the hind limb, suggested that the cathartids belong in an order separate from the Falconiformes and that a suborder should be set up for *Pandion.* Burt (1929) found that the pterylosis of woodpeckers was chiefly of value in distinguishing the order, but on this basis he was also able to distinguish certain genera (*Sphyrapicus,* for example) within the group.

The number of toes has been used rather widely as a significant feature in classification. The significance of the absence or presence of one particular toe may have been overemphasized, and perhaps this feature is not an accurate criterion in all instances; but just because it is found to be invalid in some instances and must be disregarded is no reason to rule it out in all cases. Delacour (1951:49), in referring to its invalidity in one group of birds, said, "If such an action is accepted, however, it seems logical to carry it further." Perhaps in these woodpeckers and kingfishers the "toe criterion" should be thrown out, but the proof is yet to come from other, more detailed studies; most of the features mentioned by Delacour seem to be just as plastic as the number of toes. In this same trend of thought, von Boetticher (1951) has suggested that the loss of toes may be a simple mutation, and hence the number of toes is of no great taxonomic significance. It is well known that several major changes may occur in the skeleton of domestic chickens as the result of changes in one gene complex. Rumplessness in the chicken is a good example, as is the white plumage in pheasants (Bruckner, 1941). Yet, if an entire population possessed these characters we would or should acknowledge its genetic difference, as we would if it constantly had a different number of primaries, a different bill, or a different color pattern. The *presence* of "vestigial" organs is an indication of relationship within a group; their *absence* may not be (Fisher, 1940). Further, it takes some little study to determine whether an organ is really vestigial.

Delacour and Mayr (1945) have revised the nomenclature of the Anatidae. As they noted repeatedly, detailed studies of almost every phase of duck, goose, and swan structure are necessary for clarification of the relationships. Particularly needed are studies of the merganser and shelduck "groups."

Another urgent need in the application of the findings of anatomy to taxonomic purposes is knowledge of the degree of variability in a homogeneous series within a species. This is true not only of internal structures but also of practically all the external characteristics currently used by taxonomists. Too many workers are still using inadequate series of specimens, using only the simple arithmetic mean without sufficient statistical treatment of the proper kind, and even casting out the extremes in the range of a measurement if these extremes "confuse" the problem. Notable exceptions to these practices are the studies of the genus *Junco* by A. H. Miller (1941) and of the genus *Aphelocoma* by Pitelka (1951).

Analyses of the variation in the skeleton of Recent and fossil eagles and vultures have been made by Howard (1947b) and Fisher (1944, 1947).

Quisenberry, Roberts, and Card (1941) in their genetic work on skeletal dimensions noted that differences in diameter and in area of bone surface may be more significant than differences in length. This work was a statistical study of about 400 chicken skeletons. Rensch (1940) studied relative bone sizes in *Passer montanus* and *Parus major* to check Allen's rule as regards bone mass; in some elements greater length was found in tropical forms. Latimer (1927a) found, in his investigation of postnatal growth in chickens, that the skeletons of males were heavier and continued their growth for a longer period than those of females; differences in weight were apparent in the tibiotarsus and the tarsometatarsus, but not in the femur. Hutt (1929) discussed in detail the sexual dimorphism and variability in the limb skeletons of chickens. The papers of Engels (1938a, 1938c), Baudouin (1936), Larson (1930), and Linsdale (1928) have been discussed earlier in this review.

Comparative research on individual bones, attempting to note phylogenetic trends or to differentiate taxonomic groups, has not been extensive. Ashley (1941) was able to distinguish only minor differences in the configuration of the humerus in the various species of corvids. Bones in the base of the skull, away from the jaw apparatus and the palate, should be receiving more attention as regards their significance in the classification of higher categories. Of special interest would be more investigations of the floor of the cranium. One of the few papers dealing with this region of the skull is that of Kesteven (1926) who studied the parabasal canal and the nerve foramina.

Lemmrich (1931) tried to use the bony scleral ring of the eye as an aid in taxonomy and made extensive studies of its development, gross and microscopic anatomy, and function. Some 1,400 scleral rings of 235 species were studied by Curtis and Miller (1938). They concluded that the pattern was constant, or nearly so, in the family but not in the order, and that there was no relationship between systematic position and the number of plates present in the ring. They found the ring heavier and more steep-sided in diving and swift-flying birds, which modification may account for some of the diversity within ordinal groups and some of the uniformity in families.

There are many inherent difficulties, particularly in certain elements, in distinguishing "primitive" and "advanced" characteristics (Oliver's paper of 1945 is a good illustration of this difficulty). Some bony elements cannot be relied upon to give an accurate picture of relations between different forms because of their close association with other elements in a functional unit; here, as emphasized before, the entire unit must be utilized.

We find similar adaptations within each of many of our present orders; the webbed foot, the running foot, the predatory foot, the juice-feeding mechanism, the seed-eating bill, and many other specializations are to be found in several groups. For taxonomic reasons, if for no other, it would be valuable to know the avenue of descent or evolution of these features within each order. Is there a "basic type" within the order from which these can be derived?

Can we, on the basis of the present avifauna (the fossil record is too incomplete to give much help), distinguish lines of evolution and the relation of orders, families, and genera? We need detailed anatomical studies concerning the possible polyphyletic origin of many of our "recognized" categories. Until we know something more of the basic situation in these groups, their taxonomy will probably remain as one of the most tangled areas in modern ornithology. The problem is one to which the fundamental aspects of internal anatomy can and must contribute. Within the last quarter-century the emphasis has been on the specific and subspecific categories and, with few exceptions, no work has been accomplished on the basic anatomical features of the higher categories. We are still "revising" on the basis of study skins and the incomplete anatomical evidence presented fifty years ago.

These "revisions" often have as their chief contribution the reviser's "lumping" or "splitting" attitude. Certain groups have been subjected to this treatment several times, and the anatomical foundation is still unbuilt. This does not mean that internal anatomy is all-important, but it certainly should be used along with other features. There seems little justification for continuing the erection of families, for example, without investigation of their anatomy (cf. the Irenidae of Oberholser and the Aegithinidae of Delacour). Nor is there reason to scoff at the morphologists who question such superficial characterization of higher categories. Certainly, we do not have absolute morphological criteria for many families, especially in the passerines, but we must not close our minds or discontinue the search for basic features which can clarify the situations caused by "shoe-box" taxonomy. Detailed research, similar to Fiedler's work (1951) on the jaw musculature of the oscines, might be very revealing. True, he found a high degree of constancy in birds adapted for a particular feeding habit, but the modification was not always attained in exactly the same manner, and he further stated that despite the modifications the basic pattern was often discernible. Desselberger (1931) was able to detect two separate lines of evolutionary development in the digestive system of the Dicaeidae, and Engels (1940:395) found certain cranial muscles in the Mimidae which may be absent in other passerines; Beecher (personal communication) has told me they are present in many passerines. Additional work on other groups would perhaps turn up other fruitful avenues for detailed investigation.

When this needed type of work is undertaken, a special search for additional "characters" must be made. In the past we have had much reliance placed on characteristics of the palate, formulae of muscles of the hind leg, etc., quite rightly perhaps, but the entire functioning organism must be studied and there is no reason to limit ourselves. It is further necessary to be aware of the developments in the other natural sciences and to discard, as necessary, certain time-honored concepts. One such dogma is the irreversibility of evolutionary trends. There is evidence that such trends are sometimes reversed; this adds a confusing, but inescapable, possibility that must be considered in each instance. The impact of the environment on the structure of organs is recognized, but what is not so clearly understood is that such a change in one organ of a system may influence other organs in that system or even organs in other systems—witness the changes in the bones, muscles, nerves, blood vessels, glands of the head, and often the entire gut, from esophagus to cloaca, when the feeding habit is changed. From the evolutionary viewpoint, an entire region or system may act as a single entity.

Some groups that especially need work are the: tinamous; loons and grebes; anatids; falconiforms; storks and herons; and suboscine and oscine groups. Within orders, the position of such forms as the vireos, empidonaces, warblers, flamingos, sun-grebes, sun-bitterns, various manakins, rails, and limpkins could be clarified in part at least by detailed, comparative anatomical work. The relationships of the Numididae, Phasianidae, Perdicidae, and Tetraonidae might also be investigated profitably.

EMBRYOLOGY

The whole field of general avian embryology is open. Certain birds, primarily domestic ones and the chicken in particular, have been rather intensively studied because of their economic importance or because of the ease with which they could be used in academic instruction, but how many studies have been made of the embryology of wild birds? Very few have appeared in the last twenty-five years.

Adelmann (1927) studied the development of the eye muscles in the chick, Huggins *et al.* (1942), the ossification in the nestling House Wren, *Troglodytes aedon,* and Scharnke (1931), the development of the tongue in hummingbirds and woodpeckers as straight embryological problems. Bösiger (1950) compared the rate of development of the breast musculature in the chicken, quail, and starling; he was able to distinguish characteristic rates for each species. In an investigation of the proportions of birds' wings and their changes during development, Marples (1930) found inconclusive evidence that allied forms showed similar changes in proportions. It would seem that this approach in embryology—the study of the rate of development of certain organs—might be a very useful tool in taxonomy, as well as being of interest per se, but I know of no recent papers along this line.

Watterson's paper (1942) on the morphogenesis of down feathers is one of the few recent ones on the embryology of feathers. Parsons (1932) studied seventy-eight embryos of the penguin, *Pygoscelis,* and noted, among other things, that certain features usually associated with an aquatic habitat appeared at an early age. This, as far as I know, is the only major embryological paper, of the period under consideration, that treats many features in wild birds. Latimer (1925) worked out the postnatal development of the central nervous system in the chick, with particular reference to the relative sizes of the different structures at various stages.

One of the most interesting possibilities in embryology could be the study of the function of nongenetic factors in determining bone size and shape. The papers of Glucksmann (1942), Evans (1949), and probably others of which I am unaware, show that bone shape can be influenced by mechanical stresses during development and by the morphogenetic field in which the bone lies. How much variation is possible within the bounds of the genetic constitution of the species? How great a part does the immediate environment play in causing any bone, say the femur, to be the shape we consider characteristic of that particular bone? Is the anterior curvature of the shaft of the femur, seen in many species, a genetic matter entirely or is it partly a function of the angle, position of center of gravity of the body, or use in early life? Comparative studies of individual elements in different groups of birds having different life situations would be instructive. The problem might also be attacked from the experimental side, as in the papers mentioned, by studying two related forms with different ecological niches, or by exposing different individuals of the same brood to situations in which the stresses on a certain bone were different.

Since the days of the anatomist Owen there has been confusion concerning the digits which remain on the wings of birds. The question concerns the loss of digit I and whether digits I, II, and III or digits II, III, and IV are present. Montagna (1945) working with the embryology of the domestic chicken has rather definitely shown that the existing digits are II, III, and IV. Thus the pattern of loss in birds is shown to conform to the usual situation in vertebrate animals.

MUSCLES

The homologizing of avian muscles has not received much attention in recent years. Romer in 1927 used the development of the thigh musculature of the chick as a means of verifying the view that the dorsal and ventral layers of muscle in the fish limb could be traced in the tetrapod limb. He also concluded that multiple innervation is the primitive condition in tetrapods, a fact that is of great importance. The determination of homologies through embryological study has been sorely neglected in birds, partly because the class represents a "side line" in vertebrate evolution and partly because the changes in structure often seem so major and diverse as to defy understanding. The problem is well illustrated by Romer's paper of 1944 on the lizard *Lacerta,* in which he attempted to homologize the shoulder muscles of birds with those of lower vertebrates.

Appleton (1928) attempted to homologize the muscles and nerves of the postaxial part of the tetrapod thigh, and A. B. Howell in a series of papers (1936, 1937, 1938a, 1938b) worked on the upper part of the limbs in vertebrates. Addens (1933) reviewed the state of our knowledge concerning the relationship between cranial nerves and the neural nuclei in the brain. This work is of major significance in the determination of muscle homologies. He showed that the neural nuclei are not stationary in position, in a phylogenetic sense; their location varies from group to group of vertebrates, and even within groups—perhaps in accord with Ariëns Kappers' theory of neurobiotaxis (Ariëns Kappers, Huber, and Crosby, 1936, 1:75-84). This "phylogenetic movement" may be seen in the ontogeny of individuals within a species. Further, there have been fasciculations (the grouping of fibers into bundles) or central anastomoses within the central nervous system. Addens found that, perhaps in response to direction of impulse or other similarities in function, parts of motor nerves may join with parts of other motor nerves going in the same direction. For example, he pointed out that in parrots part of the motor seventh nerve has joined to motor fifth. In other avian species part of nerve ten is with nine and part of the twelfth nerve is with the tenth. The implications of this, as far as homologies are concerned, are great—nerve roots may not be constant in content or in the parts of the brain from which they come. Thus, on simple topographical bases, some changes in innervation are apparent but not necessarily real, and changes may exist but be hidden by changes in path within the brain or possibly in the spinal cord. The true relations must be determined on the basis of embryological studies and experiments with neural degeneration and stimulation followed by cytological study. Edgeworth (1935: 220-227) discussed other general factors involved in homologizing muscles, particularly the cranial ones.

Aside from these difficulties, and assuming that much could be learned from descriptive and comparative studies, a major deterrent is that we do not have enough such basic studies to use as a foundation for setting up basic patterns. Howell, for example, used only one or two species in his work, as did Romer. Until we have this fundamental pattern demonstrated in a number of species of birds, even topographical homologies are largely speculative. Those not familiar with avian anatomy may not realize that we do not have this information and, worse, that we are not very rapidly accumulating it for future analysis. For example, no complete and detailed myology of any bird has been published since Shufeldt's myology of the raven which appeared in 1890. There have been several comparative studies of the muscles of parts of the body: Burt (1930) on limbs and tongues of woodpeckers; Scharnke (1931) on muscles of the tongue in hummingbirds and woodpeckers; Hudson (1937) on the hind limb; Fisher (1946) on wing, leg, and tail of cathartids; Beecher (1950) on jaw muscles in orioles; and others mentioned in the section on adaptations. Palmgren (1932) did detailed dissections on the leg muscles of *Regulus* and *Parus,* and, in 1949, the neck muscles of some passerines. Banzhaf (1929) described the anterior limb of *Opisthocomus* in an excellent, detailed paper.

Muscles along the vertebral column and those of the syrinx have not been investigated to any extent in recent years. Palmgren (1949) studied the muscles running between the skull and the cervical region and also the muscles of the neck proper of certain passerines. Boas (1929) compared the cervical vertebrae and cervical muscles of a series of birds. Prior to 1900 the muscles of the syrinx were worked out in some birds and were used extensively in classification. This region and that along the vertebral column (as a relatively stable area) offer areas for anatomical research that might be significant for the taxonomist as well as for the anatomist and student of function. The importance of thigh-muscle formulae in taxonomy has perhaps been overplayed, but we cannot be certain until more information is available. There is also a tendency to use structural aspects of certain muscles (pinnate condition, relations to nerves and blood vessels) as though these were always constant or at least irreversible in evolutionary development (see Beecher, 1950). We know that innervations and other topographical relations do change, and the whole matter of reversibility must be discussed on the merits of the individual instances. Edgeworth (1935:225-226) has pointed out that even simulated reversion has occurred in certain cranial muscles of mammals.

The lack of information on the musculature, at least the cranial part, is highlighted by the extensive monograph on vertebrate cranial muscles by Edgeworth *(op. cit.)*. The incompleteness of the data there for birds, as compared to other classes, is not the author's omission as much as it is the paucity of research on birds. Also revealing is a survey of the literature used by Edgeworth; few of the references postdate 1900. This same situation is perhaps reflected in Howell's paper of 1936 on the phylogenetic arrangement of the muscular system; birds are not considered.

THE NERVOUS SYSTEM

There has been considerable anatomical research on the nervous system in birds in the last twenty-five years, but the bulk of it was on primitive birds such as the kiwi, penguin, and ostrich, or on birds of interest for other reasons, for example the chicken. Much histological research has been done on the brain and spinal cord. For an excellent review of our knowledge of the avian nervous system see Ariëns Kappers, Huber, and Crosby (1936).

The study of behavior, particularly that of the higher birds, is "blossoming" now, and yet much of the very fundamental structural basis of behavior—the nervous system and its associated structures—is incompletely known for most birds, and especially for the more advanced species which seem to be the most popular for research on behavior. We speak of the evolution of behavior traits and, quite correctly, these features are being used as an aid in taxonomy. Their basis is genetic, but in part at least behavior is dependent upon structure which is even more genetically controlled. How long can we continue to discuss differences in behavior without wondering about the various details of the physical background? To study behavior without knowing the neural background is like studying mechanical power without knowing whether the power is produced by gas, steam, electricity, or water.

Craigie has perhaps published more on the details of the avian brain structure than any other individual in the time period considered, but, except for the hummingbird (1928, 1932), he has been primarily interested in the primitive birds. He has found (1940, 1941) a great homogeneity in the cerebral cortex in birds and has emphasized the derivation of the parts from the reptilian cortex. Despite the general similarity, the cortical structure varies enough to reflect the relationships within orders and suborders, the swifts and hummingbirds for example (Craigie, 1940). In this same paper Craigie pointed out that there was in the higher birds (Neognathae) a tendency toward reduction of the cortex, as compared to the paleognathine birds. In 1928 he had already noted that the most striking feature of the brains of hummingbirds was the "primitive condition" of the cerebral hemispheres. What is the significance of this? In his work on hummingbirds *(op. cit.)* he correlated the powers of flight and equilibration with a greater development of the parts of the brain controlling these abilities. He also found (1930) that the sensory centers of the fifth nerve were especially well developed in the kiwi and believed this was correlated with the tactile sense located in the bill. As regards the view that the "Paleognathae" had an origin distinct from that of the Neognathae, Craigie (1936, 1940) found no supporting evidence, and in 1941 he showed the cortex of penguins to be essentially similar to that of the ratite birds.

Muskens (1930) was able to locate certain tracts and centers involved in the associated eye movements in pigeons by using the functional approach after experimental lesions. And Sanders (1929) found the reflex centers in the brain stem of birds to be very well developed.

The papers of Huber and Crosby (1929), Brown (1935), Kuhlenbeck (1939), Jungherr (1945), and Doty (1946) are a few of the great many detailed histological papers on the nervous system of birds.

A number of workers, Crosby and Humphrey (1939a) and Kuhlenbeck (1938) on the telencephalon, Kuhlenbeck (1937) on the diencephalon, Huber (1936) on the columns of the spinal cord, Ariëns Kappers (1928) on the corpus striatum, and Larsell (1948) on the cerebellum, have attempted to set up homologies of parts of the avian nervous system with the reptilian and mammalian systems. Although much of this "dissection homologizing" will undoubtedly prove valid, the experimental method is the only certain method of establishing homologies. Weinberg (1928) thus determined the relationship between certain cranial nerves and muscles in a phylogenetic study, and Brodal *et al.* (1950) demonstrated a pontine homologue in birds. At the same time, Brodal and co-workers questioned the "accepted" homologies, most of which were not determined experimentally. I would again refer the reader to the review by Addens (1933) of the state of our knowledge of the relationships of nerves and nerve nuclei, discussed in the section on muscles (page 74). Woodburne (1936) in a detailed phylogenetic study of the trigeminal complex has found that the relative development and complexity of interconnections of this nerve are good indicators of the stage of evolution of the entire nervous system. However, in this, and most of the other studies noted above, the number of kinds of birds used is too few for generalizing about the whole class.

Data on brain size are impossible to find in the literature, and specific information on relative development of the parts of the brain in different birds is scarce.

The only major paper on spinal nerves and plexi is that of Boas (1933) who described the pelvic plexus in a variety of forms. Judging from this and older papers on the plexi there may be considerable individual variation, but who has dissected a series of birds of the same species and noted the kind or degree of variation?

Most studies dealing with the sensory organs of birds have been concerned in recent years with the physiological aspects, particularly with the capabilities of the eye. Walls (1942) and Pumphrey (1948) have very ably summarized our knowledge of the general structure and function of the eye. Perusal of these reviews will illustrate the inadequacy of our data on the comparative morphology of the avian eye. Even in those instances in which rather extensive studies of structure have been made, the functions are still often obscure. Many theories have been suggested concerning the function of the pecten. The only function widely agreed upon seems to be that it is an accessory vascular structure to aid in supplying nutriment to the eye. Menner (1938) suggested that the fingerlike shadows cast by the pecten interrupted retinal stimuli and in turn caused greater visual acuity of small, moving objects. Walls (1942), however, stated that it is unlikely that the pecten casts any shadow that could have this effect. Crozier and Wolf (1943) believed their work on the flicker response in the eye substantiated Menner's hypothesis. Thus, this latest, and in many ways most attractive, theory of the function of the pecten needs much additional study.

The ear has not been studied as extensively as the eye of birds, but Kimura (1931) and de Burlet (1934) presented reviews of available information. The latter paper may be used as a very good basis for future work on the organs of the inner and middle ears and on the canal system. A few other studies may be mentioned in passing. Dombrowsky (1925) compared the middle ears of Lacertilia and birds. Stellbogen (1930) wrote a most complete description of the ear region of the Wood Owl, *Strix aluco.* The entire inner and outer ear, including nerves, muscles, blood vessels, and bones, is described and illustrated. He treated the functional aspect, and there is a good bibliography. Ibragimova (1939) studied the inner ear region with regard to sexual variation in its structure. De Burlet (1929) investigated the general structure and innervation of the labyrinths in a series of vertebrates.

MISCELLANEOUS STUDIES

Some histological papers on the parts of the avian digestive system and its associated organs may be found, especially for domestic birds. There does not appear to have been as much gross, comparative work on the internal parts as on the mouth and jaw and the cloacal portions. In fact, searching for recent comprehensive papers on the relative lengths of parts, on coiling of the intestine, on mesenteric attachments, and other features emphasized in the early anatomical work is of little avail. Much remains to be done and many species have apparently never been dissected. As late as 1929, Böker presented the first complete analysis of the structure of the crop in *Opisthocomus,* a genus which had otherwise been investigated extensively. Desselberger (1931) was able to distinguish two lines of evolution in the family Dicaeidae on the basis of the structure of the digestive system.

In 1937 Kisseleva compared the structure of the nasal cavities of birds. Marples (1932) described the nasal glands in several species, showed their supposed homologies with glands in other vertebrates, and suggested that the higher development of such glands in marine birds was correlated with the environment. There have been no verifications of the homologies, and no extensive ones of this correlation with the environment, but Technau (1936) presented an excellent, family by family, comparative study of these glands.

ADAPTATIONS

Many of the studies to be discussed here have been mentioned previously, but in this section only the "adaptive" aspects of the papers will be considered. The outstanding avian adaptation is for flight; it will be taken up in the next section. The adaptations of the respiratory system have already been considered. We shall here concern ourselves with gross structural adaptations within the class and mostly those to be found in the skeletal, muscular, and digestive systems. This limitation is required for several reasons: (1) as stated in the beginning, microscopic anatomy may be more often associated with physiological function; (2) adaptive changes in behavior are considered elsewhere, as are modifications in reproduction; (3) the general pattern of the major changes characteristic of the class are known, if imperfectly; and (4) most of the research in this field in the last twenty-five years has been concerned with these three organ systems.

The main reason for the dynamic or functional approach in anatomy, aside from the interest attached to the complex correlation of form and function, is that the neo-Darwinians have emphasied the role of adaptations in evolution through the concept of selection of those best fitted to survive in a particular environmental situation, or those groups which, because of their inherent genetic variability superimposed on a generalized structure, can "adjust and survive" to reproduce. This is especially significant in the origin of the higher taxonomic categories, as indicated on page 71.

The problems of major functional changes are difficult, and often impossible, to study experimentally and only infrequently is the fossil record adequate to shed light on these changes in birds. Thus paleontology cannot be used as successfully here as it is in the study of the origin of, say, the vertebrate classes. We are forced then to study and interpret on one temporal level, except as we may be able to trace obvious adaptations in one member of a group back to less obvious adaptations or structures (preadaptations) in other related members of the group, as Engels (1940) has done in the thrashers of the genus *Toxostoma.*

In these birds, Engels was able to show that only slight modifications of the generalized structure of the head, of certain members of the genus, were necessary to produce an effective digging mechanism. He set up three categories of structural characteristics associated with this modification: preadaptations or structures of value to the digging habit, but which are also found in the nondigging and generalized thrashers; incidental adaptations which are of advantage in digging but which result from the development of other structures; and primary adaptations which are elaborations of existing functional mechanisms. The curved bill is the most evident modification in the digging thrashers, and this curvature results from an increase in the length of the distal part of the bill. This distal lengthening "necessitates" a longer mandibular symphysis which is advantageous but is not directly the result of the digging habit. The digging habit can come about with perhaps little change in behavior, for the pecking movements associated with the straight bill produce digging motions when associated with a curved bill.

The jaw and neck musculature of all mimids is broadly similar, and Engels has shown that the special development of certain parts of it go hand in hand with the curved bill and the digging habit. Changes in leg and wing, with terrestrial locomotion, are not always associated with modifications for digging.

Beecher (1950) has attempted to explain the apparent convergence in two genera of orioles on the theme that selection often acts on "dietary modifications of the bill and jaw musculature."

Such detailed studies as those of Engels and Beecher are much needed for a better understanding of the origin of new groups as the result of oftentimes small, but highly significant, adjustments to environmental conditions.

A number of workers have studied other adaptations of the avian skull. One of the best of the general papers treating of skulls is that of Hofer (1945). After describing the pattern of configuration in the various palatal types he proceeded to an analysis of the functional origin of each type and of the function of the parts in each. There is a detailed discussion of bill structure and function, especially of the curvature. The functional significance of the different palates and the quadrate is studied, with the situations in *Rhynchotus, Ardea,* and the woodpeckers used as detailed examples.

In 1949 Hofer analyzed the spaces or openings in the palates of reptiles and birds, attempting to trace their evolutionary history in birds. He noted that the most variable avian palate has only five such spaces and the reptilian palate has ten. With degeneration of the basipterygoid joint in birds, the interpterygoidal and pterooccipital spaces fuse. The anterior palatal vacuities in birds are often closed over with bone, but the caudal choanae always remain. The lateral palatal spaces of reptiles fuse with the adductor space in birds through loss of the transversum, which loss is apparently correlated with the increased size of the eyes in birds. The accessory palatal spaces have appeared in various places in the roof of the avian mouth and cannot therefore be considered homologous to similar spaces in the reptiles. All such changes are related to the presence or absence of movement of the palate, or of the entire rostral part, on the cranial part of the skull; in other words, the modifications are part of the development of the kinetic skull in birds.

One of the most detailed studies of the head of a single form is that by Lubosch (1929) who described the muscles, nerves, and bones of the skull of *Caprimulgus* and made an excellent analysis of the function in this streptognath skull. Moller (1932) has done much the same for *Ara macao* and has emphasied the adaptive modifications in detail. Balthasar (1935) described the anatomy of the head of *Phalacrocorax carbo* and discussed the functional integration of the muscles, tongue, and bones.

In his study of the adaptive modifications in woodpeckers, Burt (1930) delineated the modifications in the several genera and correlated them with selective pressure of the environment. Similar adaptive changes were found in most forms, but the flickers (*Colaptes*) were considered the most generalized and the three-toed woodpeckers (*Picoides*) the most specialized and furthest from the ancestral type. Burt was also able to distinguish two main lines of descent in the Picidae, on the basis of several features in the skull and musculature. Puzanov (1948) apparently studied the same modifications in Russian woodpeckers, but I have not seen the original paper.

Studies on the adaptive features of the bill mechanism in birds are too numerous to discuss each in detail, but some of the more extensive ones are listed here. The most searching papers on bill mechanics are those of Kripp (1933a, 1933b, and 1935), who has in great detail discussed the physical forces involved in the various types of bills. The treatment is from the mechanical viewpoint and is handled as mathematically as possible. Moller (1930, 1931) described the skull, tongue, and the related musculature in the Coerebidae, Trochilidae, Nectariniidae, Meliphagidae, and Zosteropidae and correlated these with the mechanics involved in their feeding habits. The functional aspects of the bill in the snipe (Schumacher, 1929) and the crossed mandibles of the Crossbill, *Loxia curvirostra* (Robbins, 1932) are known in some detail. The general pattern of the correlation between structure of tongue and feeding habits was reviewed and further elaborated in a general way by Gardner (1925) and by Engels (1938b), but more detailed studies, patterned after those of Moller (*op. cit.*), on the tongue in certain groups would be valuable, even though it is unlikely they would be of any major taxonomic importance.

The adaptations of the hind limb for various types of locomotion have been analyzed in several major papers. Perhaps the most extensive and analytical paper on adaptations for swimming and diving, published in the last twenty-five years, is that of Neu (1931) who studied coots and penguins. Dabelow (1925) also discussed the modifications for swimming; Stolpe (1932), the general adaptations for specific uses of the hind limb; Kripp (1933c), the bony specializations in storks, herons, and cormorants; Miller (1937), the changes correlated with loss of modifications for swimming and the gain of adaptations for terrestrial locomotion in the Hawaiian Goose, *Nesochen;* Richardson (1942), the convergent changes in a number of species adapted for foraging on trunks of trees; R. W. Storer (1945), the correlation of structure and terrestrial locomotion in the Alcidae; and Fisher (1946), the intra-family differences in structure and function of the appendages in New World vultures. The papers of Blechschmidt (1929), Scharnke (1930), and Steinbacher (1935) considered in detail the functional aspects of different types of bird feet.

Quite understandably, all these investigations, as well as many mentioned before, centered around the correlation of differences in gross structure with observed differences in use. Thus we have in certain instances the broad background of correlation, but we need detailed, controlled, experimental and analytical investigations. For example, much of the research just noted has relied in part on the relative development of individual muscles, or groups of muscles supposedly working toward a common action. While this is of value, it must be remembered that inferring specific actions of individual muscles or even of muscle groups on the basis of dissections of dead animals is at best very subjective and cannot take into account synergistic or antagonistic activities of other single muscles or groups, or of differential neural factors. Weights, lengths, and volumes of muscles are of course indices to their activity and can and should be used comparatively, but the specific result of the contraction of a muscle or muscle group can only be determined experimentally in living birds. Toward that end, it therefore seems necessary to perform muscle and nerve degeneration and removal experiments; such experiments are now under way at the University of Illinois. Careful analysis of movement before and after a muscle has been made inactive should provide a valuable insight of its function. It is likely, however, that other muscles may often take over the function of a deactivated muscle and hence obscure the latter's function. By successive removal of single muscles of a functional group one could eventually determine the action of the various muscles within a group. The function of ligaments and of joints could perhaps be determined in much the same way.

FLIGHT

Animal flight is one of the most complex of the easily observed aspects of life. There are so many variable factors simultaneously involved in flight that experimental analysis has thus far been impossible. The rigid, single-plane wing of an airplane, with its two or three external movable features, is very simple compared to the flexible, jointed wing of the bird. The latter has several planes (the three parts of the main wing and the alula) and adjustable length and width; the camber may be changed at will, and the wing-slotting (spacing of ends of primaries and even of secondaries and tertials, and separation of alular plane from main planes) is variable. Further, by pulling the wing tips forward or backward the position of the wing is changed in horizontal relation to the center of gravity. By up and down movement of the wing the relative vertical position of the center of gravity is changed. The inclinations of the parts of the wing plane and the alular plane are momentarily variable. And perhaps the crowning complexity is that all the wing planes may act simply as supporting surfaces, as in soaring, or at times be divided into two functional units—the proximal parts of the plane acting as a supporting surface and the distal, hand region working as a propulsive "propeller." Most of these factors apply to both soaring and gliding flight; many additional complicating features come into play when flapping flight occurs.

It seems obvious that any attempt at analysis of bird flight should first consider the relatively simple soaring and gliding mode. Analysis has proceeded along two main lines—study of functions of the individual parts of the wing and observation in the field of different mannerisms in the use of the entire wing. Thus we have studies of the inferred actions of individual muscles, bones, and feathers, and there are many papers on flapping and soaring flight and its use by various species. Let us first consider the analysis of individual aspects of the wing.

Length and width of wing usually vary with the type of flight; for the most part we associate relatively long and wide wings with soaring, short and wide wings with the rapid whirring flight of such birds as the quail, and long and narrow or short and narrow wings with speedy flapping flight. All these correlations are based primarily upon the concept of "supporting surface"—a soaring bird moving with the air needs a relatively large surface to support its weight, but a flapping bird creates its own "air currents" and by repeated movements of its wings "climbs onto" successive columns of air. The activities of the wing "replace" the natural movement of the air used by soarers. However, virtually all birds must, or at least do, use flapping motions on take-off and on landing, and occasionally at least in full flight. Hence, the possibility of flapping flight is almost always present, even in soaring birds. The difference

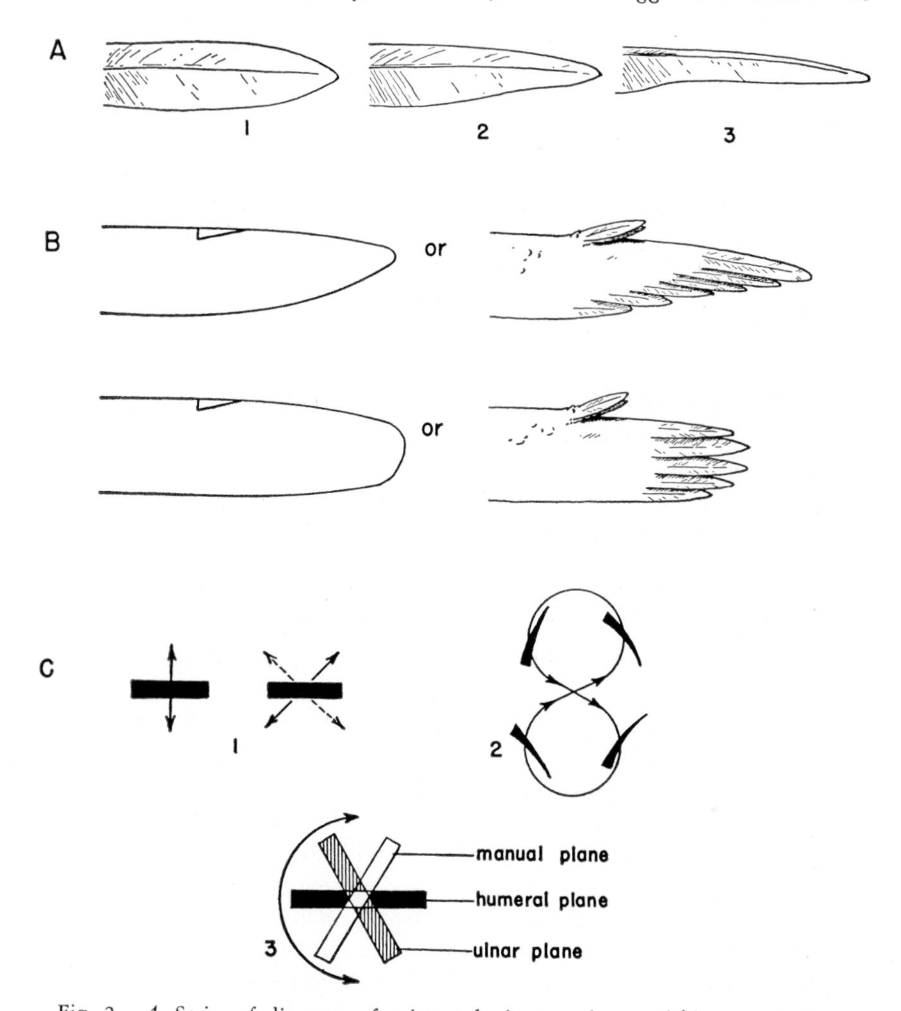

Fig. 2. *A.* Series of diagrams of primary feathers to show variable emargination on both vanes. *B.* Pointed versus rounded ends on wings, and slotting effected by spreading alula and primaries. *C1.* Diagram of cross-section of a wing plane to show possible directions of movement in relation to the plane. *C2.* Diagram to show probable rotatory movement of tip of wing, as viewed from end of wing. *C3.* Diagram to show complexity of variable but simultaneous inclinations of different planes of the wing, as might be seen in an end view.

then lies in the relative development of the parts of the mechanism. There are so many exceptions to the correlations mentioned above, in relation to length and width of wing and type of flight, that one cannot safely predict the type of flight by study of only these aspects. Gladkov (1937b) has seemingly overemphasized the importance of a single factor, length of wing.

Intermembral proportions of the wing enter into the picture. Böker (1927) studied the relative lengths of the various segments of the wing. He set up structural indices to indicate the proportions and to correlate the proportions with the type of flight. Although this was a useful pioneering work, it has now become evident that such proportions are not infallible indices to the type of flight actually exhibited by any one species. Engels (1941) showed this fallibility in hawks, and Fisher (1946) in American vultures. The relative lengths of the parts of the wing, usually based on bony elements, do vary, but this apparent variation is due in a large part to changes in the distal segments; the proximal segments appear to be more stable and less "responsive" to environmental effects. With predominantly soaring flight the distal parts of the wing are found to be longer, relative to total wing length and to body length (combined length of body vertebrae). In flapping flight it is the distal segments that usually are relatively short. But here again one cannot generalize, for in hummingbirds the humerus is very short. This is apparently the result of selection for a mechanism for speed and maneuverability, which is quite distinct from the increased support provided by the equally long, relatively, distal segments in soaring birds.

Shape of the end of the wing is important as it affects the flow of air. With a pointed tip or with slots in the end of the wing, the so-called "end effect" of an airfoil is reduced; end effect refers to the disturbance created by the end of an airfoil passing through air. In part, this turmoil of air currents is proportional to the width of the wing tip in relation to its length. Thus a pointed wing tip has less end effect than a square wing tip, and the end of a wing with primaries separated has less than a wing tip of the same width with primaries overlapping. The multi-slot wing tip, provided by emarginated and separated primaries, has been correlated with better ability to fly by Averill (1927) and Graham (1932). Averill showed that emargination or narrowing of the distal parts of the primaries increased with the size of the bird and with its migratory habits. Graham re-emphasized the importance of air passing through the slots as an aid to smoothing out the conflicting currents on the posterior edge of the wing and in producing laminar flow, which is of significance in increasing lift and forward speed.

Averill's finding that slotting increases with body size is of interest because Banks (1933), Gladkow (1936), and Poole (1938) found a decrease in wing area relative to body weight as body weight increases. If body weight increases more rapidly than does the wing area supporting it, a different mode of flight must be utilized or compensating mechanisms must be "developed." Wing slotting, as effected by emarginated primaries or by the alula, appears to be such a mechanism. In all these adaptations cognizance must be taken of differences in the type of flight usually exhibited by a species. Relative wing surface is less in flapping than in soaring birds (Poole, 1938; Fisher, 1946). There are, however, considerable variations in wing-loading among soaring birds; some, such as the Turkey Vulture, *Cathartes aura,* are lightly loaded

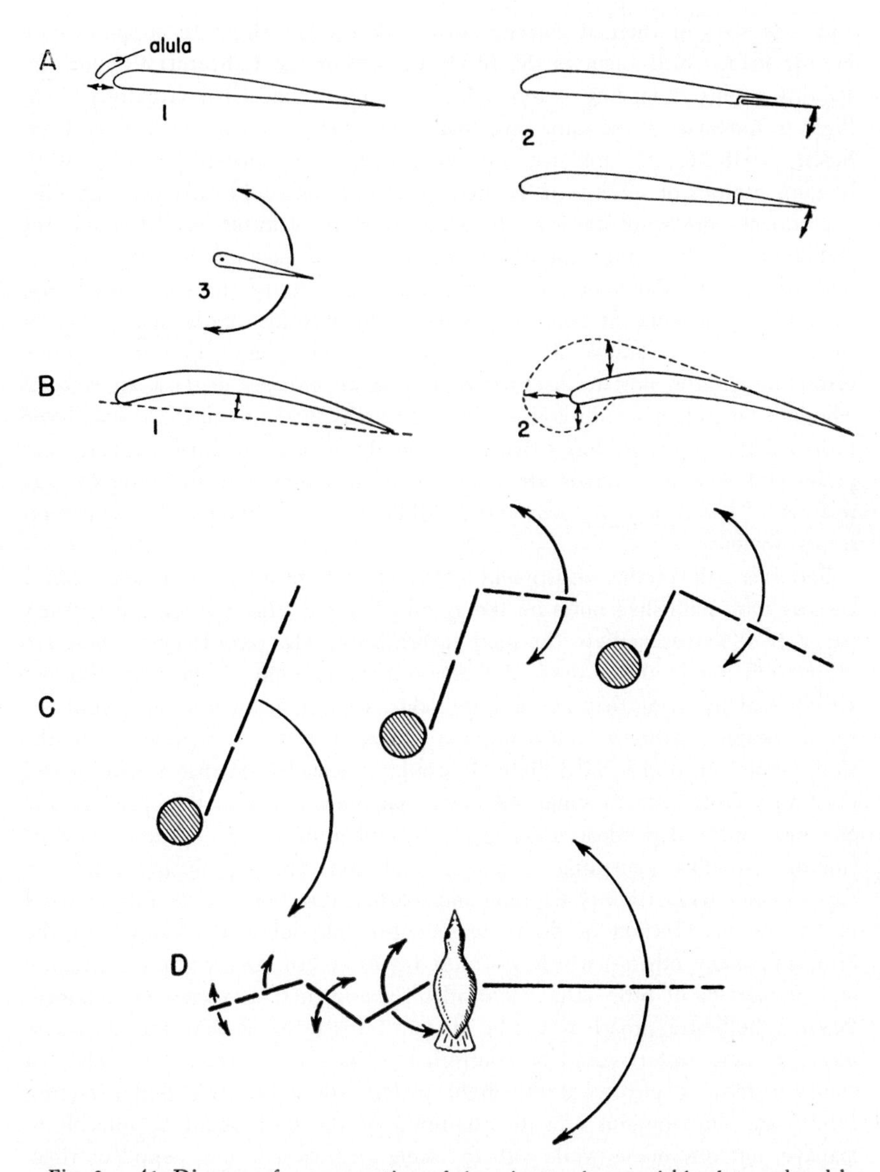

Fig. 3. *A1.* Diagram of a cross-section of the wing to show variable slot produced by alular movement. *A2.* Two types of bird "flaps" and their potential movement. *A3,* Illustration of potential "swing" of a wing plane. *B1.* Variable camber. *B2.* Diagram indicating possible changes in leading edge of wing plane—accomplished by moving marginal coverts. *C.* Line drawing of anterior view of segments of left wing to demonstrate some intramembral movements. *D.* Diagram of dorsal view of wings to indicate observable anteroposterior movements.

and may soar in thermal currents and updrafts too slight to support more heavily loaded birds such as the Black Vulture or the California Condor. Instability results if loading is too light, and strong winds may actually prevent flight in *Cathartes* at the same time that *Gymnogyps* is soaring well. (See J. H. Storer, 1948:76, 87, for data on wing-loading in various species.) With homing pigeons or other birds trained to return, one could carry on controlled experiments on wing-loading. It would not be difficult to determine the maximum weight a bird could lift at the time of take-off or could support once in the air. Differential loading of the segments of the wing might also be used to test some of our theories regarding position of the main body of the muscle. Observational data on many animals belonging to many different taxonomic groups indicate that swiftly moving appendages or those appendages whose distal ends move through a wide arc usually have the muscle masses more proximal than do those limbs that move slowly or in a restricted manner. Experimental data on animals are not present to substantiate the inferred correlation of speed of movement and position of mass, although the adaptation seems obvious.

Speed is still another constituent of flight that must be considered. Many authors have published notes on the speed of this or that species, but Cooke's paper of 1937 has perhaps the most information. The records given there are of interest, but in the analysis of flight and the relation of speed to different activities of the wing they are of little value. Indeed, I know of no records of speed, coupled with the other necessary data, that are of significance to the study of its function in bird flight. It would seeem obvious that a bird's speed must vary from zero to some unknown maximum and that the speed at any one moment is dependent upon a great number of things—altitude, rate of sinking, stimulus (pursuing, pursued, migration, feeding, mating), rate of flapping or interspersion of flapping and soaring, direction and velocity of wind in relation to direction of flight, temperature, physiological condition of the bird, and many others—which we must try to record. Observations in nature will perhaps be of little value. Controlled experimental data must be obtained. Perhaps the best approach would be to train birds to fly in wind tunnels where most of these factors could be controlled or at least measured and where a complete moving picture of the flight pattern could be made under varying conditions. The stimulus and the condition of the bird would be difficult to manage, but continuous work with the same bird, over a long period of time, and comparison with other individuals of the same species should give us a much better understanding of speed and other factors involved than we can obtain from observations in nature. Even though the problem of speed is almost untouched, Raspet (1950) has begun the analysis of speed in the Black Vulture by following this species in a slow-speed sailplane. Wilkinson (1950) described a device, based upon exposure of a photographic plate to a radioactive material, to measure the actual time spent in flight; this should be very useful in determining speeds the birds use in long flights, which in turn might be a more satisfactory speed to use in connection with the study of the relative development of wing muscles, shape and length of wing, etc.

Observations of birds in the field and aeronautical experiments show that the position of the center of gravity with relation to the supporting surface varies under different conditions. In a hawk, stooping at prey, the wings are pulled back, the center of gravity is thus moved ahead of the wings, and the anterior part of the body dips downward. The reverse occurs in steep, and perhaps even slight, climbs. We do not know how these shifts affect the action of the parts of the wing, or even the action of the muscles in changing this relative position of the center of gravity. Stegmann (1949) has studied the effect of the center of gravity on the position of the wing in flight, but I have not been able to see his paper.

The membranous patagium extending along the leading edge of the wing from the shoulder to the wrist has received little attention. Schneider's paper (1942) on the structure and function of the patagium in the Pelecanidae is the only detailed work. It is apparent that variable tension in this structure affects camber and width of wing as well as the particular properties of the leading edge—curvature, thickness, porosity, and others. Just how these variables affect flight in living birds must be determined experimentally.

Taber (1932a, 1932b) and others have briefly considered the curvature of the wing from anterior to posterior, but in all cases the information has been largely of theoretical origin and interpolated from our knowledge of the more static situation in airplanes.

The proportions of the bony parts of the wing have been discussed previously and it has been noted that they are not always reliable indices to the type of flight. However, studies of these proportions within a natural group of birds exhibiting a variety of flight patterns should make possible at least tentative correlations if at the same time the morphology of the individual bones was compared. Configuration of the bones—curvature, diameter, length and position of processes, muscular and ligamental attachments, shape and relative development of articular surfaces—is perhaps of more significance than is simple relative length. Then too, most of the past studies of these proportions have not been based on adequate samples and the statistical treatment has been too skimpy, if present at all, to indicate the probabilities. Sy (1936) and Fisher (1946) analyzed certain differences in configuration and related them to differences in flight. Sy went into great detail in his work on ligaments and the actions of joints, aspects which have been almost totally neglected.

Kaelin (1941) attempted to correlate the angle of the coracoscapular joint with the kind of flight. This work and that of Sy are the only ones, with which I am familiar, that deal with the angles and functions of joints in the wing. The wrist bones, the cuneiform and scapholunar, are unknown from the functional viewpoint and yet their conformation must be of considerable importance to the action of the wing tip, which is perhaps the most dynamic part of the wing.

In connection with the activities of joints, the best means of study might be immobilization by fusion of the ends of the bones or by insertion of internal metal splints. Such work would also eliminate several variables and make easier the analysis of function of the entire wing.

Thus far nothing has been said concerning the "motor" for flight, *i.e.,* the muscles. The general pattern of placement is known for birds, but the modifications of this pattern are not known for many. Comparative studies within a related group of birds are very much needed. We must know: (1) relative development of various muscles, measured in some quantitative way such as volume or wet and dry weights (Gladkov, 1937a; Fisher, 1946:607); (2) relative placement of the belly of the muscle; (3) relative development of tendinous and fleshy origins and insertions and their positions on the bones; and (4) the actions, coactions, and antagonistic activities of individual muscles and muscle groups. The first three points can be clarified by dissection and careful study of specimens. Some information pertinent to the fourth need can also be obtained in this manner, but the bulk of the knowledge necessary for more complete understanding of muscular activity must come from experimental work on intact muscles in living birds. The most logical, and perhaps the only successful, approach is through the neural control (see page 81).

Physiological research on the neural and metabolic aspects of flight, following the leads suggested by Groebbels (1926), Jongbloed (1938), and Pearson (1950) should be very productive.

Even with complete information on the functioning of the parts of the flight mechanism, as outlined thus far, we are left with the synthesis which at present seems almost impossible. There are several good, general reviews of the simple aeronautical principles involved and the action of the parts as viewed externally in the laboratory and in the field. See Bunnell (1930), Lorenz (1933), J. H. Storer (1948), and Slijper (1950). It is true that these and other authors have included the broader implications of internal mechanisms, but there is a wide gap in our knowledge of the correlation of "what happens" with "how it happens."

Brown (1948) has reviewed the use of high-speed photography in the study of flight and has applied it to the flapping cycle of pigeons. Much has and can be learned in this way about the sequence of events, but again this could be much more productive if carried on experimentally with some of the variables removed or at least controlled.

The most factual and quantitative approach to the study of birds in free flight is that of Raspet (1950). In a slow sailplane he was able to follow Black Vultures as closely as five meters and for long periods of time. By means of a camera mounted in the windshield he photographed various phases of flight as he tracked the bird. Most importantly, he was able to report, via radio to a ground crew, such things as altitude, airspeed, angles of bank, sinking speed, and other pertinent data to be correlated on a time sequence with the photographs. A movie record would have made the data even more complete and useful. When data such as these are integrated with the functioning of the bird's structure, we shall begin to understand something of bird flight.

The wings are of prime importance in flight, of course, but no one seems to have investigated the role of the legs in taking off. Perhaps the greatest stress on a flight mechanism is at the moment of launching into the air, and we are all aware that some birds must run on land or water to gain enough speed to take off. Other species simply jump into the air, sometimes almost vertically, and then start to flap. Differences in ability to gain speed or altitude by leg-action, at this time of major strain and urgency, must have a profound effect on the wing mechanism. A bird with weak legs may need a much stronger wing action or structure at the moment of take-off, and the reverse may be true. How much force is exerted by the legs of a bird as it jumps into the air (in the manner of a Mallard Duck, *Anas platyrhynchos*) or as it runs on land and water prior to the take-off (as a Coot does)? These and many other factors outside the wing must be considered in the analysis of the integrated flight of birds.

Bibliography

ADDENS, J. L.

1933. Motor nuclei and roots of the cranial and first spinal nerves of vertebrates. Part I. Introduction. Cyclostomes. Zeits. Anat. Entwick., 101:307-410.

ADELMANN, H. B.

1927. The development of the eye muscles of the chick. Jour. Morph. and Physiol., 44:29-87.

AMADON, D.

1943a. Bird weights as an aid in taxonomy. Wilson Bull., 55:164-177.
1943b. Bird weights and egg weights. Auk, 60:221-234.

APPEL, F. W.

1929. Sex dimorphism in the syrinx of the fowl. Jour. Morph. and Physiol., 47:497-517.

APPLETON, A. B.

1928. The muscles and nerves of the post-axial region of the tetrapod thigh. Jour. Anat., 62:364-438.

ARIËNS KAPPERS, C. U.

1928. Corpus striatum; its phylogenetic and ontogenetic development and function. Acta Psychiat. et Neurol., 3:93-113.

ARIËNS KAPPERS, C. U., G. C. HUBER, and E. C. CROSBY

1936. The comparative anatomy of the nervous system of vertebrates, including man. Macmillan Co., New York, vol. 1, xvii + 864 pp.; vol. 2, xi + pp. 865-1845.

ASHLEY, J. F.

1941. A study of the structure of the humerus in the Corvidae. Condor, 43: 184-195.

AVERILL, C. K.

1927. Emargination of the long primaries in relation to power of flight and migration. Condor, 29:17-18.

BALDWIN, S. P., and S. C. KENDEIGH

1938. Variations in the weight of birds. Auk, 40:416-467.

BALTHASAR, V.

1935. Biologisch-anatomische Untersuchungen am Kopfe des *Phalacrocorax carbo*. Zeits. Anat. Entwick., 104:593-622.

BANKS, E.

1933. The relation of weight to wing area in the flight of animals. Jour. Malayan Brit. Asiatic Soc., 8:334-360.

BANZHAF, W.

1929. Die Vorderextremität von *Opisthocomus cristatus* (Vieillot). Zeits. Morph. Ökol. Tiere, 16:113-233.

BAUDOUIN, M.

1936. Sur l'ostéologie élémentaire du Grand Cormoran *Phalacrocorax carbo subcormoranus* et sur son curieux crâne. Alauda, 8:149-168.

BEECHER, W. J.

1950. Convergent evolution in the American orioles. Wilson Bull., 62:51-86.

BELLROSE, F. C., and A. S. HAWKINS

1947. Duck weights in Illinois. Auk, 64:422-430.

BENOIT, J., *et al.*

1950. Traité de zoologie. Anatomie, systématique, biologie. Ed. Pierre-P. Grassé. Tome XV. Oiseaux. Masson et Cie, Paris, 1164 pp.

BLECHSCHMIDT, H.

1929. Messende Untersuchungen über die Fussanpassungen der Baum- und Laufvögel. Morph. Jahrb., 61:517-547.

BOAS, J. E. V.

1929. Biologisch-Anatomische Studien Über den Hals der Vögel. Kongl. Danske Vidensk. Selsk. Skrifter, Naturv. Math., Ser. 9, 1:102-222.

1933. Kreuzbein, Becken und Plexus lumbosacralis der Vögel. Danske Vidensk. Selsk. Skrifter, Naturv., Ser. 9, 5:3-74.

BÖHM, M.

1930. Über den Bau des jugendlichen Schädels von *Balaeneiceps rex* nebst Bemerkungen über dessen systematische Stellung und über das Gaumenskelett der Vögel. Zeits. Morph. Ökol. Tiere, 17:677-718.

BÖKER, H.

1927. Die biologische Anatomie der Flugarten der Vögel und ihre Phylogenie. Jour. Ornithol., 75:304-371.

1929. Flugvermögen und Kropf bei *Opisthocomus cristatus* und *Stringops habroptilus*. Morph. Jahrb., 63:152-207.

BÖSIGER, E.

1950. Vergleichende Untersuchungen über die Brustmuskulatur von Huhn, Wachtel, und Star. Acad. Anat., 10:385-429.

BOETTICHER, H. VON

1951. Etwas über Zehenreduktion bei Vögeln. Zool. Anz., 146:113-118.

BRANDES, G.

1924. Beobachtungen und Reflexionen über die Atmung der Vögel. Pflügers Arch. ges. Physiol., 203:492-511.

BREMER, J. L.

1940. The pneumatization of the head of the common fowl. Jour. Morph., 67:143-157.

BRODAL, A., K. KRISTIANSEN, and J. JANSEN

1950. Experimental demonstration of a pontine homologue in birds. Jour. Comp. Neurol., 92:23-70.

BROOM, R., and G. T. BROCK

1931. On the vomerine bones in birds. Proc. Zool. Soc. London, 1931:737-739.

BROWN, M. E.

1935. The morphology of the neurones migrated from the ganglion nodosum of the vagus in birds. Jour. Comp. Neurol., 63:127-138.

BROWN, R. H. J.

1948. The flight of birds. The flapping cycle of the pigeon. Jour. Exper. Biol., 25:322-333.

BRUCKNER, J. H.

1941. Inheritance of white plumage in *Phasianus.* Auk, 58:536-542.

BUNNELL, S.

1930. Aeronautics of bird flight. Condor, 32:269-287.

BURLET, H. M. DE

1929. Zur vergleichenden Anatomie der Labyrinth—innervation. Jour. Comp. Neurol., 47:155-169.

1934. Hohere Sinnesorgane. 2. Vergleichende Anatomie des stato-akustischen Organs. Handb. vergleich. Anat. Wirbelt., 2:1293-1432.

BURT, W. H.

1929. Pterylography of certain North American woodpeckers. Univ. Calif. Publ. Zool., 30:427-442.

1930. Adaptive modifications in the woodpeckers. Univ. Calif. Publ. Zool., 32: 455-524.

CARR-LEWTY, R. A.

1943. The aerodynamics of the drumming of the Common Snipe. Brit. Birds, 36:230-234.

COMPTON, L. V.

1938. The pterylosis of the Falconiformes with special attention to the taxonomic position of the Osprey. Univ. Calif. Publ. Zool., 42:173-211.

CONDON, H. T.

1939. The cranial osteology of certain Tubinares. Trans. Roy. Soc. So. Aust., 63:311-330.

COOKE, M. T.

1937. Flight speed of birds. U.S. Dept. Agric. Circ. No. 428:1-13.

CRAIGIE, E. H.

1928. Observations on the brain of the hummingbird (*Chrysolampis mosquitus* Linn. and *Chlorostilbon caribaeus* Law.). Jour. Comp. Neurol., 45:377-442.

1929a. The vascularity of the cerebral cortex in a specimen of *Apteryx.* Anat. Rec., 43:209-214.

1929b. Cerebral cortex of *Apteryx.* Anat. Anz., 68:97-105.

1930. Studies on the brain of the Kiwi (*Apteryx australis*). Jour. Comp. Neurol., 49:223-357.

1932. The cell structure of the cerebral hemisphere of the hummingbird. Jour. Comp. Neurol., 56:135-168.

1936. The cerebral cortex of the ostrich. Jour. Comp. Neurol., 64:389-416.

1939. The cerebral cortex of *Rhea americana.* Jour. Comp. Neurol., 70:331-353.

1940. The cerebral cortex of palaeognathine and neognathine birds. Jour. Comp. Neurol., 73:179-234.

1941. The cerebral cortex of the penguin. Jour. Comp. Neurol., 74:353-366.

CROSBY, E. C., and T. HUMPHREY

1939a. Studies of the vertebrate telencephalon. Jour. Comp. Neurol., 71:121-213.

1939b. A comparison of olfactory and the accessory olfactory buds in certain vertebrates. Papers Mich. Acad. Sci. Arts and Letters (1938) 24, Part II, Zool.: 95-104.

CROZIER, W. J., and E. WOLF

1943. Theory and measurement of visual mechanisms. X. Modifications of the flicker response contour, and the significance of the avian pecten. Jour. Gen. Physiol., 27:287-313.

CURTIS, E. L., and R. C. MILLER

1938. The sclerotic ring in North American birds. Auk, 55:225-243.

DABELOW, A.

1925. Die Schwimmanpassung der Vögel. Ein Beitrag zur biologischen Anatomie der Fortbewegung. Morph. Jahrb., 54:288-321.

DEHNER, E.

1946. An apparatus for determining the respiratory volume of large aquatic birds. Science, 103:171-172.

DELACOUR, J.

1951. The significance of the number of toes in some woodpeckers and kingfishers. Auk, 68:49-51.

DELACOUR, J., and E. MAYR

1945. The family Anatidae. Wilson Bull., 57:3-55.

DESSELBERGER, H.

1931. Der Verdauungskanal der Dicaeiden nach Gestalt und Funktion. Jour. Ornithol., 79:353-370.

DOMBROWSKY, B.

1925. Das Mittelohr der Vögel. Rev. Russ. Zool., Moscow, 5:15-35.

DOTTERWEICH, H.

1933. Ein weiterer Beitrag zur Atmungsphysiologie der Vögel. Zeits. vergl. Physiol., 18:803-809.

1936. Die Atmung der Vögel. Zeits. vergl. Physiol., 23:744-770.

DOTY, E. J.

1946. The cerebellar nuclear gray in the sparrow (*Passer domesticus*). Jour. Comp. Neurol., 84:17-31.

DURWARD, A.

1932. Observations on cell masses in the cerebral hemisphere of the New Zealand Kiwi (*Apteryx australis*). Jour. Anat. London, 66:437-477.

EDGEWORTH, F. H.

1935. The cranial muscles of vertebrates. Cambridge University Press, viii + 493 pp.

EDINGER, T.

1942. The pituitary body in giant animals, fossil and living: a survey and a suggestion. Quart. Rev. Biol., 17:31-45.

EDINGTON, G. H., and A. E. MILLER

1941. The avian ulna: its quill-knobs. Proc. Roy. Soc. Edinburgh, Sec. B, 61, Part II: 138-148.

ENGELS, W. L.

1938a. Variation in bone length and limb proportions in the Coot (*Fulica americana*). Jour. Morph., 62:599-607.

1938b. Tongue musculature of passerine birds. Auk, 55:642-650.

1938c. Cursorial adaptations in birds. Limb proportions in the skeleton of *Geococcyx*. Jour. Morph., 63:207-217.

1940. Structural adaptations in thrashers (Mimidae: genus *Toxostoma*) with comments on interspecific relationships. Univ. Calif. Publ. Zool., 42:341-400.

1941. Wing skeleton and flight of hawks. Auk, 58:61-69.

EVANS, F. G.

1949. Deformation studies of the femur under static and dynamic loading. Ann. Inst. Biol. Mex., 20:473-491.

FIEDLER, W.

1951. Beiträge zur Morphologie der Kiefermuskulatur der Oscines. Zool. Jahrb., 71:145-288.

FIORA, A.

1933, 1934. El peso de las aves. Hornero, 5:174-188, 353-365.

FISHER, H. I.

1939. Pterylosis of the Black Vulture. Auk, 56:407-410.

1940. The occurrence of vestigial claws on the wings of birds. Amer. Midl. Nat., 23:234-243.

1942. The pterylosis of the Andean Condor. Condor, 44:30-32.

1943. The pterylosis of the King Vulture. Condor, 45:69-73.

1944. The skulls of the cathartid vultures. Condor, 46:272-296.

1945a. Locomotion in the fossil vulture *Teratornis*. Amer. Midl. Nat., 33:725-742.

1945b. Flying ability and the anterior intermuscular line on the coracoid. Auk, 62:125-129.

1946. Adaptations and comparative anatomy of the locomotor apparatus of New World vultures. Amer. Midl. Nat., 35:545-727.

1947. The skeletons of Recent and fossil *Gymnogyps*. Pacific Science, 1:227-236.

FRAENKEL, G.

1934. Der Atmungsmechanismus der Vogel wahrend des Fluges. Biol. Zentralbl., 54:96-101.

FRANZ, V.

1934. Hohere Sinnesorgane. 1. Vergleichende Anatomie des Wirbeltierauges. Handb. vergleich. Anat. Wirbelt., 2:989-1292.

GARDNER, L. L.

1925. The adaptive modifications and the taxonomic value of the tongue in birds. Proc. U. S. Nat. Mus., 67, Art. 19, 49 pp.

GILBERT, P. W.

1939. The avian lung and air-sac system. Auk, 56: 57-63.

GLADKOV, N. A.

1936. Ueber den Zusammenhang Zwischen Körpergrösse und Flugart bei Vogeln. Zool. Jour. Moscow, 15:452- 471.

1937a. The weight of pectoral muscles and wings of birds in connection with the character of their flight. Zool. Jour. Moscow, 16:677-687.

1937b. (The importance of length of wing for the bird's flight.) Arch. Mus. Zool. Moscow, 4:35-47.

GLENNY, F. H.

1942a. Main arteries in the region of the neck and thorax of the Australian Cassowary. Canad. Jour. Res., 20:363-367.

1942b. A systematic study of the main arteries in the region of the heart—Aves—III. The Fringillidae. Part I. Ohio Jour. Sci., 42:84-90.

1943a. A systematic study of the main arteries in the region of the heart, Aves VI. Trogoniformes, Part I. Auk, 60:235-239.

1943b. A systematic study of the main arteries in the region of the heart. Aves: Piciformes. Proc. Zool. Soc. London, Ser. B, 113:179-192.

1943c. A systematic study of the main arteries in the region of the heart—Aves VII. Trans. Roy. Soc. Canada, Third Ser., Sec. 5, 37:35-53.

1944. A systematic study of the main arteries in the region of the heart—Aves VIII. Anseriformes. Part I. Canad. Jour. Res., 22:17-35.

1945. A systematic study of the main arteries in the region of the heart—Aves XIII. Ciconiiformes, Part I. Amer. Midl. Nat., 33:449-454.

GLUCKSMANN, A.

1942. The role of mechanical stresses on bone formation in vitro. Jour. Anat. London, 76:231-239.

GORHAM, F. W., and A. C. IVY

1938. General function of the gall bladder from the evolutionary standpoint. Field Mus. Nat. Hist., Zool. Ser., 22:159-213.

GRAHAM, R. R.

1932. The part played by emarginated feathers and the alula in the flight of birds. Bull. Brit. Ornithol. Club., 52:68-79.

GREGORY, W. K.

1935. Remarks on the origins of the ratites and penguins. Proc. Linn. Soc. New York, Nos. 45-46:1-18.

GROEBBELS, F.

1926. Die Physiologischen Grundlagen des Vogelflugs. Jour. Ornithol., 74: 362-367.

GROSS, A. O.

1928. The Heath Hen. Mem. Boston Soc. Nat. Hist., 6:489-588.

GULLION, G. W.

1950. Voice differences between sexes in the American Coot. Condor, 52:272-273.

HARTMAN, F. A.

1946. Adrenal and thyroid weights in birds. Auk, 63:42-64.

HEINROTH, O.

1922. Die Beziehungen zwischen Vogelgewicht, Eigewicht, Gelegewicht und Brutdauer. Jour. Ornithol., 70:172-285.

HOFER, H.

1945. Untersuchungen über den Bau des Vogelschädels, besonders über den der Spechte und Steisshühner. Zool. Jahrb., 69:1-158.

1949. Die Gaumenlücken der Vögel. Acta. Zool. Internat. Tidskr. Zool., 30: 209-248.

HOLST, E. VON

1943. Ueber "Künstliche Vögel" als Mittel zum Studium des Vogelflugs. Jour. Ornithol., 91:406-447.

HOWARD, H.

1947a. A preliminary survey of trends in avian evolution from Pleistocene to Recent time. Condor, 49:10-13.

1947b. An ancestral Golden Eagle raises a question in taxonomy. Auk, 64: 287-291.

1950. Fossil evidence of avian evolution. Ibis, 92:1-21.

HOWELL, A. B.

1936. The phylogenetic arrangement of the muscular system. Anat. Rec., 66: 295-316.

1937. Morphogenesis of the shoulder architecture: Aves. Auk, 54:364-375.

1938a. Morphogenesis of the architecture of hip and thigh. Jour. Morph., 62: 177-218.

1938b. Muscles of the avian hip and thigh. Auk, 55:71-81.

HUBER, G. C., and E. C. CROSBY

1929. The nuclei and fiber paths of the avian diencephalon, with consideration of telencephalic and certain mesencephalic centers and connections. Jour. Comp. Neurol., 48:1-226.

HUBER, J. F.

1936. Nerve roots and nuclear groups in the spinal cord of the pigeon. Jour. Comp. Neurol., 65:43-92.

HUDSON, G. E.

1937. Studies on the muscles of the pelvic appendage in birds. Amer. Midl. Nat., 18:1-108.

1948. Studies on the muscles of the pelvic appendage in birds. 2: The heterogeneous order Falconiformes. Amer. Midl. Nat., 29:102-127.

HUGGINS, R. A., *et al.*

1942. Ossification in the nestling House Wren. Auk, 59:532-543.

HUTT, F. B.

1929. Sex dimorphism and variability in the appendicular skeleton of the Leghorn Fowl. Poultry Sci., 8:202-218.

HUTT, F. B., and L. BALL

1938. Number of feathers and body size in passerine birds. Auk, 55:651-657.

HUXLEY, J. S.

1927. On the relation between egg-weight and body-weight in birds. Jour. Linn. Soc. London, 36:457-466.

IBRAGIMOVA, Z. I.

1939. [Sex peculiarities in the anatomical structure of the interior auditory region of birds.] Trudy Samarkand Med. Inst., 4:83-95.

JONGBLOED, J.

1938. Zur Aerodynamik des Vogelfluges. Zeits. vergl. Physiol., 25:529-540.

JUNGHERR, E.

1945. Certain nuclear groups of the avian mesencephalon. Jour. Comp. Neurol., 82:55-76.

KAELIN, J.

1941. Ueber den Coracoscapularwinkel und die Beziehungen der Rumpfform Zum Lokomotionstypus bei den Vögeln. Rev. Suisse Zool. Genève, 48:553-557.

KÄLIN, J.

1942. Ueber die Rumpfform und den Lokomotionstypus bei den Vögeln. Rev. Suisse Zool. Genève, 49:15-32.

KATTINGER, E.

1929. Sexual- und Subspecies-Unterschiede im Skelettbau der Vögel. Jour. Ornithol., 77:41-149.

KESTEVEN, H. L.

1926. The parabasal canal and nerve foramina and canals in the bird skull. Jour. Roy. Soc. New South Wales, Sydney, 59:108-123.

KIMURA, T.

1931. Morphologische Untersuchungen über das membranöse Gehörorgan der Vögel. Foliae Anat. Japonica, Tokyo, 9:91-142.

KISSELEVA, Z. N.

1937. [Comparative anatomical study of the nasal cavity of birds.] Pamyati Akad. Menzbiera. Acad. Sci. Leningrad-Moscow, pp. 175-210.

KOCH, W.

1927. Untersuchungen über die Entwicklung des Eierstockes der Vögel. II. Die phylogenetische Bedeutung der Form des Eierstockes bei den Vögeln. Zool. Anz., 71:299-303.

KÖDITZ, W.

1925. Über die Syrinx einiger Clamatores und ausländischer Oscines. Zeits. wiss. Zool., 126:70-144.

KRIPP, D. VON

1933a. Der Oberschnabel Mechanismus der Vögel (nach den Methoden der graphischen Statik bearbeitet). Morph. Jahrb., 71:469-544.

1933b. Beiträge zur mechanischen Analyse des Schnabelmechanismus. Morph. Jahrb., 72:541-566.

1933c. Die Spezialisationsreiche der Störche, Reiher una Cormorane vom konstruktiven und biotechnischen Standpunkt. Morph. Jahrb., 72:60-92.

1935. Die mechanische Analyse der Schnabel. Krummung und ihre Bedeutung für die Anpassungsforschung. Morph. Jahrb., 76:448-494.

KROGH, A.

1941. The comparative physiology of respiratory mechanisms. University of Pennsylvania Press, Philadelphia, vii + 172 pp.

KUHLENBECK, H.

1937. The ontogenetic development of the diencephalic centers in a bird's brain (chick) and comparison with the reptilian and mammalian diencephalon. Jour. Comp. Neurol., 66:23-76.

1938. The ontogenetic development and phylogenetic significance of the cortex telencephali in the chick. Jour. Comp. Neurol., 69:273-301.

1939. The development and structure of pretectal cell masses in the chick. Jour. Comp. Neurol., 71:361-387.

LARSELL, O.

1948. The development and subdivisions of the cerebellum of birds. Jour. Comp. Neurol., 89:123-190.

LARSON, L. M.

1930. Osteology of the California Road-runner, Recent and Pleistocene. Univ. Calif. Publ. Zool., 32:409-428.

LATIMER, H. B.

1925. The postnatal growth of the central nervous system of the chicken. Jour. Comp. Neurol., 38:251-297.

1927a. Postnatal growth of the chicken skeleton. Amer. Jour. Anat., 40:1-57.

1927b. Correlations of the weights and lengths of the body, systems, and organs of the turkey hen. Anat. Rec., 35:365-377.

LATIMER, H., and H. P. WAGER

1941. Weights and linear dimensions of the skull and some of the long bones of the Mallard Duck (*Anas platyrhynchos platyrhynchos*). Univ. Kansas Sci. Bull., 27:15-18.

LEMMRICH, W.

1931. Der Skleralring der Vögel. Jena Zeits. Naturw., 65:513-586.

LINSDALE, J. M.

1928. Variations in the Fox Sparrow (*Passerella iliaca*) with reference to natural history and osteology. Univ. Calif. Publ. Zool., 30:251-392.

LORENZ, K.

1933. Beobachtetes über das Fliegen der Vögel und über die Beziehungen der Flügel — und Steuerform zur Art des Fluges. Jour. Ornithol., 81:107-236.

LOWE, P. R.

1926. More notes on the quadrate as a factor in avian classification. Ibis, Ser. 12, 2:152-188.

1927. On the anatomy and systematic position of *Aechmorhynchus cancellatus* (Gmelin), together with some notes on the genera *Bartramia* and *Mesoscolopax;* the subfamily Limosinae; and the pterylosis of *Scolopax.* Ibis, Ser. 12, 3:114-132.

1928. Studies and observations bearing on the phylogeny of the ostrich and its allies. Proc. Zool. Soc. London, Part I, 1928:185-247.

1931a. On the relations of the Gruimorphae to the Charadriimorphae and Rallimorphae, with special reference to the taxonomic position of Rostratulidae, Jacanidae, and Burhinidae (Oedicnemidae olim); with a suggested new order (Telmatomorphae). Ibis, Ser. 13, 1:491-554.

1931b. An anatomical review of the "waders" (Telmatomorphae), with special reference to the families, subfamilies and genera within the suborders Limicolae, Grui-Limicolae and Laro-Limicolae. Ibis, Ser. 13, 1:712-771.

1933a. Structural diversity in charadriine genera correlated with differences in colour-pattern. Ibis, Ser. 13, 3:112-129, 351-352.

1933b. On the primitive characters of the penguins, and their bearing on the phylogeny of birds. Proc. Zool. Soc. London, 1933:483-539.

1942. Some additional factors bearing on the phylogeny of the Struthiones. Proc. Zool. Soc. London, 1942:1-20.

LUBOSCH, W.

1929. Über den streptognathen Schädel von *Caprimulgus,* nebst Bemerkungen über seine Bedeutung für die Reichertsche Theorie. Morph. Jahrb., 63 (Maurer-Festschrift), Part 2:96-151.

McDOWELL, S.

1948. The bony palate of birds. Part I. The Paleognathae. Auk, 65: 520-549.

MARPLES, B. J.

1930. The proportions of birds' wings and their changes during development. Proc. Zool. Soc. London, 1930:997-1008.

1932. The structure and development of the nasal glands of birds. Proc. Zool. Soc. London, 1932:829-844.

MAW, A. J. G.

1935. The inheritance of skeletal dimensions in the domestic fowl. Sci. Agric., 16:85-112.

MAYR, E.

1931. Die Syrinx einiger Singvögel aus Neu-Guinea. Jour. Ornithol., 79:333-337.

MENNER, E.

1938. Die Bedeutung des Pecten im Auge des Vogels für die Wahrnehmung von Bewegungen, nebst Bemerkungen über seine Ontogenie und Histologie. Zool. Jahrb., Abt. Allge. Zool. Physiol. Tiere, 58:481-538.

MILLER, A. H.

1934. The vocal apparatus of some North American owls. Condor, 36:204-213.

1935. The vocal apparatus of the Elf Owl and Spotted Screech Owl. Condor, 37:288.

1937. Structural modifications in the Hawaiian Goose (*Nesochen sandvicensis*). A study in adaptive evolution. Univ. Calif. Publ. Zool., 42:1-79.

1941. Speciation in the avian genus *Junco.* Univ. Calif. Publ. Zool., 44:173-434.

1947. The structural basis of the voice of the Flammulated Owl. Auk, 64: 133-135.

1949. Some ecologic and morphologic considerations in the evolution of higher taxonomic categories. In Ornithologie als Biologische Wissenschaft. Carl Winter, Heidelberg, pp. 84-88.

MOLLER, W.

1930. Über die Schnabel- und Zungenmechanik blütenbesuchender Vögel. I. Ein Beitrag zur Biologie des Blumenvogels. Biol. Generalis, 6:651-726.

1931. Über die Schnabel- und Zungenmechanik blütenbesuchender Vögel. II. Ein Beitrag zur Biologie des Blumenvogels. Biol. Generalis, 7:99-154.

1932. Biologisch-anatomische Studien am Schädel von *Ara macao*. Morph. Jahrb., 70:305-342.

MONTAGNA, W.

1945. A re-investigation of the development of the wing of the fowl. Jour. Morph., 76:87-113.

MOREAU, R. E.

1944a. Some weights of African and of wintering Palearctic birds. Ibis, 86: 16-30.

1944b. Rensch on the increase of heart-weight in relation to body-weight with increase in altitude. Ibis, 86:30-32.

MUSKENS, L. J. J.

1930. On tracts and centers involved in the upward and downward associated movements of the eyes after experiments in birds. Jour. Comp. Neurol., 50: 289-331.

MYERS, J. A.

1917. Studies on the syrinx of *Gallus domesticus*. Jour. Morph., 29:165-215.

NEU, W.

1931. Die Schwimmbewegungen der Tauchvögel (Blässhuhn und Pinguine). Zeits. vergl. Physiol., 14:682-708.

NICE, M. M.

1938. The biological significance of bird weights. Bird-Banding, 9:1-11.

OBERHOLSER, H. C.

1917. Ornithology.—Diagnosis of a new pycnonotine family of Passeriformes. Jour. Wash. Acad. Sci., 7:537-541.

OLIVER, W. R. B.

1945. Avian evolution in New Zealand and Australia. Emu, 45:55-77, 119-152.

PALMGREN, P.

1932. Zur Biologie von *Regulus r. regulus* (L.) und *Parus atricapillus borealis* Selys. Eine Vergleichend-ökologische Untersuchung. Acta Zool. Fenn., No. 14: 1-113.

1949. Zur biologischen Anatomie der Halsmuskulatur der Singvögel. In Ornithologie als Biologische Wissenschaft. Carl Winter, Heidelberg, pp. 192-203.

PARSONS, C. W.

1932. Report on penguin embryos collected during the Discovery investigations. Discovery Repts., 6:139-164.

PEARSON, O. P.

1950. The metabolism of hummingbirds. Condor, 52:145-152.

PITELKA, F. A.

1951. Speciation and ecologic distribution in American jays of the genus *Aphelocoma*. Univ. Calif. Publ. Zool., 50:195-464.

PLANTEFOL, A., and H. SCHARNKE

1934. Contribution à l'étude du rôle des sacs aériens dans la respiration des oiseaux. Ann. de Physiol., Paris, 10:83-133.

POOLE, E. L.

1938. Weights and wing areas in North American birds. Auk, 55:511-517.

PUMPHREY, R. J.

1948. The sense organs of birds. Ann. Rept. Smithsonian Inst., 1948: 305-330.

PUZANOV, I. I.

1948. On adaptations in Russian woodpeckers. Izvest. Akad. Nauk SSSR (Biol.), 1948:365-372.

QUISENBERRY, J. H., E. ROBERTS, and L. E. CARD

1941. Genetic studies of skeletal dimensions and their relation to body weight and egg production in the domestic fowl. Poultry Sci., 20:104-120.

RASPET, A.

1950. Performance measurements of a soaring bird. Aeronaut. Eng. Rev., 9:1-4.

RENSCH, B.

1931. Der Einfluss des Tropenklimas auf den Vogel. Proc. Seventh Internat. Ornithol. Cong., Amsterdam (1930):197-205.

1940. Die ganzheitliche Auswirkung der Grössenauslese am Vogelskelett. Jour. Ornithol., 88:373-388.

1950. Die Abhängigkeit der relativen sexualdifferenz von der Körpergrösse. Bonner Zool. Beitr., 1:58-69.

RICHARDSON, F.

1939. Functional aspects of the pneumatic system of the California Brown Pelican. Condor, 41:13-17.

1942. Adaptive modifications for tree-trunk foraging in birds. Univ. Calif. Publ. Zool., 46:317-368.

1943. Functional aspects of the inner vane of remiges. Auk, 60:44-50.

RICHDALE, L. E.

1947. Seasonal fluctuations in weights of penguins and petrels. Wilson Bull., 59:160-171.

RIDDLE, O.

1928. Sex and seasonal differences in weight of liver and spleen. Proc. Soc. Exper. Biol. and Med., 25:474-476.

ROBBINS, C. A.

1932. The advantage of crossed mandibles: A note on the American Red Crossbill. Auk, 49:159-165.

ROMER, A. S.

1927. The development of the thigh musculature of the chick. Jour. Morph., 43:347-385.

1944. The development of tetrapod limb musculature. The shoulder region of *Lacerta.* Jour. Morph., 74:1-41.

RÜPPELL, W.

1933. Physiologie und Akustik der Vogelstimme. Jour. Ornithol., 81:433-542.

SANDERS, E. B.

1929. A consideration of certain bulbar, midbrain and cerebellar centers and fiber tracts in birds. Jour. Comp. Neurol., 49:155-222.

SCHARNKE, H.

1930. Physiologische-anatomische Studien am Fuss der Spechte. Jour. Ornithol., 78:308-327.

1931. Beiträge zur Morphologie und Entwicklungsgeschichte der Zunge der Trochilidae, Meliphagidae und Picidae. Jour. Ornithol., 79:425-491.

1934. Die Bedeutung der Luftsäcke für die Atmung der Vögel. Ergeb. Biol., 10:177-206.

1938. Experimentelle Beiträge zur Kenntnis der Vogelatmung. Zeits. vergl. Physiol., 25:548-583.

SCHNEIDER, H.

1942. Aufbau und Funktion der Patagien gut fliegender Vögel. Morph. Jahrb., 87:27-84.

SCHNEIDER, M., and L. C. DUNN

1924. On the length and variability of the bones of the White Leghorn Fowl. Anat. Rec., 27:229-239.

SCHOLANDER, P. F.

1940. Experimental investigations on the respiratory function in diving mammals and birds. Hvalr. Skrifter Oslo, No. 22:1-131.

SCHORGER, A. W.

1947. The deep diving of the Loon and Old-squaw and its mechanism. Wilson Bull., 59:151-159.

SCHUMACHER, S.

1929. Zur Mechanik und Verwendungsart des Schnepfenschnabels. Zeits. Morph. Ökol. Tiere, 15:90-108.

SCHWARTZ, S. S.

1949. [New data on the relative weight of heart and liver in birds.] Zool. Jour. Moscow, 28:355-360.

SLIJPER, E. J.

1950. De Vliegkunst in het Dierenrijk. E. J. Brill, Leiden, viii+178 pp.

STEGMANN, B. K.

1949. [The center of gravity of birds and its significance for the wing position in flight.] Izvest. Akad. Nauk SSSR (Biol.), 1949:208-217.

STEINBACHER, G.

1935. Funktionelle-anatomische Untersuchungen an Vogelfüssen mit Wendezehen und Rückzehen. Jour. Ornithol., 83:214-282.

STELLBOGEN, E.

1930. Über das äussere und mittlere Ohr des Waldkauzes (*Syrnium aluco* L.). Zeits. Morph. Ökol. Tiere, 19:686-731.

STEWART, P. A.

1937. A preliminary list of bird weights. Auk, 54: 324-332.

STOLPE, M.

1932. Physiologisch-Anatomische Untersuchungen über die hintere Extremität der Vögel. Jour. Ornithol., 80:161-247.

STORER, J. H.

1948. The flight of birds analyzed through slow-motion photography. Cranbrook Inst. Sci., Bull. No. 28:xv+94 pp.

STORER, R. W.

1945. Structural modifications in the hind limb in the Alcidae. Ibis, 87: 433-456.

STRESEMANN, E.

1927-1934. Aves. In Handbuch der Zoologie by Kükenthal. Walter de Gruyter, Berlin, 7(2):xi+897 pp.

SUSHKIN, P. P.

1927. On the anatomy and classification of the weaverbirds. Bull. Amer. Mus. Nat. Hist., 57:1-32.

1929. On the systematic position of the Drepanididae. Verhandl. Sixth Internat. Ornithol. Cong., pp. 379-381.

SY, M.

1936. Funktionell-anatomische Untersuchungen am Vogelflügel. Jour. Ornithol., 84:199-296.

TABER, W. B., JR.

1932a. Curvature of wing and flapping flight. Wilson Bull., 44:75-78.

1932b. Curvature of wing and soaring flight. Wilson Bull., 44:19-22.

TECHNAU, G.

1936. Die Nasendrüse der Vögel. Jour. Ornithol., 84:511-617.

TIEMEIER, O. W.

1939. A preliminary report on the os opticus of the bird's eye. Zoologica, 24: 333-338.

TURKEWITSCH, B. G.

1936. Ein Versuch zur Systematik der Vögel und Säugetiere auf Grund der anatomischen Struktur ihres Knöchernen Labyrinths. Arch. Zool. Torino, 22: 79-122.

VOS, H. J.

1935. Über den Weg der Atemluft in der Entenlunge. Zeits. vergl. Physiol., 21:552-578.

1937. Ueber das Fehlen der rekurrenten Bronchien beim Pinguin und bei den Reptilien. Zool. Anz., 117:176-181.

WALLS, G. L.

1942. The vertebrate eye and its adaptive radiation. Cranbrook Inst. Sci., Bull. No. 19:xiv+785 pp.

WALTER, W. G.

1934. Beiträge zur Frage über den Weg der Luft in den Atmungsorganen der Vögel. Arch. Neerl. Physiol., 19:529-537.

WARNER, L. H.

1931. Facts and theories of bird flight. Quart. Rev. Biol., 6:84-98.

WATTERSON, R. L.

1942. The morphogenesis of down feathers with special reference to the developmental history of melanophores. Physiol. Zool., 15:234-259.

WEINBERG, E.

1928. The mesencephalic root of the fifth nerve. A comparative study. Jour. Comp. Neurol., 46:249-405.

WETHERBEE, K. B.

1934. Some measurements and weights of live birds. Bird-Banding, 5:55-64.

WETMORE, A.

1936. The number of contour feathers in passeriform and related birds. Auk, 53:159-169.

WILKINSON, D. H.

1950. Flight recorders: A technique for the study of bird navigation. Jour. Exper. Biol., 27:192-197.

WILLIAMS, R. G.

1937. The development of vascularity in the hindbrain of the chick. Jour. Comp. Neurol., 66:77-101.

WINDLE, W. F.

1931. The sensory components of the spinal accessory nerve. Jour. Comp. Neurol., 53:115-127.

WOLFSON, A.

1945. The role of the pituitary, fat deposition, and body weight in bird migration. Condor, 47:95-127.

WOODBURNE, R. T.

1936. A phylogenetic consideration of the primary and secondary centers and connections of the trigeminal complex in a series of vertebrates. Jour. Comp. Neurol., 65:403-501.

ZEDLITZ, O. G.

1926. Vogelgewichte als Hilfsmittel für die biologische Forschung. Jour. Ornithol., 74:296-308.

ZEUTHEN, E.

1942. The ventilation of the respiratory tract in birds. Danske Vidensk. Selskab., Biol. Medd., 17:1-50.

chapter 5

THE STUDY OF BEHAVIOR IN BIRDS . . . John T. Emlen, Jr.

INTRODUCTION

The literature of bird behavior is extensive and widely scattered. In addition to the host of papers in scientific journals, many volumes have been devoted exclusively to bird behavior by Altum, Howard, Herrick, Lack, Friedmann, Selous, Kirkman, Finn, Whitman, Armstrong, Darling, Kendeigh, and others, each containing a wealth of observation and interpretation. Much of this literature has recently been collected and admirably organized by Nice (1943) in her monograph on the Song Sparrow, *Melospiza melodia,* and by Armstrong (1947) in his *Bird Display and Behaviour.* Modern analytical studies of behavior have been brought under critical review within the last few years in the comprehensive *Handbook of Experimental Psychology* edited by Stevens (1952) and in a scholarly treatise, *The Study of Instinct,* by Tinbergen (1951a). The special behavioral characteristics of birds have been the subject of recent analytical papers by Thorpe (1951b) and Tinbergen (1951b).

This chapter is not a review of all this tremendous literature; rather it is an attempt to re-examine the broad scope and significance of the study of bird behavior and to sketch some of the modern conceptual trends as they attempt to make order and meaning out of the accumulation of recorded observations.

The Science of Animal Behavior

The study of animal behavior is one of the most basic of the biological sciences. Formerly defined simply as what an animal does, or an animal's manner of living, behavior has gradually come to be recognized as the overt expression of the co-ordinated life processes of the animal—the essence of living—toward which all organic activity and all structure in the organism are oriented. But even this broad concept of the scope and significance of behavior is inadequate for the modern worker. Behavior is more than organic expression; it is the means by which an animal maintains its relation with the environment, the vital link between the living organism and the surrounding world in which it evolved and of which it is a part. *Stimulus* and *response* are the basic attributes of environment and organism respectively in this relationship.

As with other fields of biological science, the study of animal behavior may

Manuscript received July 1, 1953.

be approached in various ways. Psychologists have been particularly concerned with response capacities and with integrative mechanisms. Physiologists have given special attention to problems of motivation and to the mechanisms of reception, conduction, and activation. A third group, the ecologists, have been primarily interested in environmental situations as releasing stimuli and in the adaptive significance of behavior patterns. An appreciation of the nature and problems of bird behavior requires some familiarity with each of these fields.

Birds as Subjects for Behavioral Research

Birds have contributed to our present knowledge and understanding of behavior in many ways. They have, perhaps more than any other group, provided a broad view of the scope of behavioral expressions in relation to life processes and life requirements. Because of the stereotyped and relatively inflexible nature of many of their responses, birds have proven to be excellent subjects for analyzing the inherited and acquired components of behavior. Various workers have found them useful subjects for analyses of stimulus-response mechanisms, particularly where the objectives of the study demanded work under natural conditions. High levels of activity and complex reproductive processes involving elaborate parental care have made them excellent subjects for studies of motivation and of cyclic behavior. Social behavior, from pairing and family association to general gregariousness, is nowhere better developed than in birds, and to birds we owe much of our present understanding of the basic principles of social organization. Proficiency in a specialized and highly efficient form of locomotion in birds has led to the development of some remarkable forms of self-maintenance behavior, including seasonal migration and territorial behavior, phenomena which hold much of interest to the general scientist.

The popularity of birds in behavioral research is also due in part to their accessibility for observation. This applies to both laboratory and field studies, but it is particularly true of the latter. Also to be considered is the wide variety of behavioral types and of situations in which birds may be observed and studied by ecologists interested in behavioral adaptations.

Acknowledgments

In writing this chapter I have sought advice and criticism from Mrs. Margaret M. Nice, Dr. Theodore Schneirla, Dr. Nicholas Collias, Dr. Robert A. McCabe, and the editor of this volume, Dr. Albert Wolfson. All have contributed significantly and most helpfully, and I wish to express my sincere appreciation to all of them. These acknowledgments should not be interpreted as indicating concurrence on all questions of interpretation. In our present state of knowledge it is quite impossible to find uniformity of opinion on the interpretation of many aspects of animal behavior.

BEHAVIORAL FORMS AND THEIR PHYLOGENY

The various components and categories of behavior may be classified vertically on the basis of levels of complexity, or horizontally on the basis of their functional application in the process of living. In this section I have attempted to present in a horizontal classification a systematic survey of the various forms of behavior exhibited by a bird in meeting the basic requirements of living. The forms included are those belonging to high levels in the vertical classification, those concerned directly with problems of survival and propagation. Simpler actions and movements such as grasping, manipulation, and locomotion are omitted on the grounds that they are components of the definitive forms, belonging to lower levels in the vertical scale of complexity.

The relationships and significance of the special behavioral forms exhibited by birds can best be appreciated when viewed in the light of known evolutionary developments in the class. Compared with reptiles, the class from which they are descended, birds are characterized by high speed and efficiency in the life processes. Nearly all of the specializations of structure as well as behavior which characterize birds are related directly or indirectly to accelerated metabolism, increased demands for fuel and oxygen, or to flight as a highly specialized and efficient means of locomotion. The success of birds as a group, their rapid adaptive radiation, and their dispersal into cold and otherwise adverse environments may be attributed largely to these developments.

Rapid evolutionary advances such as those made by the ancestral birds entail a host of interrelated structural and behavioral adaptations which, though they may be difficult to interpret in themselves, are clearly intelligible when viewed as elements in the complex pattern of evolutionary progress. Accelerated metabolism, for example, inevitably entailed increased demands for food which were met by a variety of structural and behavioral specializations. Homoiothermy could not be perfected without insulation, nor could it be developed ontogenetically without special provisions for sheltering and feeding the undeveloped young. Thus each step of progressive adaptation creates needs which must be met concurrently by functionally related adaptations in other parts of the organism or its behavior. Some of the striking behavioral specializations of birds are difficult to understand unless viewed against such a perspective of phylogeny.

The basis for the following classification of behavior forms is function. If we assume that all forms of behavior had their origin in relation to one or another of the basic requirements of living, we are justified in concluding that each of them has a natural place in such a scheme of classification. Specific behavioral forms could doubtless be transferred from one basic function to another through preadaptation or some other evolutionary process. Still, if our basic assumption is correct, a true phylogenetic relationship exists and should serve as a natural basis of classification.

In the following pages the various forms of behavior are grouped according to the vital activity in relation to which they are thought to have evolved; feeding, self-protection, plumage maintenance, and propagation. Most behavioral forms fall readily into this scheme. Others such as seasonal migration have functions in several areas and can be placed only speculatively. The survey is presented with these limitations in mind and with a realization of the hazards that exist in trying to fit a wide and varied assortment of entities into any hard and fast system of classification.

Behavior Associated with Feeding

The high nutritional requirements of birds associated with their rapid metabolic rate has inevitably led to the development of specialized and highly efficient means of securing food. Perhaps the two most interesting aspects of these developments to the biologist are (1) their great variety and (2) the clear correlation between behavior and structure.

Examination of many thousands of stomach contents and observations of feeding behavior by a host of ornithologists reveal a wide variety of interesting food habits and feeding methods. One need mention only a few examples to depict the great range of this variation: the drilling of a woodpecker for grubs, the deep diving of a loon for fish, the flower probing of a hummingbird for nectar and insects, or the precipitous plunge of the Peregrine, *Falco peregrinus,* for feathered quarry. Even within a single family or genus there is a strong tendency for each species to develop distinctive food habits (Lack, 1944). Such distinctiveness has high survival value; it may indeed be essential where two closely related species are living together in the same limited habitat (Lack, 1949).

Correlations between specialized feeding structures and specialized feeding behavior are often striking in birds. The hooked bill of a hawk, the long legs of a heron, the barbed tongue of a woodpecker, the shear-like lower mandible of the Black Skimmer, *Rynchops nigra,* are among the examples frequently cited. Any structural specialization indeed is difficult to evaluate or interpret except in terms of its utilization in behavior. The same relationship has presumably existed since the beginnings of avian evolution.

Migration is primarily a behavioral adaptation to life in the higher latitudes. The successful invasion of these regions by the ancestral birds presumably depended on the evolution of (1) structural adaptations in the form of an insulating coat of feathers together with an accelerated and regulated metabolism and (2) a behavioral adaptation, migration, by means of which they could avoid the unfavorable season. The structural adaptations are concerned with cold temperatures, the first great obstacle of these regions. Migratory behavior clearly functions in circumventing both cold and the second great obstacle, limited winter food supplies. It would be hazardous to say which of these obstacles has featured more importantly in the origin and evolution of migratory behavior, but since migration is the only major means that birds possess in meeting the problem of seasonal food decimation, I have elected to include it here in my scheme of classification. Reproductive phenomena are also closely linked with migratory behavior and actually have a far more direct bearing on the seasonal regulation of migration than does food. This physiological relationship, however, may have been secondarily acquired and does not seem to possess the vital significance to survival to be seen in the relationship of migration to food. The very existence of many of the summer resident birds in higher latitudes depends, and has presumably depended since they first occupied these regions, on the development of migratory behavior. Separate chapters in this volume are devoted to several aspects of bird migration.

Various forms of social behavior have come to feature in the food-getting of birds. Most important and most widespread of these is territorialism. Territorialism is a form of social behavior which probably had its origin in connection with reproduction (Mayr, 1935) and will be discussed more fully under that section. In many species, however, it has come to have considerable significance as a regulating factor in the apportioning of available food supplies among the members of a population. Each individual territory-holder through its intolerance of crowding assures itself a food supply. Most species are territorial only during the breeding season but a few show territorialism, either as individuals or as integrated social groups, during the nonbreeding period (Nice, 1941).

Group feeding is a form of behavior which has acquired special significance in a number of species. Flock feeding with co-operative integration of members has been described in the Double-crested Cormorant, *Phalacrocorax auritus* (Bartholomew, 1942), and the White Pelican, *Pelecanus erythrorhynchos* (Cottam *et al.,* 1942), among fish-eaters, in several ducks (personal observation) and blackbirds, Icteridae (Dawson, 1923:85), among grain feeders, and in swallows (Emlen, 1952) and mixed flocks of tropical land birds (Winterbottom, 1949) among insect-eaters.

Several species take advantage of the activities of other species in locating or securing food. Jaegers and eagles regularly obtain food by pilfering from other species, and Starlings, *Sturnus vulgaris,* are often seen to steal a worm as it is brought to the surface by a foraging Robin, *Turdus migratorius.* Cowbirds (*Molothrus*) got their name through their habit of feeding around the feet of cattle and even on their backs. Gulls follow the plow on land or the ship at sea to the same end of securing food turned up by the disturbance. The remarkable behavior of the Greater Honey Guide, *Indicator indicator,* of Africa in leading men or honey badgers to bee nests may be regarded as a specialized development of the same type of interspecies association (Chapin, 1924).

Behavior Associated with Self-protection

The special adaptational characters developed by birds for self-protection include one of the most efficient means for escaping enemies to be found in the animal kingdom, namely flight. Keen vision and hearing are also outstanding attributes of birds related to their efficiency in eluding enemies.

Behavioral adaptations for concealment, such as the crouching of the quail or the "freezing" of the incubating Woodcock, are in general less extensively developed in birds than in many other classes of animals. Hiding responses are perhaps less essential to survival in animals well equipped with an efficient means of escape, and we may probably attribute some of the conspicuous and confiding qualities of birds to their ability to escape by flight. Concealment behavior is well developed in many birds, however, in connection with nesting and other situations where direct escape would be difficult or where it would attract attention to a vulnerable nest or brood. Concealment behavior like concealment coloration is thus usually better developed in female birds than in males, and is more frequently utilized when the bird is confronted with a swift flying enemy than a stalking terrestrial predator.

Again, as in adaptations for feeding, the correlation between structure and behavior is often striking. The crouching of the baby Spotted Sandpiper, *Actitis macularia,* with eyes shut and bill on the ground, the rigid vertical neck stretching of the American Bittern, *Botaurus lentiginosus,* in its cattail surroundings, or the stealthy submergence of the Pied-billed Grebe, *Podilymbus podiceps,* in a weedbed are cases in point.

Another indirect method of self-protection is mobbing or social attack, a type of behavior observed in a wide variety of species from titmice and kinglets to crows and gulls (Nice, 1943:251). The birds apparently derive protection by swarming around the enemy, scolding and threatening it to a point where it cannot successfully hunt.

Defensive fighting is a means of self-protection which is poorly developed in birds. The fighting attack which is so conspicuous in the behavior of a blackbird, a tern, or an Osprey, *Pandion haliaëtus,* when its nest is approached is not self-defense, nor is the aggressive display of the territorial male at the start of the breeding season. Most birds when cornered or captured do not fight back but rather struggle and squeal in attempts to escape, a reaction which is a marked contrast to that expected of a rat, a weasel, or a mouse under similar conditions. Some of the larger and slower moving birds like owls, herons, or loons will, to be sure, grab, snap, and jab effectively when cornered—but generally in a less persistent and directed manner than would a dog or a raccoon similarly situated. Perhaps it is not surprising to find self-defense behavior largely restricted to species and to situations in which its employment is effective. The structural and behavioral adaptations of birds are both better developed for flight or concealment than for fighting.

The behavioral responses of birds during periods of unfavorable weather or of low visibility may also be classed as self-protective, although their significance with respect to survival is not always clear. Flocking is one of the most common and striking of these responses. Communal roosting at night by crows, robins, starlings, martins, and wagtails provide spectacular displays of flocking behavior. Various authors have noted similar tendencies to aggregate in a great variety of animals under adverse environmental conditions (see Alverdes, 1927).

Behavior Associated with Plumage Maintenance

While the development of plumage is strictly a structural adaptation, its presence in birds has necessitated the development of a number of behavioral characters concerned with its maintenance and with the sanitation and care of the skin. Preening is a form of activity concerned with feather care, which occupies much of the time of most birds between periods of feeding, sleeping, and tending a nest. In many species it appears to have been carried beyond the point of usefulness in feather maintenance and has become adapted as a part of the ritual of courtship and threat displays (Armstrong, 1947; Tinbergen, 1952). Bathing, dusting, and "anting" are other forms of behavior related to skin and plumage care which may become socialized or diverted in one way or another. Anting, a peculiar and rather rare form of plumage care only recently described, involves the rubbing into the feathers of a variety of materials of which crushed ants appear most commonly (Nice, 1943; Groskin, 1950). Its significance has not yet been definitely determined.

Behavior Related to Reproduction

While the basic essentials of individual living are accomplished by the two great categories of activity, feeding and self-protection, a third activity associated with the preservation of the race, that of reproduction, has come to play an important role in the total activities of the higher animals. This is particularly true of birds where the specialized physiological developments associated with homoiothermy and slow nervous maturation entail a long period of dependency during the early stages of growth. Mammals, the other vertebrates confronted with these problems, have solved them by internal retention of the developing individual, food manufacturing, and parental protection. In contrast to this efficient system in which only the last phase is primarily behavioral, birds shelter and feed their offspring almost entirely by behavioral means. Birds have thus developed some highly advanced forms of propagative behavior and provide a fine and varied array of materials for analytical and comparative study.

The two basic aspects of propagative behavior are the sexual aspect and the parental aspect. The first of these, involving the coming together of male and female individuals for copulation, is common to all forms of sexually reproducing animals from the protozoa up. Specializations arose in connection with the evolution of terrestrial living in the amphibians and reptiles, but the whole procedure has remained relatively simple even in the higher forms. The complex and elaborate "courtship" displays of birds appear to be primarily related to pair formation and mate retention rather than to mating itself and are thus basically social (family formation) rather than sexual. Such displays, however, may serve to stimulate sexual excitement in the performer and perhaps in the object of his attentions. Darling (1938, 1952) has reviewed evidence that paired birds deprived of the excitement of territorial or other social display through isolation often fail to breed. He also suggests that such sexual stimulation may be a primary function of territorial fighting in both colonial and non-colonial birds.

Parental behavior, that aspect of reproductive behavior which is concerned with the care and feeding of the dependent young, has its beginnings in birds each breeding season with the formation of a pairing bond, anticipating sometimes by weeks or even months the appearance of the eggs. Such a forward projection of the parental relationship is, of course, essential since the eggs, when they appear, must have an appropriate repository prepared in advance.

Pairing behavior functions as an adaptation for co-operative sharing of the work of feeding and protecting the young and has reached its most extensive development in birds. It is of particular interest to biologists in that man is one of the few species outside of the birds that has developed it. Many of the social institutions related to marriage and family behavior in man find their counterparts in the behavior of birds.

The nature of the pairing bond in birds has been given surprisingly little attention by ornithologists. In some species it appears to be little more than a simple recognition and tolerance of the mate at a time when intolerance of intruders is prominent. In others, close association, sharing of food, and defense of the mate are clearly involved. In the Cliff Swallow, *Petrochelidon pyrrhonota,* for instance, a paired bird at its nest quickly recognizes and accepts its mate on arrival while vigorously repelling any other bird that approaches. Away from the nest, however, it does not associate with its mate nor defend it from attack (Emlen, 1954). By contrast, the male California Quail, *Lophortyx californica,* associates closely with its mate whenever she is off the nest, calls her to food, and viciously drives off other males which come close (personal observation).

Most species are monogamous; a few, such as the Ring-necked Pheasant, *Phasianus colchicus,* the Red-winged Blackbird, *Agelaius phoeniceus,* and the Bishop Bird, *Euplectes hordeacea,* are polygynous; a smaller number, including the tinamous, the button quails, and perhaps the phalaropes, are polyandrous. A few, including the Prairie Chicken, *Tympanuchus cupido,* the Ruff, *Philomachus pugnax,* and the Gould's Manakin, *Manacus vitellinus,* meet only for copulation and apparently form no social pairing bond. The duration of the bond varies from a few days at the beginning of a cycle in some of the hummingbirds to the life of the birds, as in the Nutcracker, *Nucifraga caryocatactes* (Swanberg, 1951), some of the geese, and the cranes. In most species, however, the two individuals comprising the pair remain together only through a single nesting season.

The procedure of pair formation has proved an elusive problem and has been closely observed in only a few species. It would appear, however, that two general types of procedure are followed, pair formation by territory and pair formation in flocks (Lack, 1940a). In the former the male establishes himself on a territory and vigorously defends it against trespass by threats or attack. Females may be excepted from these territorial attacks if they are readily distinguishable as to sex by their appearance, but in sexually monomorphic species they may be driven off initially, as are males, and only later accepted as their distinctive response to attack reveals their sex. Various displays of plumage and song at this time may function in the process of sex recognition and the individual recognition upon which the pairing bond is built.

In pair formation in flocks, the procedure is more difficult to trace. Individual associations are gradually formed with both members contributing through displays which apparently serve to attract attention and arouse sexual excitement. In the Great Tit, *Parus major,* the stimulated male attacks indiscriminately and obtains a mate on the basis of differential response to the attacks (Hinde, 1952). In the California Quail, *Lophortyx californica,* which I have watched repeatedly, the procedure is similar except that sex is recognized at the outset. The displays are vague, at best, and ordinarily subside and disappear entirely once the bond has been formed, even though this be well in advance of the nesting season.

The activities of breeding pairs include territory defense, nest building, incubation, and care of the young. The relative roles played by the male and female in these activities vary greatly from species to species from those in which one bird, either male or female, does all of the work to those in which both share in all aspects of it.

Territorial behavior, the defense of a definite area against intrusion by individuals of the same species and occasionally other species, has already been mentioned. Its origin and true relationships are debatable, but surveys of its occurrence in a considerable number of reptiles and fish, as well as birds, suggest that the primary function may be that of a mechanism for dispersing a crowded population at times when the situation calls for independent activity (Nice, 1943). Many animals, including most of the mammals, show intolerance of close association at one time or another, but until this becomes fixed as to locality and becomes associated with specific land marks in that locality it should not be considered as true territory. What has been characterized as confidence imparted by familiarity with the area seems to influence the results of an encounter (Schjelderup-Ebbe, 1935); an animal is almost always successful, that is, dominant, on its own domain.

The evolution of territorial behavior in birds has followed a number of different lines and can be seen in various stages of development along these lines. Nice (1941) has classified the various types of territory on the basis of the period or portion of the breeding cycle during which the birds exhibit territorial behavior. Territories also vary as to size, extent to which they are used for feeding and other activities, and the rigidity with which they are defended (Meise, 1936). Some species like the Red-winged Blackbird recognize sharp territorial boundary lines which remain essentially unchanged day after day (Nero and Emlen, 1951). Others like the American Robin, *Turdus migratorius,* display aggressively to other robins at varying distances from the nest site, the amount of aggressiveness and incidence of fighting success being roughly inversely proportional to the distance from the nest (Young, 1951).

Nest-building behavior in birds is analogous with the digging activities of turtles, snakes, and alligators at the time of laying and with the den preparation, lodge construction, or nest making of numerous mammals. It takes a wide variety of forms in birds from the shallow "scrape" of the Killdeer Plover, *Charadrius vociferus,* or the floating raft of the Black Tern, *Chlidonias nigra,* to the elaborately woven hanging baskets of some of the weaver finches and orioles, or the mud houses of some swallows, and ovenbirds (*Furnarius*).

Despite the variability in nest-building behavior to be seen even within a single family of birds, the members of a species generally show a remarkable uniformity in the type of site selected, the materials used, and the manner of construction. The complex and beautifully organized movements and sequence of behavior patterns which go into the building of a nest like that of an oriole were frequently cited in the older literature as examples of purposeful or directive behavior and are today commonly used as outstanding illustrations of complex instinctive behavior.

In most species the various stages of nest building are nicely synchronized with the development of the reproductive tract preparatory to laying. This is particular true of the final stage, that of placing the lining in the nest (Tinbergen, 1939; Emlen, 1941).

Broody behavior is that phase of parental activity which provides the warmth and shelter required by the dependent eggs or young beyond that furnished by the nest. It is comparable to similar behavior occurring in mammals, but is far better developed in birds than in any other group. It generally starts at about the time of the laying of the last egg and quickly comes to dominate other forms of behavior during the period of close dependency. Sexual behavior is completely suspended in most species and even feeding may be substantially curtailed as long as the stimulus emanating from the nest full of eggs or helpless young persists. With few exceptions females are involved; males fail to show this form of behavior in many passerines and others but have it well developed in members of many of the lower orders (Kendeigh, 1952). The main characteristic is sitting or crouching with the temporarily hypertrophied and vascularized skin of the belly (the brood patch) applied to the eggs. Some species, notably the domestic hen, employ special call notes at this time and show a pronounced increase in the amount of belligerency displayed towards intruders, even potentially dangerous enemies.

Broody behavior naturally follows egg-laying, and in experiments can be induced only after a preliminary period of sexual conditioning (Whitman,

1919; Riddle, 1937). The duration of broodiness is naturally timed by the rate of the development of the embryo, which is genetically fixed for each species within rather narrow limits, and by the rate at which the young acquire independence after hatching. Complete physiological control of the body temperature may not be attained in young birds for a week or ten days after hatching (Kendeigh, 1939).

Broody behavior has apparently been completely suspended in one group of birds, the mound-birds, Megapodidae, of the Malayan-Australian region, in which the heat needed for incubation is provided by an elaboration of nest-building behavior to utilize various natural sources of heat.

In birds, provision for the feeding of dependent young is made largely by behavioral adaptations. Modification of the esophagus into a crop occurs in a number of bird groups, and specialization of the crop wall for producing nutritious materials is encountered in the pigeons and doves (Whitman, 1919). Pouchlike elaborations of the buccal cavity aid in the handling of food in Gray-crowned Rosy Finches, *Leucosticte tephrocotis* (Miller, 1941), and cell-like pits in the gizzard wall are supposedly used in a similar way by hornbills (Knowlton, 1909:502).

In many terrestrial and aquatic groups like the gallinaceous birds and the ducks, the young are hatched in an advanced condition, able to run or swim within an hour or less, and able to feed themselves by the time the yolk sac has been resorbed a day or so later. Parental behavior in most of these species is largely limited to defense, often vigorous and persistent, to occasional brooding and to calling and to picking up and dropping appropriate food items in the presence of the chicks. Special food calls have developed in many of these birds, calls which in some species have been adopted and modified by the males and incorporated along with food-showing behavior into certain aspects of courtship.

In another large category of essentially but not strictly nidicolous birds, including the pelicans, herons, gulls, terns, and hawks, food is brought to the nest and there presented to the young after an exchange of signals in which the young often peck or fondle the parent's bill. Later, as the young become larger and more active they may advance vigorously on the parent and help themselves as the item is dropped, or, where the food is carried in the gullet, reach far down into the throat of the gaping parent.

The young of most arboreal birds and of species belonging to predominantly arboreal groups are hatched in an undeveloped and helpless condition which calls for close attendance and feeding by the parents. Food is characteristically brought in the bill and, after appropriate manipulation and crushing, is delivered deep into the nestling's throat. In many species the parents swallow the food and regurgitate it for the young in a softened, partially digested condition. In the American Goldfinch, *Spinus tristis*, seeds are hulled before presentation (McCabe, personal communication). The food selected for the young is appropriate to their special needs and significantly may be quite different at first from that currently being utilized by the old birds for themselves.

Food-delivering behavior by the adult appears to be quite closely dependent upon specific stimuli emanating from the young in their food-begging behavior. Foreign objects in the nest including old egg shells and fecal material are characteristically removed by the parent. In most birds this process of sanitation is aided by the enclosing of the fecal material in a mucous sac which is readily picked up and either swallowed or carried off and dropped.

Food-delivering behavior commonly persists in response to food-begging behavior by young for two or three weeks after the young leave the nest. It may again appear under quite different circumstances as an aspect of courtship behavior, the male assuming the parental role, the female that of the dependent young (Armstrong, 1947).

The relationship between the members of a breeding pair and between parent and young are social in nature and are regarded by Allee (1931:346) and others as providing one of the main bases from which other forms of social behavior have evolved. I have, therefore, elected to survey social behavior in bird flocks under this section on behavior associated with propagation, even though much of it shows little functional relation to reproduction in its definitive form.

Most social interactions in birds are built upon either dominance-subordinance relationships or leadership-followership relationships. Schjelderup-Ebbe (1935), Allee (1936), and others have built up a considerable volume of literature demonstrating the occurrence and effectiveness of a social hierachy of dominance and subordinance in regulating social interaction in bird flocks. The system appears to apply in free-living birds as well as in confined groups and may well underlie many aspects of social behavior of birds in nature. Territorial behavior as already described is essentially localized dominance.

Leadership-followership behavior is more subtle than dominance behavior. It may parallel the latter and be indistinguishable from it, or a subordinate bird may effectively lead a dominant bird in the movements and activities of a flock. Leadership is perhaps equivalent at times to social independence, the independent individual striking out on its own, the dependent, more socially bound individuals closing in to maintain the flock unity (Lorenz, 1935). The relation of the mother hen to her chicks is an advanced type of leadership which involves solicitousness to the point where she will deprive herself of food and become thin while finding and presenting food to her offspring (Dove, 1935:530).

Large flocks of birds are generally open societies showing very little of the social interaction and organization which characterizes a closed society except as subdivisions or groupings are temporarily brought together to share in a particular activity. The bond which draws and holds such large flocks together may be in the nature of a followership response (Emlen, 1952) but is little known or understood.

THE BEHAVIORAL EQUIPMENT OF BIRDS

The distinctive characteristics and specializations of behavior in a bird are determined by the structural equipment which it possesses. Three main systems or categories of structures are involved: (1) the sensory or receptor equipment providing for the detection and analysis of stimuli and their conversion into afferent impulses, (2) the effector or motor equipment providing the mechanism of action, and (3) the integrating and co-ordinating equipment providing a system of connections between receptors and effectors. To these a fourth might be added: the motivating equipment whereby the energy resources of the body are mobilized for complex activities. The nature and performance of this equipment determines the form and limits the scope of a bird's activities. Similarly, the bird's activities determine the situation or medium in which the behavioral equipment is fashioned in evolution. Structure and behavior have thus been linked throughout the course of evolution, and one can scarcely be considered successfully without close attention to the other.

Sensory Equipment

The special sensory equipment of birds has been admirably reviewed by Pumphrey (1948) and needs only brief consideration here. The bird is dominated by visual and auditory perceptions. The chemical senses of taste and smell are for the most part poorly developed, and the tactile sense shows no structural developments of special significance for this survey of behavior.

Various workers have commented at length on the visual performance of birds, the acuity displayed by hawks, the rapid focusing adjustments of the swallow as it pursues a flying insect or the robin as it flashes in flight through the branches of a tree, or the quick response of an owl to the movement of a mouse in near darkness. Such efficient performance is a necessary concomitant of the demands placed upon a bird by its specialized mode of living.

The eye, as compared with the human eye, is particularly developed for the detection of motion and for rapid accommodation. In acuity, as measured by the minimum detectable angle, the bird's eye is better than that of most mammals and comparable to man's (Donner, 1951). As a camera, according to Pumphrey (1948:173), it is superior to the eye of man. It is considerably larger in proportion to body size and has a greater aperture and a more efficient mechanism for rapid focusing. Extended horizontal areas of high resolving power and other specializations of the retina provide a broad span of sharp vision extremely sensitive to movements.

The auditory performance of birds is also good. The ear, hidden beneath feathers and without an external pinna, is readily overlooked and internally is less elaborate in general than that of the mammal. Birds, being highly social animals, depend on auditory signals for many of their behavioral releasers. Their hearing is thus attuned particularly to sounds produced by members of their own species. Auditory acuity has rarely been measured, but is clearly great in some species, especially in owls, parrots, and pheasants. A number of birds are capable of accurate determination of the direction from which sounds are coming. Thus, a hen can locate her chicks by their calls within two degrees in the horizontal plane (W. Englemann, 1928). Owls have an elaborate, asymmetrical development of the ears associated with direction finding (Pycraft, 1898).

The structures of the inner ear associated with balance and position are well developed in birds and have been considered by Ising (1946), Yeagley (1947), and Beecher (1951) as the possible seat of the mechanism responsible for the remarkable ability of birds to orient themselves in space and find their way over long migratory or homing routes. Studies by Griffin and Hock (1949), Kramer (1952), and others have suggested, however, that the stimuli utilized in distance orientation are to a large extent visual.

Species to species variations in sensory equipment of birds are relatively slight. At least at the species level and possibly also at the generic and family levels they appear to be of less importance in determining behavioral variation than are the motor and integrative equipment.

Motor Equipment

The motor equipment of birds as a group is dominated by the specializations of the fore limbs for flight and the hind limbs for support and bipedal locomotion. Grasping and manipulating functions are thus relegated for the most part to the mouth, which is modified for a combination of these and ingesting functions. Body proportions, especially in the wing, the general rigidity of the body, and the frequency of hinge joints of limited mobility also directly influence the behavior form, while the specialized reproductive, respiratory, digestive, and excretory mechanisms of birds indirectly affect the nature of responses to environmental situations. Structures associated with sound production and display are of special importance in birds as mechanisms of communication.

The motor equipment of birds varies far more from species to species than the sensory equipment and is consequently of greater importance in comparative studies of behavioral variations within the class. We will not attempt to go further in this survey than to call to mind the interesting variations and striking adaptations in motor equipment associated with diving, swimming, climbing, and running, or with scratching, digging, vocalizing, displaying, and fighting.

Integrative Equipment

While an act of behavior is dependent on the receptors for its initiation and the effectors for its expression, the neural paths which connect the two terminal systems determine the relationship between the stimulus and the response and provide a means for regulating behavior. Essentially the functions of the integrating equipment are (1) to integrate afferent impulses from the sense organs, (2) to integrate efferent impulses into patterns of action, and (3) to select action patterns appropriate to the stimulus situation (response selection).

Evaluation of the performance of the integrating equipment of a bird is made difficult by the fact that the process of integration cannot be observed directly but only in the response. Studies of co-ordinative aspects of integration generally divide a response into its component elements and then record the relationships and independence of these elements in the compounding of a complex behavioral act. Studies of response selection attempt to weigh a response against the specific stimulus situation with which it was associated and then analyze and evaluate the relationship as it is observed.

Comparative studies of the ability of animals to respond selectively to stimulus situations of varying degrees of complexity provide a basis for recognizing several levels of discriminative performance. Smith (1951), in a recent review of discrimination in animals, has recognized three such levels: (1) simple detection of stimuli, (2) comparison and evaluation of stimuli, and (3) classification of stimuli. The first of these is involved in all behavior responses. The second occurs in taxes and tropisms and other higher forms of behavior but not necessarily in reflexes. The third appears to provide the main basis of complex behavior of the type developed in birds. Stimuli are not only perceived and evaluated but are analyzed, sorted, and classified before final reference to the effectors. Numerous simultaneous and successive stimuli which are continuously impinging on a bird in its natural environment are, furthermore, selectively analyzed and integrated in the selection of a response.

Birds are able to anlyze and classify rather complex patterns in time as well as in space and often reveal a well-developed memory. Koehler (1951) has demonstrated an ability in pigeons and Jackdaws, *Corvus monedula,* to distinguish between dot patterns involving six and seven dots respectively and between sequential auditory patterns involving six as against seven successive bell rings. Kramer's (1952) recent work with starlings on compass orientation with relation to a moving sun position seems to entail a remarkably accurate time sense. Recognition and memory of associates (avian or other) and of environmental situations is well developed in birds and features importantly in many of their activities (C. Englemann, 1951). The 86 per cent performance of Nutcrackers in finding the exact sites where they had hidden nuts several months earlier (Swanberg, 1951) represents a phenomenal place memory.

Plasticity in the selection of responses is said to be limited in birds as compared to mammals, and birds are in most cases less able to adjust to novel situations than are mammals. The ability of birds to benefit by experience is certainly not uncommon, however, although the frequency, intensity, and recency of the experiences may have to be relatively greater. Birds are good subjects for conditioning experiments and are very adept at certain types of learning, as will be discussed in a subsequent section of this chapter.

The ability to form concepts, to solve novel problems, to use tools, and to apprehend relationships in new situations seems to be limited in birds as compared with mammals, although Thorpe (1951b) reviews and discusses a long series of performances of birds which, he believes, reflects a capacity for insight. Such behavior as that exhibited by titmice and other birds in hoisting a piece of food suspended on a string (Thorpe, 1951b), the dropping of friable objects such as molluscs on hard surfaces by gulls and crows, the regular employment of a "brush" of plant fibers to apply pigment to sticks by the Bower-bird, *Ptilonorhynchus violaceus* (Gilbert, 1939) or of a plucked spine to pry out insects from cracks in bark by the Galapagos Woodpecker Finch, *Camarhynchus pallidus* (Gifford, 1919; Lack, 1947) are cited as instances of insightful behavior. Even the everyday behavior of territorial birds in recognizing their mates and the landmarks of their territories reveals an apprehension of spatial relationships. Problems of interpretation become great at these levels of behavior, and there are differences of opinion as to how such activities should be classified. These problems are also given further consideration later in this chapter.

Intelligence is a characteristic of the integrative equipment which is generally defined in subjective terms that are difficult or impossible to apply to subhumans. The elements of intelligent behavior are, however, essentially those described in the preceding paragraph.

THE NATURE AND ORIGIN OF BEHAVIOR PATTERNS

The Nature of Behavior Patterns

Birds of a given species have a distinctive way of acting under a given set of conditions. The spatial and sequential patterns of movements which constitute this distinctive way of acting may be regarded as the expression of an intrinsic character of the bird, called a behavior pattern, a character which though not measurable in physical units is often as distinctive and as valuable in classification as a feather pattern or a muscle arrangement (Delacour and Mayr, 1945; Lorenz, 1950).

Behavior patterns although composed of movements are more than mere aggregations of movements; they belong to a higher integrative level of organization possessing emergent characteristics which must be defined in terms of effect or end result. Because of this fact, and because of their uniformity and stereotypy in birds, behavior patterns have commonly been referred to in the ornithological literature as instincts. A great confusion surrounds the use of that word, however, as a result of its common misuse and of the teleological connotations often associated with it (Lack, 1943). The word instinct, furthermore, is commonly applied to strictly inherited characters, while a behavior pattern, like any structural character, is a phenotype, the result of interaction between hereditary and environmental forces.

Various hypotheses have been proposed for interpreting the nature of the behavioral phenotype in birds. Many observers, particularly those who have been impressed by subjective studies of human behavior, use a teleological or vitalistic approach which interprets behavior patterns in terms of purpose. While behavior in birds generally serves to accomplish a task, most modern workers find teleological explanations unsatisfying and prefer an objective analytical approach (see Tinbergen, 1951a). Among the advocates of objective analysis, some reflect the behavioristic approach of Watson (1914), Hull (1943), and other psychological theorists who visualize behavior essentially in terms of stimulus and response and the associative mechanisms which intervene. Others reflect the Gestalt concepts of Kohler (1929) or Tolman (1932) in which behavioral acts are viewed as the overt expressions of organized perceptions. Some interpretations emphasize the innate content of the behavior pattern (Lorenz, Tinbergen, etc.), while others hold that broad assumptions of innateness are unwarranted (Schneirla, Lehrman, etc.).

One interpretation which has recently received a great deal of attention and, for the most part, favorable acceptance by ornithologists is that developed by Lorenz (1935, 1937, 1950) and elaborated by Tinbergen (1942, 1951a) and others. This interpretation, often referred to as the *Lorenzian* or *releaser* concept, visualizes a definitive innate mechanism in the bird for each behavior pattern. Each mechanism is essentially complete in itself with motor, sensory, and integrating elements and with specific energy packets held in abeyance until a functionally related stimulus situation in the environment, a *releaser* or sign stimulus, intercedes to trip off the mechanism by removing a block which has prevented its discharge (Fig. 1). Motivational factors in the form of intrinsic impulses and hormones may raise the potential behind one of these blocks to a point where it goes off automatically to produce what is called "vacuum activity" or flows over into other channels to produce "displacement activity." In the Lorenzian view an assemblage of many such innate response mechanisms, or instincts, provides the behavior repertory of a bird. These are arranged in a hierarchical system of several levels in which a few top or central instincts dominate or otherwise influence others of a more specific nature. The former produce generalized and appetitive behavior, while the latter are concerned with specific or consummatory acts.

The Lorenzian concept in visualizing innate sensory correlates for each motor pattern provides an interesting basis for explaining the evolutionary origin and significance of many of the striking and peculiar features of a bird's plumage in terms of releasers for special behavior patterns (Lorenz, 1935). This application of the releaser concept has been used as substantiating evidence for the Lorenzian view.

A more vitalistic approach to the motivational aspects of behavior patterns is offered by Howard (1929, 1935, 1940). According to Howard a bird possesses a number of psychic states of responsiveness or "worlds." It lives in

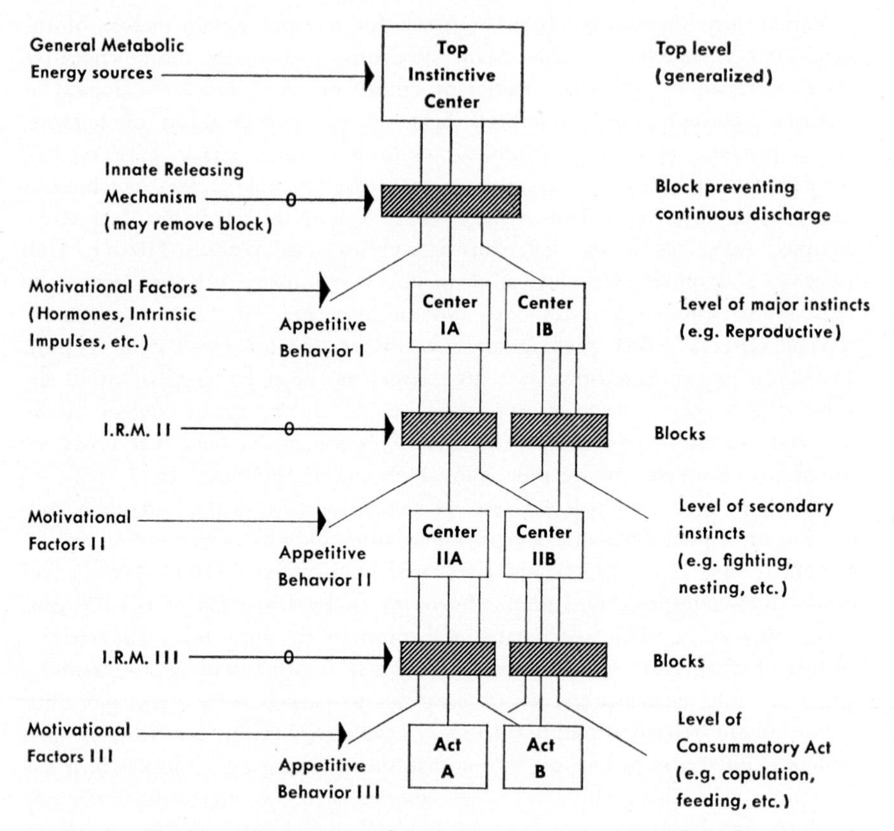

Fig. 1. The hierarchical system of instinctive centers in animal behavior as seen by Tinbergen (modified after Tinbergen, 1951).

one "world" at a time but may quickly transfer from one to another as environmental situations, particularly social situations, change and, through the sense organs, affect its physiological and thence its psychological state. Thus a Moorhen, *Gallinula chloropus,* in the nest-with-eggs world may suddenly alter its entire state of responsiveness when another bird enters its territory. The pattern of behavior exhibited is the result of innate behavior patterns guided by these general environmental situations.

Contrasting with the Lorenzian view are those of Maier and Schneirla (1935), Lashley (1938), Rand (1941a), Lack (1940b), Lehrman (1953) and others who believe that birds respond not to single elements in the environment (releasers) but to a complex Gestalt composed of many aspects in the environmental situation, and that they may simultaneously utilize, not a single, but several sensory modalities in erecting a perceptory pattern upon which effective activity is based. The response, furthermore, is often regarded not so much as a single act but as a more or less continuous series of functionally related activities. In this view a behavior pattern is not a specific entity, but merely the distinctive way an animal makes adjustments to a specific perceptory pattern it has formed with the particular neuro-motor equipment it possesses. Motivation may be expressed in terms of homeostatic disturbance and general or specific irritability rather than of drives and appetites, but nothing akin to action-specific energy is postulated. Exploratory behavior is linked to perception formation rather than to general appetitive activity.

Differences between these various concepts of behavioral organization are partly real and partly in viewpoint. While the Lorenzian view tends to focus on the individual act or movement and look outward toward the complex pattern, the Gestalt view starts with the latter and searches inward. Neither would appear to be entirely true or false, for both schools admit that a behavior pattern exhibits emergent characteristics and is more than a simple summation of movements. Both views have contributed substantially to our understanding of behavioral phenomena, and it is hoped that both will continue to be recognized for their respective worths until a more comprehensive concept can replace them. Both Lorenz (1950) and Schneirla (1952) recognize and decry the common practice of adhering to and defending one or another conventionalized theory of behavior.

Because of the diversity of views on the nature of behavioral organization it is impossible to find any one plan of treatment which would be universally acceptable for this chapter. The plan which has been adopted, treating the behavioral phenotype separately from the mechanisms of response, may be highly artificial. It is convenient, however; it also permits an approach somewhat different from that already familiar to many ornithologists through the admirable recent reviews of Thorpe (1951b) and Tinbergen (1951a).

The Morphological Basis of Behavior Patterns

Because of the definitive and precise nature of the innate response mechanism as visualized by Lorenz, it is tempting to seek a special co-ordinating center somewhere in the sensory motor system for each behavior pattern. Hess (Hess, 1943; Hess and Brügger, 1943) has lent encouragement to this type of speculation by demonstrating focal areas in the hypothalamus which, electrically stimulated, elicit complete behavior patterns of fighting, feeding, and sleeping (see Tinbergen, 1951a:108-109). It would be dangerous to assume that these areas represent the actual co-ordinating centers, however. The extensive studies of brain topology and the long search for a structural basis of learning and of other mental functions have pointed to a dispersed rather than a localized basis (Lashley, 1950; Aronson and Noble, 1945; Beach, 1948). Sperry (1952), in considering the physical basis of perception in man has rejected the older theories of isomorphism (spatial projection of an observed object on the sensory surfaces of the visual cortex) and of codal representation of external stimuli in the brain for a concept of motor organization. A perceptory pattern in this view is essentially a preparation for response in the effector organs; the awareness of such motor adjustments, presumably absent in birds, is what constitutes consciousness in man.

The Construction of Behavior Patterns

Behavior patterns are, as already noted, complex aggregations of movements, spatially and sequentially organized so that they accomplish a specific task. They may be dissected and analyzed in several ways.

Tinbergen (1951a) and others have pointed out that many behavior patterns possess distinct directional and operational elements, as the (1) aiming and (2) projecting of the tongue of a fly-catching frog. Operational and directional phases may occur simultaneously and still be analyzable, as in the egg-rolling movements of the Grey Lag Goose, *Anser anser* (Lorenz and Tinbergen, 1938), in which lateral balancing movements of the head are superimposed upon a direct retractile movement of the neck.

Many patterns contain distinct preparatory and consummatory elements. Nissen (1951) has suggested that simple reflexes and taxes are direct consummatory acts without preparatory movements and that the major parts of complex behavior patterns consist of the preparatory elements. Tinbergen (1951a) has expressed similar views, and, referring to his concept of hierarchical organization of instincts, has attributed most of the preparatory movements to high level centers, calling them appetitive behavior since they reflect the action of the basic or "executive instincts" underlying specific consummatory acts. Such preparatory or appetitive movements typically precede the consummatory act and often occur alone when a pattern sequence is interrupted or fails to run its complete course because of inadequate stimulation or a low state of physiological receptivity. Incomplete acts of this type have been termed incipient movements or "intention movements" (Heinroth, 1910). Incipient locomotive movements, as in preparation for taking flight, involve peculiar postural forms which, according to Daanje (1950), have frequently been incorporated into various display sequences in functions quite different from their natural context. Many such movements have become fixed in these new contexts as an integral part of the pattern.

Most of the movements which compose the preparatory phases of a behavior pattern appear to have a direct functional relationship to that pattern and "belong" to it. Such movements are termed autochthonous. Other movements appear to be strikingly irrelevant and are often identifiable as belonging to another pattern or instinct. Such seemingly inappropriate behavior as preening during the course of courtship, sleep-posturing in the middle of a fight, or eating and foraging during periods of fright or of sexual excitement are not uncommon in birds (Rand, 1943; Tinbergen, 1952). They have been interpreted by followers of the Lorenzian view as evidence of energy overflow or "sparking over" from one instinct group (executive pattern) to another

(Makkink, 1936; Kortlandt, 1940) and have accordingly been termed displacement activities. Regardless of their physiological interpretation, however, displacement activities have become well established in the courtship and aggressive display patterns of many birds and provide an extremely interesting problem. Tinbergen (1952) has termed those so established in a secondary context "derived activities" and has presented a convincing exposition of their frequency and importance in the behavior of many animals besides birds, including man.

The Origin and Development of Behavior Patterns

Although sperm and ova have highly interesting behavioral characteristics themselves, the behavior of an individual properly starts with fertilization and its development may be traced from the zygote to the adult or definitive condition. As in structure, certain basic elements which determine the behavioral genotype are introduced with the chromosomes. These characteristics, of course, remain undeveloped and unrecognizable until such time as the development of motor, integrating, and sensory equipment permits their expression in the phenotype. Paralleling these internal changes are comparable orderly changes in the environment of the developing individual. Factors of the relatively invariable but progressively changing environment inside the eggshell operate to direct the course of development under conditions determined largely by the genes. The environment in which development continues after hatching is slightly less stereotyped but still closely regulated, this time by the behavior of the parent bird or birds. It is not until the young bird has left the nest and the care of its parents that it is fully exposed to the highly variable environment of nature in which behavioral adjustments to unpredictable changes are paramount to survival.

From this brief sketch it may be seen that the genetic and environmental contributions to the behavioral phenotype are so intricately interdependent as to be almost inseparable even on theoretical grounds. This point has been emphasized by Carmichael (1936) and Schneirla (1952). Nevertheless, there has always been a strong interest in analyzing behavior into its "native" and "acquired" elements and determining the relative contribution of each. Birds have featured importantly in these studies.

The literature comparing the relative contributions of heredity and environment to behavior is complicated by a strong lack of agreement on definitions, a staggering multiplicity of theories, and a common failure of authors to consider parallel or contrasting points of view.

The term *instinct* is commonly applied to characters of hereditary origin, and *habit* to those developed in interaction with the environment. Such definitions are convenient in their simplicity but highly unrealistic since no character, either behavioral or structural, can develop in an environmental vacuum, nor can it be built up by the environment without a hereditary basis. Other writers recognizing the omnipresence of environmental factors during ontogeny, but still seeking a convenient division line, have directly or indirectly adopted the event of hatching or birth as a chronological indicator separating early maturation processes from later development of behavior through learning. Such a line is equally artificial and unsatisfactory, however, for many developments of post-hatching life, such as the attainment of sexual and maternal patterns are, at least in part, expressions of tissue maturation, while other patterns appearing before the hatching of the egg show elements of learning. The final criterion for distinguishing a purely instinctive act from a habit or other learned form of behavior thus seems to be the demonstration of the absence of experience during its development; at least, that is essentially the criterion on which most modern scientific analyses appear to be based. Demonstration of the complete absence of experience is extremely difficult if not impossible. The rearing of animals from birth in social isolation is a popular experimental procedure which serves to remove the postnatal social factors; prenatal influences, especially self-induced factors such as self-stimulation by peeping are far more difficult to control.

A survey of the relative roles of heredity and environment in behavioral development properly starts with the simplest forms. Reflexes and other simple movements involving single organs or body parts apparently develop with the maturation of the end organs and their neural connections. Similarly, in salamanders, the development of relatively complex locomotive movements, including the intricate co-ordinating mechanism, has been shown to parallel the maturation of neurons and the establishment of sensory-motor connections (Coghill, 1929). No corresponding work has been done on birds, but numerous workers have demonstrated that young birds reared in isolation learn to fly without "parental instruction." Grohmann (1939) and Poulsen (1951a) have found what appears to be a complete and unretarded maturation of the complex movement patterns of flight in pigeons and swallows raised from hatching in harnesses which prevented wing movements and, hence, self-induced experience.

Conflicting views are held concerning the role of self-induced learning in the development of feeding movements of baby chicks. Shepard and Breed (1913), Maier and Schneirla (1935), and others have presented observations which they believe demonstrate that experience plays a major role in the improvement shown by chicks during the first few days of post-hatching life. Kuo (1932) has suggested that even the first simple head movements of the newly hatched chick are derived from similar movements passively induced in the embryo's head by breathing. Padilla (1932) has found that chicks continuously spoon-fed in darkness for fifteen days after hatching lost the familiar pecking movements and subsequently had to be trained to feed in the normal manner of the species. Poulsen (1951a), on the other hand, has found a rapid acquisition of pecking motions after rearing in darkness and has concluded that the movements were perfected by simple maturation and that only the association of the movement with feeding was acquired by learning.

The gaping, food-begging movements of nestlings of altricial birds appear suddenly on the day of hatching (Nice, 1943:35) and thus provide good material for studies of the development of behavior. Tinbergen and Kuenen (1939) have observed that in thrushes head-waving and gaping of an unoriented nature appeared shortly after hatching in response to generalized stimuli, particularly the jarring of the nest. These movements gradually became oriented and organized as specific responses to the visual stimulus of the parent as it arrived at the nest or to the stimulus provided by various cardboard models having the approximate size, shape, and position of an adult bird on the nest rim. The initial response to the jarring of the nest would appear to reflect an inherited or instinctive mechanism which they term an innate releasing mechanism. The change towards an oriented response to a specific sign stimulus may be regarded, as these authors regard it, as the maturation of the instinctive mechanism. Various other workers including Kuhlmann (1909), Holzapfel (1939), Rand (1941b), and Lehrmann (1953) believe that learning is involved, however, and point out that since the change in behavior coincides with the gradual opening of the eyes, it could well be considered as conditioning of the generalized response through new visual experiences. Schneirla would even question the legitimacy of considering the initial gaping reaction entirely free of self-induced learning elements.

Other acts of juvenile behavior show various combinations of innate and learned elements. Craig (1912) has noted that young doves showed no special response when first presented with drinking water and did not learn to drink until, through chance pecking at objects in the pan, the water came to touch the inside of the mouth so as to induce a swallowing reaction. A consistent response was not developed until after several such experiences. Similar observations have been made on the Song Sparrow by Nice (1943) and on the domestic fowl by Breed (1911).

Bathing responses, on the other hand, may appear on first exposure to water. A young and inexperienced pigeon was observed by Whitman (1919) to react to the sight of a basin of water by squatting on the floor nearby, ducking its head and shaking its feathers in the typical manner of bathing. This bird had never bathed, but Whitman did not indicate whether it may have had experience with water in drinking. Heinroth (1938) has described similar reactions in various birds and has noted that a strengthening of the stimulus by stirring the water will induce full bathing behavior even on first exposure. McCabe and Hawkins (1946) have noted that chicks of the Partridge, *Perdix perdix,* raised in incubators went through complete dust-bathing movements on first exposure to dusty sand.

Many acts of adult behavior, such as courtship, posturing, or vocal patterns, appear in definitive form at sexual maturity or at other definite stages in post-hatching ontogeny and show a high degree of uniformity from individual to individual throughout the range of the species. Where these have been studied in birds raised in isolation a close conformity to the species pattern is often found which strongly suggests an innate derivation. Craig (1914) has found complete and typical mating and vocal patterns in doves reared in isolation, although the object on which the behavior was focused was atypical and reflected the circumstances of the individual's early environment. Many birds with relatively complex songs, however, fail to develop the pattern typical of their species when raised in isolation (Scott, 1904; Heinroth, 1924). Heinroth, drawing on a wide experience, has reported that some species develop species-specific vocal patterns without learning, while others acquire atypical patterns showing only certain basic similarities to the norm of the species and reflecting the nature of their environment during development. Such birds, he has said, quickly adopt the species' song once they have heard it, suggesting an innate predisposition to sing the normal pattern of the species. The blending of innate and acquired elements in the song of the Chaffinch, *Fringilla coelebs,* has been given special attention by Poulsen (1951b).

Various forms of behavior related to reproduction, such as nest building, pair formation, or feeding the young, involve complex patterns which appear quite suddenly in complete or nearly complete, species-specific form. The selection and placing of particular types of material in a nest or the selection and delivery of special foods to a nestling are acts which, according to the Lorenz-Tinbergen school, are inherited intact, requiring only the appropriate internal motivation and the inherently associated combination of sign stimuli from the environment for their activation. While this interpretation seems to fit the observed facts quite well and provides a useful working hypothesis, it would be well not to overlook the alternate proposals of the ontogenists who would regard such complex acts, not as pure instincts suddenly released in a fully formed condition, but as the culminating steps of a subtle learning process based on various self-induced and socially induced experiences. Selous (1933) has visualized nest building as a special development of basic sexual reactions and feeding the young as an emotionally imposed diversion of self-feeding reactions.

For purposes of analysis the development of behavior responses can be considered under three headings: (1) the elaboration of motor patterns, (2) the development of specific associations between stimulus situations and motor patterns, and (3) the elaboration of perceptual systems.

The development of motor patterns consists primarily of various maturational processes such as muscle growth, neuron growth and myelinization, the development of neuromuscular connections, the differentiation of enzyme systems, and the establishment of electro-chemical rhythms of activity in the central nervous system. Learning processes, if they are involved at all, appear to be largely or entirely of the self-induced type such as that described by Kuo (1932) for the pecking pattern of the baby chick, or the molding and improvement of motor skills through practice. Play may serve to perfect a motor activity, but it also functions in the selection and exploration of objects on which to use these activities (Beach, 1952; Nice, 1943). Learning of new motor patterns by imitation is, as noted by Thorpe (1951b), very weakly developed or absent in birds. Birds are notably poor at learning "tricks."

The general course of development of a simple motor pattern such as gaping or locomotion appears to be from generalized and diffuse to specific and particulate (Coghill, 1929). The same may be said of the more complex patterns such as those used in feeding or fighting. These activities are, however, more than motor patterns; they are complex systems of responses and as such are not comparable to simple movements. Kortlandt (1940) has noted that in complex behavior patterns in the Cormorant, *Phalacrocorax carbo,* the basic or consummatory act, which usually comes as the terminal step of the pattern, is the first to appear in ontogeny, while the other, introductory acts of more generalized character appear later in development and roughly in the reverse order of their arrangement in the definitive pattern. A pattern is thus built up by an additive process which may be considered as part of the maturational process (Tinbergen, 1951a) or as the result of associative learning, particularly sign learning as depicted in Figure 2.

Associations between stimulus situations and motor patterns provide the basis for adaptiveness in behavior, the means by which motor actions become meaningful responses. They may be divided into (1) primary associations, those formed first in ontogeny and generally retained as species-specific, and (2) secondary associations formed through modification of the primary associations.

Primary associations often seem to make their appearance rather suddenly with the first, or nearly the first, exposure of the newly hatched bird to an adequate stimulus situation. Since this stimulus situation is often quite specific for a given action, it, or at least its perceptory correlate, may constitute an actual part of the inherited mechanism. This is the view held by Lorenz, Tinbergen, and others who recognize distinct inherited entities called *innate releasing mechanisms* which function to link motor patterns with innately associated releasers or sign stimuli. An alternate view expressed by Maier and Schneirla (1935) and others points out that definitive motor patterns are, when they first appear in ontogeny, often traceable as responses to generalized pressure or vibration stimuli, and that the first post-hatching responses to visual and auditory stimuli may actually represent secondary modifications of these primitive and generalized associations acquired through simple learning processes.

Secondary associations may appear early or late as stimuli are substituted or added to those already existing in a previously established association. Such associations are, almost by definition, developed through learning of one type or another.

Much has been written on learning processes and many conflicting views

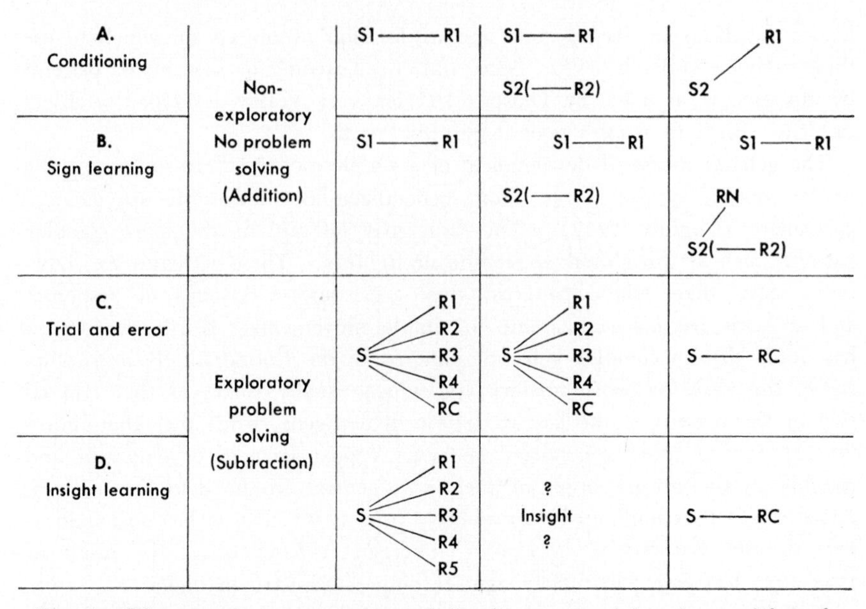

Fig. 2. Diagrammatic representations of the four types of learning modified after Kellogg, 1938. Explanation in text.

and classifications of learning types have been assayed. In a simplified presentation of the subject, Kellogg (1938) has recognized four types of associative learning in addition to the acquisition of motor skills, which he has considered as distinct. These four types of learning are diagrammed in Figure 2 to show their basic characteristics and relationships.

Conditioning (*A*) is the establishment of an additional or substitute stimulus (*S2*) in an existing stimulus-response association (Brogden, 1951). It may be induced experimentally by repeatedly approximating the new and the old (unconditioned) stimulus in a situation in which the response is reinforced by reward (Hull, 1943) or contiguity (Guthrie, 1935). The direction of conditioning is from generalized to specific discrimination. The limits are set only by the discriminatory powers of the subject. The occurrence of conditioning as a natural phenomenon in birds is difficult to detect, but the ease with which it can be induced and demonstrated under controlled experimental conditions suggests the possibility that it plays an important role in behavioral adaptations to both regular and irregular changes in the natural environment.

Sign learning resembles conditioning in that it involves the alteration or elaboration of existing stimulus-response associations. In sign learning an additional or new response (*RN*) of a preparatory nature is added in association with an auxiliary aspect of the stimulus situation, as when a dog learns to run out to meet his master (*RN*) at the distant sound of his approach (*S2*) in anticipation of his final arrival (*S1*) and the final greeting response

(*R1*). Thorpe (1951b) does not recognize sign learning as such in birds but has cited several examples of behavior which might be so classified. As already suggested, sign learning may conceivably play an important role in the process of elaborating complex behavior patterns from basic movement forms in the normal progress of ontogeny.

Trial-and-error learning is essentially the procedure by which one response is selected from an array of possible responses in a problem situation. Like the next and final form of Kellogg's classification, insight learning, it does not function in the expansion of the response repertory of an animal but is an eliminative process employed in the solution of complex problems which offer a choice of possible responses. In experimental work the "correct" response (*RC*) is reinforced by some patent reward until it becomes firmly established in the response association (learned). In wild birds trial-and-error behavior occurs in many common problem situations where adequate directive elements are lacking, as in the search for food. Repetition of exposure to nearly identical problems is requisite to learning by this procedure in laboratory experiments, and it seems likely that similar modification of responses may occur frequently in wild birds when such repetition occurs. The acquisition of skill in differentiating edible from inedible grains by the pheasant chick would be a case in point. Mostler (1935) has shown that various species of birds have to learn to reject stinging wasps as items of food by a trial-and-error process.

Insight learning, like trial-and-error learning, functions in selecting an appropriate response for a problem situation. It differs from trial-and-error learning in being sudden and in apparently eliminating the time-consuming procedure of alternately selecting and discarding the available response patterns. The selection is presumably made on first exposure to the problem through an ability to see into it by an organization of latent perceptions, or, as Thorpe (1951a) has put it, "a sudden adaptive reorganization of experience."

The occurrence of insight learning in birds is problematical as is its very existence as a legitimate form of learning. Thorpe (1951b) believes that insight and insight learning are well developed in birds and feature importantly in many of their activities in nature. Territorial behavior and homing behavior, according to Thorpe, involve an apprehension of spatial relations which is acquired by unrewarded exploration rather than by trial-and-error methods. The use of tools, the pulling up of food suspended by threads, the following of detours in reaching a hidden destination, or the carrying out of selective responses to spatially or temporally dispersed patterns of objects are cited as other responses acquired by insight learning.

In addition to the types of learning so far discussed and diagrammed in Figure 2, Thorpe in his recent reviews (1950, 1951b) has recognized two more: habituation and imprinting. Habituation may be defined as the waning or loss of an acquired stimulus-response association through lack of effectiveness of the response. It is well illustrated by the observation of Rand (1941b) that young Curve-billed Thrashers, *Toxostoma curvirostre,* at first reacted fearfully to all strange objects and had to learn what not to fear. Habituation is essentially the same as conditioning in its mechanisms and is often included with it. It differs in being negative rather than positive. Like conditioning, it is known almost entirely through experimental work, where it is often called extinction, and through studies of pet birds which lend themselves to more or less continuous observation; its role as a natural phenomenon in ontogeny is thus conjectural, although Thorpe believes that it is the simplest and one of the most universal of all learning processes.

Imprinting is a term applied to the rapid formation of stable primary stimulus-response associations or fixations during early infancy. It involves the selection of a stimulus situation for a newly developed and as yet unexpressed motor pattern and, once formed, may affect a wide variety of motor patterns. If, for example, a gosling, on hatching sees a man instead of an adult goose standing over it, it will follow the man and form an attachment which will persist even into adulthood (Heinroth, 1910; Lorenz, 1935). Imprinting resembles conditioning but differs from it in that the association formed is not a substitution but an original creation, a primary association. It resembles the sign learning of Kellogg (1938) but again differs from it in being independent of previously established associations. It differs from trial-and-error learning in that it is an additive process and not used in problem solving. Except for this latter characteristic, imprinting seems closely to resemble insight learning as defined by Kellogg. It is limited, however, by those who have described it to the formation of stable rather than temporary associations with general rather than specific stimulus situations. Lorenz, who first called attention to imprinting as a distinct and important type of association formation, thought of it as supplementing the innate releasing mechanisms which, according to him, provide the great bulk of the stimulus-response associations. Because of its limited period of occurrence in early infancy and its lasting and "irreversible" effects, he at first believed it to be an entirely distinct phenomenon not to be confused with either learning or maturation. Thorpe and others, however, have classified it as a form of learning.

Lorenz, very commendably, did not attempt to extend his concept of imprinting beyond social companions in a limited number of species. As more information has accumulated, however (Fabricius, 1951; Lorenz, 1952), variour writers (Thorpe, 1951b:264; Hutchinson, 1952) have visualized its possible extension from social situations to locality and habitat situations in a wide variety of animals, even nonavian species. Imprinting in this broader sense may well be a common process in the natural formation of primary associations in birds. Since its detection depends on the experimental introduction of a substitute situation at a critical and often very brief time in ontogeny, much work will be required before its true role in natural behavior can be evaluated.

The various types of learning have been discussed above from the point of view of association formation between stimulus and response. Several other approaches deserve attention, however, and may eventually be found to be more realistic. Maier and Schneirla (1942) have recognized a form of learning in which, through random activities, an animal "discovers" responses or modifications of old responses which fulfill or expedite the fulfillment of an organic need such as food-getting. Once so discovered, the particular activity is selected as rewarding and becomes added to the behavioral repertory of the individual. Such learning resembles trial-and-error learning but is additive rather than eliminative. It differs from both conditioning and sign learning in that contiguity of stimulus situations is not required.

Many students of behavior prefer to regard learning from the Gestalt viewpoint of perception formation. Essentially the same types are recognized, but different emphases and interpretations are given. Conditioning, habituation, sign learning and trial-and-error learning are conceived in terms of perception elaboration instead of the establishment of modification of specific stimulus-response connections. As in association formation, the innate beginnings are vague, and it is difficult to know where they start. Perceptual patterns, if they exist before hatching, must be relatively simple and generalized, based largely on tactual and proprioceptive stimuli. As the distance receptors become functional, complex and specific perceptions develop either as elaborations of the earlier generalized perceptions or as new creations (Carmichael, 1936). The emergence of eyes and ears as functional organs is a critical stage in the development of behavior, the one in which imprinting occurs. Except for changes resulting from further maturation of sensory and effector organs, subsequent behavioral development is generally thought by gestaltists to depend largely on the modification and elaboration of perceptions through experience received through all sensory modalities.

Although many complex perceptual patterns incorporating visual and auditory elements may develop from simpler more generalized forms, it is difficult with our present knowledge to evade the conclusion that others may arise, fully formed, at specified periods of ontogeny as innate perceptual patterns. After a series of experiments Lashley and Russell (1934) concluded that an apprehension of space relationships was innate in laboratory rats. According to Schooland (1942), the strikingly different reactions which ducklings and chicks of the domestic fowl show to the sight of water illustrates a difference either of perception formation or of predisposition for perception formation which to all appearances is innate.

Adaptive Plasticity of Behavior Patterns

The mechanisms by which animals adapt themselves to their environment operate at several levels: (*a*) the genetic level, regulated by natural selection and quite beyond the control of the individual, (*b*) the physiological level controlled by relatively slow metabolic adjustments in the animal's body, and (*c*) the behavioral level in which the neuromuscular system responds directly and rapidly. Behavioral adaptability reaches its highest development in animals which live a free existence in a variable environment. Behavioral specializations for such a life may emphasize either flexibility as in mammals, or specialized stereotypy as illustrated in extreme form by some of the insects.

Birds, as we have seen, have followed the latter course and, compared with mammals, are relatively stereotyped and inflexible in their individual behavior responses. Learning abilities are limited, with the result that birds are generally less able to adjust individually to unfamiliar situations than are mammals. Counteracting this individual inflexibility and perhaps responsible for the great success of birds in the complex and variable terrestrial environment is a well-developed behavioral adaptability at the population level. Numerous examples of this adaptability may be found in the adjustments which various species have made to drastic alterations of environment produced by modern man Many species of crows, starlings, swallows, and others have adopted the new and "artificial" environments of cities and towns as their principal habitat, and many others have radically altered their diets to a fare composed largely of plant and animal materials supplied by man. The California Gull, *Larus californicus,* essentially insectivorous and carnivorous, has recently turned to feeding on cherries in the orchards of Utah (Cottam, 1935). The Kea Parrot, *Nestor notabilis,* an essentially vegetarian bird by nature, has acquired a predatory habit since the introduction of sheep into New Zealand (Oliver, 1930); the flickers, *Colaptes auratus* and *C. cafer,* have adopted the tin roof as a substitute for a drumming stump and the Chimney Swift, *Chaetura pelagica,* a chimney as a substitute for a nesting tree. Typically shy species have become tame with continued and repeated exposure to man in parks where they are protected, while confiding species in previously uninhabited places such as the Falkland Islands have "learned" through experience to avoid man (Huxley, 1947). The Ruffed Grouse, *Bonasa umbellus,* was a tame and confiding bird according to reports of early settlers, but acquired a wild behavior after exposure to white man (Bump *et al.,* 1947).

Four possible explanations may be offered for this interesting adaptability at the population level: (1) genetic variants which give an appropriate behavior response to the new situation appear and are favored and selected on the basis of survival value until they have become established in the population; (2) although relatively stereotyped and inadaptable, the members of the population in each generation make direct behavioral adjustments to the new situation through learning processes; (3) the birds are already genetically preadapted to take advantage of the particular environmental changes which occur, and respond to the new stimulus situations with the same behavior patterns which they had previously used with equivalent stimulus situations; (4) individuals reared under the new conditions by adaptable or fortunate parents become adjusted to these conditions through impressions received during a susceptible period in infancy (imprinting), the adjustment becoming fixed in the population as a cultural tradition.

The first explanation, that based on genetic mutation, appears to account for the acquisition of wildness in released game farm turkeys and of tameness in confined wild turkeys (Leopold, 1944). Selection pressure is strong in both situations and apparently quickly eliminates individuals not genetically adapted to the particular situation to which the birds are exposed. Similar mechanisms may conceivably function in other instances of adaptation to environmental change; certainly there must be selective pressure for inherent wildness in natural populations exposed to heavy exploitation by man. In other cases there may be selective values in boldness or in opportunism, characteristics which have been shown (Scott, 1942) to be genetically determined in various mammals.

The second explanation based on individual learning must play a role in some adaptations. Shy birds gain confidence at the feeding shelf with experience and may learn to accept various foods with which they were previously unfamiliar. Some species are far more adaptable in these respects than others, species of wide ecological valence in respect to food habits or habitat characteristics making the fastest adjustments. Contagion or social facilitation is an important factor in inciting many types of behavior in gregarious birds (cf. Palmer, 1941; Katz, 1937), and it seems likely that association of inexperienced individuals with birds which have adopted a new behavior response facilitates the learning process.

Behavioral preadaptation, the third explanation, implies that a bird is naturally predisposed to take advantage of a new environmental situation by virtue of intrinsic response characteristics already present before the new situation presents itself. Perhaps, for instance, a brick chimney constitutes for the Chimney Swift a stimulus for nesting and roosting responses superior to the best available to it in the strictly natural environment. Phenomena attributed to structural preadaptation are numerous (see Huxley, 1942:453); behavioral preadaptation is difficult to demonstrate and remains quite hypothetical.

The fourth explanation, cultural inheritance, is likewise difficult to demonstrate with clarity but would appear to feature in many behavioral adaptations. Game keepers, aviculturalists, and falconers are familiar with the fact that birds taken from the wild as adults are difficult to tame or to induce to breed, while birds obtained as nestlings or hatched from the egg are quite tractable. An adjustment is apparently made during an early and impressionable stage of development, perhaps the age of imprinting. Social facilitation provided by the parent birds during these impressionable periods in young birds in nature must play an important part in determining subsequent behavior (cf. Nice, 1943). Such acquired responses persisting into adulthood determine the social environment of the next generation of young birds and are thus passed on as a cultural tradition. The plasticity which such a mechanism can impart to a population of individually stereotyped birds may be important in the successful adjustment of bird populations to changing environments and their success as a group.

MECHANISMS OF RESPONSE

A response mechanism in an animal is the means by which the body organizes and channels energy to specific sets of muscles or glands and there releases it according to a pattern determined by the sense organs. Our ultimate objective in analyzing response mechanisms may be to reduce them to basic terms of nerve pathways, co-ordinating centers, energy regulation, or enzyme action, but we are still very far from that goal and clearly cannot reach it precipitously. In the meantime we are obliged to try to fit our empirical observations into theoretical frameworks. Perception, motivation, learning, and intelligence are concepts of this sort, little understood biologically, but well established as psychological phenomena.

The difficulties presented by this insecure basis for biological interpretation of behavior should not be cause for the defeatist attitude which some biologists have taken toward this fundamental phase of biology. With due recognition of the difficulties and the limitations of the tools available, notable progress has been and is being made at all levels. The acute need for objectivity in observation is all too apparent, however, and interpretations should be made with caution at all times and with due regard for the Lloyd-Morgan canon of parsimony.

Two aspects of response mechanisms may be recognized, selection and activation; the two probably occur simultaneously as parts of a single process, but it is convenient to consider them separately for the present.

Selection

A bird has a considerable repertory of behavior patterns with which it responds to the large number and wide variety of stimuli that impinge upon its sense organs. The response which is selected is generally characterized by a high degree of appropriateness. In many cases, such as the foot-paddling of gulls and lapwings or the "pirouetting" of phalaropes in stirring up small invertebrates for food (Tinbergen, 1952), the functional relationships of the selection are so striking as to suggest reasoning powers to the untrained observer. Response selections, however, like response patterns are quite stereotyped and stable in birds and, even after being altered by learning, remain relatively inflexible.

The mechanism by which responses are selected in birds may be expressed in terms of either (*a*) fixed stimulus-response connections or (*b*) cognitive organization. In the first view a given sign stimulus is thought to be related to a specific response pattern in much the same way that a key is related to its lock; the behavior repertory of a bird is considered to be based on a multiplicity of such independent key-lock combinations, and selection of a particular response pattern is automatic once the effective sign stimulus has been presented. In the second view, the role of the selection mechanism is not one of matching keys and locks but of organizing the various stimuli received from an environmental situation into a perception. Such a perception should not be confused with a sensation nor with the conscious awareness of sensations. It is a complex organization of impulses derived directly from the exteroceptors and combined with the store of latent impulses residual within the individual. The course from perception to response is generally conceived to be direct; in Sperry's (1952) view, described earlier in this chapter, perceptions have their very origin and basis in the muscles which produce the response.

Basically the two concepts are quite similar and appear to be converging in the more recent writings of students of behavior. The differences are perhaps more in emphasis than in principles; the first emphasizes the effect of specific elements in the stimulus situation, the second, the total effect.

Nissen (1951) has suggested that the mechanism of response selection (determination) varies with the "openness" of the environmental situation. When the external situation is restricted or confining, as when a bird finds itself caught in a trap, selection is bypassed and activity is general and undirected. At the other extreme, in "open" situations where regulating or guiding factors are absent or few in number, a bird has no opportunity to utilize pre-existing cues or established associations and resorts to random trial-and-error methods of selection. Between these extremes is the situation in which familiar directive elements or releasers occur to guide the response selection. Most of the situations provided by natural habitats, Nissen believes, are mixtures of the three types. The particular direction a bird takes as it forages in search of food may be quite haphazard, a matter of trial and error. As familiar objects or features are encountered its movements become oriented insofar as these elements of the situation hold significance as sign stimuli for innate or learned response patterns.

The actual form of the response will depend upon (1) the configuration of the stimulus situation including any special sign stimuli present, (2) the clarity or strength of the stimulation received, and (3) the physiological state of receptiveness of the bird at that moment. The background of innate and learned stimulus-response associations determines the response pattern activated. The strength of the stimulus combined with the receptiveness of the bird determines whether the response will be complete or partial (intention movements). And, finally, the appropriateness of the current state of responsiveness or the concurrence of more than one state determines the possible inclusion of displacement movements borrowed from other response patterns.

Activation

The expression of a behavior pattern in overt action involves the release of energy. The external stimulus may be regarded as the instrument which trips off the mechanism. The energy for transmitting the impulse and for producing the action comes from the organism. The source of this energy lies in the metabolic activities of living tissues in the body; some of it is used up continuously in the maintenance of vital activities; much of it is stored for intermittent or emergency uses by the effector organs of behavior. The mobilization and discharge of this energy in behavioral action constitutes the process of activation.

The activation of a behavior pattern depends on two variables, the strength of the stimulus and the condition of responsiveness of the animal. We are here concerned with conditions of responsiveness which may vary from a level where continuous stimulation is ineffective to one in which activation appears to take place automatically in the absence of detectable external stimulation (vacuum activity of Lorenz, 1937).

The problems of activation have been approached from two distinct scientific viewpoints. The dynamics and mechanics of energy production in the animal's body and its conversion into action represent the approach followed by the biophysicist and the physiologist. To the psychologist, on the other hand, behavior activation is a matter of internal tensions or drives to be dealt with conceptually in terms of motivation, sets, and predispositions in relation to incentives.

In the search for a comprehensive view of behavior activation, specialists in the various fields have in general been unable to find common ground. Some feel that psychological and physiological phenomena belong to different integrative levels, that like forests and trees, each possesses distinctive characters which cannot be treated in the same terms. Others believe that psychological phenomena are actually nothing more than complex physiological phenomena which, to date, have defied analysis in physiological terms. Some workers have attempted to restrict themselves to terms of one or the other field, but many have found it desirable to borrow terms and concepts from both fields and attempt an amalgamation.

Students of bird behavior, attempting to utilize the contributions of modern physiology and psychology, hold varied views on the interpretation of energy mobilization and motivation. Many, following Russell (1945) or Bierens de Haan (1947), deal in teleological terms, often in subjective terms. Another group, led by Lorenz and Tinbergen, have adopted an objectivistic approach and espoused a concept of action-specific units which accumulate energy for specific responses from a general source until the threshold of release for them has been lowered to a point where ordinary environmental stimuli readily trip them off. Others question whether a concept of special energy sources or channels is warranted, whether activation cannot better be explained in terms of general metabolic energy, released in specific ways according to innate or learned patterns of excitation.

The field of comparative behavior provides a good approach to some of the fundamental principles of behavior activation. One of the basic responses of animals to stimuli is an increase in general excitability and activity, as when a shadow passing over a swarm of gyrinid beetles on the surface of a pond sets them into swirling activity. Such unoriented quantitative responses have been termed kineses and have been studied intensively in lower animals. Similar, though not necessarily homologous, phenomena occur in higher forms including birds and may be seen to particular advantage in responses to danger or sudden disturbance. At such times certain physiological responses commonly known collectively as the emergency reaction are invoked, involving rapid adjustment of the autonomic nervous system and the sudden release of epinephrin from the adrenal medulla. The behavioral response involves "fight or flight" actions, or a restrained condition of readiness to act on repetition or reinforcement of the stimulus (freezing). When restrained, the animal is highly sensitive to further stimuli of the same or a related type; its threshold of response has been lowered. The release of energy which follows is apt to be great and the action extreme, even to the extent of being displaced or irregularly directed. In a human subject we call this emotional behavior and the same term has been used frequently in subhuman animals including birds. The word emotion, however, should perhaps be reserved for psychic phenomena involving conscious sensation (see Friedmann, 1934), comprehensible only through subjective experience. In birds there is no evident need for invoking concepts of consciousness in order to explain excitability even when it is based on the same physiological processes as those which occur in man. The intense and erratic behavior of a flock of terns disturbed from their nests, or of a wild bird caught in a trap, may have the same attributes which we associate with anger and fear but cannot be shown to produce analogous conscious sensations in the birds. Until evidence of consciousness is demonstrated, it seems best to follow the Lloyd-Morgan canon that behavioral phenomena should be interpreted in objective behavioral terms.

Behavioral excitability or irritability is not always generalized; in fact it may never be completely generalized. Claude Bernard, years ago, showed that tissues require a constant internal environment (homeostasis) and that any disturbance in the chemical or physical balance of this environment results in a physiological response by the animal to re-establish it. The response may involve local circulatory adjustments, glandular activity, muscle activity, or changes in metabolism. Carrying the concept further, disturbances in the stability of the internal environment produced by external factors may affect the nervous system in ways which lead to the activation of behavior patterns that remedy the instability (Dempsey, 1951). The search for, and movements to, shelter from cold winds or from hot sun may in this way be regarded as behavioral responses to directly induced disturbances of the internal environment.

The process of living involves constant tearing down and building up of tissues and vital substances. Factors which interfere with these normal metabolic activities of the living animal act like direct disturbing factors in producing internal agitations which evoke remedial responses. The absence of adequate food or water produces such disturbances and characteristically evokes foraging movements which tend to remedy the condition. Such conditions are referred to as physiological needs, and the specific behavioral excitability or readiness to respond which accompanies them is termed a homeostatic drive or appetite.

Many of these drives have been analyzed with considerable success. A dehydration of the tissues through water deprivation (or through subcutaneous injections of salt in rats) results in an increased responsiveness to water, a "thirst" (Heyer, 1952). Rhythmic contractions of the muscles of an empty stomach produce internal disturbances which incite foraging and feeding behavior, disturbances which at the conscious sensation level are termed hunger pangs. The accumulation of lactic acid in muscle tissue directly reduces its responsiveness, producing a sensation in humans known as fatigue.

Certain chemical substances (hormones) when present in the blood, either through natural secretion of the endocrine glands or through artificial injection, induce changes in the structure and sensitivity of certain organs and produce conditions of specific excitability and sensitivity. Androgens, for instance, are associated with sexual excitability in male birds, and prolactin with parental responsiveness. Other conditions of excitability recognizable under the psychological terms of hate, disgust, grief, elation, etc., are well known to humans as subjective phenomena and may have their subconscious physiological counterparts in subhumans such as birds. Darwin (1872) described and analyzed the behavioral expressions of some of these conditions in various birds as well as mammals.

Although conditions of responsiveness constitute the internal, energy-organizing component of the activation mechanism, most of the changes in the internal chemical balance which give rise to these conditions are themselves responses to environmental stimuli. The nature of these responses is physiological, however, and quite different from that used in the direct behavior response. It differs in the rate of response, the type of organs and tissues responding, the mechanism of synapse transmission, and, often, the nature of the stimulus. While the behavior response operates through the central nervous system to the skeletal or striated muscles and is characteristically rapid, physiological responses are slow and generally involve the autonomic nervous system and visceral musculature or the glandular organs, either exocrine or endocrine. In some physiological responses, such as the emergency reaction, the response is organized quite rapidly through the autonomic nervous system and the medulla of the adrenal gland. In others, such as the thirst and hunger reactions, the response is slower, developing as metabolic disturbances set up instability in the internal environment. Finally, there are some responses, especially those related to reproductive behavior, which develop slowly over a period of weeks or months in response to environmental stimuli which often bear little or no direct relation to the behavior effected.

Changes in conditions of responsiveness are often due in part to physiological rhythms or to refractoriness and "tissue adaptation" of intrinsic origin. The regression of sexual behavior at the end of the breeding season apparently reflects physiological refractoriness (Marshall, 1951); feeding periodicity has been shown to be based on intrinsic rhythms in various mammals and may be similarly regulated in birds.

The functioning relationship or association between stimulus and physiological response may, as in behavioral responses, be either innate or learned. Proof of innateness, as we have seen, depends on the weight of negative evidence and is therefore difficult. Learned physiological responses are, on the other hand, readily demonstrated. Many of the classical experiments on conditioning, such as those of Pavlov on dogs (1927), have involved one or more physiological responses together with their related behavior attributes, or, as Tinbergen would express it, a higher, executive instinct center with its subordinate consummatory acts. The transference and fixation of fear responses to a new stimulus following a frightening experience, for instance, may involve many actions all bound together as a syndrome by the physiological emergency reaction.

Certain of the physiological states of responsiveness in birds are transitory and occur in definite seasonal rhythm in response to orderly changes in the external environment. The environmental factors which underlie these responses may be complex. In a considerable number of species seasonal change in day length has been convincingly proven to be the primary instigator of the breeding cycle with its many related activities. Even migration, only remotely related to reproduction functionally, is clearly tied in with this basic physiological rhythm (Wolfson, 1952).

A combination of several stimuli may be needed for the activation of many phases of breeding physiology and the behavior forms that belong with them. Thus, to induce full breeding behavior and laying, Starlings and House Sparrows require one or more forms of social stimuli in addition to the stimulation provided by the increased photoperiod (Burger, 1949; Polikarpova, 1940). Fulmars go through the preliminaries of nesting in response to physical factors related to the seasons, presumably photoperiod, but lay few or no eggs in the absence of stimuli provided by large colony aggregations (Fisher, 1952).

Various students of animal behavior have noted that the activation of a behavior pattern appears to remove or reduce the condition of specific responsiveness or hypersensitivity which is associated with it. The effect has been likened to that produced in a spark coil after an opposing electrode has been brought close and a spark discharged. Energy may continue to accumulate, but at least momentarily, the discharge of current reduces the head potential; the energy has been consumed by the consummatory act. Students of human behavior assert that this reduction in tension brings a pleasurable relief which is consciously or unconsciously sought and which provides an incentive for effective responses. This "hedonic" or "pleasure" principle has also been applied to lower animals including birds, and the assertion made that responses are selected insofar as they create pleasurable sensations or bring relief from distress. The whole concept of incentives and rewards, however, generally involves assumptions of striving toward a hidden goal which not all students of bird behavior care to accept. While we cannot deny the existence of incentives in the broad sense of external determinants of action, it is possible to avoid the undesirable teleological implications of striving by interpreting them in terms of releasers for executive appetitive patterns, or of extrinsic stimuli to which specific responses have become associated but which are incompletely represented in the immediate stimulus situation. The absence of essential elements or cues in a definitive stimulus situation might well account for an incomplete or exploratory type of response.

EPILOGUE

The past twenty years has seen a tremendous resurgence of interest and activity in the study of animal behavior, and we today are caught in the whirling cross-eddies of a flood of new observations and ideas. The source of this flood is multiple; psychology on the one hand is pouring in a torrent of terms and concepts stemming largely from studies of man, physiology is contributing further terms and concepts from another direction, and finally, ecology is pouring in a full share of observations and views expressed in still another technical vocabulary. The resulting maelstrom includes both confluent and conflicting currents. Some laboratory experimentalists have been inclined to ignore and wave aside the contributions of field ecologists as "old-fashioned natural history," while others with a forward view have tried to collaborate in the common objective. In the same way some ecologists have accused the laboratory worker of playing with artificial and hopelessly distorted superficialities, while others have recognized the essential role of laboratory experimentation in scientific advancement. For those who have been alert and broadly aware of current advances in all fields, the new confusion has been a challenge which is leading to new syntheses and new platforms of perspective. It is hoped that the surveys, descriptions, and comparisons presented in this chapter will provide both clarification and stimulus to workers in this vital and challenging field of investigation.

Bibliography

ALLEE, W. C.

1931. Animal aggregrations. A study in general sociology. University of Chicago Press, Chicago, ix + 431 pp.

1936. Analytical studies of group behavior in birds. Wilson Bull., 48:145-151.

ALTUM, B.

1868. Der vogel und sein leben. Niemann, Münster, xv + 240 pp.

ALVERDES, F.

1927. Social life in the animal world. Harcourt Brace, New York, ix + 216 pp.

ARMSTRONG, E. A.

1947. Bird display and behaviour. Oxford University Press, New York, 431 pp.

ARONSON, L. R., and G. K. NOBLE

1945. The sexual behavior of Anura. Bull. Amer. Mus. Nat. Hist., 86:89-139.

BAILEY, R. E.

1952. The incubation patch of passerine birds. Condor, 54:121-136.

BARTHOLOMEW, G. A.

1942. The fishing activities of Double-crested Cormorants on San Francisco Bay. Condor., 44:13-21.

BEACH, F. A

1948. Hormones and behavior. Paul Hoeber, New York, xiv + 368 pp.

1952. Play in animals. Encyclopaedia Britannica, 1952 edition, 18:70-72.

BEECHER, W. J.

1951. A possible navigation sense in the ear of birds. Amer. Midl. Nat., 46: 367-384.

BERNARD, C.

1865. An introduction to the study of experimental medicine. Trans. H. C. Greene, 1949. Henry Schuman, Inc., New York, xix + 226 pp.

BIERENS DE HAAN, J. A.

1937. Über den Begriff des Instinktes in der Tierpsychologie. Folia Biotheoretica, 2:1-16.

1947. Animal psychology and the science of animal behaviour. Behaviour, 1:71-80.

BREED, F. S.

1911. The development of certain instinctive habits in chicks. Behavior Monogr., 1:1-78.

BROGDEN, W. J.

1951. Animal studies of learning. In Handbook of experimental psychology, ed. by S. S. Stevens. John Wiley, New York, pp. 568-612.

BULLOUGH, W. S.

1945. Endocrinological aspects of bird behavior. Biol. Rev., 20:89-99.

BUMP, G., R. W. DARROW, F. C. EDMINSTER, and W. F. CRISSEY

1947. The Ruffed Grouse: life history, propagation, management. New York State Conservation Dept., Albany, xxxvi + 915 pp.

BURGER, J. W.

1949. A review of experimental investigations on seasonal reproduction in birds. Wilson Bull., 61:211-230.

CARMICHAEL, L.

1936. A re-evaluation of the concepts of maturation and learning as applied to the early development of behavior. Psychol. Rev., 43:450-470.

CHAPIN, J. P.

1924. Profiteers of the busy bee. Nat. Hist., 24:328-336.

CHILD, C. M.

1924. Physiological foundations of behavior. Henry Holt and Co., New York, xii + 330 pp.

COGHILL, G. E.

1929. Anatomy and the problem of behaviour. Cambridge University Press, London, 12 + 113 pp.

COLLIAS, N.

1944. Aggressive behavior among vertebrate animals. Physiol. Zool., 17:83-123.

1950. Social life and the individual among vertebrate animals. Ann. N.Y. Acad. Sci., 51:1074-1092.

1952. The development of social behavior in birds. Auk, 69:127-159.

COTTAM, C.

1935. Unusual food habits of California Gulls. Condor, 37:170-171.

COTTAM, C., C. S. WILLIAMS, and C. A. SOOTER.

1942. Cooperative feeding of White Pelicans. Auk, 59:444-445.

CRAIG, W.

1912. Observations on doves learning to drink. Jour. Animal Behavior, 2:273-279.

1914. Male doves reared in isolation. Jour. Animal Behavior, 4:121-133.

1918. Appetites and aversions as constituents of instincts. Biol. Bull., 34:91-107.

DAANJE, A.

1950. On locomotory movements in birds and the intention movements derived from them. Behaviour, 3:48-99.

DARLING, F. F.

1938. Bird flocks and the breeding cycle. Cambridge University Press, x+124 pp.

1952. Social behavior and survival. Auk, 69:183-191.

DARWIN, C.

1872. The expression of the emotions in man and animals. Murray, London, vi + 374 pp.

DAWSON, W. L.

1923. The birds of California. Vol. I. South Moulton Co., San Diego, xvii + 696 pp.

DELACOUR, J., and E. MAYR

1945. The family Anatidae. Wilson Bull., 57:3-55.

DEMPSEY, E. W.

1951. Homeostasis. In Handbook of experimental psychology, ed. by S. S. Stevens. John Wiley, New York, pp. 209-236.

DONNER, K. O.

1951. The visual acuity of some passerine birds. Acta Zool. Fenn., 66:1-40.

DOVE, W. F.

1935. A study of individuality in the nutritive instincts and of the causes and effects of variations in the selection of foods. Amer. Nat., 69:469-544.

EMLEN, J. T., Jr.

1941. An experimental analysis of the breeding cycle of the Tricolored Red-wing. Condor, 43:209-219.

1950. Techniques for observing bird behavior under natural conditions. Ann. N.Y. Acad. Sci., 51:1103-1112.

1952. Flocking behavior in birds. Auk, 69:160-170.

1954. Territory, nest building, and pair formation in the Cliff Swallow. Auk, 71:16-35.

ENGLEMANN, C.

1951. Beiträge zum Gedächtnis des Huhnes. Zeits. Tierpsychol., 8:110-121.

ENGLEMANN, W.

1928. Untersuchungen über die Schallokalization bei Tieren. Zeits. Psychol. Physiol. Sinnesorg. Ab. T. z. Psychol., 105:317-370.

FABRICIUS, E.

1951. Zur Ethologie junger Anatiden. Acta Zool. Fenn., 68:1-175.

FINN, F.

1919. Bird behaviour, psychical and physiological. Dodd Mead and Co., New York, x + 363 pp.

FISHER, J.

1952. The Fulmar. Collins, London, xv + 496 pp.

FRIEDMANN, H.

1929. The cowbirds. A study in the biology of social parasitism. Thomas, Springfield, xviii + 421 pp.

1934. The instinctive emotional life of birds. Psychoanalytic Rev., 21:1-57.

GIFFORD, E. W.

1919. Field notes on the land birds of the Galapagos Islands and of Cocos Island, Costa Rica. Proc. Calif. Acad. Sci. 2:189-258.

GILBERT, P. A.

1939. The bower-painting habit of the Satin Bower-bird (*Ptilonorhynchus violaceus*). Emu, 39:18-22.

GRIFFIN, D. R., and R. J. HOCK

1949. Airplane observations of homing birds. Ecology, 30:176-198.

GROHMANN, J.

1939. Modification oder Funktionsreifung? Zeits. Tierpsychol., 2:132-144.

GROSKIN, H.

1950. Additional observations and comments on "anting" by birds. Auk, 67: 201-209.

GUTHRIE, E. R.

1935. The psychology of learning. Harper and Bros., New York, viii + 258 pp.

HEINROTH, O.

1911. Beiträge zur Biologie namentlich Ethologie und Physiologie der Anatiden. Verh First Internat. Ornithol. Kongr., pp. 589-702.

1924. Lautäusserrungen der Vögel. Jour. Ornithol., 72:223-244.

1938. Das Baden der Vögel. Ornithol. Monatsber., 46:97-100.

HEINROTH, O., and M. HEINROTH

1928. Die Vögel Mitteleuropas. H. Bermühler, Berlin-Lichterfelde, 3 vols.

HERRICK, F. H.

1910. Instinct and intelligence in birds. Pop. Sci. Mo., 76:532-556; 77:82-97, 122-141.

1935. Wild birds at home. Appleton, New York, xxii + 345 pp.

HESS, W. R.

1943. Das Zwischenhirn als Koordinationsorgan. Helv. Physiol. Acta, 1:549-565.

HESS, W. R., and M. BRÜGGER

1943. Das subkortikale Zentrum der affectiven Abwehrreaction. Helv. Physiol. Acta, 1:33-52.

HEYER, A. W.

1952. Studies in motivation and retention, III. A methodological approach to the independent manipulation of tissue dehydration and time of water deprivation. Compar. Psychol. Monogr., 20:251-272.

HINDE, R. A.

1952. Behaviour of the Great Tit. E. J. Brill, Leiden, x + 201 pp.

HOLZAPFEL, M.

1939. Analyse des Sperrens und Pickens in der Entwicklung des Stars. Jour. Ornithol., 87:525-553.

HOWARD, H. E.

1907-14. The British Warblers, a history, with problems of their lives. R. H. Porter, London, 2 vols.

1920. Territory in bird life. Murray, London, xiii + 308 pp.

1929. An introduction to the study of bird behaviour. Cambridge University Press, xi + 136 pp.

1935. The nature of a bird's world. Cambridge University Press, vi + 101 pp.

1940. The Waterhen's worlds. Cambridge University Press, vii + 84 pp.

HULL, C. L.

1930. Simple trial-and-error learning: a study in psychological theory. Psychol. Rev., 37:241-256.

1943. Principles of behavior. Appleton-Century-Crofts, New York, x + 422 pp.

HUTCHINSON, G. E.

1952. Marginalia. Amer. Scientist, 40:146-153.

HUXLEY, J.

1942. Evolution the modern synthesis. Harper and Bros., New York and London, 645 pp.

1947. Notes on the problem of geographical differences in tameness in birds. Ibis, 89:539-552; 90:312-318; 91:108-116, 365-368.

ISING, G.

1946. Die physikalische Möglichkeit eines tierischen Orientierungssinnes auf Basis der Erdrotation. Ark. Mat. Astr. Fys., 32A(4), No. 18, pp. 1-23.

KATZ, D.

1937. Animals and men. Studies in comparative psychology. Longman's Green, London, xi + 263.

KELLOGG, W. N.

1938. An eclectic view of some theories of learning. Psychol. Rev., 45:165-184.

KENDEIGH, S. C.

1939. The relation of metabolism to the development of temperature regulation in birds. Jour. Exper. Zool., 82:419-438.

1952. Parental care and its evolution in birds. Illinois Biol. Monogr., 22: ix + 356 pp.

KIRKMAN, F. B.

1937. Bird behaviour. A contribution based chiefly on a study of the Black-headed Gull. Nelson, London, xv + 232 pp.

KNOWLTON, F. H.

1909. Birds of the world. Henry Holt and Co., New York, xiii+873 pp.

KOEHLER, O.

1951. The ability of birds to count. Bull. Animal Behaviour, 1:41-45.

KOHLER, W.

1921. Intelligenzprüfungen an Menschenaffen. Springer, Berlin, 194 pp.

1925. The mentality of apes. Harcourt Brace, New York, 342 pp.

1929. Gestalt psychology. Liveright, New York, x + 403 pp.

KORTLANDT, A.

1940. Eine Uebersicht der angeborenen Verhaltensweisen des mittel-europäischen Kormorans (*Phalacrocorax carbo sinensis* Shaw and Nodd.); ihre Function, ontogenetische Entwicklung und phylogenetische Herkunft. Arch. Neerl. Zool., 4:401-442.

KRAMER, G.

1952. Experiments on bird orientation. Ibis, 94:265-285.

KUBIE, L. S.

1948. Instincts and homeostasis. Psychosom. Med., 10:15-30.

KUHLMANN, F.

1909. Some preliminary observations on the development of instincts and habits in young birds. Psych. Rev. (mon. suppl.), 11:49:85.

KUO, Z. Y.

1932. Ontogeny of embryonic behavior in Aves, IV. The influence of prenatal behavior or post-natal life. Jour. Comp. Psychol., 14:109-121.

LACK, D.

1940a. Pair formation in birds. Condor, 42:269-286.

1940b. The releaser concept in bird behaviour. Nature, 145:107-108.

1940c. Courtship feeding in birds. Auk, 57:169-178.

1941. Some aspects of instinctive behaviour and display in birds. Ibis, 1941: 407-441.

1943. The life of the Robin. H. F. & G. Witherby Ltd., London, xvii + 200 pp.

1944. Ecological aspects of species formation in birds. Ibis, 86:260-286.

1947. Darwin's Finches. Cambridge University Press, x + 208 pp.

1949. The significance of ecological isolation. In Genetics, paleontology and evolution, ed. by G. Jepson *et al.* Princeton University Press, pp. 299-308.

LASHLEY, K. S.

1938. Experimental analysis of instinctive behavior. Psychol. Rev., 45: 445-471.

1950. The search for the engram. In Soc. Exper. Biol. Symposium IV. Physiological mechanisms in animal behaviour. Academic Press, New York, pp. 454-482.

LASHLEY, K. S., and J. T. RUSSELL

1934. The mechanisms of vision, XI. A preliminary test of innate organization. Jour. Genet. Psychol., 45:136-144.

LEHRMAN, D. S.

1953. A critique of Konrad Lorenz's theory of instinctive behavior. Quart. Rev. Biol., 28:337-363.

LEOPOLD, A. S.

1944. The nature of heritable wildness in turkeys. Condor, 46:133-197.

LORENZ, K.

1935. Der Kumpan in der Umwelt des Vogels. Jour. Ornithol., 83:137-213, 289-413.

1937. The companion in the bird's world. Auk, 54:245-273.

1950. The comparative method in studying innate behavior patterns. In Soc. Exper. Biol. Symposium IV. Physiological mechanisms in animal behavior. Academic Press, New York, pp. 221-268.

1952. King Solomon's ring. Methuen & Co. Ltd., London, xix + 202 pp.

LORENZ, K., and N. TINBERGEN

1938. Taxis und Instinkthandlungen in der Eirollbewegung der Graugans. Zeits. Tierpsychol., 2:1-29.

McCABE, R. A.

1947. The homing of transplanted young Wood Ducks. Wilson Bull., 59:104-109.

McCABE, R. A., and A. S. HAWKINS

1946. The Hungarian Partridge in Wisconsin. Amer. Midl. Nat., 36:1-75.

McDOUGALL, W.

1909. An introduction to social psychology, Luce and Co., Boston, 418 pp.

MAIER, N. R. F., and T. C. SCHNEIRLA

1935. Principles of animal psychology. McGraw-Hill, New York, xiii+529 pp.

1942. Mechanisms in conditioning. Psychol. Rev., 49:117-134.

MAKKINK, G. F.

1936. An attempt at an ethogram of the European Avocet (*Recurvirostra avosetta* L.) with ethological and psychological remarks. Ardea, 25:1-60.

MARSHALL, A. J.

1951. The refractory period of testis rhythm in birds and its bearing on breeding and migration. Wilson Bull., 63:238-261.

1952. Display and the sexual cycle in the Spotted Bowerbird (*Chlamydera maculata* Gould). Proc. Zool. Soc. London, 122:239-252.

MARSHALL, F. H. A.

1942. Exteroceptive factors in sexual periodicity. Biol. Rev., 17:68-90.

MAYR, E.

1935. Bernard Altum and the territory theory. Proc. Linn. Soc. N.Y., nos. 45-46:24-38.

MEISE, W.

1936. Neue Ergebnisse der Revierforschung. Mitt. Ver Sächs. Ornithol., 5:1-23.

MENNER, E.

1938. Die Bedeutung des Pecten im Auge des Vogels für die Wahrnemung von Bewegungen nebst Bemerkungen über Seine Ontogenie und Histologie. Zool. Jahrb. Abt. allg. Zool. Physiol. Tiere., 58:481-538.

MILLER, A. H.

1941. The buccal food carrying pouches of the Rosy Finch. Condor, 43:72-73.

MOSTLER, G.

1935. Beobachtungen zur Frage des Wespenmimikry. Zeits. Morph. Ökol. Tiere, 29:381-454.

NERO, R. W., and J. T. EMLEN

1951. An experimental study of territorial behavior in breeding Red-winged Blackbirds. Condor, 53:105-116.

NICE, M. M.

1941. The role of territory in bird life. Amer. Midl. Nat., 26:441-487.

1943. Studies in the life history of the Song Sparrow, II. Trans. Linn. Soc. N.Y., 6: viii + 1-328 pp.

NISSEN, H. W.

1951. Phylogenetic comparisons. In Handbook of experimental psychology, ed. by S. S. Stevens. John Wiley, New York, pp. 347-386.

OLIVER, W. R. B.

1930. New Zealand birds. Fine Arts Ltd., Wellington, viii + 541 pp.

PADILLA, S. G.

1932. Further studies on the delayed pecking of chicks. Ph.D. thesis, Univ. of Mich. Library.

PALMER, R. S.

1941. A behavior study of the Common Tern. Proc. Boston Soc. Nat. Hist., 42:1-119.

PAVLOV, I. P.

1927. Conditioned reflexes. Oxford University Press, London, xv + 430 pp.

PETRUNKEVITCH, A.

1926. The value of instinct as a taxonomic character in spiders. Biol. Bull., 50:427-432.

POLIKARPOVA, E.

1940. Influence of external factors upon the development of the sexual gland of the sparrow. C. R. (Doklady) Acad. Sci. U.S.S.R., 27:91-95.

POULSEN, H.

1951a. Maturation and learning in the improvement of some instinctive activities. Viduskabelige Meddeleser fra den Dansk Naturhistor. Forennig., 113: 155-170.

1951b. Inheritance and learning in the song of the Chaffinch. *(Fringilla coelebs* L.). Behaviour, 3:216-228.

PUMPHREY, R. J.

1948. The sense organs of birds. Ibis, 90:171-199.

PYCRAFT, W. P.

1898. A contribution towards our knowledge of morphology of the owls. Trans. Linn. Soc. London, 7:223-275.

RAND, A. L.

1941a. Lorenz's objective method of interpreting bird behavior. Auk, 58:289-291.

1941b. Results of the Archbold expeditions. No. 34. Development and enemy recognition of the Curve-billed Thrasher, *Toxostoma curvirostre.* Bull. Amer. Mus. Nat. Hist., 78:213-242.

1943. Some irrelevant behavior in birds. Auk, 60:167-170.

RIDDLE, O.

1937. Physiological responses to prolactin. Cold Spring Harbor Symposia on Quant. Biol., 5:218-228.

RUSSELL, E. S.

1945. The directiveness of organic activities. Cambridge University Press, vii + 196 pp.

SCHJELDERUP-EBBE, T.

1935. Social behavior in birds. In C. Murchison, Handbook of social psychology. Clark University Press, pp. 947-972.

SCHNEIRLA, T. C.

1946. Contemporary American animal psychology in perspective. In Twentieth century psychology, ed. by P. L. Harriman. Philosophical Library, New York, pp. 306-316.

1950. A consideration of some problems in the ontogeny of family life and social adjustments in various infra-human animals. Problems of infancy and childhood. Trans. Fourth Conf. Josiah Macy, Jr., Fndn, pp. 81-124.

1952. A consideration of some conceptual trends in comparative psychology. Psychol. Bull., 49:559-597.

SCHOOLAND, J. B.

1942. Are there any innate behavior tendencies? Genet. Psychol. Monogr., 25:219-287.

SCOTT, J. P.

1942. Genetic differences in the social behavior of inbred strains of mice. Jour. Heredity, 33:11-15.

SCOTT, W. E. D.

1904. The inheritance of song in passerine birds. Science, 19:154.

SELOUS, EDMUND

1933. Evolution of habit in birds. Constable & Co. Ltd., London, xvi + 296 pp.

SHEPARD, J. F., and F. S. BREED

1913. Maturation and use in the development of an instinct. Jour. Animal Behavior, 3:274.

SMITH, K. U.

1951. Discrimination behavior in animals. In Comparative psychology, 3rd ed., ed. by C. P. Stone. Prentice Hall, New York, pp. 316-362.

SPENCE, K. W.

1936. The nature of discrimination learning in animals. Psychol. Rev., 43:427-449.

1950. Cognitive versus stimulus-response theories of learning. Psychol. Rev., 57:159-172.

SPERRY, R. W.

1952. The mind-brain problem. Amer. Scientist, 40:291-312.

STEVENS, S. S., ed.

1951. Handbook of experimental psychology. John Wiley, New York, xi + 1436 pp.

SWANBERG, P. O.

1951. Food storage, territory and song in the Thick-billed Nutcracker. Proc. Tenth Internat. Ornithol. Cong., Uppsala, pp. 545-554.

THORPE, W. H.

1944. Some problems of animal learning. Proc. Linn. Soc. London, 156:70-83.

1948. The modern concept of instinctive behaviour. Bull. Animal Behaviour, 1:1-12.

1950. The concepts of learning and their relation to those of instinct. Sympos. Soc. Exper. Biol., 4:387-408.

1951a. The definition of terms used in animal behaviour studies. (Being a report on the Cambridge Round Table Conference.) Bull. Animal Behaviour, 1:34-40.

1951b. The learning abilities of birds. Ibis, 93:1-52, 252-296.

TINBERGEN, N.

1939. The behavior of the Snow Bunting in spring. Trans. Linn. Soc. N.Y., 5:1-94.

1942. An objectivistic study of the innate behaviour of animals. Bibliotheca Biotheoretica, Ser. D., 1:39-98.

1948. Social releasers and the experimental method required for their study. Wilson Bull., 60:6-51.

1951a. The study of instinct. Clarendon Press, Oxford, xii + 228 pp.

1951b. Recent advances in the study of bird behaviour. Proc. Tenth Internat. Ornithol. Cong., Uppsala, pp. 360-374.

1952. "Derived" activities; their causation, biological significance, origin, and emancipation during evolution. Quart. Rev. Biol., 27:1-32.

TINBERGEN, N., and D. J. KUENEN

1939. Über die auslösenden und die richtunggenbenden Reizsituationen der Sperrbewegung von Jungen Drosseln (*Turdus m. merula* L. and *T. e. ericetorum* Turton). Zeits. Tierpsychol., 3:37-60.

TOLMAN, E. C.

1932. Purposive behavior in animals and men. Appleton-Century-Crofts, New York, xiv + 463 pp.

VALIKANGAS, I.

1933. Finnische Zugvögel aus englischen vogeleiern. Vogelzug, 4:159-166.

WARDEN, C. J., T. N. JENKINS, and L. H. WARNER

1936. Comparative psychology. Ronald Press, New York, 3 vols.

WATSON, J. B.

1914. Behavior, an introduction to comparative psychology. Henry Holt and Co., New York, xii + 439.

WHITMAN, C. O.

1919. The behavior of pigeons. Posthumous works of C. O. Whitman, ed. by H. A. Carr. Pub. Carneg. Inst., Wash., 257, 3:1-161.

WINTERBOTTOM, J. M.

1949. Mixed bird parties in the tropics, with special reference to Northern Rhodesia. Auk, 66:258-263.

WOLFSON, A.

1952. Day length, migration, and breeding cycles in birds. Sci. Monthly, 74: 191-200.

YEAGLEY, H. L.

1947. A preliminary study of a physical basis of bird navigation. Jour. Appl. Physics, 18:1035-1063.

YOUNG, H.

1951. Territorial behavior in the Eastern Robin. Proc. Linn. Soc. N.Y., nos. 58-62:1-37.

chapter 6

BIRD NAVIGATION . . . Donald R. Griffin

INTRODUCTION

This paper stems from a symposium held in 1948 at the annual meeting of the American Society of Zoologists in Washington, D.C. The title of this symposium was "Mechanisms of Orientation in Migration and Homing", and the speakers were D. R. Griffin, A. G. Huntsman, E. Mayr, W. Rowan, and E. Wolf. In addition there was a spirited and stimulating participation of several others in the general discussion. One result of this discussion was the making of arrangements for a lecture tour of the United States by Karl von Frisch and the subsequent publication of these lectures in book form (von Frisch, 1950). Another result was the gradual evolution of two of the papers originally presented at the symposium into a review entitled "Bird Navigation," published in *Biological Reviews.* Since the same review of recent studies of orientation in birds is appropriate for a chapter in this book, arrangements were made to republish it here with only minor modifications which I feel to be appropriate, such as the inclusion of one or two very recent contributions and a somewhat fuller treatment of the important contributions of Kramer and his associates.

In an earlier review (1944) I attempted to summarize the evidence bearing upon the problem of bird navigation that had accumulated up to approximately 1940. Despite a world war, the ensuing decade has produced many significant advances in this field, and it has become increasingly clear that the problem of bird navigation is a dual one. The investigator is obliged to ask both ecological questions about the environmental cues which guide the migrating bird and also physiological questions concerning the sensory mechanisms by which these environmental cues may be recognized and channeled into the central nervous system. Because no wholly satisfactory answers are available to many of these questions, we find instead a variety of ingenious theories which can be classified as those, on the one hand, which postulate "something more" than the generally recognized biological mechanisms, and, on the other hand, those which assume "nothing but" types of physiological machinery that are well known in all higher vertebrates. The "something more" is usually sensory in nature—an ability to perceive terrestrial magnetism, sensitivity to

Manuscript received January 1, 1954.

infrared radiations, or some other environmental factor that cannot be detected by the human senses.

Those investigators who are not eager to postulate new sense organs tend to seek instead for adequate environmental cues perceptible to birds and man alike. But human curiosity will not let these unsolved problems rest. Because the next few years will surely produce new speculation and experimentation, it is profitable to review in some detail three theories that fall in the "something more" category and that have attracted attention in recent years, even though we shall find none of them adequate. It is also worth while to examine certain other theoretical possibilities based upon known sensory mechanisms and additional recent evidence that must be taken into account in any future consideration of bird navigation.

MECHANICAL FORCES RESULTING FROM THE EARTH'S ROTATION

The one really new theoretical idea contributed during the past decade has come from Ising (1946), who has suggested that the navigation of birds is based upon perception of mechanical forces related to the rotation of the earth. Ising discusses in rigorous fashion the physical forces upon which such sensitivity might be based; but he has left to others the quantitative comparisons of these forces with the sensitivity of actual receptor systems. The theory has been adversely criticised by Thorpe and Wilkinson (1946) and by de Vries (1948). From Ising's suggestions, I should like to select for discussion only the two which he feels to be the most promising, together with a third possibility that has since been advocated by Yeagley (1947). All three are basically the same, and all stem from the interaction of the earth's rotary motion with the motion of the bird or some part of it. In all three cases there is no doubt that the forces are *qualitatively* of the sort to which the sense organs and nervous systems of birds are able to respond. The crucial question is a *quantitative* one: are these forces large enough (*a*) relative to the absolute threshold of the mechanical receptors and (*b*) relative to other mechanical forces of the same kind to which the bird is subjected and from which it would have to discriminate the forces stemming from the earth's rotation?

One effect of the earth's rotation upon a flying bird, or any other object moving through the air, is a slight change in its apparent weight depending upon the direction of movement. Because the bird's velocity of flight either adds to or subtracts from the velocity of its rotation about the axis of the earth, a centrifugal force that is normally added algebraically to the force of gravity is slightly altered because of its flight through the air. The resulting change in weight may be considered as a change in the apparent value of g, the constant of gravitation (approximately 980 cm/sec^2). In the northern hemisphere the change in g with linear motion over the surface of the earth is given by Ising as approximately $-2U\Omega\cos\varnothing$, where U = the easterly component of the bird's velocity (cm/second), Ω = the angular velocity of the earth's rotation (7.3×10^{-5} radians/second), and $\varnothing$ = the latitude.

A bird flying east along the equator at forty miles per hour would find its weight to be less by roughly 1 part of 2,000 than when it turned and flew west. If it were circling, the easterly and westerly directions of flight might succeed each other within a few seconds, thus facilitating comparison of kinesthetic sensations. There is a related effect which, together with the departure of the earth from a perfect spherical shape, results in a variation in *g* by about 1 part in 200 between the equator and the poles. But this difference could not provide a bird with a comparison of quantitatively different sensations over short intervals of time; and differential thresholds are known to reach low values only when successive comparisons can be made rapidly. Nevertheless a bird sensitive enough to changes in its own weight might theoretically determine absolute directions from its greater apparent weight when flying west, and it might also determine its latitude by the magnitude of the whole effect which is maximal at the equator and zero at the poles.

The validity of the theory must, however, be judged on quantitative considerations of comparative sensory physiology. We might imagine that in gliding flight a bird judges its weight from stimulation of the inner ear labyrinth or the stretch receptors in the muscles and tendons that hold the wings outspread. But the forces acting upon both types of mechanoceptors result not only from the bird's weight but also from its lift and drag. To be sure, the weight and lift are balanced when the bird is maintaining constant altitude; but to judge its weight in this fashion the air speed must be held constant within approximately 1 part of 2,000. Furthermore, any variations in the lift or drag of either wing must be equally small, otherwise stray mechanical forces would affect the kinaesthetic receptors in a way that could not be distinguished from the effects of gravity. Ordinarily the air is not nearly homogeneous enough to permit such a refined process; for the minor variations in velocity of air movement (felt in an airplane as "bumps") would almost certainly interfere with the process we are postulating.

The most relevant data on differential thresholds for judging forces and weights are the results of experiments on the human deep-pressure receptors; under the best conditions the just perceptible increase in weight is about 1 part in 100. Hence the hypothesis we are discussing would require us to postulate a differential sensitivity about twenty times greater than that displayed by human mechanoceptors at their best. Even this would barely permit a bird to detect the effect; still greater sensitivity would be needed to estimate variations in its intensity.

On the other hand, one is reminded of the sensitivity of hearing and the ability of the mammalian ear to discriminate sound waves having a pressure of roughly 10^{-9} atmospheres despite the simultaneous presence of much larger pressure variations of low frequency due to winds or other causes. The analogy is scarcely a valid one, however, for two reasons: (1) The differences in frequency between the sound waves and the pressure changes is of the utmost importance in allowing a mechanism to be developed that is sensitive to one and not the other. There is no reason to believe that the mechanical effects of the earth's rotation would fall in a different frequency range from the interfering mechanical effects under consideration. (2) The mammalian cochlea is an elaborately specialized mechanism tuned to frequencies that are ordinarily called sonic; there is no evidence that birds possess any comparable structure equally specialized for great sensitivity to mechanical stimuli derived from the earth's rotation.

Despite the convincing array of criticisms of Ising's theory that have been advanced, they are all somewhat indirect and remote from the actual problem he has posed. It must be admitted that we do not have direct evidence from which we can accurately estimate a bird's differential threshold for judging its own weight or detecting the other mechanical effects discussed above.

A second effect considered by Ising in some detail concerns fluids flowing through tubes and the apparent force acting upon such a fluid as a result of the tube's motion over the surface of the earth. This effect is best analyzed by considering a small parcel of the fluid as though it were flowing by itself, without reference to the remainder of the fluid or the tube. Ising points out that such a parcel is subjected to lateral acceleration (relative to the tube), of $2\Omega U\cos\emptyset$, the same expression given above for the change in the acceleration of gravity due to a bird's motion. For one gram of a fluid moving at the equator with a velocity of 40 m.p.h. this apparent lateral force is approximately 1/3800 grams.

Ising has mentioned the blood flowing in arteries, and it is known that rather sensitive pressure receptors are located in the carotid sinus of mammals and also in the walls of certain arteries (Bronk and Stella, 1932, 1935). One might suppose that such receptors could be stimulated by accelerations imparted to the flowing blood. But the interference of other mechanical forces is probably even more serious than in the case of a flying bird attempting to judge its own weight. For the blood is impelled by the intermittent beating of the heart, and these fluctuations of hydrostatic pressure exceed by many hundredfold the pressures that could possibly be generated by the effects of the earth's rotation.

Ising constructed a laboratory apparatus which barely succeeded in demonstrating the existence of such a lateral force acting upon fluid flowing through a tube. The apparatus consisted of glass tubing formed into a loop 25 cm. in diameter, together with flexible rubber tubing through which glycerin flowed into and out of the glass loops. This rubber tubing served also as an elastic suspension for the loops of glass tubing which, according to physical theory, should be caused to rotate about a vertical axis by the flowing glycerin. The dynamics of this apparatus are analogous to those of a galvanometer in which electric current flows through a coil of wire located in a magnetic field. Hence Ising called his apparatus a "hydraulic galvanometer," considering the earth's rotation to constitute a mechanical field of force corresponding to the magnetic field of a galvanometer. Only after the most careful construction of the apparatus was it possible to demonstrate any rotation of the glass tube, even though the linear rate of flow of the glycerin was about 30 cm/sec. The difficulty of barely demonstrating this effect, even under laboratory conditions, is an indication of its small magnitude compared to the irregular mechanical vibrations present under the ordinary conditions of life—to say nothing of those encountered by a flying bird.

The whole question of possible means by which a bird might perceive mechanical forces resulting from the earth's rotation can be looked at in still another way, and this will be considered here even though it is related more directly to the theory of Yeagley discussed below. The earth's rotation gives rise to what is usually known as the Coriolis force, or, sometimes, the Eötvös force. This is an *apparent* force which causes any object moving through air or water to describe a slightly curved path over the earth's surface, simply because the earth has moved a short distance while the object was in motion. This "force" is important in computing the trajectories of such diverse objects as artillery missiles, air masses, and floating icebergs.

For our purposes I believe it is best to consider the Coriolis effect simply as a change in direction with time; in the northern hemisphere a counterclockwise rotation when viewed from above, or a clockwise rotation in the southern hemisphere. A Foucault pendulum swings back and forth for many hours, suspended in such a way that it changes its apparent direction of linear motion as the earth rotates. In the same way, any object moving over the surface of the earth comes to change its apparent direction after a time, even though it is moving in a straight line relative to some point of observation outside the earth. An important consideration is that this change in direction depends not upon the velocity of motion but merely upon time and latitude. The effect will be observed, however, only if the motion of the object is independent of the motion of the earth to a very high degree; and few moving objects in our experience are sufficiently isolated from the earth for long enough periods of time to make the change in direction appreciable.

In the case of a flying bird, however, the irregularity and turbulence of the air must ordinarily prevent any continuous, linear motion having the degree of constancy required to detect the Coriolis effect. In very still air we might suppose that a bird sets itself into a straight glide for a long enough period of time so that, owing to the earth's rotation, the straight course becomes a slightly curved one. Or, we might suppose that the bird holds itself upon a straight course by visual means such as keeping two distant landmarks exactly in line, but is obliged to steer itself slightly to the left in order to do so. The Coriolis "force" reaches its maximum at the poles and is zero at the equator, because at the equator the centrifugal component is directed upward, producing the change in weight discussed above, while at the poles it acts in a horizontal direction. One might, therefore, suppose that by judging the magnitude of this effect a bird could determine its latitude.

Since the Coriolis effect and the change in apparent weight are but two aspects of the same phenomenon, we are faced with the same quantitative physiological question discussed above. The human threshold for detection of gentle rotary movement seems to be approximately one degree per second (Dodge, 1923; de Vries, 1950; and Egmond *et al.*, 1949). This is about 240 times larger than the change in direction of motion relative to the earth's surface resulting from the Coriolis effect; for even at the poles the latter is only 1/4 minute of arc per second. A lateral force of only 0.1 gram operating against a 300 gram bird flying 40 m.p.h. would produce a deflection greater than that resulting from the Coriolis effect. At air speeds of 40 m.p.h. it would take only very slight atmospheric disturbances or slight inequality in the lift or drag of the two wings to produce a lateral force of 0.1 gram.

Direct experiments testing a bird's ability to perceive the Coriolis force are well-nigh impossible to design, for the effect is always present and cannot be altered experimentally. An indirect approach would be possible by the use of an airplane or glider. If the aircraft were trimmed so precisely that in still air it would maintain a straight gliding course and a constant air speed, without the operation of the controls, then one might expect to observe the Coriolis effect by flying this aircraft at different latitudes and noting its tendency to turn. The required precision of trimming, however, is far greater than that achieved in practice, and the maintenance of a sufficiently constant air speed for this test would also be an extremely difficult problem. A bird or airplane flying 60 m.p.h. would suffer an apparent deflection of about 18 ft. per mile due to the Coriolis effect. Anyone with flying experience will realize the difficulty of maintaining a precise enough trim to achieve such a straight flight without use of the controls and also the rarity of flying conditions sufficiently free from atmospheric turbulence to permit such a flight even should the airplane be trimmed adequately.

In short, Ising's theory that bird navigation is based upon perception of mechanical forces stemming from the earth's rotation has the great advantage of postulating a type of mechanical sensitivity that is qualitatively present in virtually all animals. But the quantitative requirements of differential sensitivity exceed by roughly two hundredfold the capabilities of any known mechanical receptors. Absolute thresholds for a given type of stimulus seldom, if ever, vary this much from one type of animal to another unless one member of the pair has a specialized sense organ lacking in the other.

SENSITIVITY TO TERRESTRIAL MAGNETISM

Several theories of bird navigation have been based upon the assumption that birds possess some means of detecting the earth's magnetic field. These were reviewed earlier (Griffin, 1944) and it was concluded that no convincing experimental evidence had been advanced in their support. The long established use of the compass in human navigation has given a degree of attractiveness to these theories which seem to maintain their popularity despite the very great physiological difficulties involved. In recent years, the chief proponent of magnetic sensitivity has been Yeagley (1947, 1951), who has suggested a modification of the older theories involving the use by birds of both terrestrial magnetism and the Coriolis force. Yeagley's theory has received wide attention but it has been severely criticized by Thorpe (1949) and Wilkinson (1949), de Vries (1948), Kramer (1948), Slepian (1948), Davis (1948), Varian (1948), Henderson (1948) and Van Riper and Kalmbach (1952). Hence it may be helpful to review the entire discussion.

Most of the older theories of sensitivity to terrestrial magnetism encountered the following difficulty. Even though a bird were assumed to be equipped with a compass, one was obliged to ask how, when it was carried into unknown territory, it could know the direction of its home relative to magnetic north. To solve this dilemma, Viguier (1882) proposed that the bird's magnetic sense enabled it to judge both the intensity and the inclination (dip) of the earth's magnetic field. These two factors vary in somewhat different fashion over the surface of the earth so that in some areas the lines of equal magnetic intensity intersect at approximately right angles the lines of equal inclination. Viguier assumed that the bird oriented itself by means of a grid equivalent to the grid of longitude and latitude used by human navigators. Thus when displaced into unknown territory it would have merely to move in such a direction that its magnetic sensations would return to those characteristic of its home. Here again we see the tendency to reduce the behavior of the bird to very simple terms by endowing it with extremely sensitive receptors. Viguier's theory attracted little interest both because of the failure to demonstrate any kind of sensitivity to terrestrial magnetism, and because in many areas the lines of equal dip and intensity are nearly parallel rather than crossing at right angles.

Yeagley has suggested a new form of two-component magnetic theory; he has proposed that birds determine their latitude by means of Coriolis force (which was discussed in the previous section) and their longitude from the variation in strength of the *vertical* component of the earth's magnetic field. In the United States the lines of equal vertical intensity take roughly the form of arcs drawn about a center located at the north magnetic pole, while the lines of equal Coriolis force are, of course, the parallels of latitude. In the eastern and central part of the United States these two lines intersect at angles of 20 to 60 degrees.

Yeagley is the first to report positive results from experiments designed to show whether or not birds were affected by the earth's magnetic field. In his "first magnetic wing experiment" conducted in 1943 two groups of birds were released sixty-five miles from their home loft, one equipped with small magnets attached to the wings, the other bearing similar pieces of nonmagnetic metal. Yeagley has calculated that the magnets produced in the vicinity of the bird's head a fluctuating, artificial magnetic field of about the same intensity as the vertical component of the earth's field.

The birds without the magnets returned much more rapidly and in larger numbers than those bearing the magnets, so the experiment is impressive at first glance. But a second "magnetic wing experiment," performed in 1945, showed no significant difference between the performance of birds with magnets and those with control weights. This second experiment is not mentioned in the 1947 paper, and in the 1951 paper we are told that it was omitted because magnetic disturbances occurred on the day of the test. Gordon (1948), Matthews (1951), and Van Riper and Kalmbach (1952) have attempted to repeat this experiment; and in all three cases the results showed no difference in homing performance between birds equipped with magnets and the controls. In the original "magnetic wing experiment" there appears to have been some difference in the method of attachment of the magnets and the control copper weights, for several of the former had dropped off the birds before they returned to their loft, while all of the latter remained attached. In view of the several earlier experiments of this sort which have led to negative results, the negative results of these three attempts at confirmation, and the negative outcome of Yeagley's second experiment, it seems likely that the one positive case resulted from some extraneous factor, such as a difference in method of attachment with consequent difference in irritation or injury.

The bulk of the evidence presented by Yeagley consists of experiments in which pigeons trained in Pennsylvania were released in Nebraska and neighboring states where the theory predicted that they would find "conjugate points" at which Coriolis force and vertical magnetic intensity were the same as at the home loft. The lines of equal vertical intensity cross a given parallel of latitude at two points, and it seemed to Yeagley that birds trained to return to a home loft in Pennsylvania should, when released in Nebraska, fly towards the point where the Coriolis force and the vertical intensity of the earth's magnetic field were identical to those of the home location.

In the course of several years of extensive experiments, Yeagley has reported that birds released in many directions from the conjugate point in Nebraska, at distances ranging up to 185 miles, showed a significant tendency to fly in the direction of the conjugate point. Only a very few, however, actually reached the mobile pigeon loft which was placed near the conjugate point, despite the fact that in some cases at least the birds were given an opportunity to fly about in the vicinity of the position at which this mobile loft was set up. Most of the data on which Yeagley's conclusions are based consisted of recoveries at some third point; these recoveries were reported by letter or telegram in accordance with instructions attached to the pigeon's leg. There appears to have been some local publicity in the newspapers although an attempt was made to keep this at a minimum. Nevertheless, it seems likely that a pigeon was more likely to be reported if it stopped in the vicinity of the mobile loft than if it landed in other regions.

The significance of these results clearly depends upon the degree to which the net direction of the whole flight (the straight line from release point to recovery point) departs from the direction predicted by the theory. The data presented in the 1947 paper show an arithmetic average deviation of 64° between the flight lines and the bearing of the conjugate point. Purely random distribution, of course, would be expected to yield an average deviation of about 90°. We are thus faced with a statistical question: what is the probability of significance of the observed deviations? Unfortunately, however, the situation does not lend itself to simple analysis. The higher probability that recoveries would be reported from the region surrounding the conjugate point has already been mentioned. In addition there is the factor of human population density. Most of the releases were to the east of the conjugate point, and the population density decreases considerably to the west of this point. Hence, there would be a certain tendency for the birds which did fly far to the west to land where they would not be found. These factors cannot be accurately evaluated; but an only slightly higher probability of recovery from the area near the "conjugate point" could easily have produced the observed results. In the section (p. 170) entitled "A Theoretical Analysis of Exploration", it is also shown how a typical case can be accounted for by simple radial scattering.

In other experiments birds were released at great distances from the conjugate point, mostly to the east. In some cases the outcome of these experiments seemed consistent with the theory; in other cases the opposite was true. Most recently Yeagley has followed pigeons from an airplane after they were released in Nebraska eighty miles east of the postulated "conjugate point." Eight of the ten birds that were followed over significant distances (forty to seventy-five miles) flew between northwest and west-northwest, while only two long flights took a wholly different direction. One additional bird was released northeast from the "conjugate point," and it also flew to the northwest. It is thus impossible to conclude from these airplane observations whether some factor was causing the birds to fly in a northwesterly direction, or whether they were indeed tending to fly toward the conjugate point. It is to be regretted that the release points were not located in several directions from the hypothetical goal of the flight; only then could one judge whether the results show a directional tendency or a tendency to seek a certain goal.

On the theoretical level, Yeagley has proposed that the sensitivity to terrestrial magnetism is based not upon any mechanical forces developed in a bird at rest, but rather upon the induced electrical voltage generated between different portions of its anatomy while it is in flight through the earth's magnetic field. These induced voltages are admittedly very small. Yeagley gives 10^{-5} volts/cm as the gradient induced in a bird flying 40 m.p.h. at the magnetic latitude of Pennsylvania. This should be compared with resting potentials of several millivolts over distances of a few microns between the inside and outside of nerve cells (gradients of at least 100 volts/cm). Several physicists have criticized Yeagley's proposed basis for bird navigation on the grounds that (1) electrostatic charges accumulating on the bird due to its flight through the air would be enormously greater than 10^{-5} volts/cm, or (2) that while voltages would indeed be induced, no closed circuit is present through which they could cause any current to flow, since all portions of the bird's tissue are simultaneously exposed to the same electrical gradient (de Vries, 1948; Slepian, 1948; Davis, 1948; and Varian, 1948).

Thorough, detailed, and searching criticisms of Yeagley's paper have also been published by Thorpe (1949), Wilkinson (1949), Kramer (1948) and de Vries (1948). The difficulties of achieving sensitivity to the Coriolis forces have been discussed in the previous section; and concerning the sensitivity to terrestrial magnetism I can only add that both before and after Yeagley's statement of his theory I have attempted to carry out conditioning experiments in which birds would be trained to respond to magnetic stimuli many times stronger than those available from the earth's field. These attempts have all yielded negative results, even when the possibility of induced electrical voltages was studied by placing the bird inside a large coil which oscillated back and forth with a sufficient speed so that the product of linear velocity and magnetic field strength considerably exceeded that encountered by a bird flying through the earth's field. Even Yeagley has reported (personal communication) that experiments of this kind in his laboratory have failed to produce positive results. Orgel and Smith (1954) have reported still another negative outcome of an attempt to elicit responses to a magnetic field.

Responses of birds to pulsed, high-frequency radio waves (from radar transmitters) have been observed both in the United States and in Europe (Drost, 1949), and these observations are cited by Yeagley as "rapidly increasing evidence" for theories of bird navigation based on electromagnetic phenomena. As Schwartzkoff (1950) has pointed out, however, the density of the energy flux in a pulsed radar beam is probably sufficient to exceed known thresholds for biological effects of electromagnetic radiation; and (Kramer, 1951b), has reported that unpulsed, continuous microwaves did not stimulate birds. One such effect, described by Barlow, Kohn, and Walsh (1947a, b) is the production of visual sensations when the human eye is stimulated either by weak alternating currents (0.2 milliamperes at 60 c.p.s.) or by the electric current induced by an alternating magnetic field of 500 gauss at 60 c.p.s. This magnetic field strength is approximately one thousand times that of the earth's field. In fact both the radar beams and the artificial magnetic fields employed by Barlow *et al.* greatly exceed any known intensity of terrestrial magnetism or its electrical by-products. On quantitative grounds it thus appears most unsound to erect theories of bird navigation based upon these observed responses of birds or men to intense electromagnetic stimuli.

We thus find after a rather detailed consideration of this new version of an old theory that none of the supporting evidence is at all satisfying on close examination. Nevertheless, the theory has achieved wide attention, and even though it seems to be wide of the mark it may prove to have stimulated many inquiries and investigations that otherwise might never have been undertaken.

INFRARED VISION

A suggestion made by Duchâtel (1901, 1902) that the visual spectrum of birds extends into the infrared has been revived recently by Wojtusiak (1946, 1949) at the University of Cracow, in a rather more extreme form than the original views (as cited by Claparède, 1903). Wojtusiak has written as follows (1946): "During the autumn migrations the birds would be guided towards warmer regions having a stronger radiation and thus appearing brighter, . . . being sensitive to infra-red rays, the birds would be able to see through the fog . . . . The birds would see not only by day but also during the night, as every body emitting radiation would be bright for them. . . . The present hypothesis opens the problem of sensibility to long wave radiation in animals. The author is carrying out experiments in order to prove its correctness." (Direct quotation, not a translation.)

This is the most extreme of the "something more" theories, and it illustrates the lengths to which it is possible to go in postulating a sensory mechanism of such fantastic scope that a migrating bird could perform its annual journeys through the simplest sort of behavior patterns. It is as though the shade of Jacques Loeb were disposing of migration as a simple "tropism" by endowing the birds with such keen receptors that their migrations become movements along an easily perceived gradient.

The only experiment on record that indicates sensitivity to infrared radiations in birds is that of Vanderplank (1934), who reported that owls responded to the radiations of very long wave lengths given off by other warm-blooded animals. This theory demands a truly impossible sort of physical detecting system capable of responding to thermal radiation between two bodies at nearly the same temperature. It is not surprising that Matthews and Matthews (1939) were unable to duplicate the results. Experiments performed many years ago by Watson and Lashley (1915) and Lashley (1916), and also more recently by Hecht and Pirenne (1940), have provided strong evidence that the visible spectrum of birds is approximately the same as that of the human eye. The threshold of the human eye has been measured as far into the infrared as 950 mμ without revealing anything but a steeply falling sensitivity (Griffin, Hubbard, and Wald, 1947). In short, theories of bird navigation based upon sensitivity to thermal radiations from bodies of low tempearture scarcely deserve serious consideration.

The fallacies of this theory of bird navigation are discussed here in the hope of discouraging such ill-conceived speculations in the future. A clear example of the results of theorizing without proper regard for quantitative considerations of sensory physiology may also be found in a proposal contained in recent papers by Beecher (1951, 1952) that "a new motion sense based on the inertia of air in the tympanic cavity apparently reports thrusting movements of the head." Air with its density of roughly 0.001 gram/cm^3 certainly seems an unpromising material from which to form a receptor designed to respond to movements of the head; the otoliths of the vertebrate labyrinth *do* have this function and have a density greater than 2. Recent reviews of the physiology of the vertebrate labyrinth have been presented by Lowenstein (1950) and Wendt (1951).

RECENT EVIDENCE FAVORING THEORIES OF NAVIGATION BASED UPON VISION

The older methods of investigating bird navigation have been supplemented during the period under review by several new techniques; but in most cases the new methods have only begun to be employed so that their ultimate contribution cannot yet be judged. For example, radar can detect flying birds at a distance (Lack and Varley, 1945), and attempts have been made to study migratory flights by this means; but no new information about orientation has yet resulted. Radioactive tagging of birds used in homing experiments has permitted automatic recording of the time of return instead of the usual, tedious visual watch by a human observer (Griffin, 1952a). Wilkinson (1950) has recently reported the development for use in homing experiments of a simple and effective device to record the fraction of the elapsed time which a bird spends in flight. Lowery (1951) has greatly refined the methods of studying nocturnal migration by observing birds against the moon. Finally the light airplane has been utilized to observe and follow individual birds during homing flights (Griffin and Hock, 1949; Yeagley, 1951; and Hitchcock, 1952).

Matthews (1952a) has reported the results of extensive homing experiments with two species of gulls, the Lesser Black-backed Gull, *Larus fuscus,* a migratory species, and the Herring Gull, *L. argentatus,* described as a restricted nomad. The migratory species showed a superior homing performance; and a few individuals seemed to head in the correct direction soon after release, although both species appeared in general to be homing "by an inefficient method, probably random exploration for known visual landmarks." Once again it was found that attaching magnets did not affect the homing ability, but that cloudy weather caused some worsening of the homing performance.

In reviewing the evidence that had accumulated up to 1941 I was led to assign a greater importance than had previously been customary to the possibility that both wild birds and homing pigeons might accomplish at least a part of their homing flights over unfamiliar territory by a process of exploration. The speeds and percentages of return in the more extensive homing experiments could be interpreted on this basis, although in all cases there were many uncertainties such as the proportion of the birds' time spent in actual cross-country flight as opposed to resting, feeding, or local flying. It was clearly desirable to know more about the actual routes flown in homing flights, and a limited attempt had been made to follow Herring Gulls from hilltops and airplanes. In 1947, however, it was possible to extend this sort of observation to much longer flights by employing Gannets, *Morus bassanus,* which are strictly marine birds so that inland territory was quite certainly unfamiliar to them (Griffin and Hock, 1949). The birds were caught at nests on an island in the Gulf of St. Lawrence and released at Caribou, Maine, approximately 100 miles from salt water in three directions—from the St. Lawrence estuary to the northwest, from an arm of the Gulf of St. Lawrence to the northeast, and from the Bay of Fundy to the southeast. Gannets are sufficiently large and conspicuous to be followed from the air with relative ease, and they proved suitable for such experiments in many other ways. Although they had difficulty taking off from land and were usually released on small bodies of fresh water where they could take off against a head wind, once in the air they continued active flights for many hours at a time without stopping to rest or feed.

Nine Gannets released at Caribou were followed for distances of 25 to 230 miles. The time which elapsed during the airplane observation of these flights ranged from 1 to 9½ hours. As shown in Figure 1, the flight paths of these nine Gannets radiated in diverse directions from the release point. In addition to birds followed from the air, nine others were released under the same conditions without any attempts at airplane following. Neglecting two birds that were weaker than the others at the time of release, the homing performance of this control group (62.5 per cent returns, average speed 81 miles/day) was not significantly different from that of the nine birds followed by airplane (62.5 per cent returns, average speed 116 miles/day). Hence it seemed unlikely that the presence of the airplane was in itself a serious disturbing factor. This danger was further reduced by flying as far as possible above the bird without losing sight of it; in practice this meant a distance of 1,500–2,000 feet. On other occasions when we flew much closer to gannets they did not seem to react to the airplane until it came within 100 feet.

A study of Figure 1 shows that many of the flight paths had a tendency to curve gradually in one direction or the other. It is possible that this curvature represents a form of spiral exploration of the sort postulated earlier. One can determine the equiangular spiral which gives approximately the best fit to the various flight paths. For instance, Gannet No. 378 flew along a course described roughly by the equation $D = 0.26\ \varnothing$, where D stands for the distance from the release point in miles, and $\varnothing$ equals the angle of rotation of the spiral in degrees. If this spiral is extrapolated, it reaches the coast after about 635 miles of flight. This Gannet actually required seventy-five hours for the return trip to its nest, and even if we allow for an indirect flight home after it reached the coast, there was still ample time for such spiral exploration. Many other exploratory search patterns could also have accounted for the observed performance of these Gannets.

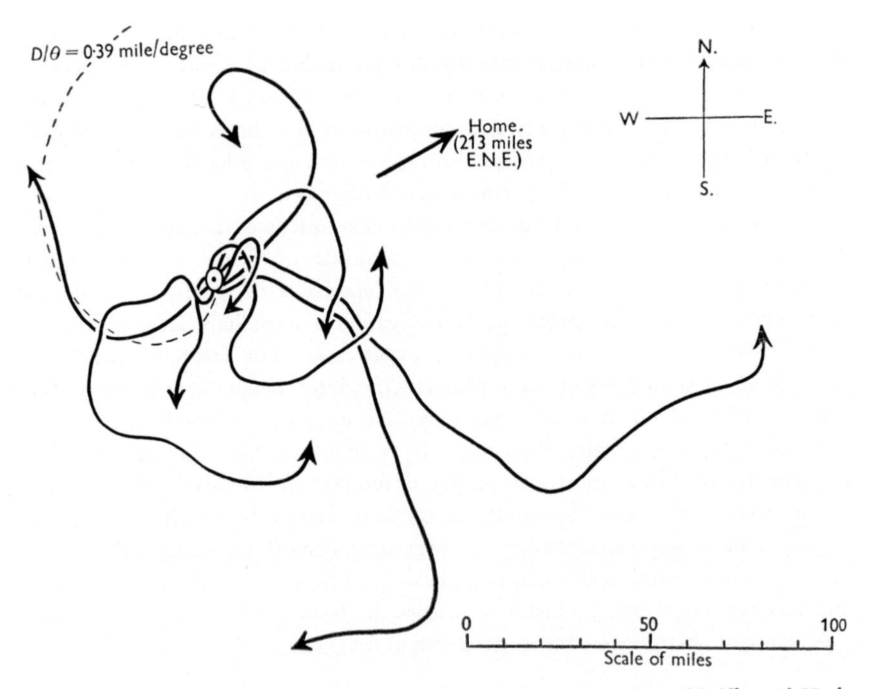

Fig. 1. Flight paths of homing Gannets observed from an airplane (Griffin and Hock, 1949). Small scale turnings and circling during soaring flights have been omitted; but in no case does the flight path indicated in this figure depart by more than three miles from the bird's actual position. The dotted line shows an equiangular spiral that is approximated by one of the flight paths.

Would any point on the coast line of Maine, Nova Scotia, or New Brunswick have been familiar territory for these Gannets? In the upper Bay of Fundy Gannets are seldom seen; but they are often observed along most other parts of the coast, so if they relied upon spiral exploration, they would have had a good chance of reaching a familiar part of the coastline in a reasonably short time. It would probably be necessary for familiar landmarks to be located only at intervals of some miles along the coast, for the Gannet's air speed is about 35 m.p.h., and a very few hours of further exploration up and down the coast would not add greatly to the total time required to return to the nest.

The question of visual memory has also caused some reluctance to accept an explanation of homing based upon exploration for familiar territory. In this connection, it is significant to cite an experiment reported by Skinner (1950). Four domestic pigeons were trained to respond to an airplane photograph of a certain area of ground and were tested at intervals for retention of the visual memory. They indicated recognition of the pattern by pecking at a particular point on the photographic image in order to obtain food; pecking at any other point was unrewarded. Even four years after they had last seen this pattern, the pigeons responded to it quickly by pecking at the point in the picture to which they had been trained. This confirms the general experience of biologists and psychologists that birds have a very well-developed mechanism for visual perception; so it is not difficult to believe that they can retain memories of specific visual landmarks.

The Gannet was selected for the experiment discussed above primarily because of ease of observation and the availability of dense colonies suitable for homing experiments. It is not an ideal species with regard to its normal migratory habits and the problems of navigation it must have learned to overcome in the course of such migratory experience. For Gannets spend their entire lives in coastal waters and while their winter range extends many hundreds of miles south of nesting grounds, this migration might be based upon a visual following of the coastline. It is thus possible that the ability to navigate by nonvisual means is poorly developed in Gannets and that other species should be studied by similar methods to determine whether they would display a more impressive ability to cover long distances without either visual landmarks or exploration. Such cases have recently been reported by Matthews and Kramer; but it will be better to discuss the results in the following section, together with Matthews' theory of celestial navigation.

A THEORETICAL ANALYSIS OF EXPLORATION

Introduction

In view of the degree to which actual flight paths of Gannets conformed with the patterns predicted by the hypothesis of spiral exploration, it seems appropriate to examine the effectiveness of various flight patterns by which a bird might search more or less systematically for a particular goal. Even though the general direction of flight may be determined on some other basis, exploration may be used to locate the actual goal of the journey. In a homing flight the ultimate goal would be the bird's nest; but since we have reason to believe that each bird has a familiar territory within which its orientation can be rapid and accurate, we may consider the goal to be the whole extent of this familiar territory. The concept of goal *area* will also permit the same discussion to cover natural migrations where the goal is usually not a specific point but a fairly extensive region. In the case of fall migration, the goal area may be the whole wintering range of the bird population in question. The following sections will show the homing performance that can be expected if a bird employs various types of exploratory flight pattern. Several simplifying assumptions will be made in deriving these equations, for they will be rough approximations at best and it seems preferable to maintain a simplicity that will permit their ready application to any consideration of homing and migratory flights, rather than to achieve mathematical rigor by developing precise but cumbersome expressions.

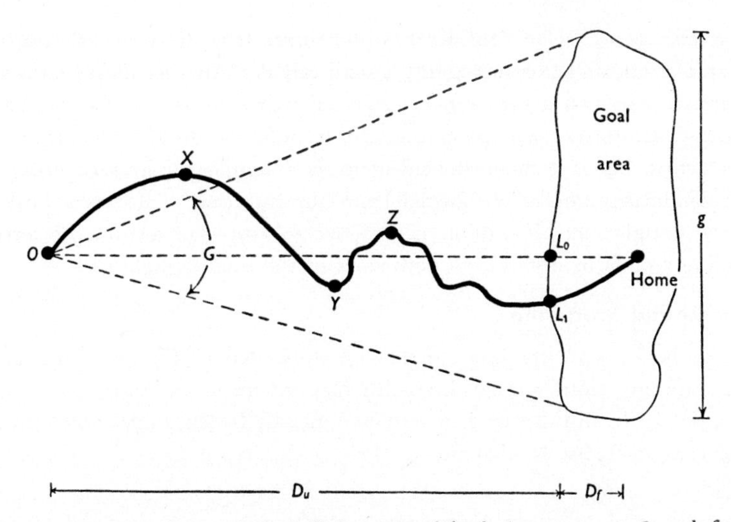

Fig. 2. Generalized hypothetical flight path of bird that starts at *O* and finds its way to a goal area; in a homing experiment this would be the familiar territory, or in natural migrations the goal area may be the range within which the individual bird will spend the next season.

Let us consider first of all the generalized situation, illustrated in Figure 2, where the bird's starting point is designated *O,* and it flies along the irregular path *OXYZ,* which eventually reaches the goal area at L_1. This irregular flight path will be longer than the straight line OL_0, connecting the starting point to the closest point within the goal area. The direct line OL_0 can be called D_u, and the shortest course home from L_0 through familiar territory will be called D_f. Using the symbol *F* to denote the actual length of flight path $OXYZL_1$, we can find a rough measure of the efficiency of the exploration process in the ratio F/D_u. If this ratio were 1, the bird's navigation would be perfect, and higher values of the ratio tell us how many times the straight line distance the bird has been obliged to fly. In order to simplify the analysis, it seems reasonable to neglect the difference between OL_0 and OL_1 and to assume that *g,* the width of the goal area, extends perpendicular to OL_0. I shall assume also that angle *G* when measured in radians equals g/D_u, an approximation which is quite accurate for small angles and introduces serious errors only when angle *G* is so large that exploration of any kind has a high probability of success.

In assuming any geometrical pattern as a hypothetical flight path we may be sure that *F,* the actual route flown by the bird, will be irregular and longer than *S,* the length of a mathematical curve that may approximately describe the bird's course. The ratio F/S defines the closeness with which the bird's route approximated the hypothetical flight pattern. When Gannets were flying courses suggestive of spiral exploration, the value of F/S seemed to lie between 1.2 and 1.4.

It is also necessary to consider the probability that the bird will reach the goal area at all; and this probability I shall call P_g. Another useful term is the distance, r, at which a bird can be expected to recognize familiar landmarks. Obviously, landmarks will be recognized at different distances depending on many factors, but it is most convenient to let r signify the average distance at which landmarks can be recognized from any direction. Thus, as a bird flies along a straight line, it will in general be able to scan a band of territory extending r units of distance on both sides of the line of flight.

Linear Radial Scattering

Let us begin with the very simple case illustrated in Figure 3, homing by radial scattering along straight lines that may extend in any direction from the release point. P_g in this case is determined directly by the angle subtended at O by the goal area plus $2r$, that is,

$$P_g = \frac{G + \frac{2r}{D_u}}{2\pi} \qquad (1)$$

or, using the approximation that $G = g/D_u$,

$$P_g = \frac{G + 2r}{2\pi D_u} \qquad (2)$$

The length of the flight pattern, S, will vary rather little as the direction of flight turns away from OL_0. Among the cases of successful homing, S/D_u will have a maximum value of $\frac{1}{\cos\left(1/2\,G + \frac{r}{D_u}\right)}$ so that the average value of S/D_u for all successful cases of homing will not greatly exceed 1. This is the basis for the statement that homing by radial scattering results in almost as rapid returns as though the birds knew the correct direction in which to fly.

As an example of the application of this simple concept of radial scattering, let us consider a hypothetical case in which homing pigeons are trained to fly to a mobile loft. Suppose that the mobile loft is transported into unfamiliar territory and that the pigeons are released for a few hours of flight around the new location so that they become familiar with a circular area 8 miles in radius or 16 miles in diameter. They are then carried to a distance of 70 miles, in closed boxes, and released. If they exhibit simple radial scattering, and if $r = 2$ miles, $P_g = \frac{16 + 4}{(2\pi)(62)}$. In other words, we would expect that approximately one pigeon in twenty would reach the goal area.

An experiment very similar to this has actually been reported by Yeagley (1947, release no. 5). Seventeen pigeons were trained to a mobile loft, which was then transported into unfamiliar territory. The birds were allowed a few short flights in the vicinity of the new location of the mobile loft and were then released at 70 miles. Of the seventeen birds released, one returned to the loft. We cannot conclude that these pigeons relied solely upon simple radial scattering, and certain other groups of Yeagley's pigeons performed

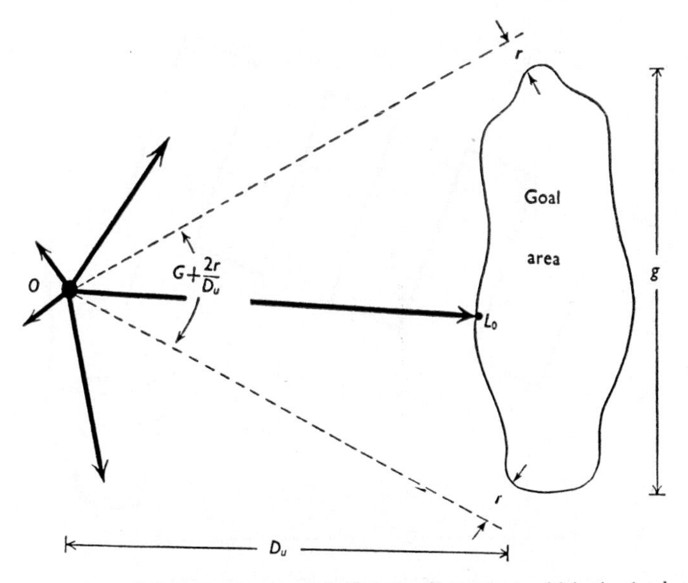

Fig. 3. Linear radial scattering; r stands for the distance at which the landmarks can be recognized.

better, although in most cases there were no returns at all. But when the actual fraction of returns agrees so closely with the calculated values of P_g, one certainly cannot exclude the possibility that homing was accomplished by methods no more refined than the simple type of radial scattering described above. Claparède (1903) clearly expressed this concept of radial scattering, and yet even today its relevance to many types of homing is not generally appreciated.

Rectangular Search Pattern

It is clear that a bird's probability of reaching a goal area would be considerably increased if flight along a straight line were replaced by some search pattern which enabled it to scan a band of territory having a width greater than $2r$. Many types of search pattern could be postulated, but two of the simplest are discussed in this and the following section because they are reasonably economical of the bird's time and effort and because they can be described by simple equations. In the first type the bird is assumed to fly along the pattern illustrated in Figure 4, scanning an area whose width is approximately $b+2r$. Such a pattern clearly improves a bird's chance of success, and provided that g is large compared to a and b, we may write

$$P_g = \frac{G + 2b + 2r}{2\pi D_u}. \qquad (3)$$

The length of the flight path, S, will be given approximately by

$$S = (a + b)\,\frac{D_u}{a}. \qquad (4)$$

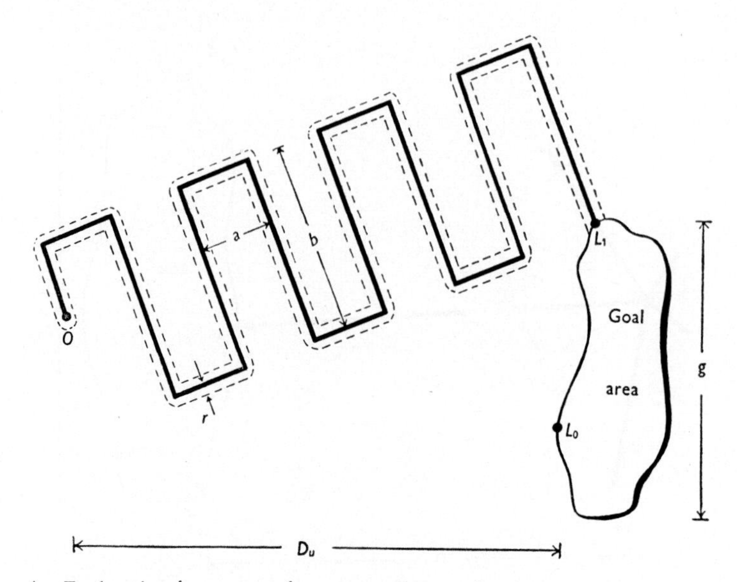

Fig. 4. Exploration by means of a rectangular search pattern.

It is helpful for many purposes to consider the ratio S/D_u, for this is the factor by which the bird's flight path is increased over the direct course, due to its exploratory searching. In a rectangular search pattern we may obtain this ratio directly from (4) and write

$$\frac{S}{D_u} = \frac{a+b}{a}. \quad (5)$$

Minor deviations from (4) and (5) will result if the zigzag flight path does not start and end at the points on the pattern shown in Figure 4; but such deviation will never be large and will be quite negligible whenever there are several legs to the pattern.

One special case of the rectangular search pattern occurs when $a = 2r$ so that the bird completely scans a band of territory whose width is $b+2r$. Such a pattern would result if on each leg of the path the bird kept just barely in view the territory seen on the previous leg. Under these circumstances,

$$\frac{S}{D_u} = 1 + \frac{b}{2r}. \quad (6)$$

Clearly the most economical search patterns of this type will be those in which a is roughly equal to the width of the familiar territory.

Expanding Search Pattern

Another interesting type of search pattern is illustrated diagrammatically in Figure 5. It differs from the rectangular type in that the territory scanned is an isosceles triangle with its apex at O. Again, I have assumed that the lateral legs of the pattern would be parallel. If we let e stand for the angle formed

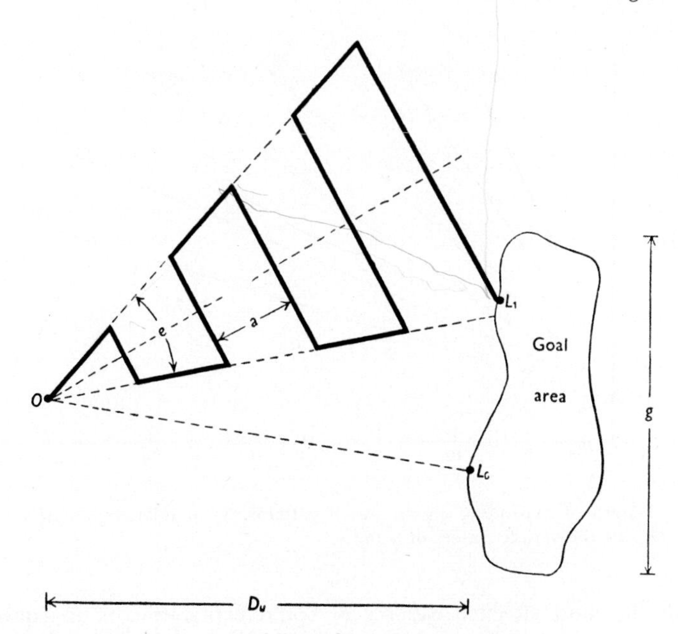

Fig. 5. Exploration by means of expanding zigzag search pattern.

at O by the sides of this triangle, S can be expressed in terms of e, a, and D_u. On the basis of the same assumptions which have been made above, we may write the following approximations:

$$S = \frac{D_u}{\cos \frac{1}{2}e} + D_u \tan \tfrac{1}{2}e \left(\frac{D_u}{a} + 1 \right) \tag{7}$$

$$\frac{S}{D_u} = \frac{1}{\cos \frac{1}{2}e} + \tan \tfrac{1}{2}e \left(\frac{D_u}{a} + 1 \right). \tag{8}$$

The probability of success in such an expanding, zigzag pattern is obviously given by the ratio of $2e + g$ to the arc of a complete circle, so that

$$P_g = \frac{e}{\pi} + \frac{g}{2\pi D_u}. \tag{9}$$

Figure 6 shows the approximate numerical values for S/D_u in expanding zigzag patterns of exploration such as that illustrated in Figure 5. Over a considerable range of values for e and a, S/D_u remains reasonably small.

Spiral Exploration

The previous sections have dealt with flight patterns having a linear axis; but it is clear that such exploration can never achieve a value of P_g approaching one, while a spiral path such as that illustrated in Figure 7 can virtually be certain of ultimate success. Since the homing experiments carried out with some species of birds such as Herring Gulls have yielded 70 to 95 per cent returns, and since the flight paths of Gannets suggested spiraling, this sort of exploration must also be considered.

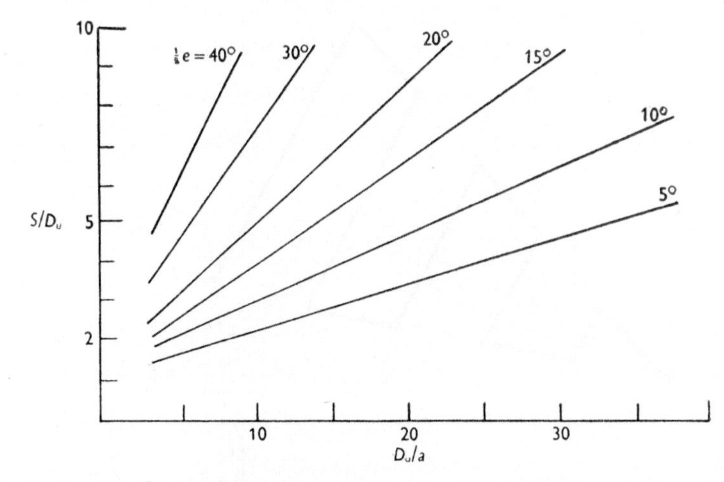

Fig. 6. Length of expanding zigzag search patterns, S, in relation to direct course to goal area, D_u, for the various values of a and e.

One of the most effective patterns of spiral exploration is an equiangular spiral of the type $D = k\theta$, where D is the radial distance from the release point and θ is the angle through which the spiral has rotated. If we let a equal the distance between loops of such a spiral, $a = 2\pi k$. If we assume that no point of terrain is overlooked by the searching bird, $a = 2r$. Such a spiral, however, results in an extremely long flight path, and in reality the bird will be searching not for a point but for a goal area. The exploratory flight would be greatly shortened by increasing a to a distance comparable to the width of

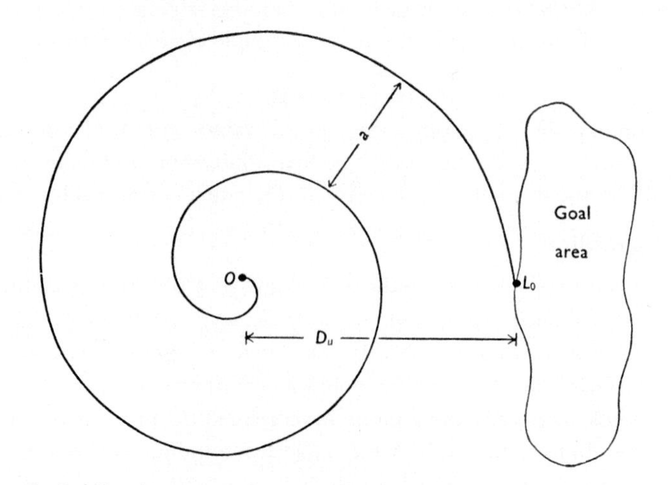

Fig. 7. Exploration by means of an equiangular spiral.

the goal area. The actual flight paths of Gannets do suggest spirals with a large value of a. Having raised this possibility we must admit that its navigational basis is not at all clear. But even at the risk of raising new problems in the course of a hypothetical solution of old ones it seems worthwhile to consider the mathematical relationships involved in such spiraling.

It is most convenient to express both the length of the spiral, S, and the radial distance from the release point, D, in units of k miles, so that the equation of the spiral becomes simply,

$$D = \theta. \tag{10}$$

The value of S is then given precisely by

$$S = \frac{1}{2}\left[D\sqrt{D^2+1} + \log_e\left(D + \sqrt{D^2+1}\right)\right]. \tag{11}$$

But this expression can be simplified without serious error provided the spiral contains more than one turn, for then the second term of the radical and the log term both become negligible, so that (11) can be replaced by

$$S = \frac{D^2}{2} \text{ or } \frac{S}{D} = \frac{D}{2}. \tag{12}$$

This simplification will produce a maximum error of 7 per cent if $\theta = 2\pi$. Recalling that S and D were both expressed in units of k miles, we may now return to any convenient unit of distance, and substitute $\frac{a}{2\pi}$ for k. This gives us the simple and useful approximation,

$$\frac{S}{D_u} = \pi \frac{D_u}{a}. \tag{13}$$

Although valid only for spirals containing more than one turn, (13) is a useful index of the effectiveness of spiral exploration in cases such as the flights of Gannets described above.

For the Gannets released at Caribou, D_u may be taken as roughly 150 miles. In the flight path most closely approximately a spiral (no. 378) a appears to be about 94 miles; or, according to (13) S/D_u would equal 5. In experiments described below, homing pigeons have been followed by air over an entire flight from release point to the home loft, and F/D_u, the ratio of actual flight distance to the direct course, was sometimes as large as 3. Hence spiral exploratory flights involving two to five turns do not seem impossible with wild birds released in unknown territory. The chief problem in such cases is to explain the basis upon which the bird could navigate along curvatures of such large radius. Perhaps this is accomplished with reference to the sun, for the recent investigations of Matthews and Kramer show that the sun can be used by birds for reasonably accurate orientation.

Discussion

These theoretical considerations can be applied not only to homing experiments but to certain types of natural migrations. If we postulate that a bird flying over relatively trackless areas of land or water has some approximate means of setting its course, plus or minus several degrees, we might well find that even a small goal area could readily be located by some variant of the search patterns described above. An appreciation of these quantitative possibilities of various patterns of exploration may help to clarify our thinking about the cases where birds migrate to small oceanic islands, such as the migration of the Bronze Cuckoos, *Chalcites lucidus,* between New Zealand and the Solomon Islands. In this case the goal area may be considered to subtend an angle lying between twenty and forty degrees at the starting point of the migration in New Zealand. Assuming the expanding zigzag type of exploration discussed above we might assign a value of 20 to the ratio D_u/a, and a value of 30 degrees to the angle G. If we then postulate that angle e of Figure 5 has a value of 20 degrees (which would give a value of S/D_u close to 5), the birds could be assured of reaching the goal area provided they had some navigational system capable of pointing their expanding search pattern within 25 degrees of the direct course to the center of the goal area—that is, capable of confining their exploration to a sector of 50 degrees or slightly less than one-seventh of the entire compass rose.

In this section we have clearly been dealing with gross oversimplifications of any real routes which birds might be expected to fly under natural conditions. Minor irregularities of the flight path can be taken into account by thinking in terms of F, rather than S, and estimating the ratio F/S from cases where actual following by airplane has given some indication of its value for a particular species. But from any realistic point of view it must be recognized that the actual routes flown are unlikely to conform in more than the most general fashion to the patterns illustrated in Figures 3 to 7. If we find, for example, that the quantitative results of homing experiments with a particular species can be explained on the basis of one of these idealized patterns, this does not prove that the birds followed this pattern rather than one of a number of others that would also serve to bring them to familiar territory within the time available.

In fact, Wilkinson (1952) has demonstrated that the results of the homing experiments with Gannets, as well as most of those with other wild birds, can be explained by postulating a purely random search in which each bird is assumed to fly in approximately a straight line for a certain distance, then turn through any angle at all, and continue this process until familiar territory is reached. If the mean length of the legs of such a random search is assumed to be of the order of 20 to 100 miles, the quantitative results as well as the routes observed from airplanes can be accounted for. But these many possibilities of accounting for the quantitative homing performance of wild birds by various types of exploration should not be allowed to distort one's perspective, for the entire phenomenon of bird navigation cannot be explained away in any such fashion, as I shall attempt to make clear in the following sections.

RECENT STUDIES OF HOMING PIGEONS

The problem of navigation by homing pigeons has received considerable attention during the past ten years. Yeagley's theory was advanced primarily to explain the homing of pigeons, and only incidentally for application to wild birds. While the homing of trained racing pigeons is different in many ways from the migration or homing of wild birds, there is every reason to believe that similar sensory mechanisms of orientation are probably involved in both cases. Some of the recent evidence concerning homing pigeons points definitely in the direction of the "nothing but" type of theory. Nicol (1945) has reported cases in which pigeons were led seriously astray in the absence of visual landmarks upon which they had apparently become dependent. Heinroth and Heinroth (1941) and Platt and Dare (1945) have reported additional cases in which pigeons showed a great deterioration in homing performance when released in unfamiliar territory. Heinroth and Heinroth have aptly summarized their results, and those of many previous investigators, in the following words: "Never did a pigeon find its way home if it was released 100 kilometers or more from its loft without previous experience; even birds trained by several short flights (up to 30 km) did not return from great distances." But more recent evidence, to be discussed below, indicates that in these cases the birds were not of the best stock, or were not properly trained in the sense that motivation or physical stamina for long flights was inadequate.

There have been three separate studies of homing pigeons by direct tracing of the routes flown by means of small airplanes. Yeagley's evidence from this source has been discussed above. I maintained a small colony of racing pigeons southeast of Cayuga Lake near Ithaca, N.Y., during 1946 and 1947, and these birds were trained in a manner designed to provide evidence concerning the amount of wandering which they had done before the longer homing flights (Griffin, 1952b). They were not released earlier in the afternoon than two to three hours before sunset, and their return to the loft was checked sufficiently often to establish whether they had returned before the end of the day or whether they had remained out overnight. In most of the releases at more than twenty miles, they were followed by airplane, and in the principal experiments airplane observations were made after each successive release at increasing distances.

When pigeons four to five months old were carried to gradually increasing distances up to seventeen miles, their homing flights proved to be reasonably direct. Four such birds were next carried twenty-four miles in the opposite direction to a release point in unknown territory. This twenty-four-mile release point was on the shore of Seneca Lake, another of the Finger Lakes which is very similar in geological formation and topography to Cayuga Lake, near the southern end of which lay the territory familiar to these pigeons. Furthermore, this release point in unknown territory was located at a point on Seneca

Lake corresponding to a release point on Cayuga Lake from which the pigeons had returned rapidly on several previous occasions. The purpose of the experiment was to determine whether the similarities of topography would lead these pigeons astray. Would they fly south, as they had when released eight miles from home at the southeast corner of Cayuga Lake?

The outcome of this experiment was that the birds did start south—the direction which one would expect if they had indeed been misled by the topography. They continued south for two and one-fourth miles and then turned through 90°, traced a rough circle back to the release point, and then once again headed toward the south. On the second occasion, they flew three miles south before turning. After this, they flew in several other directions and when last seen from the air were heading northeast. Three of these four birds failed to reach home at all. The fourth required almost five hours for the return flight; but when it was again carried to the south end of Seneca Lake a few days later, it reached home in forty-five minutes. Such an increase in homing speed on a second trip to the same release point has been reported for Herring Gulls (Griffin, 1943) and also for swallows (Wojtusiak, 1949). It is an easily understandable effect if we assume that the first return flight from unknown territory succeeds only after exploratory flights, and that the birds profit from such experience and use the memory of their first trip in orienting themselves for a more direct flight home after the second release.

It should be stressed, however, that the experiment described above employed pigeons less than a year old. The same sort of experiment was attempted the following year, but not with the same release point because by that time the available pigeons had flown over a wider area and the southern end of Seneca Lake might have been familiar territory. Instead, a flock of twelve pigeons was carried northwest from Ithaca, along a line that lay close to the west shore of Cayuga Lake. Each successive release point was only three to five miles beyond the previous one; and on each occasion the birds were followed from the air. Up to and including the release at twenty-five miles they were set free within a mile or two of Cayuga Lake, and after several minutes of preliminary circling they flew directly to the lake, turned right (south) and flew home along its shore. The next release was at thirty-two miles, and the birds were now released for the first time close to the east shore of Seneca Lake which was in plain view from treetop altitude at this release point. After the usual preliminary circling these birds flew directly to the shore of Seneca Lake, and two birds did turn right shortly afterwards, flying north and away from home. Neither found its way back to the loft, but one was picked up twenty-eight miles north-northwest from the release point. There is thus reason to believe that these two birds were indeed misled by the topographical similarity to previous release points.

The remaining birds of the flock were not so easily confused and flew a surprisingly direct course home over what was probably unfamiliar territory.

In subsequent releases the surviving birds of the flock were carried 28, 43, 55, 72, and 100 miles northwest, and in most cases the distance between release points was great enough, in view of the airplane observations of the previous flights, to make it reasonably certain that for the first few miles at least the pigeons were in unfamiliar territory. These birds suffered heavy losses, and by the time the 100-mile point was reached only two remained; but the airplane observations showed that in several cases the initial direction of the homing flights was too close to the correct bearing of the home loft to be explained by chance scattering or exploration.

These releases were all made in the afternoon, with one exception, and it was originally planned to compare releases at the accustomed time of day with others made early in the morning, but the heavy losses precluded this test. In view of the findings of von Frisch (1950) and others that precise navigation of insects is often based upon the position of the sun, similar procedures must be considered in attempting to explain the essentially correct orientation of pigeons in unfamiliar territory, particularly in view of the generally recognized deterioration of their homing ability under heavily overcast skies.

Another series of airplane observations of homing pigeons has recently been reported by Hitchcock (1952). After preliminary training up to 30 miles from their lofts, one- and two-year-old pigeons were released and followed over what was probably unfamiliar territory for distances of 70 to 106 miles. In most cases there was considerable deviation from the correct direction, and losses were heavy. There was often a tendency for the birds to fly in the direction of their previous training flights, even though this led them farther away from home. Despite these departures from the direct course home, there was ample evidence that some few birds were able to determine an approximately correct direction early in the flight, and sometimes these birds were seen to break away from the main flock in the direction of home. Further studies of this sort appear promising, especially when it becomes feasible to identify and follow single birds so that the behavior of the best performers can be compared to that of the average birds.

Most recently a substantial contribution to our knowledge of the homing ability of pigeons has been reported by Matthews (1951-53). Using pigeons a few months of age raised especially for his experiments by experienced racers, he found that the initial direction of flight within a mile or two of the release point was correlated with the homing performance of the birds, as judged by the usual standards of speed and per cent returns. Some pigeons when released in unfamiliar territory showed a clear tendency to fly in the direction of their previous training flights. Hence, in certain experiments their training was purposely confined almost wholly to one direction, and the birds were then taken many miles into unfamiliar territory in an entirely different direction. Those birds which appeared to have learned to fly in a particular *direction* suffered heavy losses when treated in this way; a very similar result has also been reported by Dinnendahl and Kramer (1950), Kramer and von St. Paul (1950b), and Kramer and Seilkopf (1950). In other flocks of pigeons, however, Matthews demonstrated a type of homing that has long been believed to exist but has heretofore proved elusive when sought by the careful experimenter. In these later experiments he carried pigeons far into unfamiliar territory, in a totally different direction from that of their previous training, and a majority headed within thirty to forty degrees of home while still within view of the release point. Kramer and von St. Paul (1952) have reported additional instances of the same type. Such rapid and essentially correct orientation cannot be explained by any of the simpler theories discussed above; and these experiments seem to be the keystone of a body of evidence showing that we have to deal with three distinct levels of homing ability in pigeons.

The first and simplest type of homing I shall call for convenience Type I; it is reliance on visual landmarks within familiar territory and the use of exploration or some form of undirected wandering when released in unfamiliar territory. This type has been clearly demonstrated in some flocks of pigeons, such as those described above that were released near Seneca Lake; and the observed flight paths of Gannets can certainly be accounted for on this basis. Type II homing might then be designated as that by which birds are able to fly in a certain *direction* even when crossing unfamiliar territory. With pigeons this is most likely to be a direction that the birds have flown in a majority of their previous training flights. Type II homing appears to have been under way in some of the longer airplane observations of pigeons described above, in certain of the flights followed by Hitchcock, and in the earlier experiments of Kramer *et al.*, and of Matthews. The work reported by Schüz, Rüppell, and by Rowan, discussed in the next section, indicates a similar directional tendency when wild migratory birds are released in unfamiliar territory. Type III homing ability goes one step further and allows the bird possessing it to choose approximately the correct direction of its home even when it is carried into unfamiliar territory in a new and unaccustomed direction. To date, the most convincing demonstrations of this third and most impressive type of homing have been those provided for pigeons by Matthews (1951), by Kramer and von St. Paul (1952), and by Matthews (1953c) for the Manx Shearwater, *Puffinus puffinus.* But we can probably assume that Type III homing was also involved to some degree in other flights of pigeons discussed above.

To the extent that future investigations indicate a general validity for this classification of the homing ability into these three types, it may prove very helpful to make a clear distinction between them, since all three may be intermingled in the same homing flight and theories applicable to one may be irrelevant for another of the three types. It is tempting to speculate that Type II homing might involve flying at an appropriate angle to the sun, although the results of Matthews' experiments clearly rule out any simple, insect-like adherence to a fixed angle between flight direction and the sun's position, so any such theory must assume that the birds make some allowance for the time of day. Type II navigation apparently based on the sun has been reported in the Common Tern, *Sterna hirundo,* by Griffin and Goldsmith (1955).

Type III homing is, of course, the most baffling of all; but it is a pleasure to report that real progress towards its elucidation has been achieved very recently. Matthews (1951-53) has suggested a theory based upon the use of the sun's position in the sky. Assuming that a bird could be aware of at least the approximate time since sunrise, it might judge its latitude by estimating the altitude of the sun above the horizon. Supporting evidence for some sort of sun navigation can be found in several cases where pigeons (and also wild birds) showed better homing performance in clear weather than when obliged to fly under an overcast sky. Additional support for this general type of explanation has recently come from the work of Kramer and his associates, but since most of these studies have employed wild birds rather than pigeons they will be discussed in the following section. Very recently Matthews (1953c) has reported further homing experiments with Manx Shearwaters that serve to amplify in an important manner the earlier work of Lack and Lockley (1938).

Matthews released fifteen shearwaters from Skokholm Island (southwest of Wales) at Cambridge, England, certainly a totally unfamiliar inland point. The day was clear and most of the fifteen headed within a few degrees of the correct direction while still under observation from the library tower. Return-times of less than twenty-four hours were recorded for the 240 mile flight, and all the remaining birds returned the following night. But on two subsequent releases at Cambridge *under a heavy overcast* forty shearwaters scattered at random, and the fastest took some days to reach their nests, while some never returned at all. This is by far the clearest evidence yet put forward for the importance of clear skies in accurate homing over unfamiliar territory. Matthews' theory of sun navigation will be discussed in the following section.

EXPERIMENTS WITH BIRD MIGRATION

In all general discussions of bird navigation there is implicit the hope of explaining not only the ability of a bird to navigate during homing experiments but also during the long, natural migrations. The difficulties of direct experiments or even extensive observations of individual migrating birds have resulted in the present situation in which the bulk of the experimental evidence accumulated to date has stemmed from homing rather than migrating birds. Notable exceptions will be discussed below, however, after reviewing several scattered reports and suggestions which are relevant to the general problem.

It might be expected that the extensive birdbanding programs of the past thirty years would have produced valuable evidence concerning bird navigation.

Many thousands of recoveries of banded birds have indeed been recorded, and in hundreds of these reported cases the birds had traveled long distances between the point of banding and recovery. Such records lend a tangible aspect to the description of migratory routes. They seldom suffice, however, to map with adequate precision the actual flight path followed by any one individual, because a long period of time elapses between banding and recovery—long relative to the time necessary for direct flight by the bird between the two points. Only rarely is a bird recovered within a few days at a point hundreds of miles away so that the record establishes unequivocally the fact that it flew a straight or nearly straight course. In this connection, it is not generally appreciated how great a distance is frequently covered by birds in a day's time, especially by the larger species. For example, I once observed a large flock of Snow Geese, *Chen hyperborea,* in arctic Alaska at a date when they had completed their spring migration to the breeding range. This flock was seen to fly 120 miles along the coast in four hours, although apparently engaged merely in a search for food or nesting sites.

One group of recent papers supports the general notion that wind direction or air pressure patterns play an important role in determining the direction of bird migrations (Suffern, 1949; Odum, 1948; and Lowery, 1951). Lowery has analyzed a very extensive series of data which reveal that, under some conditions at least, nocturnal migratory flights do follow the general direction of the winds and are considerably different from one night to another if the wind shifts its direction. These studies were made by visually estimating the direction of flight of night migrants seen through telescopes against the illuminated surface of the moon and correcting the raw data for the geometrical distortion involved in this method of observation. Lowery's organized observations on a large scale have raised this method from the status of an occasional spectacle to an important source of information not obtainable in any other manner. It is possible that the correlation between wind direction and average direction of flight has some other basis than a simple tendency to fly downwind; and the method does not permit differentiation between species, so if some species behave differently from others this alone will complicate the results. But despite these limitations the method is a promising one.

It has been pointed out that even the famous migration route of the Pacific Golden Plover, *Pluvialis dominica fulva,* may not involve such spectacular and precise navigation as has often been supposed. The available records of these birds seen from ships in the northeast Pacific do not all lie along a straight line between their breeding range and the wintering area (Griffin and Hock, 1949). A comment concerning this species has been presented by Preston (1949), who has stated that there is a rather consistent cloud formation lying parallel to the western coast of North America but some hundreds of miles to the west. This might form an excellent ecological cue capable of guiding the birds from Alaska to the Hawaiian Islands. While still an attractive avenue for speculation, the search for ecological cues along natural migratory routes has not been actively pressed, aside from this suggestion by Preston.

A successful attempt to deal directly with actual migratory flights of wild birds has been reported by Rowan (1946) in the form of an experiment which supplements his well-known studies of the relationship between length of daylight and the timing of the migrations and breeding of birds. Common Crows, *Corvus brachyrhynchos,* were caught during the summer as young birds in the vicinity of Edmonton, Alberta. They were held in captivity until late autumn when adults of this species had left the area for their winter range, which banding evidence had shown to be located 1,500 miles to the southeast in the states of Kansas and Oklahoma. To assure that these young birds would have to fly over unfamiliar territory they were released at least 60 miles southeast of the area where they had been trapped. As a result of an intensive local publicity campaign thirty-one out of the fifty-four birds released were recovered, and thirteen had flown a significant distance from the release point. Seven of these thirteen recoveries were within the angle of about twenty degrees subtended at the release point by the winter range of the population, which may be considered the goal area of these inexperienced young birds making their first attempt at a migration alone and under unfavorable conditions of cold. Of the remaining six birds, all were recovered within twenty degrees of a direction that pointed towards some part of the winter range. The two most serious departures from this direction occurred in cases where the bird was not recovered until several days after release, so that some wandering after failure to achieve a successful migration is not unreasonable. Rowan closes his account of this experiment with the following words: "It seems to me that one is compelled to describe this performance as an *inherited sense of direction,* whether one likes this habitually spurned definition or not, or whether it means anything or nothing in the present state of knowledge."

A similar experiment with European White Storks, *Ciconia ciconia,* was carried out in Germany many years ago, but the full details have only recently been made available (Schüz, 1934, 1949; and Mayr, 1952). These storks were captured at Rossitten on the Baltic coast of East Prussia; and previous returns of banded birds had shown that the normal route for the fall migration of this population was to the southeast, around the eastern end of the Mediterranean, and thence to Africa. On the other hand, storks nesting west of the Rhine valley normally migrate to the southwest, reaching Africa through Spain and Morocco. Young storks from Rossitten were transported to western Germany, banded and released; and the recoveries provide significant data. Those set free before the wild storks had migrated flew southwest, apparently joining the local population for the fall migration. Of greater interest are the records obtained from other groups of young storks that were held in captivity until the wild members of the species had left Europe altogether. Even when released at Rossitten the young birds migrating without benefit of the company of adults scattered more widely than normal, three being recovered in the Alps to the southwest of their starting point. A group of twenty released at Frankfurt were traced south into the Alps; and the largest group (144), released at Essen, took an initial direction definitely to the west of south until they too reached the Alps. The results do not provide a wholly convincing answer to the question for which they were designed, whether or not the tendency to migrate southeast is an inherited behavior pattern in the East Prussian population. But it is entirely clear that these inexperienced birds had an inherited behavior pattern that led them to fly in a generally southerly direction and deviations of thirty degrees or so are minor in comparison to this important fact.

A third experiment of this general type involved Hooded Crows, *Corvus cornix,* that were already engaged in their spring migration through Rossitten. Previous banding had shown that this population wintered in central and western Germany and was on its way to a breeding range that included the Baltic states, Finland, and the western portion of Russia. Soon after capture, 507 of these crows were released at Flensburg, Schleswig-Holstein, just south of the Danish border; and almost all of the recoveries during the ensuing summer fell in an area in the Scandinavian countries to the west of the normal summer range. In other words, these crows continued to migrate in the same northeasterly direction after being displaced roughly 500 miles to the west, into what was almost certainly unfamiliar territory. Here again we see the migratory habit expressed in the form of a tendency to fly in a certain direction, plus or minus perhaps twenty or thirty degrees.

Other instances of the same sort of directional tendency have been recently reviewed by Mayr (1952), and the parallel to what I have called Type II navigation in homing birds is certainly striking. While this evidence does not tell us how the birds maintained the approximate direction that they did, it does serve to clarify to some extent the sort of behavior pattern with which we are dealing.

Laboratory studies of the sensory basis of orientation in birds have not been undertaken by many investigators in recent years. Dijkgraaf (1947) and Matthews (1952c) have attempted to train birds to head in a certain direction inside an opaque experimental chamber, food being the reward for correct choice. It proved impossible, however, to demonstrate any ability to discriminate "absolute" directions without visual or auditory cues from the immediate surroundings. Schwartzkopff (1949, 1952a, b) has determined the frequency range and sensitivity of hearing in birds, as well as their sensitivity to vibrations and their ability to localize the direction in which a sound source is located. But by far the most important set of laboratory studies of bird orientation have been those of Kramer, von St. Paul, Hoffmann and their associates (1948-53) at the Max Planck-Institut für Meeresbiologie in Wilhelmshaven.

The first of these experiments dealt with a fundamental new observation: under some circumstances at least the *Zugaktivität,* or migration restlessness of caged migratory birds, was directional (Kramer, 1948, 1949, and 1950a, b). Even within small outdoor cages the birds are reported to fly back and forth in the direction of their normal migratory flight, or to flutter on a perch heading most of the time in the appropriate direction. The directional tendency was not a precise one; but in the more consistent individuals all headings during a period of two or three minutes fell within an angular spread of about ninety degrees (Kramer, 1951a). Magnetic fields had no effect on these directional tendencies within the cages; but sky light was an important controlling factor. A warbler, *Sylvia atricapilla,* pointed southeastwards when allowed a clear view of the night sky in a rural location; but when exposed to the glow of city lights reflected from clouds it headed towards this brighter portion of the sky. This suggests that the brightness pattern of the night sky may be utilized as a directional cue by nocturnal migrants; and it is true, other factors being equal, that the night sky in the northern hemisphere is slightly brighter to the south. Much more evidence would be necessary, however, before such a type of orientation could be considered proven, especially in view of the many factors such as clouds and artificial lights that alter the average pattern of night sky brightness. Ornithologists will recall, however, the occasional disasters suffered by migratory birds from bright artificial lights such as lighthouses and airport ceilometer searchlights, particularly under unusual weather conditions involving poor visibility. Conceivably artificial lights are something that nocturnal migrants must learn to discount, and this could be one reason that lighthouse casualties seem to have decreased over the years since powerful lighthouses were first erected.

In a most significant experiment one Starling, *Sturnus vulgaris,* that was pointing northwest in a similar cage during the spring migration continued to show this heading when its view of the sky was limited to six equally spaced square windows, each subtending about twenty degrees (Kramer, 1952). Through these windows the birds could see nothing but six patches of sky slightly above the horizon; and none of the windows afforded a direct view of the sun. If mirrors were placed outside the windows so as to alter by ninety degrees the direction from which light reached the bird, its heading shifted by approximately the same angle, as illustrated in Figure 8. The orientation seemed to depend primarily upon the light arriving from the portion of the sky nearest to the sun—perhaps because this portion would provide the brightest of the six windows. Some orientation persisted under cloud cover of moderate thickness, but not under a heavy overcast; and Kramer feels that Starlings can probably perceive the sun's position through approximately as much cloud as can a human observer. No evidence was found of an

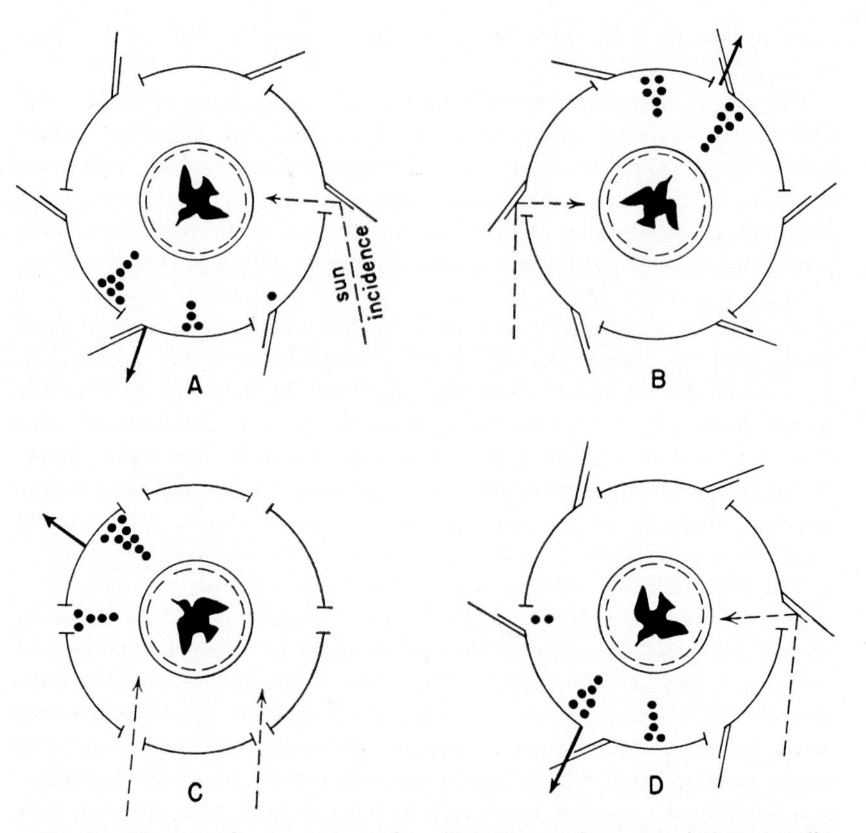

Fig. 8. Diagram of an experiment by which Kramer demonstrated that a starling could choose a definite direction with reference to the pattern of light from the sky. Each solid dot indicates the bird's average position during a ten-second period; each figure represents fifteen consecutive periods of ten seconds. In *C* the light from the sun reaches the bird directly as indicated by the broken arrows, and the bird's average heading is roughly 120° from the direction of the incident sunlight. In *A, B,* and *D* the direct light from sun and sky is cut off by shades; but reflected light is admitted by means of mirrors indicated by the inner and shorter line at each window. The bird's average position is still roughly 120° from the direction of the reflected sunlight. In no case was the sun itself visible to the bird, so light from that portion of the sky close to the sun must have a predominant importance in this type of orientation.

ability to use the polarization of the sky light, as bees are now known to do (von Frisch, 1950). Montgomery and Heinemann (1952) have reported negative results of attempts to train pigeons to respond to the plane of polarization of light.

Adapting the directed migration restlessness to a more readily controlled experimental situation, Kramer and von St. Paul (1950a) also succeeded in training both Starlings and pigeons (Kramer and Riese, 1952) to obtain food in a definite compass direction from the center of the cage, *provided that the sky was visible* through the six 20-degree windows. The only basic factor that was different in this experiment from that of Dijkgraaf cited above was the fact that six patches of sky were visible in an apparatus identical to that shown in Figure 8, *A*. Without a view of the sky Dijkgraaf could not train birds to seek food in a definite compass direction; with the sky visible Kramer could.

Still more significant was the fact that a Starling trained in this way to seek food in a definite direction did almost as well when tested at a wholly different time of day from the hours during which the training had taken place. That is, a bird trained to head in a particular direction during the morning hours immediately chose the same direction when placed in the experimental cage in mid-afternoon. This indicates an ability to allow for the sun's motion across the sky, perhaps by keeping track of the time of day and being aware of the direction in which the sun should lie at various times after daybreak. Indeed there was some evidence that a Starling can more easily learn to seek food in a certain compass direction (regardless of the time of day) than it can learn what to us would seem a much simpler problem, namely to obtain food by always heading directly towards the sun. One Starling also reacted in the same manner to an incandescent lamp that was substituted for the natural sun, seeking food in the direction relative to this artificial sun that would have been correct at the time, relative to the real sun. The bird's awareness of time is related to the same physiological mechanism responsible for 24-hour activity rhythms which persist under constant conditions, for Hoffman (1953a, b) has reported that a bird accustomed to a shifted schedule of light and darkness chooses a different direction as would be expected from the "resetting of its clock." These experiments are still in progress, and interested readers should look forward eagerly to a complete account of the work, for it is the most significant development in the understanding of bird orientation that has occurred in our generation.

In reflecting upon this recent evidence for visual, celestial navigation in birds, it is well to bear in mind that the avian eye is equipped with a unique structure, the pecten, that would appear ideally suited in many ways to facilitate looking at the sun. The pecten, for which a variety of functions have been suggested (Menner, 1938; Walls, 1942; and Crozier and Wolf, 1943), is certainly not equipped with visual receptor cells, but is instead a highly vascular, heavily pigmented, pleated fold extending inwards from the fundus of the eye and covering a substantial area of what, in a mammalian eye, would be peripheral retina. If we try to imagine ourselves viewing the horizon and the sky through the eyes of a typical diurnal bird, at any one instant the two pectens would appear as enormous blind spots, situated in the upper part of the two visual fields. The edges of these blind spots would be deeply serrated; and if for example a point on the horizon was imaged on the fovea, one of these blind spots might well lie in the proper position to receive the image of the sun. In this case the heavy pigmentation of the pecten would presumably absorb the brilliant light of the sun's image, and the rich blood supply would tend to carry away the resulting heat. One might even go so far as to postulate that the angular position and movement of the sun is perceived by birds in terms of particular folds or serrations of the pecten.

If we assume for the sake of argument that birds estimate the sun's altitude above the horizon, it would not be an unduly great additional step to postulate that they might also pay attention to the rate of change of its altitude with time. This would help a bird engaged in Type III homing considerably, for a given combination of altitude and rate of change of altitude occurs at a given season only at one latitude. That is, while a given altitude of the sun can occur at 8:00 A.M. at one latitude or at 10:00 P.M. at some more northern latitude, the rate at which it is climbing will be different in the two cases. In any event a rather accurate estimation of latitude could be made by a bird on the basis of accurate perception of either the sun's altitude plus an awareness of the time of day, a combination of altitude and rate of change in altitude with time, or a combination of all three.

Matthews (1951a, 1953a, 1953c) has spelled out in some detail a theory of sun navigation based on the considerations outlined above. He also describes experiments in which some disorientation was caused by holding the birds indoors where they could not see the sun for several days and by subjecting them to an abnormal schedule of light and darkness. But as Kramer (1953a) has pointed out, the precision of visual estimation of the sun's altitude and rate of change of altitude which must be postulated by Matthews' theory is too great to be credible without more convincing evidence. Kramer's recent results indicate that pigeons can head in the general direction of home only a few seconds after their release from opaque shipping containers. Although his results confirm Matthews' evidence that orientation is much poorer under an overcast than under a clear sky, Kramer feels that Matthews' theory of sun navigation in its present form cannot account for the rapid orientation of pigeons released in unfamiliar territory. With this conclusion I agree, although the new evidence concerning the ability of birds to use the sun for orientation is a most important step towards a full understanding of the whole phenomenon.

SUMMARY

Recent theories and observations dealing with the navigation of birds have been critically discussed and analyzed. The most original theory advanced during the past ten years is Ising's suggestion that birds perceive mechanical forces related to the earth's rotation and orient themselves by means of the variation of these forces with latitude. These mechanical effects can be considered from several points of view: a change of apparent weight depending upon the direction of flight and upon latitude; forces acting on blood flowing through arteries; or a deflection of an otherwise straight flight path into a slightly curved one (Coriolis effect). This theory has the attraction at first glance of requiring only a qualitative sort of mechanical receptor that is known to be present in birds and all other highly organized animals. But serious difficulties arise when quantitative questions of sensory physiology are faced. In any of its forms, Ising's theory requires a sensitivity to mechanical forces or accelerations about two-hundred times greater than the highest values that have been measured experimentally, even under favorable laboratory conditions.

The theory that has attracted most attention in recent years has unquestionably been Yeagley's hypothesis that navigating birds, especially homing pigeons, determine their latitude from the Coriolis force and their longtitude from the vertical component of the earth's magnetic field. In addition to the difficulties encountered by Ising's theory, there is no significant evidence for sensitivity to the magnetic field of the earth. The experimental evidence presented by Yeagley is open to serious question, and the results of his experiments can probably be accounted for by inadequate experimental procedures or by undirected exploration on the part of the birds.

A theory of bird navigation based upon perception of infra-red radiations has been revived by Wojtusiak; but evidence in its support seems to be entirely lacking.

Further evidence has been accumulated which indicates that under many circumstances the long distance flights of birds can be accounted for by assuming a recognition of familiar landmarks within familiar territory, and a more or less systematic search or exploration when the birds find themselves in unknown surroundings. This type of explanation appears particularly applicable to the homing of certain wild birds after artificial transportation away from their nests. Gannets have been followed from a light airplane during the first few hours of their homing flights over unfamiliar territory. They flew in all directions with no significant tendency to head directly toward their nests. The flight paths were, for the most part, gradual and somewhat irregular curves suggestive of spiraling but also open to interpretation as purely random exploration.

An analysis of various types of exploratory flight paths shows that most of the recorded homing flights of wild birds can be explained by assuming that they employed any one of a number of types of search patterns which would increase the probability of reaching a goal area that lay in an unknown direction. Equations have been presented to show the quantitative results to be expected from linear radial scattering, from zigzag search patterns, and from spirals. These types of exploration may possibly apply to migratory routes where topographical factors or other easily perceived cues are inadequate. Given a means of heading in the approximate direction of the goal area, birds could employ some variant of these search patterns to good effect at least in the terminal portion of the journey. Airplane observation has served at least one important function in demonstrating that birds may deviate widely from the straight-line type of flight that used to be taken for granted and that is implied to the uncritical reader by maps depicting artificial homing experiments or natural migratory routes by straight lines. Whenever actual flight paths have been traced by any method at all, the resulting information has proved enlightening; and it seems clear that further progress will be made when the actual courses flown by individual migrants can be determined.

Recent studies of homing pigeons, both by observing their flight paths from airplanes (Griffin and Hitchcock) and by observing their initial directions of flight near the release point (Matthews and Kramer), have shown that three distinct types of homing can occur. Type I is simple reliance on "contact flying" or orientation based on visual landmarks in familiar territory plus exploration when the birds find themselves over unfamiliar terrain. Type II is the choice of a particular direction (in pigeons this is usually the training direction) even when the bird is released in unfamiliar territory. Type III is the selection of the correct direction of home from a point in unfamiliar territory even though home lies in an unaccustomed direction. Several examples of the first two types can be found among the results obtained with both wild birds and pigeons by several different investigators. Type III homing has to date been convincingly demonstrated only in pigeons, by Matthews and by Kramer and von St. Paul, and in the Manx Shearwater (Matthews, 1953c); but its existence must be taken into account in all considerations of homing and migration.

Direct experiments with migratory flights of birds released in unfamiliar territory have demonstrated that several species take the approximate direction of the normal migration in their species even without guidance by experienced older birds. Experiments by Kramer and his associates have demonstrated such directional tendencies in both nocturnal and diurnal migrants even when confined in small cages, *provided that the sky was visible.* In similar experimental cages, Starlings and pigeons have been trained by Kramer and his associates to seek food in a particular compass direction. The birds appeared to base this orientation on the light reaching them from six equally spaced, twenty-degree, square windows through which sky slightly above the horizon was visible but not the sun itself. This type of orientation in a definite compass direction on the basis of light from the sky persisted even when the bird was placed in the experimental cage at a wholly different time of day from the hours to which the training had been confined. Apparently these birds are able to keep track of the time of day and correct for the sun's passage across the sky.

It is speculated that the pecten may play some role in the use of the sun for celestial navigation.

Matthews has advanced a detailed theory of sun navigation which assumes that birds determine their position on the earth's surface by visual estimation of the altitude and rate of change of altitude of the sun, together with an accurate awareness of the time of day. Recent experimental evidence presented by Kramer and others indicates, however, that under favorable conditions pigeons can choose the correct direction for a homing flight within so short a time that an explanation of their orientation by Matthews' theory requires what at present seems an incredibly precise judgment of the time of day and the rate of change of the sun's altitude.

Bibliography

BARLOW, H. B., H. I. KOHN, AND E. G. WALSH

1947a. Visual sensations aroused by magnetic fields. Amer. Jour. Physiol., 148:372-375.

1947b. The effect of dark adaptation upon the electric threshold of the human eye. Amer. Jour. Physiol., 148:376-381.

BEECHER, W. J.

1951. A possible navigation sense in the ear of birds. Amer. Midl. Nat., 46: 367-384.

1952. The unexplained direction sense of vertebrates. Sci. Monthly, 75:19-25.

BRONK, D. W., and G. STELLA

1932. Afferent impulses in the carotid sinus nerve, I. The relation of the discharge from single end organs to arterial blood pressure. Jour. Cell. Comp. Physiol., 1:113-130.

1935. The response to steady pressures of single end organs in the isolated carotid sinus. Amer. Jour. Physiol., 110:708-714.

CLAPARÈDE, E.

1903. La faculté d'orientation lointaine. Arch. Psychol., 2:133-180.

CROZIER, W. J., and E. WOLF

1943. Theory and measurement of visual mechanisms, X. Modifications of the flicker response contour, and the significance of the avian pecten. Jour. Gen. Physiol., 27:287-313.

DAVIS, L.

1948. (Remarks on) The physical basis of bird navigation. Jour. Appl. Physics, 19:307-308.

DE VRIES, H. L.

1948. Die Reizschwelle der Sinnesorgane also physikalisches Problem. Experientia, 4:205-213.

1950. The mechanics of the labyrinth otoliths. Acta Oto-laryng., Stockholm, 38:262-273.

DIJKGRAAF, S.

1947. Über das Problem der Fernorientierung bei Vögeln. Öst. Zool. Zeits., 1:314-324.

DINNENDAHL, L., and G. KRAMER

1950. Heimkehrleistungen italienischer und deutscher Reisetauben. Vogelwarte, 15:237-242.

DODGE, R.

1923a. Habituation to rotation. Jour. Exper. Psychol., 6:1-35.

1923b. Thresholds of rotation. Jour. Exper. Psychol., 6:107-137.

DROST, R.

1938. Über den Einfluss von Verfrachtungen zur Herbstzugzeit auf den Sperber, *Accipiter nisus* (L.). Zugleich ein Beitrag zur Frage nach der Orientierung der Vogel auf dem Zuge ins Winterquartier. C. R. Ninth Cong. Ornithol. Internat., 9:503-521.

1949. Zugvögel perzipieren Ultrakurzwellen. Vogelwarte, 15:57-59.

DUCHÂTEL.

1901-1902. Faculté de directions du pigeon voyageur. Ann. Psychol. Zool., 1:22; and 2:48. (Cited by Claparède.)

EGMOND, A. A. J. VAN, J. J. GROEN, and L. B. W. JONGKEES

1949. The mechanics of the semicircular canal. Jour. Physiol., 110:1-17.

FRISCH, K. VON

1950. Bees, their vision, chemical senses, and language. Cornell University Press, Ithaca, pp. 89-109.

GORDON, D. A.

1948. Sensitivity of the homing pigeon to the magnetic field of the earth. Science, 108:710-711.

GRIFFIN, D. R.

1943. Homing experiments with Herring Gulls and Common Terns. Bird-Banding, 14:7-33.

1944. The sensory basis of bird navigation. Quart. Rev. Biol., 19:15-31.

1952a. Radioactive tagging of animals under natural conditions. Ecology, 33:329-335.

1952b. Airplane observations of homing pigeons. Bull. Mus. Comp. Zool., 107:411-440.

1952c. Bird navigation. Biol. Reviews, 27:359-393.

GRIFFIN, D. R., and T. GOLDSMITH

1955. Initial flight directions of homing birds. Biol. Bull., 108 (In press).

GRIFFIN, D. R., and R. J. HOCK

1949. Airplane observations of homing birds. Ecology, 30:176-198.

GRIFFIN, D. R., R. HUBBARD, AND G. WALD

1947. Sensitivity of the human eye to infra-red radiation. Jour. Opt. Soc. Amer., 37:546-554.

HECHT, S., and M. H. PIRENNE

1940. The sensibility of the nocturnal Long-eared Owl in the spectrum. Jour. Gen. Physiol., 23:709-717.

HEINROTH, O., AND K. HEINROTH

1941. Das Heimfinde-Vermögen der Brieftauben. Jour. Ornithol., 89:213-256.

HENDERSON, G. H.

1948. Physical basis of bird navigation. Science, 107:597-598.

HITCHCOCK, H. B.

1952. Airplane observations of homing pigeons. Proc. Amer. Philos. Soc., 96:270-289.

HOFFMAN, K.

1953a. Die Einrechnung der Sonnerwanderung bei der Richtungsweisung des sonnerlos aufgezogenen Stares. Naturwissenschaften, 40:148.

1953b. Experimentelle Änderung des Richtungsfindens beim Star durch Beeinflussung der "inneren Uhr." Naturwissenschaften, 40:608-609.

ISING, G.

1946. Die physikalische Möglichkeit eines tierischen Orientierungssinnes auf Basis der Erdrotation. Ark. Mat. Astr. Fys., 32A, No. 18: pp. 1-23.

KRAMER, G.

1948. Neue Beiträge zur Frage der Fernorientierung der Vögel. Ornithol. Ber., 1:228-238.

1949. Über Richtungstendenzen bei der nächtlichen Zugunruhe gekäfigter Vogel. In Ornithologie als Biologische Wissenschaft. Carl Winter, Heidelberg, pp. 269-283.

1950a. Orientierte Zugaktivität gekäfigter Singvögel. Naturwissenschaften, 37:188.

1950b. Weitere Analyse der Faktoren die Zugaktivität des gekäfigten Vogels orientieren. Naturwissenschaften, 37:377-378.

1951a. Eine neue Methode zur Erforschung der Zugorientierung und die bisher damit erzielten Ergebnisse. Proc. Tenth Internat. Ornithol. Cong., pp. 269-280.

1951b. Versuche zuz Wahrnehmung von Ultrakurzwellen durch Vögel. Vogelwarte, 16:55-59.

1952. Experiments on bird orientation. Ibis, 94:265-285.

1953a. Wird die Sonnenhöhe bei der Heimfindeorientierung verwertet? Jour. Ornithol., 94:201-219.

1953b. Danebenfliegen und Überfliegen beim Heimflug von Brieftauben. Vogelwarte, 16:146-148.

KRAMER, G., and E. RIESE

1952. Die Dressur von Brieftauben auf Kompassrichtung im Wahlkäfig. Zeits. Tierpsychol., 9:245-251.

KRAMER, G., and U. VON ST. PAUL

1950a. Stare (*Sturnus vulgaris,* L.) lassen sich auf Himmelrichtungen dressieren. Naturwissenschaften, 37:526-527.

1950b. Ein wesentlicher Bestandteil der Orientierung der Reisetaube: Die Richtungsdressur. Zeits. Tierpsychol., 7:620-631.

1952. Heimkehrleistung von Brieftauben ohne Richtungsdressur. Zool. Anz. Suppl. Bd., 16:172-178.

KRAMER, G., and H. SEILKOPF

1950. Heimkehrleistung von Reisetauben in Abhängigkeit vom Wetter, insbesondere vom Wind. Vogelwarte, 15:242-247.

LACK, D., and R. M. LOCKLEY

1938. Skokholm bird observatory homing experiments. British Birds, 31:242-248.

LACK, D., and G. C. VARLEY

1945. Detection of birds by radar. Nature, 156:446.

LASHLEY, K. S.

1916. The color vision of birds, I. The spectrum of the domestic fowl. Jour. Animal Behavior, 6:1-26.

LOWENSTEIN, O.

1950. Labyrinth and equilibrium. Sympos. Soc. Exper. Biol., 4:60-82.

LOWERY, G. H.

1951. A quantitative study of the nocturnal migration of birds. Publ. Univ. Kansas Mus. Nat. Hist., 3:361-472.

MATTHEWS, G. V. T.

1951a. The sensory basis of bird navigation. Jour. Inst. Navigation, 4:260-275.

1951b. The experimental investigation of navigation in homing pigeons. Jour. Exper. Biol., 28:508-536.

1952a. An investigation of homing ability in two species of gulls. Ibis, 94: 243-264.

1952b. The relation of learning and memory to the orientation and homing of pigeons. Behavior, 4:202-221.

1953a. Sun navigation in homing pigeons. Jour. Exper. Biol., 30:243-267.

1953b. The orientation of untrained pigeons: a dichotomy in the homing process. Jour. Exper. Biol., 30:268-276.

1953c. Navigation in the Manx Shearwater. Jour. Exper. Biol., 30:370-396.

MATTHEWS, L. H., and B. H. C. MATTHEWS

1939. Owls and infra-red radiation. Nature, 143:983.

MAYR, E.

1952. German experiments on orientation of migrating birds. Biol. Reviews, 27:394-399.

MENNER, E.

1938. Die Bedeutung des Pecten im Auge des Vogels für die Wahrnhmung von Bewegungen nebst Bemerkungen über seine Ontogenie und Histologie. Zool. Jahrb. Abt. Allge. Zool. Physiol. Tiere, 58:481-538.

MONTGOMERY, K. C., and E. G. HEINEMANN

1952. Concerning the ability of homing pigeons to discriminate patterns of polarized light. Science, 116:454-456.

NICOL, J. A. C.

1945. The homing ability of the carrier pigeon: its value in warfare Auk, 62:286-298.

ODUM, H. T.

1948. The bird navigation controversy. Auk, 65:584-597.

ORGEL, A. R., and J. C. SMITH

1954. Test of the magnetic theory of homing. Science, 120:891-892.

PLATT, C. S., and R. S. DARE

1945. The homing instinct in pigeons. Science, 101:439-440.

PRESTON, F. W.

1949. The Pacific flyway of the Golden Plover. Auk, 66:87-88.

ROWAN, W.

1946. Experiments in bird migration. Trans. Roy. Soc. Canada, Third Ser., Sec. 5, 40:123-135.

RÜPPELL, W.

1944. Versuche über Heimfinden ziehender Nebelkrähen nach Verfrachtung. Jour. Ornithol., 92:106-132.

SCHÜZ, E.

1934. Vom Storch-Versuch 1933 der Vogelwarte Rossitten. Vogelzug, 5:21-25.

1949. Die Spä-Auflassung ost-preussischer Jung-Störch in Westdeutschland durch die Vogelwarte Rossitten, 1933. Vogelzug, 14:63-78.

SCHWARTZKOPFF, J.

1949. Über Sitz und Leistung von Gehör und Vibrationsinn bei Vögeln. Zeits. vergl. Physiol., 31:527-608.

1950. Zur Frage des "Wahrnehmens" von Ultrakurzwellen durch Zugvögel. Vogelwarte, 15:194-196.

1952a. Untersuchungen über die Arbeitsweise des Mittelohres und das Richtungshören der Singvögel unter Verwendung von Cochlea-Potentialen. Zeits. vergl. Physiol., 34:46-68.

1952b. Über den Gehörsinn der Vögel. Jour. Ornithol., 93:91-103.

SKINNER, B. F.

1950. Are theories of learning necessary? Psychol. Rev., 57:193-216.

SLEPIAN, J.

1948. Physical basis of bird navigation. Jour. Appl. Physics., 19:306.

SUFFERN, C.

1949. Pressure patterns in bird migration. Science, 109:209.

THORPE, W. H.

1949. Recent biological evidence for the methods of bird orientation. Proc. Linn. Soc. London, 160:85-94.

THORPE, W. H., and D. H. WILKINSON

1946. Ising's theory of bird orientation. Nature, 158:903-904.

VANDERPLANK, F. L.

1934. The effect of infra-red waves on Tawny Owls (*Strix aluco*). Proc. Zool. Soc. London, 1934:505-507.

VAN RIPER, W., and E. R. KALMBACH

1952. Homing not hindered by wing magnets. Science, 115:577-578.

VARIAN, R. H.

1948. (Remarks on) A preliminary study of a physical basis of bird navigation. Jour. Appl. Physics, 19:306-307.

VIGUIER, C.

1882. Le sens de l'orientation et ses organes. Rev. Philosophique, 14:1-36.

WALLS, G. L.

1942. The vertebrate eye and its adaptive radiation. Cranbrook Inst. Sci., Bull. No. 19, pp. 365-367.

WATSON, J. B., and K. S. LASHLEY

1915. Homing and related activities of birds. Papers Dept. Marine Biol., Carnegie Inst., 7:1-104.

WENDT, G. R.

1951. Vestibular functions. In Handbook of experimental psychology, ed. by S. S. Stevens. John Wiley, New York, pp. 1191-1223.

WILKINSON, D. H.

1949. Some physical principles of bird orientation. Proc. Linn. Soc. London, 160:94-99.

1950. Flight recorders. A technique for the study of bird navigation. Jour. Exper. Biol., 27:192-197.

1952. The random element in bird 'navigation'. Jour. Exper. Biol., 29:532-560.

WOJTUSIAK, R. J.

1946. Hypothesis of sensibility to infra-red rays as an attempt to explain some problems of orientation in animals. C. R. Sci. Math. Nat. Acad. Polon., pp. 28-29.

1949. Polish investigations on homing in birds and their orientation in space. Proc. Linn. Soc. London, 160:99-108.

YEAGLEY, H. L.

1947. A preliminary study of a physical basis of bird navigation. Jour. Appl. Physics, 18:1035-1063.

1951. A preliminary study of a physical basis of bird navigation, II. Jour. Appl. Physics, 22:746-760.

Several recent publications add significant new information and ideas to those discussed in this chapter. Of particular importance is a monograph by G. V. T. Matthews, "Bird Navigation," Cambridge University Press, 1955. Other important recent papers not included in Matthews' bibliography are the following:

HOFFMAN, K.

1955. Versuche zu der im Richtungsfinden der Vögel enthaltenen Zeitschätzung. Zeits. Tierpsychol., 11:453-475.

KRAMER, G.

1955. Ein weiterer Versuch die Orientierung von Brieftauben durch jahreszeitliche Änderung der Sonnenhöhe zu beeinflussen. Gleichzeitig eine Kritik der Theorie des Versuch. Jour. Ornithol., 96:173-185.

RAWSON, K. S.

1955. Sun compass orientation and endogenous activity rhythms of the starling (*Sturnus vulgaris* L.). Zeits. Tierpsychol., 11:446-452.

RAWSON, K. S., and A. M. RAWSON

1955. The orientation of homing pigeons in relation to change in sun declination. Jour. Ornithol., 96:168-172.

chapter 7

THE ANNUAL STIMULUS FOR MIGRATION: EXPERIMENTAL AND PHYSIOLOGIC ASPECTS[1] . . . Donald S. Farner

INTRODUCTION

Among the fascinating aspects of bird migration are its cyclic nature and its temporal precision. Twice annually, in a migratory species, there must be some type of mechanism which causes the development of the complex migratory behavior pattern. It is the purpose of this discussion to present an inventory of our knowledge concerning the nature and mechanisms of the periodic stimulation of migration. For purposes of this treatise, migration is defined as a regular, usually annual, movement of at least a portion of a population from the breeding area to a nonbreeding area, and a return of at least a portion of the individuals to the breeding area. It is definitely oriented and periodic. Care must be exercised in excluding, as nonmigratory, many so-called vagrant and sporadic movements; some of these may represent initial phases in the development of more typical migratory movements or modifications of more typical migratory patterns. The traditional German designation (Weigold, 1924, and others) of "instinct" and "weather" migrants, although basically sound, likewise should be applied with caution. It is likely that these two categories represent the extremes of types of migratory behavior (Schildmacher, 1952a). Between these extremes lie many intermediate cases. It is not unlikely in some instances that "weather" types may represent transitional stages in the evolution of instinct types.

With their aerial mobility, high metabolic rate, and ability to acquire instinctive behavior patterns phylogenetically, birds are well equipped for the development of migratory behavior. Because of these "preadaptations" for migration and further because of the peculiarly scattered distribution of migratory habits among the families and orders of birds, it appears not unlikely (Grinnell, 1931; Thomson, 1942, 1949; Farner, 1950; Phillips, 1951) that migratory behavior may have evolved several or many times in the course of the evolutionary history of modern birds and that, in studying migration, we may actually be confronted with many subtle cases of convergent evolution.

Manuscript received June 25, 1953.

[1] Previously unpublished data on *Zonotrichia leucophrys gambelii* cited herein are from investigations supported by funds provided for biological and medical research by the State of Washington Initiative Measure No. 171.

This in turn may well mean that the selective processes, the stimulatory mechanisms, the mechanisms of navigation and orientation, and other aspects of migration are different in different species (Thomson, 1949, 1951; Farner, 1950; Phillips, 1951).

With this suggestion in mind, Farner (1950) has enumerated and discussed the pitfalls associated with the interpretation of experimental data and observations on migration in general and the stimulation of migration in particular. Among these are the tacit tendency to regard all migration as having a common origin, uncritical application of conclusions concerning one species to other species and the erection of general theories on the basis of a single or a few species, erroneous assumption that the correlation of two phenomena necessarily represents a cause-and-effect relationship, and excessive generalization from small quantities of data.

With respect to causation in bird migration, two groups of environmental factors, *proximate* and *ultimate,* may be recognized (Baker, 1938, 1947; Thomson, 1942, 1949, 1950). The latter consist of the factors which have exerted a strong positive selection of those individuals which developed a certain hereditary migratory pattern and those factors which have exerted a negative selective influence on those individuals which failed to do so. These *ultimate* factors are therefore those which have made the migratory pattern useful to the species and have allowed it to survive. Hence with respect to spring migration, birds with hereditary behavior patterns which bring the migrating individuals to areas more favorable to reproductive activity at the more favorable times would represent a genetic stock with enhanced possibilities for survival. The importance of maximum food supply, both in quality and quantity, and maximum daylight for procuring it, has become increasingly apparent with respect to the rearing of young (Lack, 1950) and possibly also with respect to the net energy available for production of eggs (Kendeigh, 1941). The possible importance of avoiding undesirable summer conditions of the winter range also must not be overlooked. In the case of postbreeding migration, enhanced survival would develop in those stocks whose migratory patterns remove them to areas of less rigorous climate, more abundant food, longer periods of daylight for feeding, or other advantages during the nonbreeding season. The physiologic basis of such selection has been better defined for certain temperate and subarctic breeders as a result of the investigations by Kendeigh (1934) on the House Wren, *Troglodytes aëdon,* with respect to tolerance of low temperatures with short daily photoperiod; by Kendeigh (1945) on hunger resistance in relation to environmental conditions in several species; by Seibert (1949) on caloric requirements and caloric intake in relation to environmental temperature and length of photoperiod in several species; by Kendeigh (1949) on the English Sparrow, *Passer domesticus,* with respect to caloric intake and caloric requirements in relation to environmental temperatures and daily photoperiod; by Scholander *et al.* (1950) on several species with respect to caloric requirements as a function of environmental temperature; by Wallgren (1952) on the caloric requirements as a function of environmental temperature in the migratory Ortolan Bunting, *Emberiza hortulana,* compared with the closely related nonmigratory Yellow Bunting, *Emberiza citrinella;* by Salt (1952) on caloric loss by finches of the genus *Carpodacus* as a function of environmental temperature and atmospheric water-vapor pressure; and by Schildmacher (1952b) on the European Redstart, *Phoenicurus phoenicurus,* with respect to minimum environmental temperature tolerance. Obviously the ability of the bird in winter to attain the required increase in caloric intake in the face of shorter daily photoperiods for feeding (Rowan, 1931) must be critical with respect to the establishment of the limits of winter range as well as in the evolutionary development of migratory behavior. Caution must be exercised with respect to oversimplification, not only because of the variety of possible physiologic limitations and the meagerness of our knowledge about them, but also because migration, as an inherited instinctive behavior pattern, may often have a strong historical imprint (Mayr and Meise, 1930; Tugarīnov, 1949; Moreau, 1951) and therefore cannot necessarily be rationalized alone in terms of current conditions.

The *proximate factors* include those which twice annually bring the migratory bird into actual migration. This may involve factors necessary for the development of a physiologic state necessary for migration (*Zugdisposition* of various German and Finnish investigators) as well as those very immediate factors which serve as stimuli for the actual release of migratory behavior. This categorization may be an oversimplification (Verwey, 1949). In this treatise the "annual stimulus of migration" is interpreted, as in the sense of Thomson (1926), in terms of the environmental and internal factors which are responsible for the development of the physiologic condition necessary for migration as well as those which cause immediate release of migratory behavior.

It should be observed that the distinction between *proximate* and *ultimate* factors probably can be made only with respect to *typical migrants* (Thomson, 1942, 1949; Drost, 1951), which have been referred to variously as "instinct migrants" ("Instinktvögel" of various German authors), "innenweltbedingte Zugvögel" (Putzig, 1938b), "echte trekvogels" (van Oordt, 1943, 1949), and "introverse trekvogels" (Vleugel, 1948). In these species the proximate factors operate to cause the initiation of migration in advance of the seasonal occurrence of the *ultimate factors* (if such are still operative), which have served as the basis for selection in the evolution of the migratory behavior. In "weather migrants" movements occur in direct response to improvement or deterioration of environmental conditions of the nature of these *ultimate factors.* An evolution from a weather-migrant type of behavior to a typical-migrant behavior then would be defined primarily in terms of the development of migratory response to a secondary periodic factor or series of factors which initiate migration in advance of the seasonal changes in environment to which the migratory pattern is adapted (Thomson, 1926, 1936a, b, 1951). This would emphasize the previous suggestion that there are in existence many intermediate situations between weather migration and typical migration. For various reasons, the remainder of this treatise will be directed primarily towards those cases which, at least in appearance, may be regarded as typical migration.

Thomson (1951) is certainly correct in observing that the proximate factors, including the immediate stimuli, for migration must vary from species to species and must be different in spring and in fall. There is also merit in his suggestion of the possibility ". . . that the annual cycle of the bird's life is linked at only one point with environmental stimuli; that an internal rhythm has been established; and that all but one of the events in the cycle occur as the result of the mere effluxion of time, following refractory periods. . . ." Major objectives of research on the annual stimulation of migration must be to discover the periodic factors responsible for the initiation of migration, to learn how these factors actually operate and the nature of physiologic changes effected by them, and to ascertain the relationship of the migratory cycle to other annual cycles. It is the function of this treatise to present an inventory of progress thus far and to present a hypothesis to rationalize the currently available information.

Two periods may be recognized in the history of our knowledge of the annual stimulation of migration.

The *period of observation* (1825-1925) is characterized by theories, usually unifactoral, based solely, or at least largely, on uncontrolled observations. Many of the theories bestowed on birds untenable attributes such as intelligence and ability to plan. Many confused the factors of annual stimulation and the selective factors which fix the response mechanism. The hypotheses and theories proposed during this period, in one way or another, have suggested, implied, or anticipated most of the factors and ideas of our current concepts. As a rule, however, these theories were generalized from restricted observations, and although frequently proposed as general theories, they failed to have general application. The important contributions of this period are aptly summarized by Wachs (1926).

The *period of experimental investigations,* which is characterized by the combination of observational and experimental approaches to the problem of the annual stimulation of migration, began with the first experiments with Slate-colored Juncos, *Junco hyemalis,* in Alberta by Rowan (1925). These experiments lead to the first of a series of hypotheses, by Rowan and others, in which migration is regarded as a sexual phenomenon.

THE EXPERIMENTAL APPROACHES

The experimental investigations of the annual stimulation of migration have employed a necessarily restricted number of approaches.

Experimental Migration

This involves a planned treatment (castration, prolonged photoperiod, injection of hormones, etc.) followed by release of the subjects with attempts to obtain recoveries. Sometimes the mere disappearance of such birds from the locality has been interpreted as an indication of migration; obviously such may be a precarious inference. Experimental migration has been employed in the investigations of Rowan (1929, 1930, 1932), Wolfson (1940, 1942), Hann (1939), and Putzig (1937, 1939a, 1939c). It is not within the province of this paper to discuss the use of experimental migration in the study of orientation in migration; Schüz (1952) has recently published an excellent résumé of its application in this respect.

Zugunruhe

Zugunruhe is the characteristic activity displayed by caged migrants during the migratory season. It is most conspicuous in nocturnal migrants which normally show little or no nocturnal activity during the nonmigratory period. This phenomenon is discussed at length in a subsequent section. As an experimental approach the investigation of *Zugunruhe* has the advantage of being measurable quantitatively and further that the experimental subjects may be observed continuously for as long a period as desired. Responses to experimental treatments can be recorded precisely and quantitatively. The difficulties of this approach are those of evaluating the relationship of the behavior of the caged bird to that of the bird under natural conditions. Is *Zugunruhe* similar or analogous physiologically to migratory behavior? Although there are reasons for a cautious affirmative answer, it is obviously impossible to be certain of the degree of similarity.

Investigation of the Mechanisms of the Gonadal Cycles

The response of the gonads of many species to increased daily photoperiod is spectacular. It is a phenomenon which presents a nice quantitative basis for experimental investigation. Experimental manipulation of the gonadal cycle was first employed (see section on gonadal hypotheses) in studying migration because it was felt that the gonads exerted a primary regulatory role with respect to the migratory cycle. More recently (Wolfson, 1942, 1945, 1952a, b), a justification of this experimental approach has developed in the possibility that the stimulation of gonadal development and migratory behavior may involve similar or parallel mechanisms, possibly involving the anterior pituitary in both cases. If the stimulatory mechanisms are similar in the two phenomena, it is then logical to assume that important suggestions concerning the development of migratory behavior, which is difficult to measure, can be learned from the investigation of the readily measurable gonadal response.

Metabolic Investigations

In general this approach has involved the characterization of differences in metabolism between migratory and nonmigratory species or races, characterization of differences in metabolism of the migratory and nonmigratory periods, metabolic relation of migration to other activities of the bird, etc. The tools of measurement have included measurements of fat deposition, changes in body weight, oxygen uptake, release of carbon dioxide, net caloric intake, etc., applied under various experimental conditions. Experimentally this approach has involved alterations of metabolism induced by changes in photoperiod, changes in environmental temperature, administration of thyroid and thyrotropic hormones, etc. It seems obvious now that each migratory period must be preceded by the development of a gradually improved physiologic state leading finally to a general metabolic condition in which there is sufficient energy available for migration. This emphasizes the importance of this approach to the study of the annual stimulation of migration.

It appears patent that a fundamental understanding of the nature of the annual stimulation of migration will be attained only after extensive experimental investigations. However, the experimental approach necessitates many artificial conditions and the control of variables in an unnatural manner. It is consequently necessary to remember always in the use of information derived from such experiments that the migratory bird operates in a complex environment with many variables and that migration involves profound and extensive physiologic and psychologic changes within the bird. The importance of recognizing the entire ecologic, physiologic, and psychologic aspects has been emphasized by Tugarīnov (1949) and Promptov (1949).

ZUGUNRUHE

Because *Zugunruhe,* the characteristic activity of caged migrants, particularly nocturnal migrants, has been investigated rather extensively as an approach to the physiology of the development of migratory behavior, it seems logical and pertinent to present here a brief discussion of this phenomenon. The restlessness of caged birds during the normal migratory period apparently has been well known for a long time. For example, von Homeyer (1881) cited Naumann's (1822) description of it in caged Nightingales, *Luscinia megarhyncha,* in February. *Zugunruhe* was also known to Palmén (1876); Wachs (1926) stated that it was described in some detail by Eckström in 1828. The initial significant investigations were those of Wagner (1930) who recorded the activities of Whitethroats, *Sylvia communis;* European Robins, *Erithacus rubecula;* Bluethroats, *Cyanosylvia* [*Luscinia*] *svecica cyanecula;* Song Thrushes, *Turdus ericetorum;* European Blackbirds, *Turdus merula;* and Redwings, *Turdus musicus;* it was noted that this restlessness in caged birds corresponded fairly closely in daily and annual patterns to natural migratory behavior, although the spring period of *Zugunruhe* was of longer duration than the spring migratory period.

In later papers (Wagner, 1936; Wagner and Schildmacher, 1937) data were presented on the development of *Zugunruhe* in passerine birds transported out of their normal range. Also Wagner (1937) presented data which suggested to him that the development of *Zugunruhe* during the migratory season is somewhat dependent, varying with the species, on the amount of food available. In Song Thrushes, low temperatures appeared to be stimulatory or augmentative. In European Robins and Whitethroats it was found that the intensity of light in the experimental room at night was an important factor. Promptov (1949), in studying *Zugunruhe* in young cuckoos, presumably *Cuculus canorus,* found that *Zugunruhe* could be reduced with decreased light or increased food. Numerous investigations have been made (Ahlquist and Palmgren, 1935; Palmgren, 1937, 1938, 1943, 1944a; Siivonen, 1936; and Palmgren, 1936) concerning causal and modifying factors as well as the fundamental patterns of *Zugunruhe* in the European Robin, Garden Warbler, *Sylvia borin,* and other species.

Of considerable interest is the report of Promptov (1949) that *Zugunruhe* develops in young Scarlet Grosbeaks, *Carpodacus erythrinus,* at a specific age rather than at a specific time in fall. Promptov's observations are based on a small number of individuals. This matter should be investigated further.

Investigations by Merkel (1937, 1938, 1940) on Whitethroats, European Robins, and other species have made noteworthy contributions to the physiology of *Zugunruhe.* It was concluded that the development of *Zugunruhe* involves two physiologic phases, based on the earlier suggestions of Groebbels (1930): (1) *Zugdisposition* characterized by changes in metabolism resulting in an accumulation of fat and, more important, the ability to replenish rapidly the weight (primarily fat) lost in periods of *Zugunruhe,* or presumably in actual migration; and (2) *Zugstimmung,* the actual initiation of migratory behavior, expressed as *Zugunruhe* in caged birds, which the author presumed to be caused by increased secretion of thyroid hormone which mobilizes energy-rich reserves. Temperature was found to be an important modifying factor both in the appearance of and in the intensity of *Zugunruhe.* Recorded *Zugunruhe* has been the source of the basic data in the previously cited experiments of Schildmacher (1933, 1934a, 1937, 1938b), Stadie (1938, 1939), Giersberg and Stadie (1934), and Putzig (1937, 1938c). The entire phenomenon of *Zugunruhe* has been reviewed briefly by van Oordt (1943, 1949) and Steinbacher (1951) and much more thoroughly by Palmgren (1944b, 1949), who regards *Zugunruhe* as an expression of fundamental physiologic changes in which environmental factors may have important developmental, stimulatory, inhibitory, and modifying roles.

In America some recent attention has been given to this phenomenon. Ivor

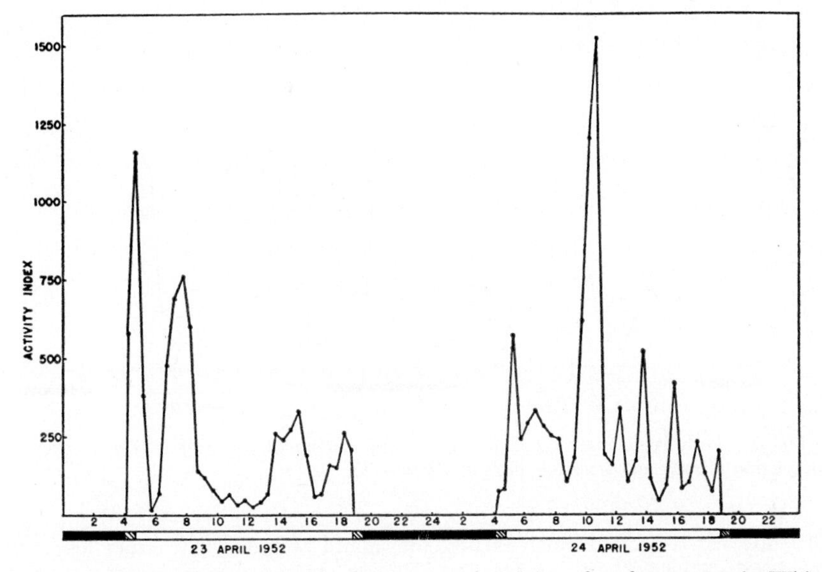

Fig. 1. Forty-eight-hour record of the rate of activity of a first-year male White-crowned Sparrow during prenuptial-like molt just prior to the onset of *Zugunruhe.* At the base of the figure, black bar designates the period of darkness; diagonally hatched bar, civil twilight; and open bar, sunrise to sunset.

(1944) has noted restlessness in caged Rose-breasted Grosbeaks, *Pheucticus ludovicianus,* at the time for normal migration. Eyster (1952) has reported the results of activity recordings on English Sparrows, Slate-colored Juncos, White-crowned Sparrows, *Zonotrichia leucophrys,* and White-throated Sparrows, *Zonotrichia albicollis.* He noted spring nocturnal unrest in Slate-colored Juncos and White-throated Sparrows, but none in English Sparrows. White-crowned Sparrows showed nocturnal unrest throughout the year except during molt. However maxima in activity were observed in spring and fall. Farner and Mewaldt (1953a, b) and Farner, Mewaldt, and King (unpublished) have made extensive recordings of the diurnal activity patterns of caged White-crowned Sparrows both in natural outdoor conditions of light and temperature and under experimental conditions. The results, at least in gross aspects, are quite consistent with the experience of European investigators in the recording of *Zugunruhe* and with Eyster's (1952) observations on White-crowned Sparrows. Much of the data of Farner, Mewaldt, and King remain to be analyzed; however, it has been noted (Farner and Mewaldt, 1953b) that in midwinter an elevation of environmental temperature to 22°C., an increase in photoperiod to fifteen hours per day, or a combination of both cause the development of extensive nocturnal activity. It is tempting to regard this as analogous with migratory behavior but, in the present status of our knowledge, caution is certainly indicated as Thomson

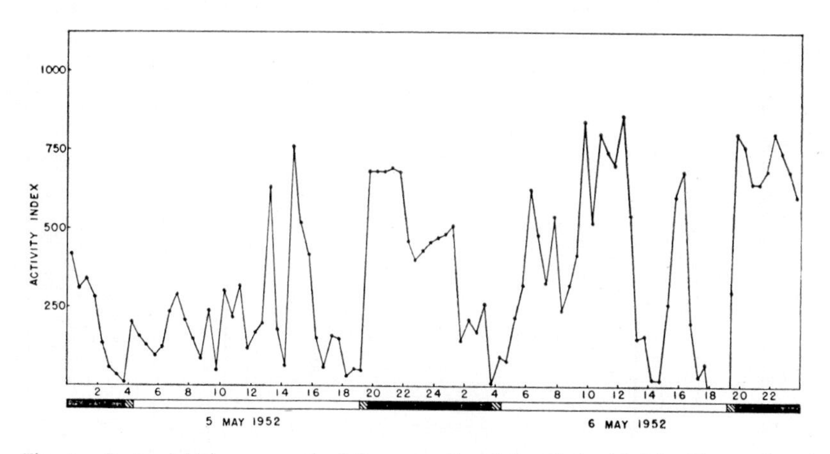

Fig. 2. Forty-eight-hour record of the rate of activity of the bird in Fig. 1 after th completion of molt and after the onset of *Zugunruhe*.

(1936b) has suggested much earlier. It should be noted that either lengthening photoperiod or raising environmental temperature creates a more favorable metabolic situation either by reduction of caloric loss in thermoregulation or by providing increased opportunity for caloric intake. It could be speculated then that this nocturnal activity may be simply a device for physiologic dissipation of the excess energy ("productive energy" of Kendeigh). On the other hand, one could also speculate that this more favorable metabolic situation is a basic requirement in many species for the development of migratory activity. Certainly the studies of Groebbels (1928, 1930, 1932), Merkel

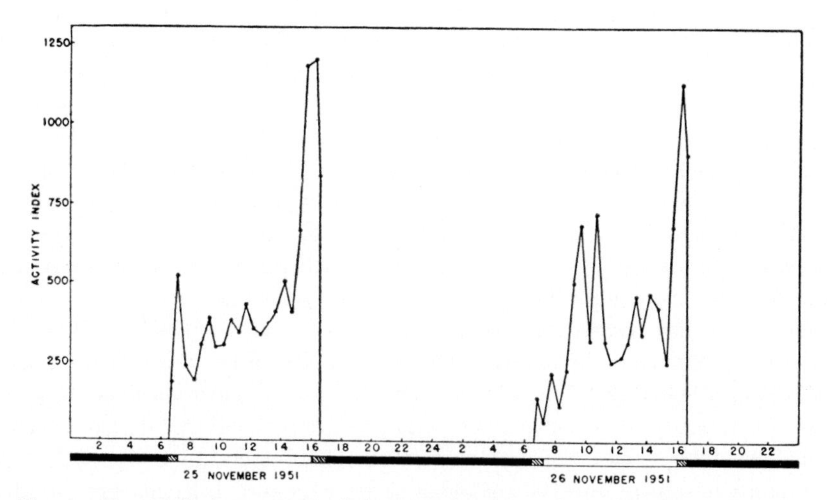

Fig. 3. Forty-eight hour record of the rate of activity of an adult female Clark Nutcracker. This species has not shown nocturnal activity at any time of the year.

(1937, 1938, 1940), Kendeigh (1934, 1944, 1949), Seibert (1949), and Wallgren (1952) lend a sound basis for this type of reasoning. Perhaps this more favorable metabolic situation may lead directly to migratory activity with other external environmental factors playing only a relatively minor role. However, one must not fail to recognize the probable existence of mechanisms which "direct" the course of expenditure of such productive energy (migration, molt, or reproductive activity). These suggestions with respect to the relation of *Zugunruhe* to an improved metabolic situation are consistent with the phenomenon of premigratory fat disposition to be discussed subsequently.

It is of importance to note that Ball (1952) in his important studies of migration on the Gaspé Peninsula has indicated that there is some evidence of the development of a restless behavior in migratory passerines prior to departure in fall. It is also of interest to note that the nocturnal pattern of migration in thrushes as observed by him is quite similar to the patterns of *Zugunruhe* recorded in thrushes by European investigators.

THE GONADAL HYPOTHESES

In his pioneer experiments Rowan (1925, 1926, 1929, 1931, 1946) subjected Slate-colored Juncos in winter to artificially increased daily photoperiods. The testes of these birds gradually developed and increased in size, whereas in the controls the testes remained at a size and development normal for the season. Rowan then associated the increasing size and development of the gonads of the experimental birds with the similarly increasing size and development in spring migrants. When light-treated birds were released in midwinter, many disappeared, whereas controls with undeveloped gonads remained in the vicinity. This was interpreted as an indication of migration on the part of the experimental birds.

Rowan (1930, 1932, 1946) also conducted experiments on migration with American Crows, *Corvus brachyrhynchos.* In winter releases of crows, which had been subjected to artificially increased day length, some northwesterly movements were obtained; there were also southeasterly movements; also some individuals were sedentary. Castrates, similarly treated and released, with a single exception (described as a partial castrate), were sedentary or moved in a southeasterly direction. Noncastrated controls which received no light treatment were sedentary or moved in a southeasterly direction typical of normal migration in autumn. These results appear to indicate the necessity of the testes in the stimulation of northward migration and constitute the strongest available argument for an important regulatory role on the part of the gonads. Experiments involving treatment with certain hormonal preparations were inconclusive.

Rowan (1926, 1929) first proposed that migration, spring or fall, is stimulated by hormones secreted by the testes or ovaries at a certain stage of partial development and that the regression and recrudescence of the gonads is caused by the decrease and increase in day length in spring and autumn. Later, in consideration of the results from the experiments with Crows, Rowan (1931, 1932) revised his theory to the effect that fall migration is probably not dependent on any particular stage of regression but only on regression, castration representing the maximum regression. Still later however, Rowan (1946), although still placing emphasis on the role of the gonads, suggested that the pituitary and "the entire physiology of the animal" are involved in the stimulation of migration.

Schildmacher (1933, 1934a, 1934b) has reported results from experiments on young and adult European Redstarts which have been interpreted (Bullough, 1945) as support for a hypothesis of gonadal stimulation of migration. It was reported that small injections of female sex hormone caused a cessation of migratory behavior in fall in caged birds, whereas migratory behavior persisted when larger injections were made. Schildmacher, in interpreting these results, assumed that fall migration is the result of decrease in sex hormones, whereas spring migration is stimulated by an increase in sex hormones. He then suggested that the small doses counteracted the stimulating effect of decreasing sex-hormone level, whereas the large doses actually produced a simulation of springtime migratory behavior. These experiments have been criticized, with apparent justification, on several points by van Oordt (1943, 1949), Steinbacher (1933), and Desselberger and Steinbacher (1934). Stadie (1939) was unable to confirm Schildmacher's results with similar experiments on European Redstarts. Unfortunately the experiments of both Schildmacher and Stadie involved very small numbers of experimental animals. The same is true for the earlier experiments of Giersberg and Stadie (1934) in which a simulated *Zugunruhe* was reported following the injection of female sex hormone preparations in Whitethroats. Merkel (1938) suggested that Schildmacher's results were the consequence of increased metabolic rate. One must agree with Thomson's (1936b) observation that none of these experiments involving injections of hormones have produced results on which definitive conclusions may be based.

In a number of migratory species it has been possible to correlate an incomplete migration or lack of migration with incomplete gonadal development in nonbreeding birds (van Ordt, 1928, 1931; Putzig, 1938b; Wynne-Edwards, 1939; Bullough, 1945; and others). These correlations have been interpreted by Bullough (1945) as evidence of a possible primary role of the gonads in the regulation of migration. However, these correlations need not necessarily indicate a cause-and-effect relationship.

In addition to those of Rowan (1926, 1932), hypotheses assuming a primary regulation of migration by the gonads have been suggested by Cahn (1925), Bergtold (1926), Heape (1931), Lincoln (1950), Bullough (1945, 1951), and Marshall (1951). It should be pointed out, however, that Rowan (1926, and more particularly 1946) has recognized the necessity of a much broader physiologic basis for migratory behavior. Farner (1950) has summarized the evidences and arguments against the general validity of the simple unifactoral gonadal hypotheses. These include, in part: migration by castrates (Putzig, 1937, 1939a; Hann, 1939; Drost, 1941); the improbability of identical functions of the ovaries and testes or the hormones produced by them; the fact that the hypotheses are based almost exclusively on correlations which need not represent cause-and-effect relations; and the failure of gonadotropic preparations (Wolfson, 1945) to cause the premigratory deposition of fat in Oregon Juncos, *Junco oreganus,* although a primarily somatotropic preparation was found to evoke both gonadal development and fat deposition. More recently Farner and Mewaldt (1953b) have been able to demonstrate with White-crowned Sparrows, *Zonotrichia leucophrys,* that a development of nocturnal activity similar to that displayed during spring migration can be induced by raising environmental temperature without development of the gonads. If this induced nocturnal activity is the same as the nocturnal activity displayed during the period of spring migration, it would appear that no primary role can be assigned to the gonads with respect to the development of the necessary physiologic condition for migration or the actual release of migratory behavior. Putzig (1938d) has developed a similar argument on the basis of his observations that, in some caged passerines, the development of nocturnal activity does not necessarily accompany the premature gonadal development induced by increased photoperiod. It should be emphasized, however, that the presently available evidences do not warrant the preclusion of contributory and modifying gonadal influences in the total physiologic picture of the development and release of migratory behavior. For example, Schildmacher and Steubing (1952) have reported experiments on male Bramblings, *Fringilla montifringilla,* which suggest that it is testosterone produced by the developing testes in spring which may be responsible for the premigratory deposition of fat. It should be noted further that the available information does not necessarily preclude the possibility that the gonads may have a primary regulatory role in the initiation of migration in some species. On the other hand a primary causal and regulatory role with respect to migration in birds in general seems extremely improbable. It should be emphasized in this respect that the very nature of selection of migratory and reproductive patterns is certain to have had a tendency toward a synchronization regardless of the physiologic relationships between the two cycles. With this and the possibility of a multiple phylogenetic origin of migration in mind, it is patent that extreme caution must be exercised with respect to proposing an immediate causal relation between the gonadal and migratory cycles.

Rowan (1946:129) has logically observed that ". . . the marked changes induced in the pituitary and gonadal activity are surely but tangible symptoms of a more general and deep-seated effect." For the present, then, we must continue to note that the available evidences cited in support of the gonadal hypotheses actually support a more profound physiologic explanation as well or better, and further, that some of the evidence actually denies a primary stimulatory role on the part of the gonads. These misgivings about the general applicability of the gonadal hypotheses are certainly consistent, at least in part, with those of Schäfer (1907), Eifrig (1924), Bissonnette (1937), Merkel (1938), Putzig (1938a), Toschi (1939), Woodbury (1941), van Oordt (1949), Promptov (1949), Collias (1950), Bourlière (1950), Dircksen (1951), Phillips (1951), and others.

THE THYROID HYPOTHESES

The investigations of Riddle and Fisher (1925), Häcker (1926), Watzka (1934), Miller (1937), and Höhn (1949) indicate that there are seasonal cycles in thyroid function in many avian species and (Höhn, 1950) that there is sufficient evidence to indicate that in birds, as in mammals, extensive periods of cold weather evoke increase thyroid activity. Riddle, Smith, and Benedict (1932), in comparing the metabolism of the migratory Mourning Dove, *Zenaidura macroura,* and the nonmigratory Rock Dove, *Columba livia,* suggested that the failure of the thyroid gland to respond to cold weather in the former might be responsible for its migratory behavior. Doubtless this suggestion refers to the relative selective value of the development of a migratory behavior pattern in a species in which the thyroid mechanism for increasing metabolism in cold temperatures is inadequate.

It should be indicated here that most investigations and hypotheses concerning the thyroid gland in relation to migration have been directed either towards the thyroid gland's role in the development of the necessary metabolic condition for migration or towards its role in the immediate release of migratory behavior. Sometimes the two concepts have been confused. Wagner (1930) was able to obtain a simulated *Zugunruhe* in his experimental Whitethroats with thyroid extracts and suggested that the thyroid hormone may have a role in the natural stimulation of *Zugunruhe.* Similarly Merkel (1937, 1938, 1940) was able also to produce a simulated *Zugunruhe* in caged Whitethroats and European Robins with injections of relatively small doses of thyroxin or thyrotropic hormone preparations; larger doses interrupted or inhibited *Zugunruhe.* Merkel suggested that the thyroid gland could have an integral function in the annual stimulation of migration; particularly he suggested that a very slight increase in thyroid activity could be responsible for the initiation of fall as well as spring migratory behavior in birds in metabolic condition to migrate. He felt that his data and conclusions were in agreement with the concept of cyclic thyroid function as advanced by Häcker (1926), Küchler (1935), and Elterich (1936). Although Groebbels (1930) suggested that decreased thyroid activity may be involved in the development of the metabolic condition necessary to migrate, this is not necessarily incompatible with Merkel's hypothesis of thyroid release of migratory behavior. Merkel (1937, 1938, 1940) has suggested further that the difference between the slight increase in thyroid activity necessary for stimulation of migration and the greater amount necessary to cause molting makes these two processes mutually exclusive.

Putzig (1937, 1938b) has given extensive consideration, on the basis of histologic studies, to the possible role of the thyroid gland in migration. Particular attention has been given (1938b) Lapwings, *Vanellus vanellus,* and certain other limicoline species. In general the data are quite variable; however, in the Lapwing the thyroid gland during spring migration usually contains a certain amount of chromophobic colloid suggestive of a certain degree of activity. In the early fall migration (*Frühwegzug*) the epithelium is described as having a good functional appearance with some follicles containing little or no colloid. Putzig has conjectured that *Frühwegzug* is associated with a metabolic condition dominated by elevated thyroid secretion. Putzig (1938d) has suggested further that the thyroid gland in migratory birds may show, in addition to the well-known responses to temperature changes, an intrinsic rhythm which may be important in migration. Experimentally he found that injection of rather large doses of thyrotropic hormone into European Robins in *Zugdisposition* in fall resulted in a simulated or enhanced *Zugunruhe,* whereas smaller doses were ineffective. These results were therefore somewhat different than those obtained by Merkel (1937, 1938, 1940) on Whitethroats and European Robins. Both investigators, however, used a very small number of experimental birds. Putzig (1938b, 1939a, b) apparently considered the role of the thyroid as a part of a more intricate endocrine and metabolic pattern in the development of migratory behavior rather than as an immediate triggering mechanism.

Schildmacher and Rautenberg (1952) have reported that the daily injection of 0.2 mg. of thyroxin in Bramblings and Chaffinches, *Fringilla coelebs,* may result in a sufficiently increased food intake so that there is an increase in body weight despite a higher metabolic rate. If this phenomenon actually occurs under natural conditions, it would be possible to rationalize increased thyroid activity with the characteristic metabolism of the migratory period.

Schildmacher (1952a) has actually characterized the period of beginning of spring migration as one of increased thyroid activity. He has suggested that the fall migratory period becomes possible with the termination of the dissimilatory effects of sex hormones of the breeding season and with the termination of the marked elevation of thyroid activity of the postnuptial molt.

Although the data obtained by Putzig (1937, 1938b, 1938d) and Merkel (1937, 1938, 1940) and the suggestions of Schildmacher (1952a) are interesting, it is still not possible to designate precisely the role of the thyroid gland in migration; certainly the evidence does not indicate a primary regulatory role. In assessing the possible role of the thyroid gland in the regulation of migration we must accept the warning of Thomson (1936b) that the simulated *Zugunruhe* obtained with injections of thyroid and thyrotropic preparations may not necessarily represent true migratory behavior. We must certainly agree with Höhn (1950) both in his observation that the role of the thyroid gland in migration is still speculative and with his suggestion that it receive more attention in future research.

METABOLIC ASPECTS OF MIGRATION—THE RELATION OF FAT DEPOSITION TO THE DEVELOPMENT OF MIGRATORY BEHAVIOR

Although there are substantial differences in important details, hypotheses suggesting the development of a distinctive metabolic condition prior to migration have been suggested by Groebbels (1928, 1930, 1932), Merkel (1937, 1938, 1940), Kendeigh (1934, 1945, 1949), van Oordt (1943, 1949), Wolfson (1942, 1945), Seibert (1949), and Schüz (1952). Many aspects of these hypotheses have been anticipated by Rowan (1926), Wachs (1926), and others.

It is of interest to note that some of the hypotheses are designed primarily to explain an accumulation of energy reserves, principally fat deposits, as a necessary prerequisite for migration or as the reflection of a favorable metabolic balance necessary for migration. On the other hand, several (Kendeigh, 1945, 1949; Seibert, 1949) suggest that migration is forced in fall by an unfavorable metabolic situation resulting from the greater loss of energy in thermoregulation and a decreased energy intake because of decreased photoperiod; presumably as conditions become more favorable in spring the return movement becomes physiologically possible. Actually these two types of hypotheses are not necessarily mutually exclusive. However, it would seem that a mechanism of the latter type is more properly to be associated with weather migrants (*aussenweltbedingte Zugvögel* of Putzig), for it would appear that, in many typical migrants, the beginning of migration cannot be associated with such environmental changes. This discussion is therefore constructed for those species in which migration actually begins in advance of the periodic appearance of the environmental conditions which make migration necessary for survival of the species.

The association of fat deposition with the development of migration is of long standing. It was noted by Naumann, for example, as early as 1822 (Wachs, 1926). The observations and data of Zedlitz (1926), Groebbels (1928, 1930, 1932), Linsdale and Sumner (1934b), Merkel (1937), Baumgartner (1938), Shaw (1939), Hagen (1942), Wolfson (1945), and Meinertzhagen (1951) suggest, in a variety of species, that an increase in weight involving fat deposition is characteristic of the premigratory period and that there are consequently characteristic differences in weight cycles between migratory and nonmigratory forms.

Considerable information has been accumulated on premigratory fat deposition in spring in the finches of the genus *Zonotrichia.* Linsdale and Sumner (1934a, b) have published data on the Golden-crowned Sparrow, *Zonotrichia coronata,* which indicate a pronounced increase in weight prior to spring migration. Wolfson (1945) has shown this to be, at least in part, the result of deposition of fat. Blanchard (1941) has found in the migratory *Zonotrichia leucophrys pugetensis* that there is similarly a marked deposition of fat before departure in spring; Wolfson's (1945) data on the same subspecies supply additional details. Blanchard and Erickson (1949) have found a similar situation in the migratory *Zonotrichia leucophrys gambelii* on the basis of inspection of subcutaneous fat depots. These observations are confirmed by the more quantitative and extensive data of Farner, Mewaldt, and McGreal (unpublished) obtained by extraction of carcasses. In the case of the nonmigratory race *Zonotrichia leucophrys nuttalli,* this "premigratory" increase in weight was found not to occur (Blanchard, 1941). Odum (1949) has presented extensive data on the weight of White-throated Sparrows taken in the winter range in Georgia. Two peaks, one in midwinter and a second just prior to northward migration, are evident. More recently Odum and Perkinson (1951) have shown that there is a pronounced premigratory deposition of lipids in spring in this species. Data from preliminary experiments by Farner, Mewaldt, and McGreal (unpublished) with *Zonotrichia leucophrys gambelii* indicate that two distinct increases in fat deposition occur in response to increased photoperiod and increased environmental temperature, respectively. The former apparently requires a minimum of about fourteen hours of light per day.

Wolfson's (1940, 1942, 1945) observations and experiments on the migratory races of the Oregon Junco, *Junco oreganus,* under both experimental and natural conditions in California, indicate clearly that an increase in weight, because of increased fat deposition, occurs prior to spring migration. It was found that this would develop prematurely with artificial increases in daily photoperiod. This phenomenon does not occur in nonmigratory *Junco oreganus pinosus.* Later investigations by Wolfson (1952b) indicate that there is also a premigratory fat deposition in the migratory Slate-colored Junco and that there is also a fat-deposition response to increased daily photoperiod in this species. Schildmacher and Steubing (1952) have reported that increased fat deposition can be obtained in male Bramblings with increased daily photoperiods, treatment with preparations from pregnant-mare serum, or implants of testosterone. In Belgium, de Bont (1947) has demonstrated with Chaffinches that increasing the daily photoperiod can result in fat deposition in migrant birds but fails to do so in sedentary individuals. Koch and de Bont (1952) found a marked difference in the pattern of standard metabolism between migratory and sedentary Chaffinches. Also a marked increase in weight and fat deposition was again noted in the migratory Chaffinch with increased photoperiod; this did not occur in the sedentary form.

Kirkpatrick (1944) found that female Ring-necked Pheasants, *Phasianus colchicus,* increase in weight in spring but that there is no corresponding increase in males. These data are similar to those of Wilson (1911) for the Red Grouse, *Lagopus scoticus,* and to those of Hagen (1942) for the Willow

Grouse, *Lagopus lagopus.* Mr. T. D. Burleigh (personal communication) has informed me that in Blue Grouse, *Dendragapus obscurus,* in Idaho, females are quite fat in spring, whereas males are not. Conceivably this situation, which may be common in nonmigratory species, could result from increased estrogen secretion in spring; the fattening effect of estrogen in the domestic fowl is well established. In other words, it is possible that those nonmigratory species in which only the female deposits fat in spring represent quite a different situation than those migratory species in which both sexes deposit fat before migration. This problem is one that merits further investigation.

As a broad generalization, as Schildmacher (1952a) and others have suggested, it appears that among temperate-zone species the deposition of fat in fall is a rather common phenomenon whereas the spring deposition of fat is generally a characteristic of migratory birds. There are noteworthy exceptions, such as the female galliform birds as noted in the paragraph above, and possibly others as noted below. Nice's (1937) very extensive data on the Song Sparrow, *Melospiza melodia,* in Ohio, however, do not conform with the general pattern for migratory species. Wolfson (1945) has suggested that this may be the result of the failure to separate resident and migrant individuals. Nice (1946) has consequently reanalyzed and published her data in accordance with migrant and resident status. The data on winter visitants do not indicate a correspondence with the weight cycle in the migrant races of the Oregon Junco and the White-crowned Sparrow in California. Nice (1946) has suggested that climatic differences between Ohio and California may account for the differences. It seems equally probable that fundamental physiologic differences between the species may be involved. The extensive treatise on bird weights by Baldwin and Kendeigh (1938), like that of Nice (1937, 1946), does not support a general hypothesis of weight increase and fat deposition prior to spring migration. This may not necessarily be evidence against the hypothesis because, as Wolfson (1945) has indicated, the data were not analyzed from the standpoint of migration, and further, because of individual differences in weight, premigratory increases in weight may be obscured. On the other hand it must be conceded that premigratory deposition of fat does not necessarily occur in some species. Putzig (1939b) has suggested that although birds with ample energy reserves are more likely to migrate, the premigratory accumulation of energy reserves is not a necessary physiologic prerequisite for migration. Obviously there is a great need for reliable information on weight cycles both in migratory and nonmigratory species; particularly desirable are series of data for individual birds. There is an equally great need for information on the normal temporal patterns of fat deposition and fat mobilization.

There has been a tendency to place considerable emphasis on the premigratory fat deposition in terms of a reservoir of energy to be used in migration.

However, the data of Kendeigh (1949), Seibert (1949), Pearson (1950), and Koch and de Bont (1952) on energy requirements of small birds indicate that the maximum possible energy reserves cannot be of great significance as compared to daily intake of energy. Equally important at least is the fact that deposition of fat is a reflection of a favorable energy balance, i.e., that the intake of energy is exceeding current requirements, thus allowing a daily balance which can be used for additional physiologic activity such as migration. Although the premigratory deposition of fat can occur only as a result of a more favorable energy balance, most physiologic aspects of it are quite obscure. Groebbels (1928) for example, suggested that the premigratory fattening in fall is not the result of increased energy intake but rather is the result of better utilization of food and altered metabolism perhaps as the result of endocrine changes such as the absence of the dissimilatory effects of sex hormones. He suggested that a type of physiological castration might be involved. He also (1932) emphasized the daily period available for obtaining food, environmental temperature, and energy requirements in a subsequent discussion. Merkel (1937, 1938, 1940) has suggested that both an increased energy intake and a decreased energy requirement are involved. Koch and de Bont (1952) were unable to demonstrate a suppression of standard metabolic rate during fat deposition in migratory Chaffinches and believe that Merkel's suggestion of reduced metabolic rate cannot hold. In commenting on the premigratory deposition of fat in spring, Kendeigh (1949) has pointed out that increasing environmental temperatures and longer photoperiods for energy intake result in a favorable energy balance in which unused "productive energy" may be stored in fat depots or used in migration; in nonmigratory forms this productive energy is used, as soon as it occurs, in reproductive activity, with none therefore being available for fat deposition. Also noteworthy is the limited experimental evidence on male Bramblings (Schildmacher and Steubing, 1952) indicating that male sex hormones may be partially responsible for the spring deposition of fat and that a certain degree of elevation of thyroid activity in Bramblings and Chaffinches (Schildmacher and Rautenberg, 1952) may increase food intake sufficiently to cause a gain in weight. One may speculate that under natural conditions these phenomena could develop in response to increased pituitary activity evoked by increased photoperiod, a possibility that is suggested by Wolfson's (1952) investigations with Slate-colored Juncos.

Unquestionably much serious thinking must go into consideration of the cyclic physico-chemical relationship between the bird and its environment and the mechanisms which regulate these relationships. To Groebbels (1928, 1930, 1932), Merkel (1937, 1938, 1940), Putzig (1938b, 1939b), Kendeigh (1934, 1949), Seibert (1949), Promptov (1949), and Koch and de Bont (1952) goes much credit for orientation of thinking in this respect. Unquestionably the requirements of thermoregulation, food procurement and other basic vegetal functions have a physiologic priority with respect to available energy. But scant progress has been made in understanding the mechanisms which determine how the excess productive energy is to be used.

In this respect Wolfson's (1952b) investigations of the refractory period in the gonadal and fat deposition cycles in Slate-colored Juncos are of interest. This refractory period occurs after a period of gonadal activity; during it increased photoperiod does not initiate development of the gonads or deposition of fat. The refractoriness of the gonad-stimulating mechanism is quite well known in a variety of species and has been discussed critically by Burger (1949) and Marshall (1951). Wolfson's investigations on Slate-colored Juncos indicate that long daily photoperiods extend the refractory period, whereas short daily photoperiods bring it to termination more quickly. Unpublished data obtained in my laboratory with *Zonotrichia leucophrys gambelii* are consistent with these observations. The investigations of Schildmacher (1939) on European Redstarts and European Robins, those of Miller (1949) on Golden-crowned Sparrows and, more particularly, those of Benoit *et al.* (1950) on ducks indicate that the seat of refractoriness of the gonad-stimulating mechanism is doubtless in the anterior pituitary. It seems therefore very probable, as Wolfson has previously suggested, that in some species at least, the development of the necessary physiologic state for spring migration as indicated by the accumulation of fat deposits and the development of the gonads are both functions of a change in the anterior pituitary resulting from increased photoperiod. With respect to spring migration in temperate-zone species it appears, therefore, that we must think in terms of altered physico-chemical relationships with the environment resulting in increased productive energy and a control of the disposition of this productive energy through endocrine mechanisms.

There is a further question with respect to the relationship of the altered metabolic state, as indicated by fat deposition, and the immediate release of migratory behavior. Does migratory behavior itself result from the development of this altered metabolic state (*Zugdisposition*) or is an additional immediate stimulus required? The scanty evidence indicates either to be possible. Perhaps the situation varies in different species. If the release of *Zugunruhe* in caged birds is the same as release of natural migratory behavior, it would appear (Farner and Mewaldt, 1953b and unpublished data) that in migratory White-crowned Sparrows, under certain conditions at least, the development of a favorable energy balance by increasing photoperiod with additional feeding time or by increasing environmental temperature, thus reducing energy loss, may be all that is necessary in the development of spring migration. It should be noted that Verwey (1949) has questioned the validity of *Zugdisposition* as a real functional entity. Certainly it may represent different conditions in different species. The available information on immediate environmental stimuli will be discussed subsequently.

THE ROLE OF THE ANTERIOR PITUITARY

The rhythmic reappearance of the apparently characteristic metabolic condition (*Zugdisposition*) necessary for migration has led naturally to reflection concerning a fundamental regulatory organ with an intrinsic rhythmicity or which responds to a rhythmic environmental cycle of proper frequency. The necessity of such a mechanism to determine the disposition of productive energy has been indicated above. The previously discussed hypotheses involving the gonads and the thyroid gland were attempts to establish mechanisms. The inadequacies of these hypotheses have been indicated in an earlier paper (Farner, 1950) and elsewhere in this discussion. Among the most obvious possibilities of such a fundamental regulatory organ is the anterior pituitary gland. This has been suggested by Bissonnette (1937), Putzig (1938b, c, 1939a), and Wolfson (1942, 1945, 1952b), among others. Positive evidence for such a hypothesis is admittedly fragmentary. Wolfson (1945), in experiments on Oregon Juncos, has found that injection of a gonadotropic preparation from pregnant-mare serum resulted in a good gonadal response in the males of both migratory and resident races but that the characteristic premigratory fat deposition failed to occur in the males of the migratory race. In another series of experiments involving rather small numbers of birds and begun, unfortunately after the beginning of spring gonadal recrudescence, he obtained results which indicated that both gonadal recrudescence and premigratory deposition of fat could be obtained by injection of a preparation, Antuitrin G, containing largely somatotropic hormone but also small amounts of other anterior pituitary hormones. In simultaneous experiments, the injection of a chorionic-gonadotropic preparation caused some gonadal recrudescence but no fat deposition. Cytologic studies of the anterior pituitary, particularly in respect to the Golgi apparatus, indicated that there is increased activity as the photoperiod increases and that the response is rather strikingly different between resident and migrant races. For several reasons, including the small numbers of birds involved and the necessary assumption that the fat deposition obtained was actually an indicator of the development of the metabolic condition necessary for migration, the results of these experiments are suggestive rather than conclusive in nature.

It should be recalled at this point that Merkel (1937, 1938, 1940) and Putzig (1938a) in experiments with European Robins and other species in fall have been able to obtain a simulated *Zugunruhe,* at least in some cases, with properly selected dosages of thyrotropic hormone preparation. Consideration of these experiments probably should be in respect to the *immediate release* of migration and not in consideration of the development of the metabolic state necessary for migratory behavior. Furthermore the results of these experiments, because of the small numbers of birds involved and because of the rather profound effects of disturbed thyroid function, are very difficult to interpret. As mentioned above, the suggestions of Schildmacher and Steubing (1952) and Schildmacher and Rautenberg (1952) with respect to thyroid and gonadal roles in the metabolism of the spring migratory period could be explained in terms of a primary pituitary regulation.

Actually the arguments favoring a hypothesis of primary regulation by mechanisms involving the anterior pituitary are therefore mostly indirect. They may be summarized as follows: (1) a scanty amount of direct experimental evidence as cited above; (2) the somewhat parallel relationships, in many temperate-zone species, of the gonadal and migratory cycles with respect to photoperiod and the improbability that this parallel relationship between gonadal and migratory cycles represents a cause-and-effect relationship; (3) the gonadal response to increased photoperiod involves the anterior pituitary (see Benoit, 1950, for résumé of evidence) thus suggesting that the somewhat parallel behavior of the migratory cycle is also the result of a mechanism involving this gland; (4) the refractory period, which follows a period of gonadal development, involves refractoriness of the anterior pituitary to increased daily photoperiods (Schildmacher, 1939; Miller, 1949; Benoit *et al.*, 1950); furthermore, it is also a period of refractoriness with respect to photoperiodically stimulated premigratory fat deposition (Wolfson, 1952a, b).

It should be pointed out here that change in daily photoperiod, i.e., periodically increasing or decreasing day lengths, has been suggested, by one mechanism or another, as basic to migratory behavior in the writings of many investigators including von Homeyer (1881), Schäfer (1907), Bretscher (1915), von Lucanus (1923), Eifrig (1924), Rowan (1925, 1926, 1931), Groebbels (1928), Wachs (1926), Wetmore (1926), Thomson (1936a, b), Bissonnette (1937), Toschi (1939), van Oordt (1943, 1949), and Wolfson (1942, 1945). That increasing day length could serve as the basis of the physiologic condition necessary for migration has been experimentally demonstrated or strongly suggested by Rowan (1926, 1929) for Slate-colored Juncos by actual departures; by Wolfson (1942, 1945) for migratory races of Oregon Juncos by fat deposition and actual departures and for Slate-colored Juncos (1952) by fat deposition; by Putzig (1938c) for European Robins, European Redstarts, and Garden Warblers on the basis of recording of *Zugunruhe;* by Schildmacher (1937, 1938b) for European Redstarts and European Robins on the basis of *Zugunruhe;* by de Bont (1947) for Chaffinches on the basis of fat deposition; and by Miller (1948) for Golden-crowned Sparrows on the basis of fat deposition. More recently Wolfson and Winn (1948) and Wolfson (1952b) have emphasized the cumulative effect of light in the gonadal responses and deposition of fat.

Although a hypothesis involving a cyclic function of the anterior lobe of the pituitary gland resulting from stimulation because of increased day length and decline in function because of decreased day length is attractive, there can be no general application of it in such a simple form. Few migratory cycles correspond symmetrically to the annual pattern of decreasing and increasing day lengths. Likewise such a simple hypothesis would be untenable for transequatorial migrants and for many types of migrations which occur in the tropics (Moreau, 1931). The first two objections can be circumvented, at least in a large part, by consideration of the occurrence of refractory periods (Bissonnette, 1937; Wolfson, 1952a), the cumulative nature of the effects of light (Wolfson, 1952a), and varying thresholds with respect to increased photoperiod. Although Wolfson (1952a, b) has suggestive evidence from temperate-zone fringillids, final analysis of the applicability of these suggestions must await detailed studies on transequatorial and tropical migrants. It has been suggested by Witschi (1935) that some gonadal cycles may be the reflection of an inherent internal cycle involving the pituitary gland; possibly the same could be true in some instances for the migratory cycle. Moreau (1931) has suggested that there may exist all degrees of variation of migratory cycles from those which are completely dependent on photoperiodism to those with a complete dependence on internal cycles.

THE MECHANISM OF THE STIMULATION OF THE ANTERIOR PITUITARY BY LIGHT

Although this interesting problem has been investigated almost exclusively with respect to gonadal response to increased photoperiod, it is reasonable to assume that information obtained therefrom may be useful in consideration of a role of the anterior pituitary in the development of the physiologic state necessary for migration. The coincidence of refractoriness in the gonadal and fat deposition cycles (Miller, 1948; Wolfson, 1952a, b), assuming fat deposition to be an indicator of the physiologic state necessary for migration, suggests that such reasoning may be useful. It is well known that in a large number of species an increase in daily photoperiod will result in a development of the gonads (see Burger, 1949, for summary). Burger (1949) has also summarized the investigations on the relationship of wave-length to gonadal response; apparently the most effective wave lengths are those which lie in the yellow-red. With respect to intensity, it would appear that the rate of gonadal development is a function of intensity from an undetermined minimum, which probably is different for different species, to a maximum which definitely differs with different species (Burger, 1949; Bartholomew, 1949; Wolfson, 1952a, b). With respect to photoreception there is considerable evidence (Burger, 1949) that the eye is the primary receptor although the remarkable experiments performed in Benoit's laboratory (Benoit, 1935a, b, c, 1937, 1950; Benoit and Ott, 1944) on ducks indicate, in this species at least, that there is in addition an encephalo-hypophysial receptor system which does not involve the eyes.

Wolfson and Winn (1948) and Wolfson (1952b) have obtained experimental data on Slate-colored Juncos and White-crowned Sparrows which strongly support the thesis that daily photoperiod, *whether constant or gradually increasing,* induces an increment of physiologic change which is directly proportional to the length of the daily photoperiod up to a maximum of sixteen hours for the species studied. According to Wolfson (1952a), one may think of the summation of increments reaching a threshold after a period of summation or induction, at which time the various responses become manifest. Wolfson (1952a) also found that, once initiated, the rate of response is a direct function of the length of the daily photoperiod. Furthermore it was found that reduction of daily photoperiod to nine hours resulted in regression of partially developed testes.

Recently Kirkpatrick and Leopold (1952) have found that in Bobwhite Quail, *Colinus virginianus,* it is possible to induce gonadal development with a total of ten hours of light per day *if* one hour of it were used to interrupt the dark period. Further, the rate of gonadal development was found to be inversely proportional to the length of the longest dark period per day. These authors have emphasized the importance of the dark period in photoperiodic response. A similiar emphasis has been indicated by Jenner and Engels (1952) on the basis of similar experiments and similar results with White-throated Sparrows and Slate-colored Juncos. Although these concepts are by no means physiologically impossible, one is nevertheless tempted to seek explanations alternative to the "dark-dependent phase" of Jenner and Engels (1952) and the "dark period as an inhibiting factor" of Kirkpatrick and Leopold (1952). Another explanation might be proposed in terms of a persistent activity of the pituitary, in the release of gonadotropic hormones, or a persistence of gonadotropic hormones in the blood for a substantial period after the cessation of light. Should such a period have the duration of two hours or more and should the pituitary begin liberating gonadotropic hormone promptly after the beginning of lighting, it could be possible that these experiments functioned primarily by lengthening the daily period of release of gonadotropic hormone by the anterior pituitary. There are in the literature some investigations which are consistent with this suggestion. Benoit (1937) obtained a greater gonadal development in male ducks which received a standard period of dim light (nonstimulating in controls) plus two and one-half hours bright light for ten and one-half minutes per hour than in similar individuals which received the standard period of dim light plus one two and one-half hour period of bright light at night. Burger *et al.* (1942) found that spermatogenic activity in Starlings could be obtained with a total of ten hours light consisting of six hours of continuous light and eight hours in which alternate light and dark periods of five seconds duration were administered. The spermatogenic activity thus obtained was the same as in controls which received fourteen hours of uninterrupted light per day. Farner *et al.* (1953) have obtained results from intermittent lighting of *Zonotrichia leucophrys gambelii* which are consistent with such an explanation. In lighting experiments on poultry Dobie *et al.* (1946) investigated the effects on egg production of variously spaced periods of two- and eight-hour periods of light per day. They found that egg production was distinctly improved if the two-hour period began four hours after the end of the six-hour period and ended four hours before the beginning of the six-hour period. Staffe (1950, 1951) in investigations on egg production by the domestic fowl reported that hens treated with twenty-second shocks of intense light at 4:00 and 4:45 A.M. each day produced as many eggs as those which received continuous artificial light from 4:00 A.M. to daylight. Similar results have been reported by Weber (1951).

In each of the investigations described in this section the results could be rationalized by simply assuming that a "carry-over period" follows each photoperiod and that during the "carry-over" period (Farner *et al.*, 1953) there is a persistence of the gonadotropic effect developed during the photoperiod. Such a hypothesis has the merit of simplicity; however, further experiments are needed to establish its validity. Obviously more research is necessary to understand the mechanism of the gonadal response; much more research is also needed to understand whether a similar mechanism is involved in the development of the metabolic state necessary for migration.

THE IMMEDIATE RELEASE OF MIGRATORY BEHAVIOR

As mentioned above, the present fragmentary knowledge indicates that it is possible either that the development of *Zugdisposition* may by itself culminate in the release of migratory behavior or that once a state of *Zugdisposition* is attained, migratory behavior may be released by an additional environmental stimulus. The latter is apparently in accord with the conclusions reached by van Oordt (1943, 1949) and Bourlière (1950) in their analyses of the available information on the physiologic basis of the initiation of migration; their conclusions reflect strongly some of the thinking of Groebbels (1932) and Merkel (1938). This would conform then with a rather broad principle in animal behavior—the development of a requisite physiologic state for a particular response, with the actual response then being evoked by a specific stimulus or releaser. That the former, however, is possible, is suggested by the investigations of Farner and Mewaldt (1953b) on White-crowned Sparrows. Possibly the situation varies in different migratory species. However, it seems patent that true migratory movements are always preceded by the gradual development of a distinctive metabolic state—*Zugdisposition.*

It is not within the province of this paper to cite and discuss the almost innumerable papers which are concerned with the role of meteorologic and other external environmental factors which may serve as the immediate releasers of migratory behavior, although this aspect of the problem must enter into the construction of a general working hypothesis of the annual stimulation of migration. The possible roles of these factors, both as releasing and modifying influences, have been discussed at length by, among others, von Homeyer

(1881), Cooke (1913), Wachs (1926), Rowan (1931), Groebbels (1932), Kendeigh (1934), Lincoln (1950), Palmgren (1936, 1937), Palmgren *et al.* (1939), Nice (1937), Toschi (1939), Thomson (1942, 1949), von Haartman and Bergman (1943), van Oordt (1943, 1949), Vleugel (1948), Tugarīnov (1949), Promptov (1949), Drost (1951), Bagg *et al.* (1950), Williams (1950), Phillips (1951), Dircksen (1951), and Schüz (1952).

Of particular interest, of course, are those cases where there is evidence that the bird in *Zugdisposition* was actually stimulated to migrate or to develop migratory behavior by an external stimulus, such as a change in temperature, which is effective only during *Zugdisposition*. Palmgren (1936), on the basis of field observations, has suggested that a decline in temperature is necessary to cause migration of Goldcrests, *Regulus regulus,* once *Zugdisposition* has developed. Siivonen and Palmgren (1936) recorded an increase in *Zugunruhe* in a Song Thrush in fall following a decline in temperature. Palmgren (1937) has also reported the release of spring *Zugunruhe* in caged European Robins with an increase in temperature. Putzig (1937, 1938a) and Schildmacher (1938a) noted enhanced *Zugunruhe* in European Robins in spring with increased environmental temperature; probably this does not represent an actual *release* of migratory behavior however. Putzig (1938a, 1939a) also presented evidence that *Zugunruhe* in this species in fall was released by decreased environmental temperatures.

Merkel (1938) has suggested that Whitethroats and European Robins in *Zugdisposition* in fall may be stimulated to migrate by external factors, such as a decline in temperature. This he believed to be effected through a slight increase in thyroid activity. Farner and Mewaldt (1953b) have noted the initiation of nocturnal activity or the enhancement of light-induced nocturnal activity in winter and early spring in migratory White-crowned Sparrows with increases in environmental temperature. It seems possible, however, that this represents a case of increased productive energy directed into this activity rather than a stimulation of the release of migratory behavior in birds in *Zugdisposition*. This should emphasize again the caution which must be exercised in the interpretation of data from experiments on *Zugunruhe* in caged birds.

Vleguel (1948), on the basis of his observations of the winter movements of certain species of waterfowl and shorebirds in the Netherlands, has suggested that certain species, or populations thereof, may be in *Zugdisposition* throughout the winter. This would constitute a basis for winter movements in response to meteorologic changes and spring departures which vary accordingly. Schüz (1952) has made a similar suggestion with respect to birds whose migration varies extremely with meteorologic conditions, particularly those which arrive in the breeding area early in spring and depart late in fall, and whose migratory routes are relatively short. The migratory White-crowned Sparrows studied by Farner and Mewaldt (1953b) could conceivably represent this type of situation.

These suggestions, although hypothetical, are important and should be subjected to experimental investigations.

It should be noted that very little attention has been directed to the possibility of a Gestalt type of releasing situation. This certainly warrants investigation.

A WORKING HYPOTHESIS OF THE ANNUAL STIMULATION OF MIGRATION

The hypothesis proposed herein is an attempt to rationalize and integrate the fragmentary information from experimental investigations with the greater body of information derived from direct observations in the field. The available experimental data, as indicated in the previous pages, come primarily from several species of finches, thrushes, and old-world warblers. Since most of these species confine their migration to the temperate zone and since we have no information on the development of spring migration of those that have transequatorial migration, this hypothesis is constructed primarily for passerine species whose migration is confined to the temperate and subtropical parts of the northern hemisphere. Although certain elements of it may well be applicable to transequatorial migrants, experimental data on the development of spring migrating behavior in such species is necessary before any general extension of the hypothesis should be attempted.

It is proposed that in spring, with the lengthening of photoperiod and with increased mean temperatures, an improvement of energy balance develops because of lower energy requirements for thermoregulation, an increased daily period for intake of food, and possibly, in some instances, improved feeding conditions. This improvement in metabolic state may undergo a temporary reversal during the prenuptial molt, during which migratory behavior usually does not develop. The anterior pituitary has long since recovered from the refractory period because of the influence of the long winter nights and is now stimulated to activity by the cumulative effects of the lengthening photoperiod. The activated pituitary appears to influence the development of the favorable metabolic balance and quite possibly regulates the ways in which the excess energy is used. Also it now begins to exert its gonadotropic effect. There is possibly also an increase in thyroid activity which is very possibly associated with the prenuptial molt. Through the continued existence of the favorable metabolic balance and possibly, in addition, through the continued activity of the pituitary, the bird is brought into the physiologic condition necessary for migration, i.e., *Zugdisposition*. *Zugdisposition* may be characterized by the accumulation of substantial fat reserves, a remarkable ability to restore these reserves when depleted, a tendency to sleep more lightly, and a tendency to develop nocturnal restlessness. Either the continued persistence of *Zugdisposition* per se, or the influence of environmental stimuli, or a combination of both, results in the release of the migratory behavior pattern and the beginning of migration. Doubtless a flock behavior pattern is involved in the final development of migratory behavior. It is suggested that the role of temperature in the development of *Zugdisposition* and in the development of the gonads is related only to its effect on the energy required for thermoregulation. To that extent, then, higher mean temperatures in spring, by an energy-sparing effect, may contribute to a more rapid rate of development of *Zugdisposition* and a more rapid rate of gonadal development. It also appears best, at this time, to regard the role of the gonads in the development of spring migration as of a definitely secondary order.

The development of fall migration is somewhat more difficult to rationalize. Obviously again there is the development of a favorable energy balance at the end of the reproductive season and molting season in the case of the adults and at the end of the growing season in the case of the young of the year. Possibly in most migratory forms the pituitary is now refractory so that the gonads are inactive, with a consequent saving of energy. This favorable metabolic balance leads again to the development of a condition of *Zugdisposition,* apparently with characteristics similar to spring *Zugdisposition.* Again a persistence of *Zugdisposition* per se, the intervention of environmental factors such as possibly a drop in temperature, or a combination of both, results in the release of migratory behavior.

It should be noted that it is assumed that spring *Zugdisposition* is associated definitely with an active anterior pituitary, whereas fall *Zugdisposition* may be associated with a light-refractory anterior pituitary. It is tentatively assumed also that this refractory period is sufficiently long and well developed to preclude any *substantial reactivation* of the gonads and accompanying sexual behavior. Although the interpretation of the physiologic mechanism is different, we agree basically with Bullough's (1943) observation that the anterior pituitary of migrant forms is not susceptible to activation in late summer and fall, whereas it is susceptible for considerable periods, at least, in many nonmigrants. It is believed that the thinking in this hypothesis is consistent with the data of Marshall (1949, 1951, 1952) with respect to both reproductive and migratory cycles despite the rather substantial differences in interpretation.

As indicated herein previously, it is obviously scientifically precarious to assume that mechanisms of similar details may exist in the migratory species of the three families from which the data are drawn. However, since the fragmentary nature of the available data dictates the necessity of thinking still in quite general terms, this combination of data seems justifiable. I am by no means of the opinion that the ultimately acceptable theories of the annual stimulation of migration will necessarily retain any substantial part of the hypothesis. It is presented as an interpretation of the available information. It is hoped that it will stimulate experimental investigations which will provide the much needed information for developing a sound understanding of this fundamental and interesting aspect of avian migration.

ACKNOWLEDGMENTS

This review actually represents a revision of my previous review "The Annual Stimulus for Migration" (Condor, 52:104-122). Dr. Albert Wolfson, Dr. George E. Hudson, Mr. T. D. Burleigh, and Dr. L. R. Mewaldt have made many important suggestions and criticisms; Dr. Igor Kosin has given invaluable assistance with the Russian papers. Although I am profoundly grateful for this assistance, I, of course, assume all responsibility for the material and interpretations as presented. Figures 1, 2, and 3 are reproduced from *Bird-Banding,* volume 24; grateful acknowledgment is made for their use herein.

Bibliography

AHLQUIST, H., and P. PALMGREN

1935. Ett försök att utröna sambandet mellan burfåglars flyttningsoro och väderleksläget. Ornis Fennica, 12:44-54.

BAGG, A. M., W. W. H. GUNN, D. S. MILLER, J. T. NICHOLS, W. SMITH, and F. P. WOLFARTH

1950. Barometric pressure-patterns and spring bird migration. Wilson Bull. 62:5-19.

BAKER, J. R.

1938. The evolution of the breeding seasons. In Evolution: Essays on aspects of evolutionary biology . . ., ed. by G. R. de Beer. Oxford University Press, pp. 161-177.

1947. The seasons in a tropical rain-forest (New Hebrides). Part 7. Summary and general conclusions. Jour. Linn. Soc. London, 41:248-258.

BALDWIN, S. P., and S. C. KENDEIGH

1938. Variations in the weights of birds. Auk, 55:416-467.

BALL, S. C.

1952. Fall migration on the Gaspé peninsula. Peabody Mus. Nat. Hist., Yale Univ. Bull. 7, vii + 211 pp.

BARTHOLOMEW, G. A.

1949. The effect of light intensity and day length on reproduction in the English Sparrow. Bull. Mus. Comp. Zool., 101:433-476.

BAUMGARTNER, A. M.

1938. Seasonal variations in the Tree Sparrow. Auk, 55:603-613.

BENOIT, J.

1935a. Nouvelles expériences relatives à la stimulation par la lumière du développement testiculaire chez le canard. C. R. Acad. Sci., Paris, 201:359-362.

1935b. Stimulation par la lumière artificielle du développement testiculaire chez des canards aveuglés par section du nerf optique. C. R. Soc. Biol., 120: 133-136.

1935c. Stimulation par la lumière artificielle du développement testiculaire chez des canards aveuglés par énucléation des globes oculaires. C. R. Soc. Biol., 120:136-139.

1937. Facteurs externes et internes de l'activation sexuelle. II. Étude du méchanisme de la stimulation par la lumière de l'activité testiculaire chez le canard domestique. Rôle de l'hypophyse. Bull. Biol. France et Belg., 71:393-437.

1950. Reproduction—caractères sexuels et hormones—déterminisme du cycle sexuel saisonnier. In Traité de zoologie, ed. by Pierre-P. Grassé, Vol. XV. Masson et Cie, Paris, pp. 384-478.

BENOIT, J., I. ASSENMACHER, and F. X. WALTER

1950a. Résponses du méchanisme gonado-stimulant à l'éclairement artificiel et de la préhypohyse aux castrations bilatérale et unilatérale, chez le canard domestique mâle, au cours de la période de régression testiculaire saisonnière. C. R. Soc. Biol., 144:573-577.

1950b. Activité gonadotrope de l'hypophyse du canard domestique, au cours de la régression testiculaire saisonnière et de la prépuberté. C. R. Soc. Biol., 144: 1403-1407.

BENOIT, J., P. MANDEL, F. X. WALTER, and I. ASSENMACHER

1950. Sensibilité testiculaire aux hormones gonadotropes hypophysaires, chez le canard domestique, au cours de la périod de régression testiculaire saisonnière. C. R. Soc. Biol., 144:1400-1403.

BENOIT, J., and L. OTT

1944. External and internal factors in sexual activity; effects of irradiation with different wave-lengths on the mechanism of photostimulation of the hypophysis and on testicular growth in the immature duck. Yale Jour. Biol. and Med., 17:27-46.

BERGMAN, G.

1950. Experimentella undersökningar över sömndjupet hos olika småfågelsarter. Ornis Fennica, 27:109-124.

BERGTOLD, W. H.

1926. Avian gonads and migration. Condor, 28:114-120.

BISSONNETTE, T. H.

1937. Photoperiodicity in birds. Wilson Bull., 49:241-270.

BLANCHARD, B. D.

1941. The White-crowned Sparrows (*Zonotrichia leucophrys*) of the Pacific seaboard: environment and annual cycle. Univ. Calif. Publ. Zool., 46:1-178.

BLANCHARD, B. D., and M. M. ERICKSON

1949. The cycle in the Gambel Sparrow. Univ. Calif. Publ. Zool., 47:255-318.

BONT, A. F. DE

1947. Le métabolisme des graisses chez les oiseaux migrateurs et sédentaires. Le Gerfaut, 37:57-62.

BOURLIÈRE, F.

1950. Physiologie des migrations. In Traité de zoologie, ed. by Pierre-P. Grassé, Vol. XV. Masson et Cie, Paris, pp. 1089-1099.

BRETSCHER, K.

1915. Beobachtungen über die Vogelpsyche. Naturwiss. Wochenschr., N. F., 14:389-392.

BULLOUGH, W. S.

1942. Observations on the colonies of the Arctic Tern (*Sterna macrura* Naumann) on the Farne Islands. Proc. Zool. Soc. London, 112A:1-12.

1943. Autumn sexual behavior and the resident habit of many British birds. Nature, 151:531.

1945. Endocrinological aspects of bird behavior. Biol. Rev., 20:89-99.

1951. Vertebrate sexual cycles. Methuen and Co. Ltd., London, viii + 117 pp.

BURGER, J. W.

1949. A review of experimental investigations on seasonal reproduction in birds. Wilson Bull., 61:211-230.

BURGER, J. W., T. H. BISSONNETTE, and H. D. DOOLITTLE

1942. Some effects of flashing light on testicular activation in the male Starling (*Sturnus vulgaris*). Jour. Exper. Zool., 90:73-82.

CAHN, A. R.

1925. The migration of animals. Amer. Nat., 59:539-556.

COLLIAS, N. F.

1950. Hormones and behavior with special reference to birds and the mechanisms of hormone action. In A symposium on steroid hormones, ed. by Edgar S. Gordon. University of Wisconsin Press, Madison, pp. 277-329.

COOKE, W. W.

1913. The relation of bird migration to the weather. Auk, 30:205-221.

DESSELBERGER, H., and G. STEINBACHER

1934. Weibliches Sexualhormon und Vogelzug II. Kritische Bemerkungen zu der Arbeit von H. Schildmacher. Vogelzug, 5:169-170.

DIRCKSEN, R.

1951. Vogelvolk auf weiter Reise. C. Bertelsmann, Gütersloh, 191 pp.

DOBIE, J. B., J. S. CARVER, and J. ROBERTS

1946. Poultry lighting for egg production. State College of Wash., Inst. Agric. Sci., Agric. Exper. Stations, Bull. 471, 27 pp.

DROST, R.

1941. Zug einer kastrierten Amsel, *Turdus m. merula* L. Vogelzug, 12:163.

1951. Study of bird migration 1938-1950. Proc. Tenth Internat. Ornithol. Cong., pp. 216-240.

EIFRIG, G.

1924. Is photoperiodism a factor in the migration of birds? Auk, 41:439-444.

ELTERICH, C. F.

1936. Über zyklische Veränderungen der Schilddrüse in den einzelnen Geschlechtsphasen der Taube. Endokrinologie, 18:31-37.

EYSTER, M. B.

1952. Mechanically recorded nocturnal unrest in captive songbirds. Abstract of Papers, A.O.U. Seventieth Stated Meeting, p. 3.

FARNER, D. S.

1950. The annual stimulus for migration. Condor, 52:104-122.

FARNER, D. S., and L. R. MEWALDT

1953a. The recording of diurnal activity patterns in caged birds. Bird-Banding, 24:55-65.

1953b. The relative roles of diurnal periods of activity and diurnal photoperiod in gonadal activation in male *Zonotrichia leucophrys gambelii* (Nuttall). Experientia, 9:219-221.

FARNER, D. S., L. R. MEWALDT, and S. IRVING

1953. The roles of darkness and light in the activation of avian gonads with increased daily photoperiods. Science, 118:351-352.

GIERSBERG, H., and R. STADIE

1934. Ueber experimentelle Auslösung des Zugtriebes durch weibliches Sexualhormon. Vogelzug, 5:173-176.

GRINNELL, J.

1931. Some angles in the problem of bird migration. Auk, 48:22-32.

GROEBBELS, F.

1928. Zur Physiologie des Vogelzuges. Verh. ornithol. Gesellsch. Bayern, 18:44-74.

1930. Bausteine zu einer Physiologie und Histophysiologie des Zugvogels. I. Mitteilungen. Physiologische Untersuchungen an helgoländer Zugvögeln. Zeits. wissenschaftl. Biol. Abt. C. Zeits. vergl. Physiol., 12:682-702.

1932. Der Vogel. Bau, Funktion, Lebenserscheinung, Einpassung. Erster Band. Atmungswelt und Nahrungswelt. Gebrüder Borntraeger, Berlin, xi + 918 pp.

HAARTMAN, L. VON, and G. BERGMAN

1943. Der Herbstzug an zwei Orten in Südfinnland und seine Abhängigkeit von äusseren Faktoren. Acta Zool. Fenn., 39:1-33.

HÄCKER, V.

1926. Über jahreszeitliche Veränderungen und klimatisch bedingte Verschiedenheit der Vogelschilddrüse. Schweiz. Med. Wochenschr., 7:337-341.

HAGEN, Y.

1942. Totalgewichts-Studien bei norwegischen Vogelarten. Unter besonderer Berücksichtigung der biologischen Verhältnisse bei Raubvögeln, Eulen, und Waldhühnern. Arch. Naturgesch. Zeits. syst. Zool., N. F., 11:1-173.

HANN, H. W.

1939. The relation of castration to migration in birds. Bird-Banding, 10:122-124.

HEAPE, W.

1931. Emigration, migration and nomadism. W. Heffer and Sons, Cambridge, x + 369 pp.

HÖHN, E. O.

1949. Seasonal changes in the thyroid gland and effect of thyroidectomy in the Mallard in relation to moult. Amer. Jour. Physiol., 158:337-344.

1950. Physiology of the thyroid gland in birds: a review. Ibis, 92:464-473.

HOMEYER, E. F. VON

1881. Die Wanderung der Vögel mit Rücksicht auf die Züge der Säugethiere, Fische und Insekten. Th. Grieben's, Leipzig, 415 pp.

IVOR, H. R.

1944. Bird study and semi-captive birds: the Rose-breasted Grosbeak. Wilson Bull., 56:91-104.

JENNER, C. E., and W. L. ENGELS

1952. The significance of the dark period in the photoperiodic response of male juncos and White-throated Sparrows. Biol. Bull., 103:345-355.

KENDEIGH, S. C.

1934. The rôle of environment in the life of birds. Ecol. Monogr., 4:299-417.

1941. Length of day and energy requirements for gonad development and egg-laying in birds. Ecology, 22:237-248.

1944. Effect of air temperature on the rate of energy metabolism in the English Sparrow. Jour. Exper. Zool., 96:1-16.

1945. Resistance to hunger in birds. Jour. Wildlife Mgmt., 9:217-226.

1949. Effect of temperature and season on energy resources of the English Sparrow. Auk, 66:113-127.

KIRKPATRICK, C. M.

1944. Body weights and organ measurements in relation to age and season in Ring-necked Pheasants. Anat. Rec., 89:175-194.

KIRKPATRICK, C. M., and A. C. LEOPOLD

1952. The role of darkness in sexual activity of the quail. Science, 116:280-281.

KOCH, H. J., and A. F. DE BONT

1952. Standard metabolic rate, weight changes and food consumption of *Fringilla c. coelebs* L. during sexual maturation. Ann. Soc. Roy. Zool. Belg., 82:1-12.

KÜCHLER, W.

1935. Jahreszyklische Veränderungen im histologischen Bau der Vogelschilddrüse. Jour. Ornithol., 83:414-461.

LACK, D.

1950. The breeding season of European birds. Ibis, 92:288-316.

LINCOLN, F. C.

1950. Migration of birds. U.S. Government Printing Office, Washington, D.C., 102 pp.

LINSDALE, J. M., and E. L. SUMNER

1934a. Variability in weight in the Golden-crowned Sparrow. Univ. Calif. Publ. Zool., 40:309-320.

1934b. Winter weights of Golden-crowned and Fox Sparrows. Condor, 36:107-112.

LUCANUS, F. K. H. VON

1923. Die Rätsel des Vogelzuges. 2nd ed. Hermann Beyer und Söhne, Langensalze, xi + 243 pp.

MARSHALL, A. J.

1949. Weather factors and spermatogenesis in birds. Proc. Zool. Soc. London, 119:711-716.

1951. The refractory period of testis rhythm in birds and its possible bearing on breeding and migration. Wilson Bull., 63:238-261.

1952. The interstitial cycle in relation to autumn and winter sexual behavior in birds. Proc. Zool. Soc. London, 121:727-740.

MAYR, E., and W. MEISE

1930. Theoretisches zur Geschichte des Vogelzuges. Vogelzug, 1:149-172.

MEINERTZHAGEN, R.

1951. [Remarks on fat and body weight in migrating birds.] Proc. Tenth Internat. Ornithol. Cong., p. 293.

MERKEL, F. W.

1937. Zur Physiologie des Vogelzugtriebes. Zool. Anz., 117:297-308.

1938. Zur Physiologie der Zugunruhe bei Vögeln. Ber. Ver. Schles. Ornithol., 25 (Sonderheft): 1-72.

1940. Neuere Untersuchungen über die Ursachen des Vogelzug-Triebes. Natur und Volk, 70:167-178.

MILLER, A. H.

1948. The refractory period in light-induced reproductive development of Golden-crowned Sparrows. Jour. Exper. Zool., 109:1-11.

1949. Potentiality for testicular recrudescence during the annual refractory period of the Golden-crowned Sparrow. Science, 109:546.

1951. Further evidence on the refractory period in the reproductive cycle of the Golden-crowned Sparrow. Auk, 68:381-383.

MILLER, D. S.

1937. Effects of thyroxin on plumage of the English Sparrow. Jour. Exper. Zool., 71:293-309.

MOREAU, R. E.

1931. Equatorial reflections on periodism in birds. Ibis, 13th ser., 1:553-570.

1951. The migration system in perspective. Proc. Tenth Internat. Ornithol. Cong., pp. 245-248.

NICE, M. M.

1937. Studies in the life history of the Song Sparrow, I. Trans. Linn. Soc., N.Y., 4: vi + 247 pp.

1946. Weights of resident and winter visitant Song Sparrows in central Ohio. Condor, 48:41-42.

ODUM, E. P.

1949. Weight variations in wintering White-throated Sparrows in relation to temperature and migration. Wilson Bull., 61:3-14.

ODUM, E. P., and J. D. PERKINSON

1951. Relation of lipid metabolism to migration in birds: seasonal variations in body lipids of the migratory White-throated Sparrow. Physiol. Zool., 24: 216-230.

OORDT, G. J. VAN

1928. Studies on the gonads of summering birds, I and II. The Knot and the Turnstone. Tijds. Nederl. Dierk. Vereen., 1:25-30.

1931. Studien über die Gonaden übersommernder Vögel, III. Zeits. mikrosk-anat. Forsch., 25:539-560.

1943. Vogeltrek. 2nd ed. E. J. Brill, Leiden, xi + 145 pp.

1949. Vogeltrek. 3rd ed. E. J. Brill, Leiden, xii + 148 pp.

PALMÉN, J. A.

1876. Über die Zugstrassen der Vögel. W. Engelmann, Leipzig, 292 pp. Original not seen. The information cited herein is from von Homeyer (1881), Wachs (1926), and Välikangas (1946).

PALMGREN, P.

1936. Über den Massenwechsel bei *Regulus r. regulus* (L.). Ornis Fennica, 13:159-164.

1937. Auslösung der Frühlingszugunruhe durch wärme bei gekäfigten Rotkehlchen, *Erithacus rubecula* (L.). Ornis Fennica, 14:71-73.

1938. Studien über den zeitlichen Ablauf der Zugerregung bei gekäfigten Kleinvögeln. Ornis Fennica, 15:1-16.

1943. Zur Tagesrhythmik der Finkenvögel. Ornis Fennica, 20:99-103.

1944a. Tagesrhythmik gekäfigter Kleinvögel bei konstanter Dauerbeleuchtung. Ornis Fennica, 21:25-30.

1944b. Studien über die Tagershythmik gekäfigter Zugvögel. Zeits. Tierpsychol., 6:44-86.

1949. On the diurnal rhythm of activity and rest in birds. Ibis, 91:561-576.

PALMGREN, P., G. BERGMAN, E. Å. FABRICIUS, L. VON HAARTMAN, and O. LEIVO

1939. Beobachtungen über die Zugverhältnisse bei einem Wetterfrontdurchgang in Südfinnland. Vogelzug, 10:154-169.

PEARSON, O. P.

1950. The metabolism of hummingbirds. Condor, 52:145-152.

PHILLIPS, A. R.

1951. Complexities of migration: a review. Wilson Bull. 63:129-136.

PROMPTOV, A. N.

1949. Sezonnye migrat͡sii ptit͡s kak biofiziologicheskai͡a problema. Izvestii͡a Akademii Nauk, SSSR serii͡a Biologicheskai͡a, 1949:30-39.

PUTZIG, P.

1937. Von der Beziehung des Zugablaufs zum Inkretdrüsensystem. Vogelzug, 8:116-130.

1938a. Beobachtungen über Zugunruhe beim Rotkehlchen (*Erithacus rubecula*). Vogelzug, 9:10-14.

1938b. Der Frühwegzug des Kiebitzes. Jour. Ornithol., 86:123-165.

1938c. Weitere Versuche über die Beziehungen der Keimdrüsen zum Zugverhalten. Vogelzug, 9:189-200.

1938d. Die Triebkräfte des Vogelzugs. Umschau, 42:866-869.

1939a. Keimdrüsen und Heimzug. Ber. Ver. Schles. Ornithol., 24:36-41.

1939b. Beiträge zur Stoffwechselphysiologie des Zugvogels. Vogelzug, 10: 139-154.

1939c. Sechste Rückmeldung einer kastrierten Nebelkrähe (*Corvus cornix*) in Heimzugrichtung. Vogelzug, 10:171-172.

RIDDLE, O., AND W. S. FISHER

1925. Seasonal variation of thyroid size in pigeons. Amer. Jour. Physiol., 72:464-487.

RIDDLE, O., G. C. SMITH, and F. G. BENEDICT

1932. The basal metabolism of the Mourning Dove and some of its hybrids. Amer. Jour. Physiol., 101:260-267.

ROWAN, W.

1925. Relation of light to bird migration and developmental changes. Nature, 115:494-495.

1926. On photoperiodism, reproductive periodicity and the annual migrations of birds and certain fishes. Proc. Boston Soc. Nat. Hist., 38:147-189.

1928. Reproductive rhythm in birds. Nature, 122:11-12.

1929. Experiments in bird migration, I. Manipulation of the reproductive cycle: seasonal histological changes in the gonads. Proc. Boston Soc. Nat. Hist., 39:151-208.

1930. Experiments in bird migration, II. Reversed migration. Proc. Nat. Acad. Sci., 16:520-525.

1931. The riddle of migration. Williams and Wilkins, Baltimore, 151 pp.

1932. Experiments in bird migration, III. The effects of artificial light, castration and certain extracts on the autumn movements of the American Crow (*Corvus brachyrhynchos*). Proc. Nat. Acad. Sci., 18:639-654.

1937. Effects of traffic disturbance and night illumination on London starlings. Nature, 139:668-669.

1938a. London starlings and seasonal reproduction. Proc. Zool. Soc. London, Ser. A., 108:51-77.

1938b. Light and seasonal reproduction in animals. Biol. Reviews, 13:374-402.

1946. Experiments in bird migration. Trans. Roy. Soc. Canada, 3rd ser., Section V, 40:123-135.

ROWAN, W., and A. M. BATRAWI

1939. Comments on the gonads of some European migrants collected in East Africa immediately before their spring departure. Ibis, 14th Ser., 3:58-65.

SALT, G. W.

1952. The relation of metabolism to climate and distribution in three finches of the genus *Carpodacus*. Ecol. Monogr., 22:121-152.

SCHÄFER, E. A.

1907. On the incidence of daylight as a determining factor in bird-migration. Nature, 77:159-163.

SCHILDMACHER, H.

1933. Zur Physiologie des Zugtriebes, I. Versuche mit weiblichem Sexualhormon. Vogelzug, 4:21-24.

1934a. Zur Physiologie des Zugtriebes, II. Weitere Versuche mit weiblichem Sexualhormon. Vogelzug, 5:1-9.

1934b. [Reply to H. Desselberger and G. Steinbacher, Weiblicher Sexualhormon und Vogelzug.] Vogelzug, 5:171-172.

1937. Zur Physiologie des Zugtriebes, III. Versuche mit künstlich verlängerter Tagesdauer. Vogelzug, 8:107-114.

1938a. Zur Auslösung der Frühlings-Zugunruhe durch Wärme bei gekäfigten Rotkehlchen, *Erithacus r. rubecula* (L.). Vogelzug, 9:7-10.

1938b. Zur Physiologie des Zugtriebes, IV. Weitere Versuche mit künstlich veränderter Belichtungszeit. Vogelzug, 9:146-152.

1939. Über die künstliche Aktivierung der Hoden einiger Vogelarten im Herbst durch Belichtung und Vorderlappenhormone. Biol. Zentralbl., 59:653-657.

1952a. Untersuchungen zur Zugdisposition der Zugvögel. Die Wissenschaft vom Vogel und die Volkswirtschaft. Herausgegeben vom Kulturbund zur demokratischen Erneuerung Deutschlands, Zentralkommission Ornithologie und Vogelschutz, Berlin. Reprint, 9 pp.

1952b. Stoffwechselphysiologische Studien an männlichen Gartenrotschwänzen *Phoenicurus ph. phoenicurus* (L.). Biol. Zentralbl., 71:238-251.

SCHILDMACHER, H. and W. RAUTENBERG

1952. Über die Wirkung kleiner Mengen von Thyroxin auf das Körpergewicht bei Finkenvögeln. Biol. Zentralbl., 71:397-405.

SCHILDMACHER, H., and L. STEUBING

1952. Untersuchungen zur hormonalen Regulierung des Fettwerdens der Zugvögel im Frühjahr. Biol. Zentralbl., 71:272-282.

SCHOLANDER, P. F., R. HOCK, V. WALTERS, and L. IRVING

1950. Adaptation to cold in arctic and tropical mammals and birds in relation to body temperature, insulation, and basal metabolic rate. Biol. Bull., 99:259-271.

SCHÜZ, E.

1952. Vom Vogelzug. Grundriss der Vogelzugskunde. Paul Schöps, Frankfurt am Main, 231 pp.

SEIBERT, H. C.

1949. Differences between migrant and non-migrant birds in food and water intake at various temperatures and photoperiods. Auk, 66:128-153.

SHAW, T. H.

1939. Variability in the body weight of the Brambling. Bull. Fan Mem. Inst. Biol., Zool. Ser., 9:241-250.

SIIVONEN, L.

1936. Die Stärkevariation des nächtlichen Zuges bei *Turdus ph. philomelos* Brehm und *T. musicus* L., auf Grund der Zuglaute geschätzt und mit der Zugunruhe einer gekäfigten Singdrossel verglichen. Ornis Fennica, 13:59-63.

SIIVONEN, L., and P. PALMGREN

1936. Über die Einwirkung der Temperatursenkung auf die Zugstimmung bei einer gekäfigten Singdrossel (*Turdus ph. philomelos* Brehm). Ornis Fennica, 13:64-67.

STADIE, R.

1938. Experimentelle Untersuchungen über den Wandertrieb gekäfigter Gartenrotschwänze, *Phoenicurus ph. phoenicurus* (L.). Ber. Ver. Schles. Ornithol., 23:65-80.

1939. Licht- und Schattenseiten des Zugphysiologischen Experiments. Proc. Ninth Cong. Ornithol. Internat., pp. 343-354.

STAFFE, A.

1950. Weitere Untersuchungen über die Wirkung des Lichtschocks auf die Legeleistung. Der Geflügelhof, 13:446-449, 510-514.

1951. Belichtung und Legeleistung beim Huhn. Experientia, 7:399-400.

STEINBACHER, G.

1933. Weibliches Sexualhormon und Vogelzug. Kritische Bemerkungen zu der Arbeit von H. Schildmacher: Zur Physiologie des Zugtriebes. Ornithol. Monatsb., 41:81-84.

STEINBACHER, J.

1951. Vogelzug und Vogelzugforschung. Waldemar Kramer, Frankfurt am Main, 184 pp.

THOMSON, A. L.

1926. Problems of bird-migration. Witherby and Co., London, xvi + 350 pp.

1936a. Bird migration. H. F. and G. Witherby, London, 224 pp.

1936b. Recent progress in the study of bird-migration: a review of the literature, 1926-35. Ibis, 13th Ser., 6:472-530.

1942. Bird migration. 2nd ed. H. F. and G. Witherby, London, viii + 192 pp.

1949. Bird migration. 3rd ed. H. F. and G. Witherby, London, 183 pp.

1950. Factors determining the breeding seasons of birds. Ibis, 92:173-184.

1951. Reproduction, migration and moult: factors controlling the annual cycle in birds. Proc. Tenth Internat. Ornithol. Cong., pp. 241-244.

TOSCHI, A.

1939. La migrazione degli uccelli. Supplemento alle Ricerche Zool. appl. Caccia, 292 pp.

TUGARINOV, A. J.

1949. Sovremennoe sostoi͡anne ucheniīa o sezonnykh mīgrat͡sīiakh ptīt͡s. Izvestīi͡a Akademiī Nauk SSSR, Serīi͡a Bīologīcheskai͡a, 1949, 7-29.

VÄLIKANGAS, I.

1946. J. A. Palmén's theories on migratory routes of birds in light of later, especially Finnish, observations and results of ring-marking. Soc. Scient. Fenn. Års. 24B (2):1-34.

VERWEY, J.

1949. Migration in birds and fishes. Bijd. Dierk., 28:477-504.

VLEUGEL, D. A.

1948. Enkele waarnemingen over "vorstvlucht" en "randtrek" in het Sloe-Schengengebied tijdens de winters van 1935/1936 en 1936/1937. Ardea, 36:143-162.

WACHS, H.

1926. Die Wanderungen der Vögel. Ergeb. Biol., 1:479-637.

WAGNER, H. O.

1930. Über Jahres- und Tagesrhythmus bei Zugvögeln. (I. Mitteilung). Zeits. vergl. Physiol., 12:703-724.

1936. Über den Jahresrhythmus verschiedener Grasmücken (*Sylvia*) in Mexico. Vogelzug, 7:109-112.

1937. Der Einfluss von Aussenfaktoren auf den Tagesrhythmus während der Zugphase. Vogelzug, 8:47-54.

WAGNER, H. O., and H. SCHILDMACHER

1937. Über die Abhängigkeit des Einsetzens der nächtlichen Zugunruhe verfrachteter Vögel von der geographischen Breite. Vogelzug, 8:18-19.

WALLGREN, H.

1952. On the dependence of standard metabolism upon environmental temperature in the Yellow Bunting (*Emberiza citrinella* L.), and the Ortolan Bunting (*E. hortulana* L.). Ornis Fennica, 29:44-48.

WATZKA, M.

1934. Physiologische Veränderungen der Schilddrüse. Zeits. mikrosk. — anat. Forsch., 36:67-86.

WEBER, W. A.

1951. Influence of the light shock on the laying potential. Proc. Ninth World's Poultry Cong., 2:99-101.

WEIGOLD, H.

1924. VII. Bericht der Vogelwarte der Stattl. Biologischen Anstalt auf Helgoland. Jour. Ornithol., 72:17-68.

WETMORE, A.

1926. The migrations of birds. Harvard University Press, Cambridge, vii + 229 pp.

WILLIAMS, G. G.

1950. Weather and spring migration. Auk, 67:52-65.

WILSON, E. A.

1911. The weight of grouse. In The grouse in health and disease, Vol. I. Smith Elder and Co., London, pp. 130-146.

WITSCHI, E.

1935. Seasonal sex characters in birds and their hormonal control. Wilson Bull., 47:177-188.

WOLFSON, A.

1940. A preliminary report on some experiments on bird migration. Condor, 42:93-99.

1941. Light versus activity in the regulation of the sexual cycles of birds: the role of the hypothalamus. Condor, 43:125-136.

1942. Regulation of spring migration in juncos. Condor, 44:237-263.

1945. The role of the pituitary, fat deposition, and body weight in bird migration. Condor, 47:95-127.

1952a. Day length, migration, and breeding cycles in birds. Sci. Monthly, 74:191-200.

1952b. The occurrence and regulation of the refractory period in the gonadal and fat cycles of the junco. Jour. Exper. Zool., 121:311-326.

WOLFSON, A., and H. S. WINN

1948. Summation of day lengths as the external stimulus for photoperiodic responses in birds. Anat. Rec., 101:70-71.

WOODBURY, A. M.

1941. Animal migration—periodic-response theory. Auk, 58:463-505.

WYNNE-EDWARDS, V. C.

1939. Intermittent breeding of the Fulmar (*Fulmarus glacialis* (L.)) with some general remarks on non-breeding in sea-birds. Proc. Zool. Soc. London, 109A: 127-132.

ZEDLITZ, O.

1926. Vogelgewichte als Hilfsmittel für die biologische Forschung. Jour. Ornithol., 74:296-308.

chapter 8

DIRECT STUDIES OF NOCTURNAL BIRD MIGRATION . . . George H. Lowery, Jr., and Robert J. Newman

During the past decade much effort has been devoted in America to the direct investigation of bird movements through the night sky. Use has been made of two types of inquiry, which may be conveniently called "flight-call counting" and "study by means of the moon." One of the most singular paradoxes in current ornithological research is the uncanny consistency with which these two techniques, the one auditory and the other visual, have led to seemingly contrary conclusions. To provide a basis for interpreting this duality in data, we shall preface a summary of the results themselves with a discussion of the two methods that have produced them.

FLIGHT-CALL COUNTING

Flight-call counting, sometimes referred to as "chip counting," has been utilized most productively to date in the work of Ball (1952), who employed data so obtained as the main basis for a book-length treatise dealing with autumnal bird migration on the Gaspé Peninsula. Stated in its simplest terms, the method consists merely of recording the number of flight calls heard at a given place in a stated interval of time and then comparing the results with the figures obtained at other times and places. But as practiced by Ball, flight-call counting has become a highly developed art, whereby it is possible to judge directions of flight and often even to classify the records according to species, as in the case of the thrushes of the genus *Hylocichla.*

The possibility provided by flight-call counting of studying some kinds of nocturnal migrants separately, species by species, is one of three currently unique advantages. The others are that it permits one to check on migration during the dark of the moon and that it gives one an awareness of activity at very low elevation, where the present visual methods do not work well. Furthermore, auditory studies make direct use of the original counts just as they are taken down in the field, without difficult and time-consuming mathematical adjustments. Convenient though this feature is, it at the same time conceals an important limitation. The technique retains its mathematical simplicity only because no way has been found to use flight calls as a measure of the amount of migration taking place in a definite unit of space. The only

Manuscript received January 15, 1954.

progress in this direction has been provided by Ball, who has estimated that the loudest calls of thrushes can be heard under favorable circumstances at a horizontal distance of 2,000 feet and at a vertical distance of 1,500 feet.

The most serious defect in the auditory detection of bird movements at night is that the ratio of the number of call notes heard to the number of birds passing is almost certainly not a constant one. Every student of the problem agrees that frequently individual birds seem to call more than once during the time when they are within earshot. Conversely, it is possible that vast flights of migrants may wing by without uttering a sound. Still more disconcerting is the fact that much nocturnal migration passes at elevations above the 1,500 feet that, by Ball's calculations, is the greatest vertical distance at which even the far-carrying notes of thrushes can be heard. A further limitation of the auditory approach is that, for maximum effectiveness, it requires quiet surroundings. It is thus not well suited to the many situations where there are competing sounds, such as the noises of the city or the roar of the surf. All of these shortcomings may be summed up in the conclusion that the perceptibility of migration by auditory means varies markedly with varying circumstances.

STUDY BY MEANS OF THE MOON

Most of the bird students in this country already know that it is possible to see a part of the migration taking place at night by pointing a telescope at the moon and watching for the passing objects fleetingly silhouetted against its illuminated face. In fact, some 2,500 people have shared the actual experience of witnessing the parade of migration in this manner. Their magnificent efforts in a common cause have brought together over ten thousand hours of observation representing over 325 localities scattered over the North American continent from Canada to Panama. During lunar studies of migration, the moon is envisioned as an upright clockface, and the slant of the pathway of each passing object is identified in terms of the imaginary clock numbers (Fig. 1). A detailed description of the observational procedure has been given in a special publication of the Museum of Zoology of Louisiana State University (Newman, 1952). Revision and reissue of this booklet is being deferred so that lessons learned during the work of 1952 and 1953 may be incorporated.

The mere counting of lunar silhouettes as an index to migration is open to the same fundamental criticism as the counting of flight calls. At some times the moon provides an opportunity to record a higher proportion of the birds passing than at other times. The varying observational potential of the moon, however, is a more easily estimable quantity and thus permits corrective treatment. In what has always seemed to us, his former colleagues, a brilliant analysis of the situation, Rense (1946, 1950) laid down the mathematical principles that have formed the basis of all subsequent corrective procedures. A further explanation of these principles and a description of the first complete calculating system developed from them accompanied the report on their large-scale applica-

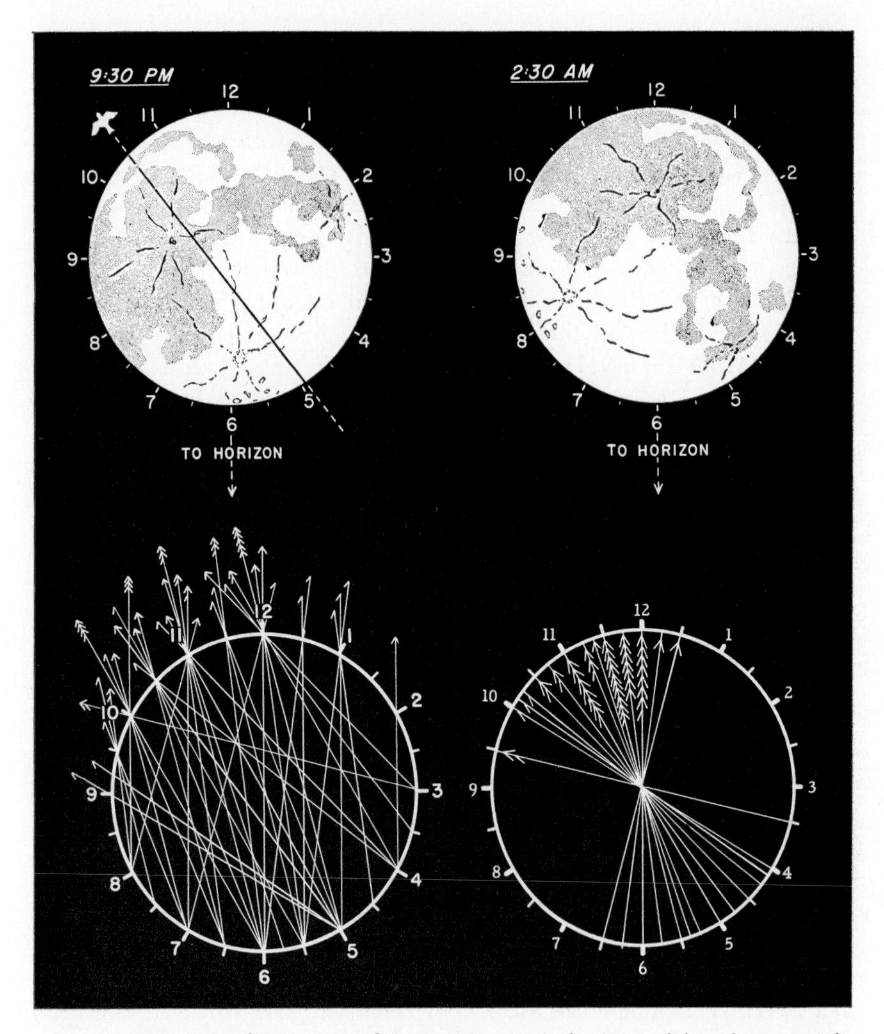

Fig. 1. Flight co-ordinates as used in the lunar method. *Upper left and upper right:* These diagrams illustrate how a flight path across the moon may be identified in terms of numbers on an imaginary clockface, constantly oriented with 6 o'clock nearest the horizon regardless of the rotation of the moon's topographic features. The bird shown is proceeding from 5 o'clock to 10:30. *Lower left:* The original co-ordinates of the 86 pathways recorded in an actual hour of observation. *Lower right:* The same data plotted with all pathways of the same slant (and therefore of the same direction) expressed as a single co-ordinate through the center of the circle. The two latter diagrams demonstrate how an apparently confused jumble of co-ordinates may conceal a coherent directional flow of birds. (Reproduced from *A Quantitative Study of the Nocturnal Migration of Birds* by permission Univ. Kansas Mus. Nat. Hist.)

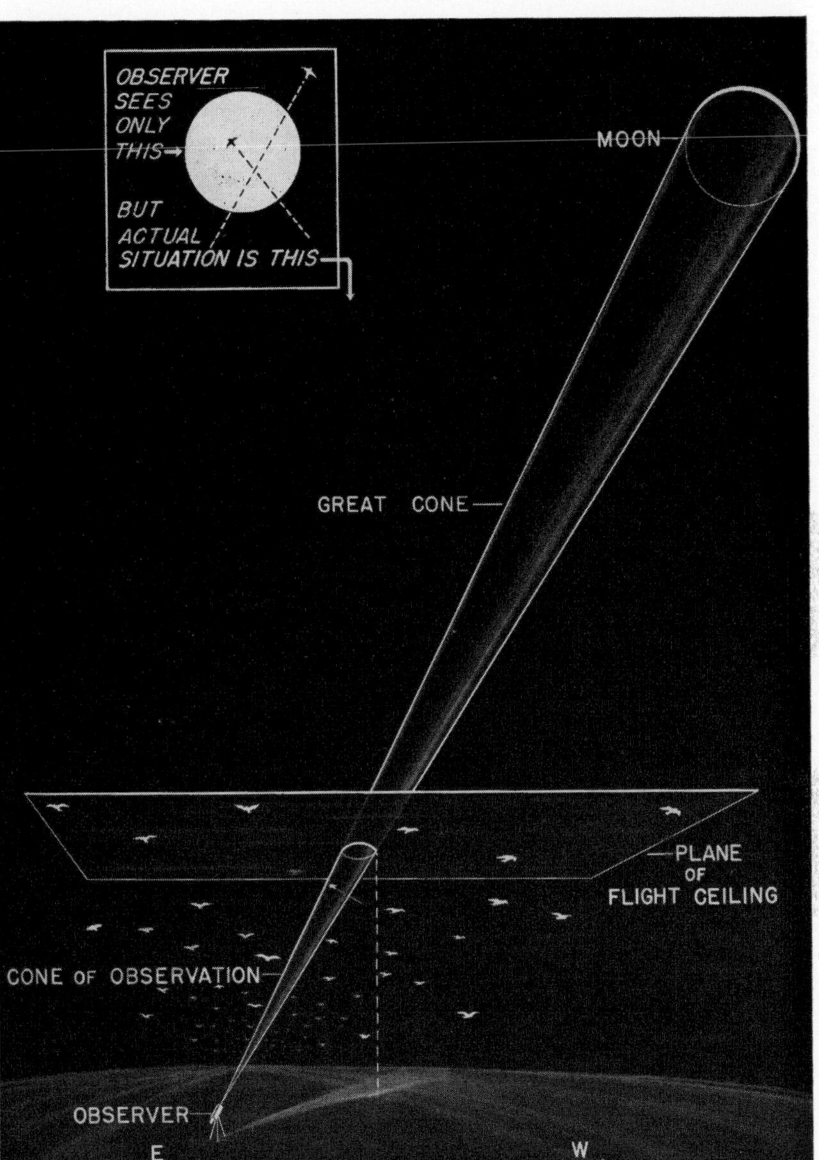

Fig. 2. The field of observation, showing its two-dimensional aspect as it appears to the observer and its three-dimensional actuality. The *flight ceiling* is the highest level at which birds are flying; the *great cone* is the entire observation space between the telescope and the moon; the *cone of observation* is that part of the great cone lying beneath the flight ceiling. In the illustration the breadth of the cone is greatly exaggerated. (Reproduced from *A Quantitative Study of the Nocturnal Migration of Birds* by permission Univ. Kansas Mus. Nat. Hist.)

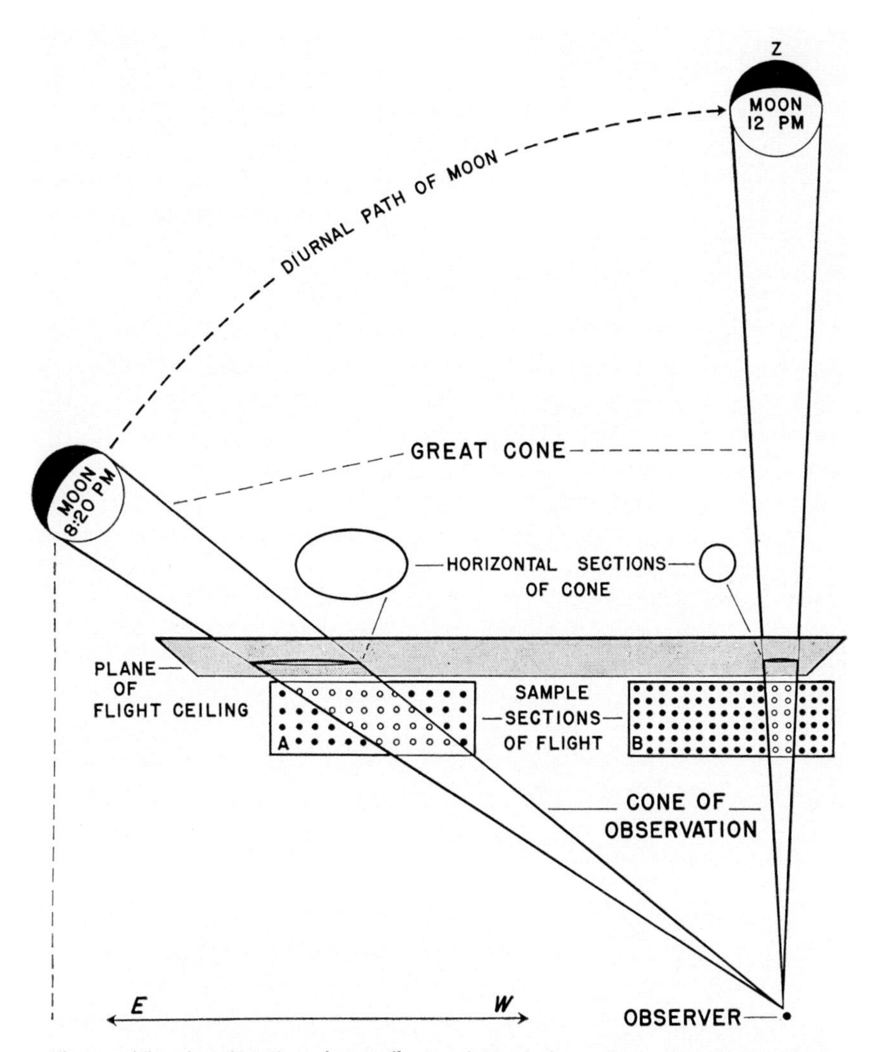

Fig. 3. The changing size of the effective field of observation. The sample sections A and B represent the densities of flight at 8:20 and 12:00 P.M., respectively. With twice as many birds in the air at midnight, when the moon is at the zenith (Z), as there were at the earlier hour, only half as many are visible because of the decrease in the size of the cone of observation. Note that when the moon is overhead a horizontal section of the cone is circular, but when the cone is inclined this circle becomes elongated into an ellipse. (Reproduced from *A Quantitative Study of the Nocturnal Migration of Birds* by permission Univ. Kansas Mus. Nat. Hist.)

tion to data collected in the spring of 1948 (Lowery, 1951). The supply of these papers, as well as the special publication dealing with observational procedures, is exhausted, though circulating copies can still be furnished on a loan basis by the Louisiana State University Museum of Zoology. It is therefore appropriate to restate here in a general way why untreated counts of lunar silhouettes are misleading and to explain what is being done to make them more meaningful.

The reasoning on which the corrective measures are based is in part theoretical and in part as thoroughly grounded as a theorem in geometry. Let us examine the certainties in the situation first. The idea that all long-range migration is performed on essentially horizontal planes, or at least that the ups and downs involved tend to cancel out, causing the lines of flight to regress on horizontal planes, seems self-evident. Consequently much of the process can be validly analyzed in terms of what occurs on one typical horizontal plane. Keeping this idea in mind, imagine a night and a moment when the full moon is directly overhead. At such a time the observer peering straight upward at the moon through a telescope is looking into an observation-space that has the shape of a long, narrow cone similar to that in Figure 2 but vertical. Any plane horizontal to the earth (such as any of the planes on which the birds are assumed to be flying) cuts this cone in a right section, describing a circular area of visibility that presents an equal breadth to all birds from whatever direction they are coming. Looking into such an observation space, the observer has just as good an opportunity to see the birds flying eastward or westward as he does to see the birds flying northward or southward. But let us consider the situation, as illustrated by the 8:20 P.M. position in Figure 3, when the moon is still at a low elevation and the cone of observation is inclined to the east. Then a horizontal plane cuts the cone in an elongate figure, an ellipse whose long axis extends from east to west and whose short axis extends from north to south. Under these circumstances, one may expect to see a higher proportion of the birds flying from north to south, across the long axis, than one will see of the birds flying from east to west, across the short axis.

This directional disproportion in the visibility of migrating birds is an inescapable fact, but correction can be made with great mathematical rigor. The angles at which the different flight directions cross the elliptical area of visibility can be determined from the recorded lunar pathways previously mentioned. Then the comparative breadths of the ellipse for each angle of approach can be computed to find the corrective ratios that will equalize them.

There is, however, another potential factor affecting the comparative visibility of migration at different positions of the moon. Most bird flight occurs in a stratum of air quite close to the earth. When the moon is low, a relatively large portion of the telescopic cone lies in the stratum of migration; but, as the moon moves upward, carrying the cone toward a vertical position, less and less of the observation space remains at the levels where birds are flying (compare the two cones of observation in Figure 3). To overcome this difficulty, the dimensions of the effective cone during each hour of observation may be computed at an assumed median elevation of flight. Then the number of birds seen in a given hour can be converted to the theoretical number of birds that

NIGHTLY FLIGHT DENSITY SUMMARY Form C-d Computer FRC

NIGHT OF 22-23 September 1953 STATION Maryland: Laurel

Sector	Average Times of Observations EST													Sector Total	Per Cent
	5:30	6:30	7:30	8:30	9:30	10:30	11:30	12:30	1:30	2:30	3:30	4:30	5:30		
N8 E ENE							200							200	–
N6 ENE NE															
N4 NE NNE				70			200							270	–
N2 NNE N									200					200	–
N1 N NNW				80										80	–
N3 NNW NW					200	200								400	–
N5 NW WNW				300	200									500	–
N7 WNW W				100	900	200	200	1,200	200		100	60	70	3,030	1
S8 W WSW			1,300	2800	1,900	1,300	3,600	5,000	1,100	500	300	300	500	18,600	8
S6 WSW SW		100	2,400	6,800	12,100	15,000	10,500	17,000	6,800	10,100	1,900	2,000	100	84,800	37
S4 SW SSW			3,100	8,200	12,500	16,000	13,700	9,300	11,900	9900	2600	1,600	200	89,000	38
S2 SSW S		80	4,000	4200	2,400	5,000	2,500	2,900	1,200	1,100	600	400	30	24,410	14
S1 S SSE		90	3,000	400	500	1,600	700		1,200	300	70	60		7,920	3
S3 SSE SE			200	200		200								600	–
S5 SE ESE			300	300	200									800	–
S7 ESE E															
Station Density		270	14,300	23,450	30,900	39,500	31,600	35,400	22,600	21,900	5,570	4,420	900	230,000±	
T. A. Bird Counts		26	303	330	300	371	200	215	141	120	60	89	33	2188	

Fig. 4. Facsimile of a nightly flight density summary sheet. The "T. A. Bird Counts" on the bottom rows are the hourly bird counts adjusted for time-out periods. Densities are shown for each directional sector in each hour of observation. "Station Densities" are the hourly totals of the sector densities. For a delineation of the sectors themselves, see Fig. 5.

would have been seen in a space a mile wide had birds been passing on the mile front in the same density as on the visible segment of front included in the cone. Thus, when the section of the cone cut by the horizontal plane of flight at the median elevation is .01 of a mile in breadth, the number of birds seen may be multiplied by 100 to obtain the assumed number passing in a space a mile wide. The resulting figure, expressing the rate of migration over an observation station in terms of birds per mile of front per hour, is called a flight density. Figure 4 shows the type of data accruing from these procedures. This summary of flight densities indicates the pattern of variation in the migration over Laurel, Maryland, on the night of September 22-23, 1953, as computed from observations made by Chandler S. Robbins working alone with a wire recorder.

The main reason for expressing the quantity of migration in this manner is not to discover the actual number of birds passing in a flight a mile wide, but merely to reduce all observations to an equal comparative basis, weighting them properly for the varying amounts of time and space in which they were secured. But the present tables of adjustment factors were derived on the assumption that the practical upward limits of nocturnal migration are more or less stable and that they are low enough to permit an observer with a 20-power telescope to see nearly all of the birds that enter the cone of observation. Though the latter assumption seems reasonable enough on theoretical grounds, there remains a possibility that the factors over-correct for the variations that they propose to remedy. Fortunately, as observations accumulate, they themselves are providing a test of the validity of the mathematical method.

The analysis of lunar flight co-ordinates derives its research stature from the fact that it permits more precise numerical measurements of migration as a mass movement than does any other method applicable either by night or by day. A considerable portion of diurnal migratory activity doubtless takes place through the screening foliage of the trees, where the presence of nonmigrating birds of migratory species adds to the observer's confusion. Under these conditions, accurate space-defined sampling of the rate and frequency of passage is next to impossible. Such low-level migratory activity seems less practicable after dark, especially as a prolonged performance. We may surmise with a fair degree of confidence that the major part of nocturnal migration is performed in the open sky, where few nonmigrants are intruding and where telescopic observation provides a reliable check on the numbers of birds in flight. When statistically expressed as density-rates, the telescopic counts can be combined and contrasted in a variety of objective correlations to determine what factor is producing an observed effect. In this respect they seem more reliable than flight-call counts, which cannot be so definitely identified with the dimensions of the space in which the recorded birds are passing. The way in which, without the disturbing influence of artificial light, moon-watching enables the observer actually to *see* a part of the migration is an important additional feature, one presumed to yield more dependable approximations of directional trends of flight than other nocturnal means permit. All of these advantages are heightened by the proven appeal of the method and its suitability for widespread use, attributes that have led to the accumulation of data in impressive quantity.

Nevertheless, bird studies by means of the moon have important limitations. Ideal though they are for exploration of the vast common denominator of nocturnal migration—those features of behavior that most night migrants share—they provide little insight into the variations characteristic of the separate species. Indeed, the counts may even suffer in some circumstances, in the tropics, for example, from contamination by objects other than birds. So far moon-watching for ornithological purposes has been restricted mainly to the five-day period centered on the full of the moon; and, although work at Baton Rouge has demonstrated the practicality of extending the watch to a fifteen-day period, half of the nights in the month and more than half of the hours of darkness will always be unavailable for this kind of study because the moon is absent from view or because its lighted portion is drastically reduced in size. Just as the moon cannot tell us what is happening in total darkness, so does it fail to enlighten us concerning the behavior of migrating birds at times of complete overcast. And, finally, telescopic observations provide larger samples of birds flying at high elevations than of birds flying at low elevations.

In spite of the difficulties associated with both the auditory and visual methods, the direct study of nocturnal migration in action has already uncovered new information and provided stimulating bases for conjecture regarding a variety of aspects of the phenomenon. In the remaining sections of this chapter, we shall summarize this material, making use of results obtained through autumnal flight-call counting on the Gaspé by Ball (1952), lunar migration data recorded in the spring survey of 1948 and analyzed by Lowery (1951), and a sampling of the unpublished observations secured in the fall through the nation-wide moon-watching projects of 1952 and 1953 and now being processed at Louisiana State University.

DISTRIBUTION OF NOCTURNAL MIGRANTS IN THE SKY

In the spring of 1948, ornithologists watching the moon made a discovery of critical importance. This is that night migrants exhibit a remarkably uniform horizontal dispersion through the air above an observation point. Herons, geese, and shorebirds have been seen crossing before the disc of the moon in close formation; but nearly all small birds traveling at night seem to fly neither in definite flocks nor in narrow streams. Evidence for this was found in spring in the even flow of migrants observed, the infrequency with which more than one bird was seen in front of the moon at once, and the close correspondence between counts made at two telescopes stationed a few feet apart. In fact, only 1.1 per cent of the 7,432 observations of lunar silhouettes in 1948 involved more than one bird at a time. These findings have crucial bearing upon the further significance of telescopic counts of nocturnal migrants. They mean that birds are distributed through the night sky with enough uniformity to permit fairly representative sampling even within the extremely narrow limits of visibility provided by a single telescope. Such, of course, would not be the case if the majority of migrants habitually traveled in compact groups.

Speaking for the autumnal movements of thrushes on the Gaspé, Ball has expressed assurance that grouping does occur, probably as a rule. In support of this assertion, he has pointed to the uneven distribution of call notes, citing particularly his records in the half hour before dawn on the morning of September 22, 1949. Retracing just after daylight the path along which he had heard flight calls at variously spaced intervals, he found a similar unevenness in the distribution of thrushes after they had descended to the ground.

Autumnal lunar counts pertinent to this problem are available in great quantity but are not scheduled for statistical analysis in the immediate future, other analyses having commanded higher priority. In the absence of a really

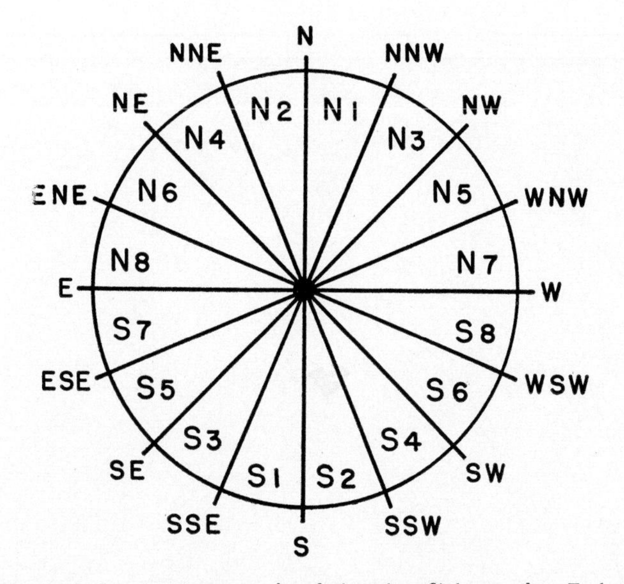

Fig. 5. Standard directional sectors for designating flight trends. Each zone covers a span of 22½°. The arrangement is according to the position of the sectors on an overhead moon, a mirror image of their compass positions on earth. (Reproduced from *A Quantitative Study of the Nocturnal Migration of Birds* by permission Univ. Kansas Mus. Nat. Hist.)

critical comparison, both the data and our personal experience convey an impression that fall flight may not be quite as consistently dispersed as flight in spring. In several instances the counts made at telescopes set up within sight of one another have been less closely correlated at this season. Furthermore, on nights of heavy migration, many observers have remarked on a tendency of birds to come in bursts. For almost half a minute the moon may remain vacant. Then suddenly the observer is bombarded with a rapid fire of silhouettes that tax his capacity to call out their co-ordinates. The surprising thing about these bursts, however, is that they seldom suggest birds in flocks. Usually the paths crisscross, and the objects themselves display a variety of sizes, shapes, and qualities of focus, suggesting that many of them are not even at the same level. In spite of the fact that the autumnal passage of over a hundred thousand birds before the moon has now been recorded, definite flocks thought to be passerine have been reported very rarely.

EFFECT OF WEATHER ON MIGRATION

The fact that we can determine with considerable accuracy by the telescopic method the directions in which the birds of a representative sample are flying in the darkness overhead permits us to analyze the direction of migratory movements at night with respect to meteorological conditions. Observations

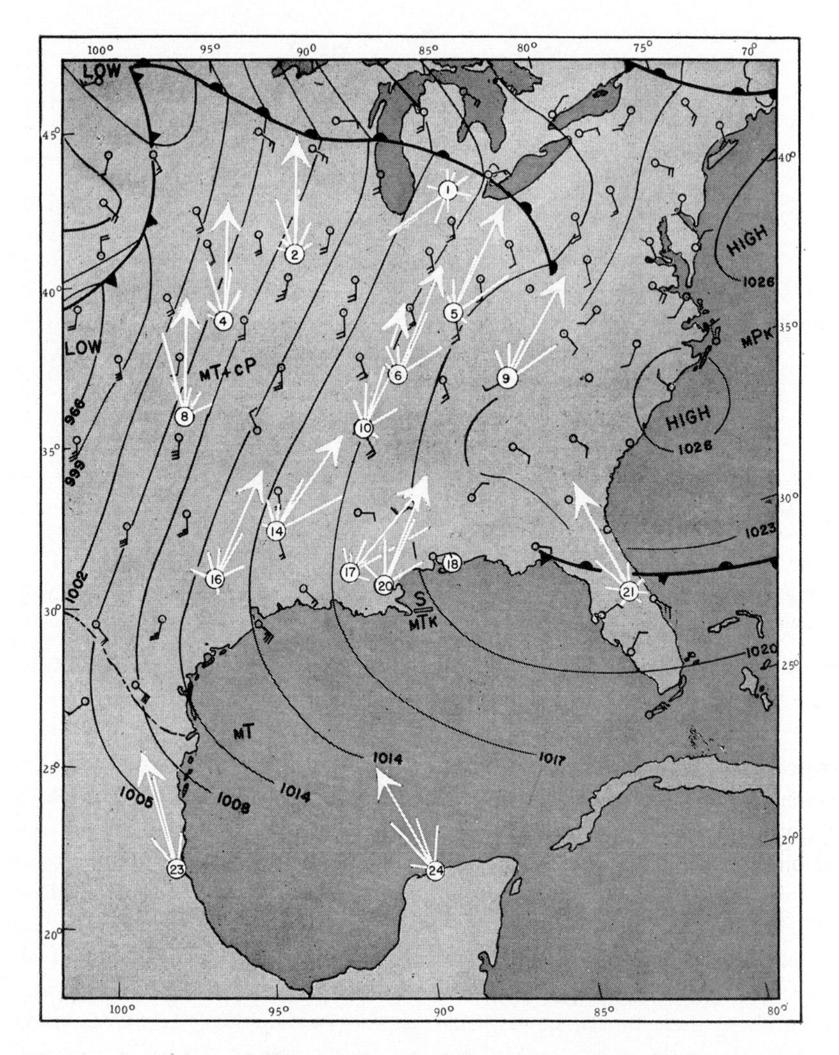

Fig. 6. Comparison of flight trends and surface weather conditions on April 23-24, 1948. The meteorological data were taken from the U. S. Weather Bureau Daily Weather Map for 12:30 A.M. (CST) on April 24. The lines with the arrowheads represent the vector resultants; the other lines are sector vectors, the relative lengths of which show the proportion of birds recorded for each sector. (Reproduced from *A Quantitative Study of the Nocturnal Migration of Birds* by permission Univ. Kansas Mus. Nat. Hist.)

at twenty-eight stations in the spring of 1948, many simultaneously, led to the determination of the direction of flight of over 7,000 birds. This information was expressed in terms of the nightly flight densities (birds per mile of front) at each station for each of sixteen directional sectors (Fig. 5). These sector densities were considered as lines of thrust, plotted on weather maps for the

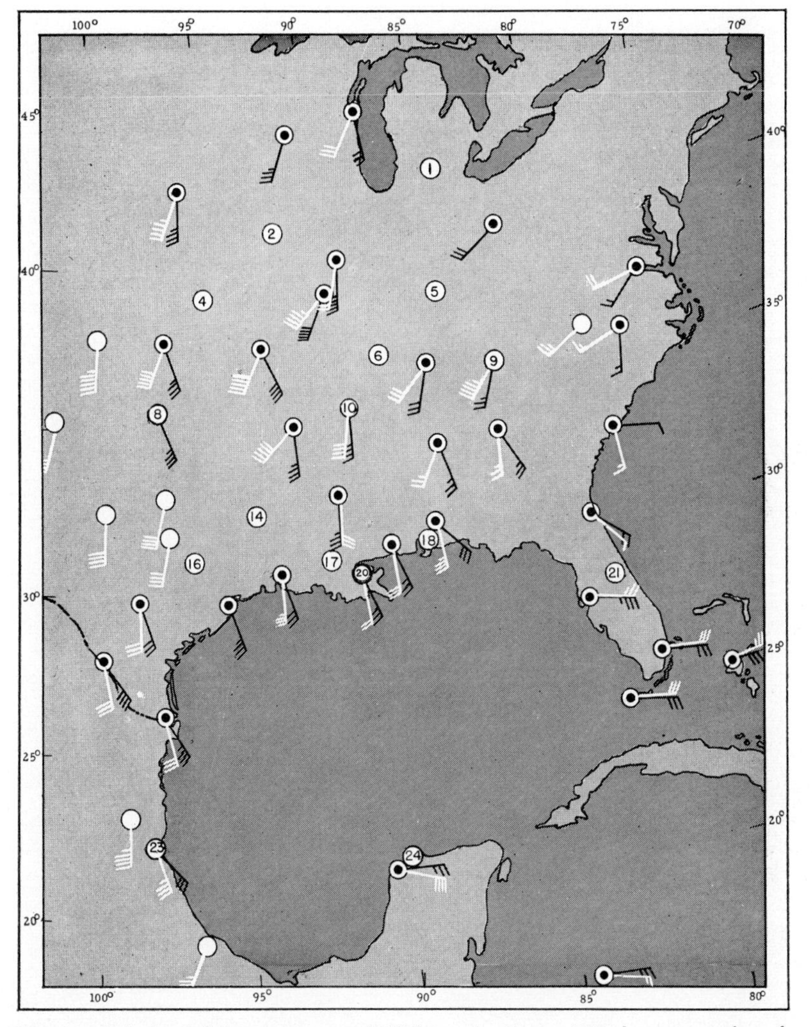

Fig. 6a. Winds aloft at 10:00 P.M. (CST) on April 23. Winds at 2,000 feet above mean sea level are shown in black; those at 4,000 in white. The numbered positions locate the stations shown in Fig. 6. (Reproduced from *A Quantitative Study of the Nocturnal Migration of Birds* by permission Univ. Kansas Mus. Nat. Hist.)

appropriate dates, and subjected to vector analysis to determine the vector resultant, representing the "average" direction of flight at the locality in question.

These initial studies, as well as the data now in the process of analysis, support the conclusion that the bulk of a night's migration generally proceeds with the wind. Figures 6 and *6a* show the situation that obtained on the night of April 23-24, 1948. In Mexico and in the central part of the United

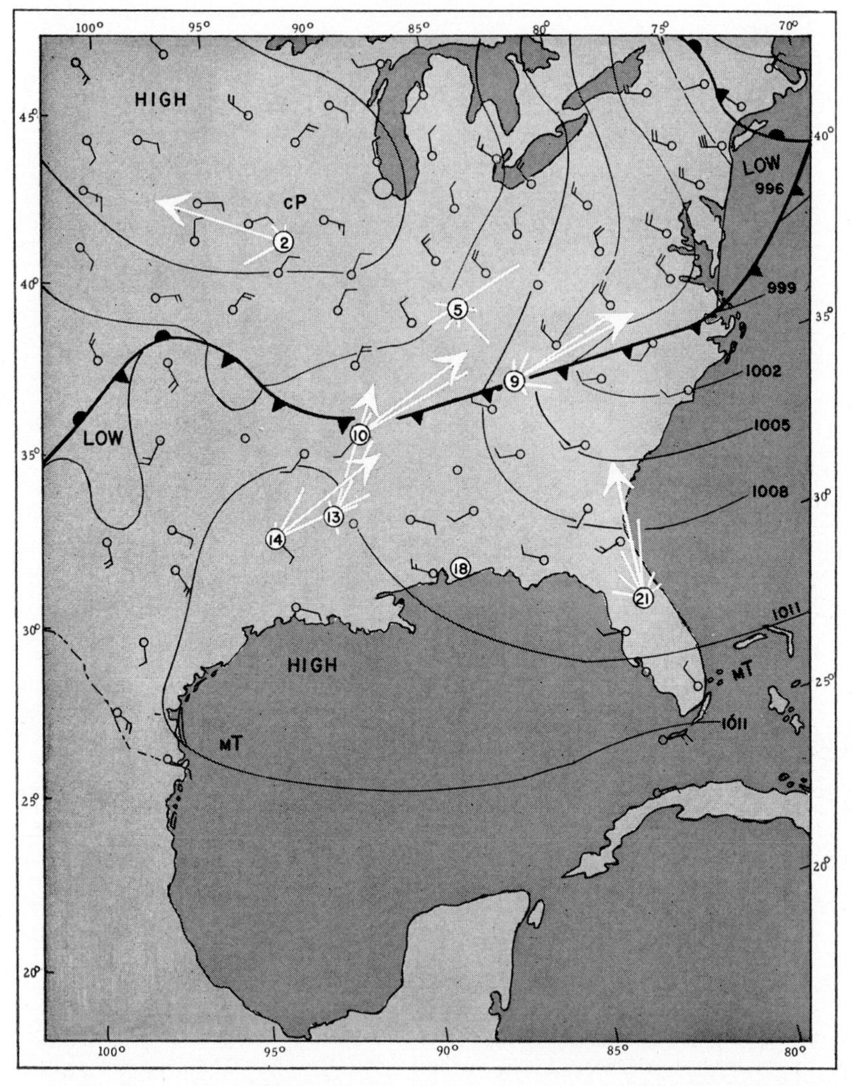

Fig. 7. Comparison of flight trends and surface weather conditions on May 21-22, 1948. The meteorological data were taken from the U. S. Weather Bureau Daily Weather Map for 12:30 A.M. (CST) on May 21. For further explanation, see legend of Fig. 6. (Reproduced from *A Quantitative Study of the Nocturnal Migration of Birds* by permission Univ. Kansas Mus. Nat. Hist.)

States there is evident a marked correlation, at sixteen simultaneously operating stations, between the direction of bird flight and the general flow of air. On the night of May 21-22, 1948, an entirely different directional movement of birds is correlated with a different pattern of continental air flow associated

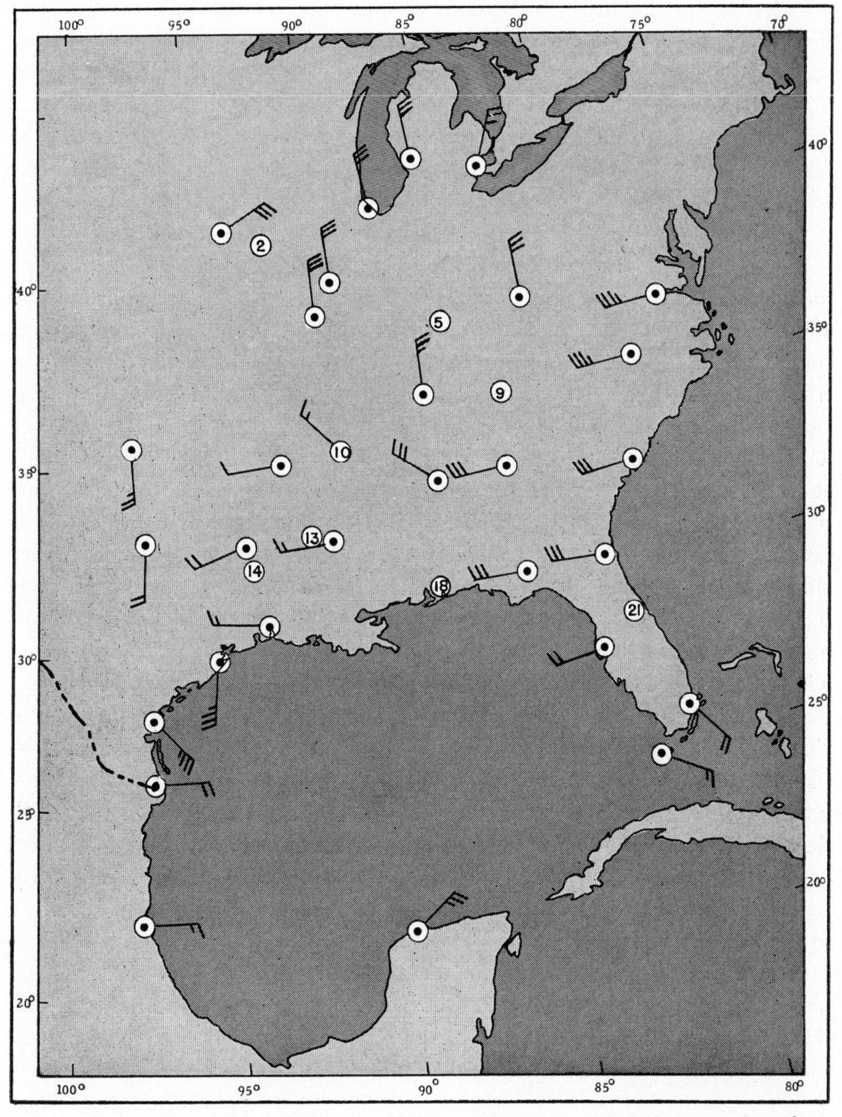

Fig. 7a. Winds aloft at 10:00 P.M. (CST) on May 21. Winds at 2,000 feet above mean sea level are shown in black; those at 4,000 in white. The numbered positions locate the stations shown in Fig. 7. (Reproduced from *A Quantitative Study of the Nocturnal Migration of Birds* by permission Univ. Kansas Mus. Nat. Hist.)

with the movement of the cold front that was being pushed down the breadth of the eastern United States by a high pressure system (Figs. 7 and 7*a*).

The detailed study now in progress of the directional flow of migration as revealed at the hundreds of stations in operation in the fall of 1952 and the fall of 1953 is expected to bring these correlations into still sharper focus. At times, while the wind has been blowing from the south, the strongest flight vectors have actually turned into the north quadrants, indicating a migrational flow diametrically opposite to the normal trend. This effect has so far been most noticeable among sets of southern data. At northern latitudes adverse winds seem to bring migration to a standstill rather than to reverse it. Confirmation of these impressions must await statistical evaluation.

These findings integrate smoothly with certain conclusions reached by European investigators engaged in direct studies of diurnal migration. Deelder and Tinbergen (1947) have shown that the higher birds fly, the greater becomes the angle between the direction of their flight and the direction of the wind. In other words, daytime migrations at the upper levels tend to be performed with the wind, while migrations at lower levels tend to proceed into the wind. This principle seems to resolve the conflict between the results obtained at night with the telescope and the insistence of some ornithologists that migrating birds almost always head into the wind. During the day attention is drawn to the wind-bucking tactics of birds flying within easy visual range close to earth. At night the fact that the interceptory potential of the telescope increases with distance favors the detection of the migrants moving in the upper air streams, with the wind. At the same time, the extreme degree to which nocturnal migration is affected by the wind might be taken to indicate that night migrants lack a very precise mechanism of orientation. This conclusion, if warranted, would do much to resolve the difficulties encountered by Kramer (1952, 1953), who has adduced powerful evidence to show that birds determine direction by the sun but has been at a loss to explain how they find their way after dark. Perhaps nocturnal migrants orient themselves before the sun disappears, and if blown off course or otherwise deviated from the set direction during the night, simply make the proper correction by reference to the sun of the following day.

Another feature of nocturnal migration seemingly associated with changes of weather has been the intermittency of maximal flight densities. In fall these seem usually to occur with the passage of cold fronts and the attendant southward flow of air. Because of the tremendous numbers of birds involved, they well merit the term "avalanche" that has been applied to similar flood passages in Scandinavia. Instances in point are: 992 birds in 6 hours and 53 minutes at Harlingen, Texas, on the night of September 4-5, 1952, seen by L. Irby Davis and Marshall Johnston; 1,276 birds in 6 hours and 4 minutes at Arlington, Virginia, on the night of September 30—October 1, 1952, seen by Mr. and Mrs. Irwin C. Hoover and Mr. and Mrs. Russell H. Hoffman; 1,557 birds in 6 hours and 45 minutes at Commerce, Texas, on the night of October 1-2, 1952, seen by Nora O'Neil and associates; 1,084 birds in 8 hours and 34 minutes at St. George Island, Florida, on the night of October 2-3,

1952, seen by Herbert L. Stoddard, Sr., and Leon Neel; 1,661 birds in 10 hours and 25 minutes at Towson, Maryland, on the night of September 22-23, 1953, seen by R. D. Cole and associates.

Ball has discounted both the influence of the wind on flight directions and the influence of cold fronts on the volume of migration. He has summarized his experiences as follows: "Analysis of wind direction during several migration seasons fails to support it as an important factor influencing the numbers and flight direction of Gaspé migrants. Large thrush movements have been recorded only on nights of relatively low wind velocity."

THE INFLUENCE OF TOPOGRAPHICAL FEATURES

Years ago, at the close of a pioneer study of nocturnal migration by means of the moon, H. A. Winkenwerder (1902a, b) announced proof that night migrants tend to be channeled along watercourses. Especially convincing to him were data obtained by a telescope situated on the east bank of the Rock River, just south of Beloit, Wisconsin. Here, on two successive nights in May there was a tremendous increase in the counts of silhouettes during the hour when the observation cone was pointing along the course of the river. These counts were not corrected for changes in the size of the field of observation, and subsequent attempts to adjust them by the modern method of processing have failed because of ambiguities in the directions given. Whether or not the apparent maxima recorded over the river represented the real maximum flight densities for the nights in question remains uncertain.

The more recent lunar data thus far analyzed have produced no clear support for Winkenwerder's ideas. The very fact that, as just discussed, migrational vectors seem to veer with the wind clashes with the concept of a rigid adherence to flight lines that are topographically defined, though the question at least remains as to how migrants behave on nights of calm. Working at the Museum of Zoology at Louisiana State University, Mrs. Frances James is currently concentrating on the problem of rivers and their effect on migration. Prominent in her study are comparative data obtained by the use of two simultaneously operating telescopes set up on opposite sides of a river. When these instruments face the rising moon the observer on the west bank is looking across the water while the observer on the east bank is looking away from it. If migration is occurring in greater density over the river, the first telescope should reveal fewer birds at the outset than the second one. Later, when the moon is over the river, putting both cones of observation in an equally favored position, the counts should agree closely. And finally, as the moon moves westward, the count from the scope on the east bank (whose cone alone is now over the river) should gain ascendancy. Pending the completion of Mrs. James' research, definite statements concerning the role of rivers in nocturnal migration would be premature. Possibly the routes of certain classes of birds lie along rivers while those of other birds do not. If so, a

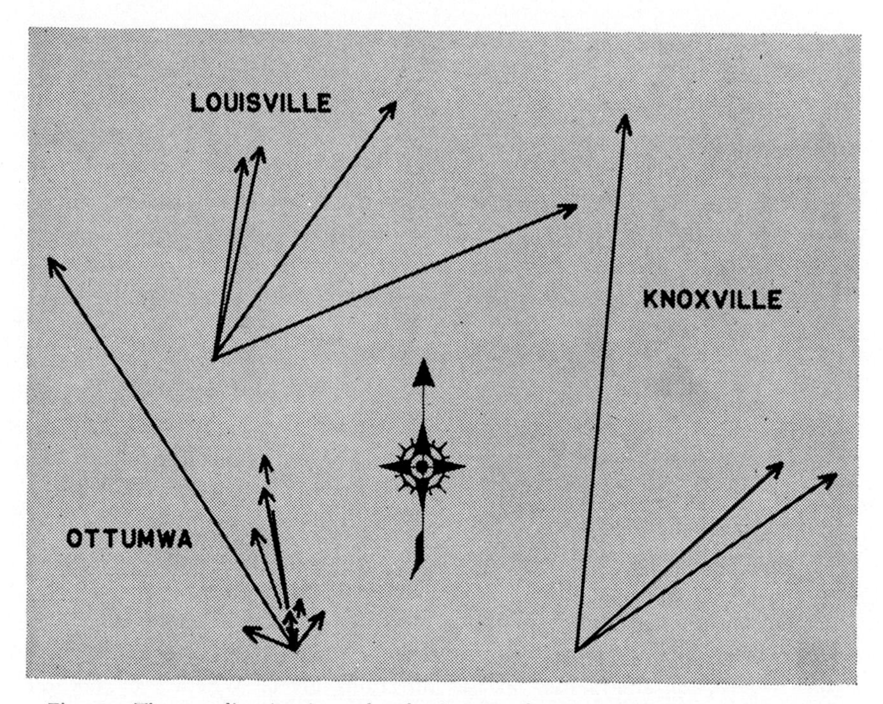

Fig. 8. The net directional trends of migration for several nights in 1948 at three stations. Each arrow is the vector resultant for a particular night, its length expressing the nightly density as a percentage of the total station density for all of the nights represented. (Reproduced from *A Quantitative Study of the Nocturnal Migration of Birds* by permission Univ. Kansas Mus. Nat. Hist.)

very complicated sort of analysis may be required to establish the fact. It may be mentioned, however, that in the fall of 1952, through the kind cooperation of Dr. Carl Welty and the Department of Biology of Beloit College, tests were carried out with a pair of telescopes stationed along the Rock River, the very area that produced Winkenwerder's data. The original results were not duplicated.

The general impression conveyed by the observations assembled in the spring of 1948 was that of broad-front movement, unmodified by the effect of topographical features. There were places where a strong directional trend was maintained from night to night with little variation even though the station was located in featureless terrain seemingly devoid of "leading lines" (see beyond). Contrariwise, at some other stations great variations in the overall trend of migration occurred on different nights (Fig. 8), even though there were marked physiographic features present for the birds to follow. Such evidence, of course, is by no means conclusive. Better understanding of the relative importance of broad-front and narrow-front movements is certain to be reached through the detailed comparisons made possible by the much denser network of telescopes simultaneously in operation in the autumns of 1952 and 1953.

When the topographical problem was studied in 1948, the question emphasized was whether night-flying birds use rivers and other linear topographical features as aids in finding their way during migration. Meanwhile, in Europe the ornithologists who were making direct studies of diurnal movements of birds were coming to the conclusion that even daytime migration is basically a broad-front performance, usually accomplished without orientation by topographical clues. According to the current consensus abroad, migrating birds may become concentrated in a stream along the visible lines provided by features of the terrain or by the borders between different types of habitat; but they do so because they are reluctant to cross the line and to fly over an unfavorable habitat, not because they need these visible lines to guide them to their destination. Because these linear features of the terrain tend to lead migrants away from a direct course, they have come to be called "leading lines." Whether leading lines play a very important part in migration at night is a matter not yet fully evaluated. One might expect to find the reduced visibility at night minimizing the influence of leading lines; but at the other speculative extreme one might reason that, unable to use the type of solar orientation demonstrated by the work of Kramer and others, night migrants may find reference to topographical features an indispensable adjunct to effective navigation.

Once again Ball's chip-counting procedures have produced evidence of a very different sort. It would seem that thrushes beginning their migrations from the interior highlands of the Gaspé follow the little tributary streams from the draw in which they have nested down radially into the main river valley, whereupon they generally descend the valley even when they must for the time being proceed northward to do so. Ball has postulated that the descending horizon line presented to birds flying down valleys is the orienting stimulus directing these performances.

MIGRATION OVER WATER

The reaction of migrants to the large bodies of water that are frequently interposed in their paths is really only a special case of the effect of topographical features, but it is one having aspects that warrant separate discussion. In view of the now repeatedly observed reluctance of land birds to cross even small bays and narrow estuaries in the daytime, it is not surprising that leading lines have their most noticeable influence along the borders of the sea. There the resulting tendency of migrants to follow the shore line has caused the British to coin a special term for it. They call it "coasting."

In line with these principles, Ball has found no direct evidence that thrushes from Anticosti Island or Labrador cross the Gulf of St. Lawrence to reach the Gaspé. He is furthermore convinced that the resident populations of thrushes on the Gaspé are sufficient to account for all of the thrushes which he heard migrating at night in the course of his four-year study. Only once in this period did he observe other passerines that he presumed might have made the over-water flight across the Gulf of St. Lawrence.

Counterbalancing these facts and conclusions is the ample evidence that coasting is not a simple, unmodifiable reaction or, perhaps, even the typical one. In the Netherlands, where the relation of diurnal migration to topography has been most searchingly examined (van Dobben, 1953), observers have concluded that the willingness of birds to accept a coastal leading line depends in part upon the extent to which the trend of the shore deviates from their so-called "standard direction," which usually represents the direct course to their ultimate goal. Tail winds, high-level flying, and the joint participation of many birds in a mass movement likewise act to overcome the psychological hazard posed by water barriers. Then again, as van Dobben has remarked, a lone observer is inclined to get an exaggerated idea of the relative volume of the low-level coastwise flights, since he is in a position to witness them close at hand and in full continuity but at best can perceive the higher-level, seaward departures at only one of the many points where they are taking place. Reviewing what is known of the migratory behavior of that one-third of the summer bird population of Europe wintering in Africa south of the Sahara, Moreau (1953) has pictured trans-Mediterranean migration as a broad-front movement involving no demonstrated tendency to favor the short crossings except on the part of soaring birds.

Here, however, our primary concern is with the direct observation of migratory behavior in coastal situations after dark. On occasion, at locations where the shore line roughly parallels a north-south line of flight, the moon has disclosed what could be interpreted as coasting flights closely contained by the leading line of the land's edge. Such was our experience on April 21-22, 1948, at Tampico, Tamaulipas, Mexico, where a dearth of observations in the early hours, when the telescopic cone lay over the water, was succeeded by tremendous flight densities in the 10 to 11 P. M. interval, when the cone passed over the beach. Figure 9, embodying a type of analysis that may be applied to terrain problems, shows the situation pictorially. The critical reader will notice that the computed prevailing direction of flight, which varied only two degrees on three successive dates, actually veered slightly to sea. This circumstance, together with the fact that the hour of maximum density corresponded not only with the passage of the moon over the beach but also with the expected peak in temporal pattern, considerably weakens the force of these data as proof that the leading line principle is effective at night. Further attempts to test the matter on the western Gulf coast, at various localities in Texas, have met with little success. Along this strand, renowned for the most spectacular daytime manifestations of coasting on this continent, beach stations have continually failed to record nocturnal migrants in appreciable number.

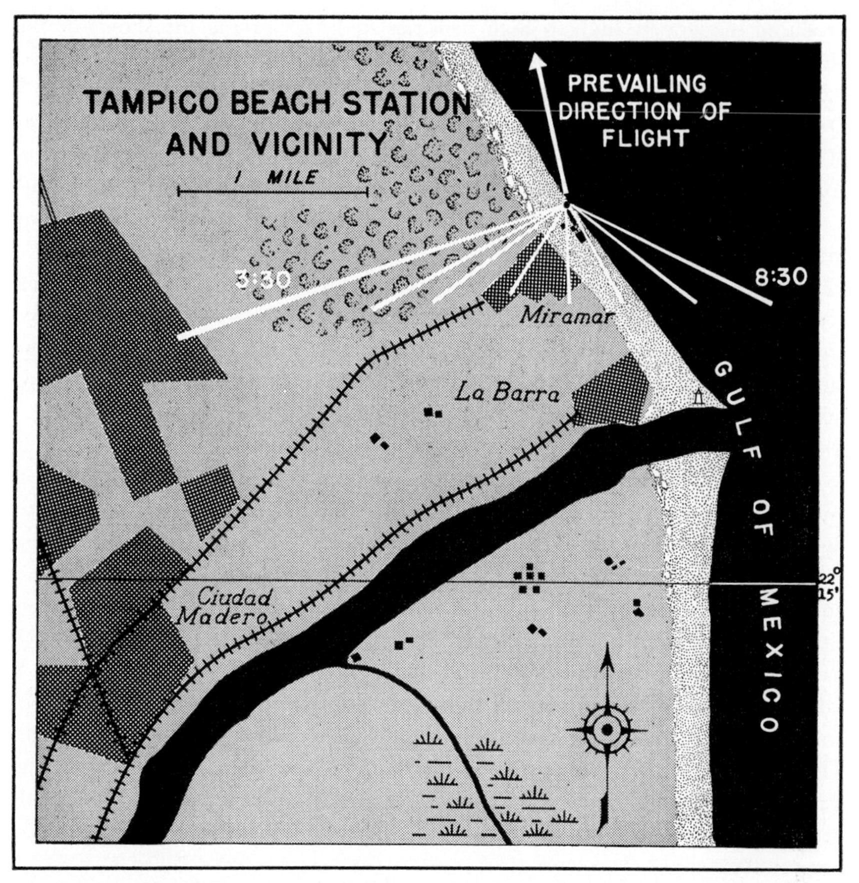

Fig. 9. Terrain analysis of the migration at Tampico, Tamps., on the night of April 21-22, 1948. The tapering white lines represent the hourly projections of the cone of observation on the earth's surface at the mid-point of each hour of observation. The third line from the right shows the average position of the cone in the 10 to 11 o'clock interval when all the birds seen were flying over the beach. (Reproduced from *A Quantitative Study of the Nocturnal Migration of Birds* by permission Univ. Kansas Mus. Nat. Hist.)

As might be predicted on the basis of the diurnal studies in the Netherlands, lunar watches from positions where the coast of departure tends to cross the line of direct migration at right angles yield rather different results. In spring, flights of substantial magnitude have been recorded of migrants leaving the northern coast of Yucatán and heading out over the wide expanse of the Gulf of Mexico (Lowery, 1946, 1951). Although only two all-night telescopic counts have been made in Yucatán, one of these was the third largest secured anywhere in 1948. The two nights yielded, respectively, average hourly flight densities over water of 3,900 and 3,000 birds per mile of migratory front. Subsequent data, obtained in the fall migrations of 1952 and 1953, at stations on the coasts of Louisiana and northwest Florida, produced moderately high to high densities of birds leaving the shores of the United States and heading southward out over the Gulf. The Florida records, accumulated through the diligence of H. L. Stoddard, F. M. Weston, and Frank Dachille, are the more impressive in bulk but are complicated by an array of multiple vectors interpretable as the expression of simultaneous coastwise and seaward movements. The Louisiana observations secured at Grand Isle, a barrier beach separated from all large areas of firm ground by miles of marshland, exhibit the initial phases of trans-Gulf migration in purer form. Not only are the directional trends less diffuse, but a check is provided through counts made by a second team of observers located on an offshore oil rig, eight miles from land and almost due south of the Grand Isle station. The latter results are not significantly different with respect either to direction or magnitude from those obtained on the island.

The seaward departure of transients from land masses at night is likely to result in longer sustained flights than most transients normally make in any one stage of their migrations. We may postulate that nocturnal migrants, flying too high to react always to leading lines on the terrain, frequently launch out over great bodies of water unintentionally or at least without trepidation and then, after several hours of flight, are compelled to make the best of their situation. Although the completion of these flights may be fraught with hazards (Bullis and Lincoln, 1952; Packard, 1947; Lowery, 1946; etc.), landfalls are made by a large enough proportion of them (Paynter, 1953; Lowery and Newman, 1953; etc.) to insure against decimation of the species involved. The possibility exists, however, that the drastic diminution in numbers of the Bachman's Warbler, *Dendroica bachmani,* in recent decades may be the result of mass fatalities in trans-Gulf crossings, disasters from which the species has not yet recovered.

Notwithstanding this substantial progress, the subject of transmarine migration has not been divested of contradictions and controversy. Great strides forward could be made by adapting the lunar methods to use aboard ship and by ringing the periphery of the Gulf of Mexico with telescopes simultaneously pointed at the moon.

THE NIGHTLY TEMPORAL PATTERN OF MIGRATION

The "nightly temporal pattern of migration" is a phrase that has been applied to the hour-to-hour changes in the numbers of birds flying over an observation station. In no other single respect do the auditory and visual methods of study lead to more astonishingly divergent results than in the contributions they have made regarding this pattern of temporal variation.

Ball's experience has been that migration as reflected in the flight calls of thrushes takes place in two separate periods—the first in the early hours of the evening before 10 P. M., the second in the hours just before dawn. The morning flight is by far the more impressive. During ten seasons of listening,

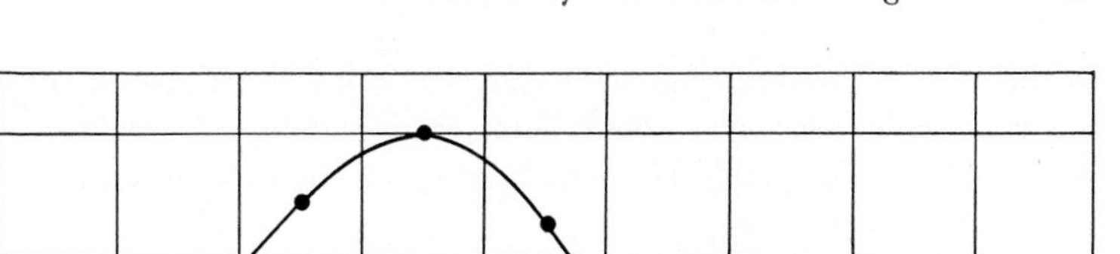

Fig. 10. Nightly temporal pattern of spring migration as indicated by telescopic observations of 1948. The curves are both based on hourly values plotted as a percentage of the peak value but were arrived at by two different methods as described in the text.

Ball has recorded 32,700 thrush calls after midnight, but only 1,221 calls before 10 P. M.—a ratio of 27 to 1! Moreover, except for one large evening flight of 450 birds, fully 90 per cent of these migrants were heard in the hour before dawn. These facts suggest to Ball that some thrushes arise an hour or two before sunrise and migrate from thirty to sixty miles before daylight brings them down. He has found that the bimodal nightly pattern of thrush calls is not peculiar to the Gaspé or to autumn. It holds just as true in Connecticut and in spring.

Against this carefully studied background, it is astounding to discover that the pattern of flight densities computed from the numbers of birds seen at night behaves in a manner that is almost exactly opposite. Figure 10 shows the volume of flight from hour to hour as evidenced by the data obtained through the nationwide moon-watching project of the spring of 1948. The upper curve is a plotting of the hourly means of the flight densities for all stations and all nights, expressed as percentages of the peak value *after* computation of the means. It therefore represents a statistical procedure wherein nights of heavy flights exercise a vastly greater control than nights of reduced activity. The lower curve shows the result obtained when the separate sets of data for single nights at single stations are expressed as hourly percentages of their respective peak values *before* computation of the means. This procedure combines the individual temporal patterns in such a way that they make equal contribution to the final curve, regardless of the total number of birds concerned in them. The two resulting lines differ in slope but conform in the general trend of their curvature. Both point to migrations of maximum magnitude in the hour before midnight—the very time when the listener on the Gaspé sits beneath a silent sky.

Analyses carried out in 1948 led to the hypothesis that this rise and fall in the nightly temporal pattern of flight density is the unconstrained manifestation in nature of those hour-to-hour variations in migratory restlessness that European investigators have observed in caged birds and called *Zugunruhe*. As such, it might be envisioned as an inherent twenty-four-hour rhythm, triggered perhaps by external stimuli but involving a timing mechanism that is largely independent of the surrounding environment. Already, however, certain inconsistencies in the accumulating evidence warn us to be cautious in our pronouncements. It is to these inconsistencies and their thorough exploration that the first large-scale evaluation of the data collected since 1948 is now being addressed.

If temporal pattern is not moon-controlled, if it is not an artifact produced by the mathematical procedure, and if it is not just the normal distribution of a series of chance events, then the same hour-to-hour trend should prevail on the seventh to third nights preceding the full of the moon as on the five nights surrounding it and on the third to seventh nights following. Each of these five-day periods embraces markedly different positional relations of the moon with respect to the various hours of the night; and so too the correction factors, which depend on the positions of the moon, vary in their application with respect to time. Thus, if the computations for the three different intervals lead to three discordant density-time curves, perfection of the correction factors may be sought in those values that bring the patterns into harmony. Whatever the outcome of this stringent test, the techniques of density calculations should emerge from it with an increased measure of dependability. This is the chief reason why temporal pattern has been chosen as a starting point in the current series of analyses dealing with various aspects of nocturnal migration.

None of the possibilities mentioned is sufficient to reconcile the testimony of the visual method with the auditory temporal pattern shown by Ball. Whatever the exact hour-to-hour variation in the volume of migration and whatever the factors that govern it, the untreated telescopic counts alone serve to demonstrate two things irrefutably. They prove that flights of great magnitude are typically in progress near the middle of the night, and they show that almost always the visible presence of migrants before the moon dwindles into nothingness before the eyes of the astonished observer in that very predawn interval when passing chips so frequently assail his confused faculties with a rising wave of sound.

One obvious explanation would be that migrants are near enough to the observer to be heard only when rising to or descending from upper levels where most migration is performed. Aware of the telescopic findings of 1948, Ball sought to test this hypothesis by climbing to high elevations to listen for flight calls in the middle of the night. He heard nothing.

CONCLUDING REMARKS

Migrational behavior is doubtless subject to geographic variation as well as to variation by species. If we bear this probability in mind as we consider in turn each of the points of conflict between the auditory and visual evidence, much of the mystery surrounding these contradictions disappears. With respect to both types of variation, Ball's exposition may be predicated on a special situation. Indeed, he has not really claimed otherwise. Lying at a more northern latitude than most of the localities where visual methods have been applied intensively and surrounded on three sides by expanses of water, the Gaspé Peninsula may be the stage for initial phases of migratory behavior differing from manifestations of the phenomenon under full momentum. Similarly, thrushes, with their visual adaptations to a life in deep forest shade, may have nocturnal abilities that permit them to cope with the hazards of low-level flight and to perform migrations of a type that would be disastrous to other passerines.

Thus it becomes apparent that the contrasts in the conclusions with which we are dealing here are not necessarily contrasts induced by the methods that were employed in reaching them. The probability is rather that these contrasts stem in large part from the fact that the conclusions relate on the one hand to studies on a broad scale and on the other hand to studies that are sharply focused on one type of bird in a local situation. That this may not be the whole picture is suggested by the contradictions that relate to the temporal pattern of nocturnal migration. Here each method of study has proven itself capable of producing positive evidence that contraverts negative evidence of the other. When we hear birds and see none, we cannot say that no birds are there; and the reverse is, of course, equally true. Both situations have been encountered in one night in one locality by observers participating in our research program. Indeed, there appears frequently to be an inverse relationship between the number of birds seen through the telescope and the number of call notes counted. We can interpret these facts to mean that in the middle of the night most migration is taking place at altitudes beyond the range of audibility. It might be, however, that chipping has an echo-sounding function, causing the frequency of call notes to be inversely correlated with altitude.

Ball, at the time of the writing of his paper, had conducted a few lunar observations on the Gaspé. Results were negative. If they were continued to the point where they assumed statistical significance and he still failed to see birds, the hypothesis that Gaspé migration takes place at an unusually low level would become an established fact, and the many contradictions previously discussed would become understandable. The work in Europe prepares us to expect differences in the reaction both to wind and to leading lines on the part of high-level and low-level migrants. Furthermore, we should bear in mind that the two types of study have not concentrated on exactly the same aspects of the topographical problem, the auditory approach having been used mainly in connection with flight along valleys, and the analyses of visual data having so far dealt mainly with the possible effect of large rivers and seacoasts.

Ball's stimulating work has shown a pressing need for the proper integration of the visual and auditory approaches to the study of nocturnal migration. Each method is really complementary to the other, and the two techniques working together should permit ornithologists to explore the intricacies of migration with new effectiveness. We have every confidence that the vast corps of lunar observers who have so indefatigably devoted time and effort to a joint undertaking will continue on a dual basis the researches they have so splendidly begun.

Bibliography

BALL, S. C.

1952. Fall bird migration on the Gaspé Peninsula. Bull. Peabody Mus. Nat. Hist., 7:1-211.

BULLIS, H. R., JR., and F. C. LINCOLN

1952. A trans-Gulf migration. Auk, 69:34-39.

DEELDER, C. L., and L. TINBERGEN

1947. Waarnemingen over de vlieghoogte van trekkende vinken, *Fringilla coelebs* L., en spreeuwen, *Sturnus vulgaris* L. Ardea, 35:45-78.

DOBBEN, W. H. VAN

1953. Bird migration in the Netherlands. Ibis, 95:212-234.

KRAMER, G.

1952. Experiments in bird orientation. Ibis, 94:265-285.

1953. Wird die Sonnenhöhe bei der Heimfindeorientierung verwertet? Jour. Ornithol., 94:201-219.

LOWERY, G. H., JR.

1946. Evidence of trans-Gulf migration. Auk, 63:175-211.

1951. A quantitative study of the nocturnal migration of birds. Univ. Kansas Publ., Mus. Nat. Hist., 3:361-472.

LOWERY, G. H., JR., and R. J. NEWMAN

1953. Central southern region. Audubon Field Notes, 7:276-279.

MOREAU, R. E.

1953. Migration in the Mediterranean area. Ibis, 95:329-364.

NEWMAN, R. J.

1952. Studying nocturnal bird migration by means of the moon. Special publ. Mus. Zool., Louisiana State Univ., 49 pp.

PACKARD, F. M.

1947. Notes on the occurrence of birds in the Gulf of Mexico. Auk, 64:130-131.

PAYNTER, R. A., JR.

1953. Autumnal migrants on the Campeche Bank. Auk, 70:338-349.

RENSE, W. A.

1946. Astronomy and ornithology. Popular Astronomy, 54:55-73.

1950. Some notes on the astronomical method of studying bird migration. Popular Astronomy, 58:287-294.

WINKENWERDER, H. A.

1902a. The migration of birds with special reference to nocturnal flight. Bull. Wisconsin Nat. Hist. Soc., 2:177-263.

1902b. Some recent observations on the migration of birds. Bull. Wisconsin Nat. Hist. Soc., 2:97-107.

chapter 9

BREEDING BIOLOGY OF BIRDS . . . David E. Davis

The breeding biology of birds has naturally received ample attention from ornithologists in recent years. This review will discuss trends and advances in our knowledge of breeding biology since 1933 when the American Ornithologists' Union published its *Fifty Years' Progress in American Ornithology.* The splendid monograph of Nice (1937, 1943) covers many aspects of research in the years 1933-1942. The review is not intended to be an exhaustive critique of studies and will not try to mention every paper on breeding biology. It will cite notable examples of research trends and comment critically on some problems. Bent's *Life Histories* (1919-1953), although the early volumes are out of date, contain references to the major articles for each species. The excellent French compendium (Grassé, 1950) has a fine chapter by Noel Mayaud (pp. 539-652) that summarizes breeding biology from the conventional viewpoint.

The plan of the review is first to discuss developments in methods of research; second, to discuss research in the sequence from pairing through fledging of the young. In addition, problems of general biological interest will be discussed at various times.

The term "breeding biology" encompasses the activities of adults and young during the period of reproduction from pairing of adults to fledging of young. It could include behavioral aspects (territorialism, courtship) but these will be mentioned only when specially pertinent. For this review breeding biology will be assumed to start with pairing, although some aspects of migratory activities might be included. Following pairing, the construction and location of the nest will be considered. The laying of eggs, incubation, and hatching follow in sequence, and the care of the young in the nest and the fledging completes the cycle of breeding biology.

METHODS

The basic method for the study of breeding biology still consists of observation unaided by elaborate apparatus. Generally speaking, the observer watches the adults and the nests and records in a notebook the activities of the birds. Frequently the time is recorded for each event or at definite intervals. Odum (1941), in a summary of methods and objectives, listed the phases of

Manuscript received February 15, 1954.

breeding biology and suggested appropriate methods for each phase. He suggested keeping records in simple notebooks and urges the use of maps. Colored bands or other marks are essential for studies of individual birds, which must be trapped for marking. Odum's review concluded with a detailed list of desirable data. Mechanical devices for recording visits to the nest have been developed (Baldwin and Kendeigh, 1927; Odum, 1945; Kluijver, 1950) but have not been generally used. Moreau (1939) trained African natives to record data in a routine manner. Perhaps the significant recent development in methods has been the extensive use of colored bands, thereby permitting identification of the individual. The simple method of observation unaided by extensive apparatus has been fruitful; in research the observation is the objective, and apparatus (microscope, scalpel, oscillograph, etc.) are merely devices for assisting the observer. Indeed, ornithologists may be proud of the research accomplished without extensive apparatus.

A beginning in experimentation (manipulation of conditions) is discernible in recent years, although most such studies involve the behavior of adults. The early use of dummies to stimulate behavior of wild birds (Allen, 1934; Chapman, 1935) has been followed by a number of experimental studies of behavior. Recently Nero *et al.* (1951) moved the nests to study territorial behavior. Some persons (Emlen, 1941; Davis, 1942a) have altered the number of eggs in a nest to attempt to influence the clutch-size. There are, of course, a large number of experimental studies of the physiology of reproduction but most are laboratory studies and only a few (Collias, 1950) are related to natural conditions. The time is ripe for field experimentation in the physiological aspects of breeding biology.

A notable development in recent years is the study of life histories of tropical birds. The work of British officials has been going on for years, but recently some splendid work has been conducted by persons residing in South and Central America (Skutch, 1949; Sick, 1947; Wagner, 1945).

This review will attempt to summarize studies that present "adequate" data to support the conclusions. The word adequate is difficult to define and depends upon the variability of the sample. In general, data are here considered adequate if they permit the detection of 10 per cent difference between sets of observations at a confidence level of 5 per cent or if around thirty observations are reported. This means that variation due to sampling would give the particular difference only 5 times out of 100. It is fully realized that these standards are arbitrary and in many cases unwise. However, an attempt to set minimum standards of quality is worthwhile. A specific example may illustrate the use of the standards to reject data. Girard (1941) studied nesting of Mallards, *Anas platyrhynchos,* and found 267 nests. Of duration of incubation he said (p. 238), "Records made for this study show that the incubation period of the Mallard is about 25 days, varying two or three days either way." No data are given to establish the conclusion; there is no statement of how many incubations were observed. Since the author did not give number of nests, mean duration, and standard deviation, it is not possible to compare his data with other data. In many cases an author failed to report data which he surely had collected. Consider, for example, the excellent paper of Beer and Tibbitts (1950). On page 71 they stated, "The data gathered from 153 nests considered to have complete clutches showed that the Red-wing [*Agelaius phoeniceus*] averages 3.7 eggs per nest, with a range of from two to six eggs." But they give an unsatisfactory measure of variability, and hence the data are difficult to compare with any other sample. Unfortunately they did not give a table of eggs per nest. Many studies are omitted from this review because of lack of "adequate" data.

Another aspect of this problem is the use of studies involving only a few nests. Consider the numerous examples of thorough studies of one or two nests, as for example Nice and Thomas (1948) or Purchon (1948). Variation may be so great from nest to nest that no generalization can be developed as in the following case. Nohring (1943) studied three nests of the Pied Flycatcher, *Muscicapa hypoleuca.* In one nest the male did not feed the female, in another such feeding was rare, but in a third the male fed the female regularly. Many papers are omitted from this review because they treat only a few nests.

The breeding biology of birds can be divided into several stages, although of course the reproductive cycle is a continuous series of events. The following discussion therefore will be divided into sections on pairing, the nest, eggs, incubation, the young, and duration of the breeding season.

PAIRING

The first definite act in the breeding cycle is the pairing of the birds. By pairing is meant the formation of a psychological bond between male and female. The time of formation and the duration of the bond varies greatly from species to species and in some groups (hummingbirds, manakins) hardly exists. (The term *mating* is not used here because it may mean pairing, copulation, or even courtship). Actual pairing may occur long before the breeding period as in many ducks (Hochbaum, 1944; Girard, 1941). But typically pairing occurs after the male has selected a territory and shortly before nest construction, as for example in the House Wren, *Troglodytes aedon* (Kendeigh, 1941:48). However, in some species (American Goldfinch, *Spinus tristis,* Stokes, 1950:109; Black-capped Chickadee, *Parus atricapillus,* Odum, 1941) the pairing takes place while the birds are still in flocks, while in other cases (Eastern Kingbird, *Tyrannus tyrannus,* Davis, 1941) pairing occurs before territories are chosen. Laskey (1950) described the pairing of dominant male and female Cowbirds, *Molothrus ater,* a species that lays its eggs parasitically in the nests of other birds. Apparently within an area one male and one female become dominant over others of the same sex and copulation occurs only between these dominant individuals.

Courtship behavior is an integral part of breeding biology and may occur in different species in any or even all parts of the cycle. The establishment of territory is also an essential part of the cycle. Typically the male defends an area which ultimately serves for raising the young, although there is much variation among species. After establishment of territory, reproduction truly begins. Copulation generally occurs shortly after pairing but may continue in some species during incubation. Unfortunately, copulation is rarely observed and hence little is known about its time and frequency. Presumably these aspects of the breeding cycle are under physiological control. Recent research has called attention to several aspects of pairing that were formerly poorly known. For example the importance of the bond for nesting success and the reality of the bond between members of a pair have been recognized. Another example is the realization that pairing may occur in many species before the establishment of territories.

Social Nesting

In recent years several studies have shown that some species do not regularly pair but nest in groups. Ryves (1934) showed that the male Corn Bunting, *Emberiza calandra,* is polygynous and may have as many as seven females. Lack (1935) found a similar situation in the Bishop-bird, *Euplectes hordeacea.* Ritter (1938) described the communal nesting habits of the California Woodpecker, *Balanosphyra formicivora.* Davis (1942b) summarized a series of papers on the phylogeny of social nesting in an aberrant group of cuckoos in which the more primitive species nest in pairs but the more advanced kinds nest communally and have lost all pairing behavior. Wilson (1946) reported similar social nesting in an Australian "Magpie," *Gymnorhina dorsalis.*

Social parasitism has received some attention in recent years, although the results were confirmatory in nature rather than original. Makatsch (1936) summarized the available information on cuckoos, and Chance (1940) gave his old data and some new data in detail.

Age at Sexual Maturity

Age at breeding is an intricate problem requiring attention. Information can be obtained from banded birds as has been done for Yellow-eyed Penguins, *Megadyptes antipodes,* by Richdale (1949a) or by anatomical studies as was done by Wright and Wright (1944) for Redwings. Richter (1953) found that male Dippers, *Cinclus cinclus,* in certain areas did not breed till their third year, apparently because of an excess of males in the population. Such studies require data on a large number of individuals before generalizations can be developed. Some data will be cited later in this chapter.

THE NEST

Construction

The nest is frequently constructed by both sexes, although in many cases, as, for example, in manakins and hummingbirds, only the female builds. Generalized observations are available for a number of species to show the role of each sex, and some recent studies give detailed data for several species. Nice (1937:94) observed that the male Song Sparrow, *Melospiza melodia,* carries material in preliminary activities but that the female does the actual building. Hann (1937:168) noted that the female Ovenbird, *Seiurus aurocapillus,* alone builds the nest. The male House Wren (Kendeigh, 1941:24) constructs foundations for several nests in his territory and the female lines one of them for use. Kuusisto (1941) gave some detailed observations of frequency of trips to the nest while building but the data are hard to analyze for conclusions. A comparison of the role of each sex in closely related species might suggest evolutionary or survival significance of the differences.

A number of recent studies have obtained quantitative data on the duration of construction. Walkinshaw (1941:7) found that construction for fifty-four nests of the Prothonotary Warbler, *Protonotaria citrea,* averaged 3.3 days in Michigan. Putnam (1949:158) determined that the average time for construction of eleven nests of Cedar Waxwings, *Bombycilla cedrorum,* was 5.6 days (S.D. = 1.6). Stokes (1950:119) found an average construction time for forty-five goldfinch nests of 9 days. Further, a statistically significant decline occurred as the season progressed, from 13.0 days during July 1-15 to 5.6 days during August 16-31. Such a decline has been reported for other species but not adequately documented. Gibb (1950:512) reported considerable difference in construction time of nests of individual tits but did not analyze his data in detail. Petersen and Young (1950:468) divided the construction period of Purple Grackle, *Quiscalus quiscula,* nests into stages and gave figures for the average duration but failed to mention the number of observations. Clearly, detailed studies of nest construction are a fertile field for investigation. Such studies could suggest the role of weather factors in the activity of a bird or indicate the influence of habitat on construction.

Location

The location of the nest has received considerable attention in recent years, especially from the ecological-minded game managers. Provost (1947:487) gave detailed data and a diagram of the relation of waterbirds nests to vegetation and the depth of a pond. Each species was found within a fairly narrow band, although Coots were widely distributed. Glover (1953) found that 85 per cent of 97 nests of the Pied-billed Grebe, *Podilymbus podiceps,* were within 50 feet of open water in a marsh. Girard (1939) found that Shoveller, *Spatula clypeata,* nests averaged 61 feet from water and 56 per cent were in short grass. Randall (1941:311) gives a fine example of a detailed study (Table 1). He records the cover type for 257 Ring-necked Pheasant, *Phasianus colchicus,* nests and gives detailed maps for several fields. He determines "acreage use values" by dividing the number of nests in a cover-type by the acreage of the type. For example, 59 per cent of the nests were found in alfalfa, but since alfalfa was the most common cover-type, when placed on an acreage basis, the result was 4.4 per cent in contrast to roadsides with 19.8 per cent. Hann (1937:165) gave interesting data for the location of Ovenbird nests in reference to trees or bushes. Of 60 nests 58 per cent were not under a tree or bush. Schierer (1952) found that 62 per cent of 380 White Stork, *Ciconia ciconia,* nests were on public buildings, 35 per cent on private buildings, and the rest in trees. Howell (1942:549) gave a table of heights of American Robin, *Turdus migratorius,* nests from the ground. The geometric mean was 16.4 feet. (S.D. = 21.4). Howell also contrasted the number of first nests in evergreens or in deciduous trees with the number of later nests in these types. From his data one can calculate that 69 per cent of 49 first nests

TABLE 1. Distribution of Nests of Ring-necked Pheasants by Dates and Cover-Types (Randall, 1941)

Date of First Egg	Roadside	Fence Row	Waste Land	Alfalfa Clover	Small Grain	Pasture	Potatoes	Misc.	Total
April 1-15	1	2	2	1	0	1	0	0	7
April 16-30	4	3	5	8	1	0	0	5	26
May 1-15	4	6	6	33	5	3	0	4	61
May 16-31	1	1	6	63	10	1	0	3	85
June 1-15	2	0	5	32	8	0	0	0	47
June 16-30	2	0	2	14	1	0	0	0	19
July 1-15	2	0	3	2	0	0	2	0	9
July 16-31	0	1	1	0	1	0	0	0	3
Totals	16	13	30	153	26	5	2	12	257
Per cent Use[a]	19.8	18.7	5.0	4.4	1.0	1.5	0.2	5.5	

[a] See text for explanation.

were in evergreens, whereas only 44 per cent of 52 later nests were in evergreens. The difference is significant at the 5 per cent level. Apparently Robins prefer fairly dense cover for nesting and hence in the early spring avoid the bare deciduous trees. Kozicky and Schmidt (1949:357) gave details on the distribution of Clapper Rail, *Rallus longirostris,* nests. They pointed out that 72 per cent of 62 nests were within 12 feet of a ditch which supported a growth of saltmarsh grass. Putnam (1949:157) recorded the species of trees used for nest sites by Cedar Waxwings. Of 99 trees, 27 per cent were cedar, 27 per cent were apple, 14 per cent were pear, and the rest belonged to 7 other kinds. Data concerning the relative abundance of trees in the area would be interesting to show whether waxwings preferred cedar and apple or whether these are merely the most common trees. Siivonen (1939) found that 78 per cent of 460 nests of the Song Thrush, *Turdus ericetorum,* were in firs. Stokes (1950:117) gave data on relative abundance of plants and the location of 230 American Goldfinch nests. Although about 50 per cent of the plants in the area were elderberry, 68 per cent of the nests were in elderberry. He also noted that the nest was almost always placed within 2 feet of the top of the shrub and gave a table of the height from the ground of 278 nests. The arithmetic mean was 5.1 feet (S.D.=1.85). Girard (1941:234) gave a graph of the cover-type in which 267 Mallard nests were found. About 60 per cent were in grass. McCabe and Hawkins (1946) listed the cover-type for Hungarian Partridges, *Perdix perdix,* in Wisconsin. Colquhoun (1951:234) gave detailed data for the location of Wood Pigeon, *Columba palumbus,* nests. About one-third were in evergreens and most were 5 to 15 feet above the ground.

Studies of the locations of nests are significant for an understanding of population size or changes. The abundance of a species may depend on some minute detail of the habitat which is only detectable by careful analysis. When such requirements are discovered, the population can be managed more effectively. From the speciation viewpoint, the analysis of variation in nesting site may provide information about trends in evolution.

EGGS

Laying

The laying of the eggs is the culmination of the preparatory activities in the breeding cycle. The actual date of laying depends on a variety of physiological, environmental, and psychological influences. Darling (1938) advanced the hypothesis that mutual courtship-stimulation influenced the start of laying in gulls. Hoogerwerf (1937) reported that several White Storks, *Ciconia ciconia,* build nests on a platform and that the members using each platform begin laying simultaneously.

The initiation of laying is dependent upon a complex series of physiological events but the external environment may determine the actual day. Few studies of the relation of laying to environmental factors are available under experimental or natural conditions. Nice (1937:99) interpreted her data to indicate that high temperatures stimulated laying. Kluijver (1951) presented probably the most complete set of data on the initiation of laying. He compares air temperatures and date of laying by Great Tits, *Parus major,* in Holland from 1912 to 1943. His paper should be consulted for details because of the wealth of excellent data. Differences of habitat were not consistently associated with differences in date of laying. Atmospheric pressure, rainfall, humidity, and sunshine showed little relationship with initial date of laying. But temperature is correlated with the date. Kluijver (1951:54) developed the idea of a "warmth-sum" necessary for initiation of laying but in a later paper (1952) rejected the warmth-sum as merely a correlation without a causal relation. Paludan (1951:42) from two years of observation concluded that temperature had little effect on the initiation of laying in Herring, *Larus argentatus,* or Lesser Black-backed, *Larus fuscus,* gulls, because in two years the period of time between arrival and laying was the same although there was a great difference in temperature. Kuerzi (1941:20) presented interesting data that indicate that Tree Swallows, *Iridoprocne bicolor,* may suspend egg laying for as much as seven days at times of cloudy, cold weather. Lack and Arn (1947) found that the Alpine Swift, *Apus melba,* began nesting about May 31 in eight years of bad weather and about May 17 in nine years of good weather. Richdale (1951:157) reported that weather does not affect the date of laying in Yellow-eyed Penguins, except indirectly.

Data of this type are hard to obtain and hard to analyze but are nevertheless highly desirable. A basic difficulty is that one should measure the microclimate where the bird is living but usually the only available weather records pertain to a city several miles away. For example, since suburban areas commonly have lower temperatures than do urban areas, a study of relation of temperature to nesting of Robins in the suburbs should use temperatures recorded in the suburbs rather than on top of some building in the city. In hilly areas temperatures in the valleys may differ greatly from those on the hills.

The relation between date of initiation of laying and age has been determined in a few cases. Ruiter (1941:195) reported that for 23 yearling European Redstarts, *Phoenicurus phoenicurus,* the date of laying the first egg averaged May 19, whereas for 61 adults the date averaged May 12. Laskey (1943) found that yearling Eastern Bluebirds, *Sialia sialis,* laid nine days later than did the adults. Kluijver (1951) found that age of the male Great Tit has no relation to date of laying but that yearling females laid eggs 2.1 days later than did older birds. Schüz (1950:218) reported that White Storks attain the complete nesting sequence in stages. Birds two years old may search for a nest site. About 9 per cent of the three-year-old birds copulate and lay. About 23 per cent more of the four-year-olds raise broods and about 28 per cent more of the five-year-olds raise broods. Thus about half the birds have raised broods by the sixth year.

Construction of the nest may continue during egg laying in some species (Tricolored Redwing, *Agelaius tricolor,* Emlen, 1941:212; Cedar Waxwing, Putnam, 1949:158). Indeed, Davis (1940:200) found that the Ani, *Crotophaga ani,* brings in sticks and leaves during the entire incubation period although this behavior is hardly true construction. In many species, however, there is an interval between the completion of the nest and the laying of the first egg. Hann (1937:171) reported that the first Ovenbird egg is laid within three days of completion of the nest. Fautin (1941:108) gave data for an unspecified number of nests (124?) in two colonies of Yellow-headed Blackbirds, *Xanthocephalus xanthocephalus.* Sixty-two per cent laid their first egg the first day after the nest was completed; 24 per cent on the second; 11 per cent on the third; 4 per cent on the fourth. Walkinshaw (1941:7) gave data for several years showing that the average time between completion of nest and laying the first egg in 54 nests of Prothonotary Warbler was about two days.

The available data indicate that many species lay their eggs in the morning. Hann (1937:171) reported that the Ovenbird lays its eggs in the morning but gave only meager data. Putnam (1949:158) gave a model tabular presentation of data. The mean time between "last observation before laying" and "first observation after laying" was 6:29 A.M. solar time. Stockton and Asmundson (1950:478) found that 40 per cent of domesticated Turkey, *Meleagris gallopavo,* eggs were laid before noon and furthermore that time of day did not influence fertility or hatchability. An exception to the morning laying is found in the Ani (Davis, 1940:200) which frequently lays in the afternoon. Skutch (1952) summarized observations on the time of laying and of hatching for a number of tropical forms. The data show that most passerine birds lay shortly after sunrise. There is a suggestion that although many species lay the second egg twenty-four hours after the first, some species may lay the second egg twenty-five to twenty-six hours after the first.

The interval between eggs has been studied in detail for a few species. Emlen (1941:210) reported that the Red-wing lays an egg every day; Hann (1937:171) reported the same for the Ovenbird, and Putnam (1949:147) presented data for 13 Cedar Waxwing nests showing that an egg was laid each day. Observations are not sufficiently detailed to know the number of hours between laying but it is possible that the interval is more than twenty-four hours (as in chickens) and that each day the egg is laid later. Chance (1940) summarized his previous evidence and added some new evidence to show that the European Cuckoo, *Cuculus canorus,* lays on alternate days. He reports that cuckoo A in five seasons laid 76 eggs at an interval of 2 days, 1 at 3 days, 4 at 4 days, and 3 at 5 days. Other cuckoos laid 44 eggs at an interval of 2 days, 4 at 4 days, 1 at 6 days, and 1 at 7 days.

Data concerning the time between nestings is scarce. It is important to distinguish between renesting after destruction of a nest and laying of a second clutch. Stokes (1950:120) found great variation in renesting time for 6 American Goldfinches, as did Kuerzi (1941:23) for Tree Swallows. Nice (1937) stated that Song Sparrows lay 4 days after a nest is destroyed and gives data for the interval after destruction (8 nests) and between broods (7 nests). Although the latter interval is greater in this sample, the data are inadequate to develop a generalization. Sowls (1949:265) found that for several ducks the interval of time between the destruction of a nest and starting of a new one was proportional to the stage of incubation. The later the stage of incubation, the longer the interval. Seubert (1952) found no correlation between stage of incubation and renesting interval in pheasants kept in a 7.8-acre pen. Paludan (1951:60) found no correlation for Herring Gulls of time till renesting and the stage of nesting. The intervals averaged 11.9 (S.D. = 0.9) days. Klomp (1951) found that Lapwings, *Vanellus vanellus,* renested 12 days after removal of eggs by humans and that an individual bird may renest four times although it does not have a second brood. Rinkel (1940) reported that Lapwings averaged 7.7 days (22 cases) between destruction of their clutch and the start of the new clutch. More data are needed concerning the time interval between destruction of nest and laying another set (renesting) in relation to the stage of the breeding cycle at the first nest. Some birds (Ruffed Grouse, Bump *et al.,* 1947:364) rarely renest.

Some data are available on the interval between first and second nests. Kendeigh (1941:54) found that for House Wrens the interval between the first brood's leaving the nest and the initiation of the second nest varied from 3 to 17 days for 57 cases. The modal interval was 9 days. Putnam (1949: 172) observed that Cedar Waxwings lay the first egg of the second clutch anytime from the day before fledging at the first nest to 3 days after. Kluijver (1951:58) gave a table showing the interval between the date of laying the first egg of the first and of the second clutches of the Great Tit. The mean calculated from his Table 22 for second clutches (not renests) is 47.15 days (SD = 5.1 days) or about 4-6 days after fledging young.

Clutch-Size

The number of eggs in a clutch is known in a general way for most temperate zone species. The standard reference texts give the number of eggs laid in some routine phrase such as "generally 3-5 eggs." But detailed frequency distributions have rarely been obtained until recent years. Such distributions are necessary to determine whether observed differences might be due to chance sampling and are essential in a study of changes of clutch-size with latitude, from season to season, between years, according to age of bird, and with many other variables or factors. Data of a general type are available for many tropical birds also. For example, Phillips (1948-1951) gave records for the number of eggs of Ceylonese birds.

A clutch is usually defined as the number of eggs in an uninterrupted series. However in actual practice the clutch-size is the number of eggs found in the nest. For example Paynter (1949) found an average of 2.38 eggs in 1,011 Herring Gull nests, yet there is considerable evidence from observing nests and sectioning ovaries (Davis, 1942c) that the clutch-size is 3 eggs. The difference presumably is due to loss of some eggs from some nests.

Pheasants lay or at least ovulate many more eggs than are found in the nest (Buss *et al.,* 1951). The number of eggs in a nest may, in some cases, represent several females, as in the case of Wood Ducks, *Aix sponsa* (Mc-

Laughlin and Grice, 1952). It is most unfortunate that the data that are easily obtained (number of eggs in the nest) are not the true clutch-size. Perhaps for detailed studies of seasonal changes and latitudinal changes one should study ovaries histologically. This method permits an analysis of the problem in many species. For example a series of papers (see Buss *et al.,* 1951) described the number of eggs laid by pheasants as determined by a count of ovulated follicles. These authors found that some hens lay as many as twice the number usually found in a nest. The problem is most acute in the communal Anis (Davis, 1942b) which lay eggs in a common nest. The only way to determine clutch-size with confidence is the analysis of ovaries.

Data on clutch-size for a number of species have been listed in Table 2. In all but a few cases it was necessary to calculate the standard deviation from the author's original data (A "normal" distribution was assumed although this assumption is not entirely satisfactory). The standard error can readily be calculated by persons interested in further analysis. Some reports had to be omitted because proof was lacking that the clutches were complete. For example, Marples (1934) presented voluminous data on five species of terns, and Schreurs (1941) presented data for 199 Red-backed Shrike nests, *Lanius collurio.* But there is doubt that the clutches were complete or were all reported. Some data from incomplete nests may have inadvertently been included in Table 2.

Although most of the reports are self-explanatory, several need special comments. Lack's (1947b) voluminous data on the Partridge, *Perdix perdix,* permitted him to draw detailed conclusions. Late layings are smaller than early layings. Average clutch-size is greater in northern and eastern Europe than in England. Considerable annual variation in clutch-size occurs. Randall (1941) seems to be the only author to give detailed data on a vitally important game species. McLaughlin and Grice (1952:249) have splendid data on Wood Ducks but present it in summary form so that little can be done with it. The clutch-size in 918 "successful" nests was 13.3 and in 509 "not successful" nests was 12.2, but no tests of significance were made nor are frequency distributions given. Clutch-size can be calculated from the graph on page 252 of their study. A graph shows that abandonment was highest for nests with few eggs (1-5) and many eggs (more than 25). Lack (1950c) compiled a mass of data from several countries, some of which are recorded in Table 2.

The table shows that the Roseate Tern, *Sterna dougallii,* clearly has larger clutches in England than in Australia (the difference is significant at the 5 per cent level). The difference in clutch-size between the Great Tit and the Blue Tit, *Parus caeruleus,* is statistically significant, as is the difference between the two subspecies of White-crowned Sparrows, *Zonotrichia leucophrys,* between the Prothonotary Warbler in Tennessee and in Michigan, and between

TABLE 2. SIZE OF CLUTCHES

Species	Clutches	Mean	Standard Deviation	References[a]	Place
Pied-billed Grebe *Podilymbus podiceps*	97	6.18	0.40	Glover, 1953	Iowa
Guanay Cormorant *Phalacrocorax bouganvillii*	89	3.13	0.94	Vogt, 1942	Peru
Wood Duck *Aix sponsa*	664	13.60	4.82	McLaughlin, 1952	Massachusetts
Common Eider *Somateria mollissima*	110	3.25	1.05	Gross, 1938	Maine
Common Eider *Somateria mollissima*	162	3.53	1.17	Paynter, 1951	New Brunswick
Common Eider *Somateria mollissima*	1131	4.04	1.01	Lewis, 1939	St. Lawrence
Marsh Hawk *Circus cyaneus*	60	5.05	0.76	Hammond, 1949	U.S.A.
European Partridge *Perdix perdix*	4051	14.60	2.38	Lack, 1947	England
Ring-necked Pheasant *Phasianus colchicus*	157	10.60	3.18	Randall, 1941	Pennsylvania
Clapper Rail *Rallus longirostris*	104	9.97	2.10	Kozicky, 1949	New Jersey
Clapper Rail *Rallus longirostris*	71	8.38	1.56	Stewart, 1951	Virginia
American Coot *Fulica americana*	37	8.84	1.27	Provost, 1947	Iowa
American Woodcock *Philohela minor*	122	3.96	0.20	Mendall, 1943	Maine
Herring Gull *Larus argentatus*	1011	2.38	0.71	Paynter, 1949	New Brunswick
Herring Gull *Larus argentatus*	217	2.91	0.34	Paludan, 1951	Holland
Lesser Black-backed Gull *Larus fuscus*	242	2.75	0.56	Paludan, 1951	Holland
Sandwich Tern *Sterna sandvicensis*	3831	2.45	0.45	Dircksen, 1932	Germany
Roseate Tern *Sterna dougallii*	2656	1.03	0.16	Serventy, 1951	Australia
Roseate Tern *Sterna dougallii*	373	1.43	0.50	Serventy, 1951	England
Oystercatcher *Haematopus ostralegus*	84	3.01	0.68	Dircksen, 1932	Germany
White-rumped Swift *Micropus cafer*	93	2.00	0.00	Moreau, 1942	Africa

TABLE 2 (Cont.). SIZE OF CLUTCHES

Species	Clutches	Mean	Standard Deviation	References[a]	Place
Common Swift *Apus apus*	170	2.24	0.48	Lack, 1951	England
Common Swift *Apus apus*	79	2.76	0.52	Lack, 1951	Switzerland
Alpine Swift *Apus melba*	970	2.30	0.53	Lack, 1947	Switzerland
Skylark *Alauda arvensis*	55	3.87	0.70	Haun, 1931	Germany
Crested Lark *Galerida cristata*	68	4.18	0.84	Haun, 1931	Germany
Wood Lark *Lullula arborea*	99	4.17	0.70	Haun, 1931	Germany
Purple Martin *Progne subis*	84	4.94	0.74	Allen, 1952	U.S.A.
Tree Swallow *Iridoprocne bicolor*	68	5.20	0.84	Kuerzi, 1941	Connecticut
Yellow-billed Magpie *Pica nuttalli*	70	6.50	0.92	Linsdale, 1937	California
Pied Flycatcher *Muscicapa hypoleuca*	275	6.43	1.09	von Haartman, 1951	Finland
Pied Flycatcher *Muscicapa hypoleuca*	123	7.44	0.91	Campbell, 1950	England
Pied Flycatcher *Muscicapa hypoleuca*	49	5.82	1.10	Berndt, 1939a	Germany
Spotted Flycatcher *Muscicapa striata*	309	4.25	0.77	Summers-Smith, 1952	England
Great Tit *Parus major*	112	10.92	1.74	Gibb, 1950	England
Great Tit *Parus major*	174	9.83	1.43	Lack, 1950c	Sweden
Great Tit *Parus major*	8809	9.32	1.88	Lack, 1950c	Holland
Great Tit *Parus major*	339	10.27	1.81	Lack, 1950c	S. England
Blue Tit *Parus caeruleus*	3455	10.65	2.16	Lack, 1950c	Holland
Blue Tit *Parus caeruleus*	312	11.64	2.16	Lack, 1950c	S. England
Coal Tit *Parus ater*	119	8.19	1.38	Lack, 1950c	Sweden
Coal Tit *Parus ater*	2759	8.69	1.65	Lack, 1950c	Holland

TABLE 2 (Cont.). SIZE OF CLUTCHES

Species	Clutches	Mean	Standard Deviation	References[a]	Place
Crested Tit *Parus cristatus*	182	4.92	0.89	Lack, 1950c	Sweden
Crested Tit *Parus cristatus*	1143	7.07	1.27	Lack, 1950c	Holland
Willow Tit (Chickadee) *Parus atricapillus*	346	8.24	1.71	Lack, 1950c	Holland
Wren-tit *Chamaea fasciata*	84	3.92	0.52	Erickson, 1938	California
House Wren *Troglodytes aedon*	98	5.46	1.10	McAtee, 1940	Maryland
Southern House Wren *Troglodytes musculus*	38	3.78	0.69	Skutch, 1953	C. America
American Robin *Turdus migratorius*	127	3.39	0.62	Howell, 1942	New York
European Blackbird *Turdus merula*	298	3.94	0.75	Lack, 1949	England
Song Thrush *Turdus ericetorum*	179	4.13	0.67	Lack, 1949	England
Song Thrush *Turdus ericetorum*	437	4.68	0.75	Siivonen, 1939	Finland
Eastern Bluebird *Sialia sialis*	102	4.44	1.02	Laskey, 1939	Tennessee
English Robin *Erithacus rubecula*	534	4.97	0.65	Lack, 1946	England (April)
English Robin *Erithacus rubecula*	364	5.16	0.80	Lack, 1946	England (May)
Wood Warbler *Phylloscopus sibilatrix*	216	6.03	0.58	E. Lack, 1950	England
Cedar Waxwing *Bombycilla cedrorum*	65	2.85	0.90	Putnam, 1949	Ohio
Western Magpie *Gymnorhina dorsalis*	46	3.46	0.62	Wilson, 1946	Australia
European Starling *Sturnus vulgaris*	105	4.85	1.08	Lack, 1948	England
European Starling *Sturnus vulgaris*	1,785	5.14	1.11	Lack, 1948	Holland
European Starling *Sturnus vulgaris*	101	4.54	1.15	McAtee, 1940	Maryland
European Starling *Sturnus vulgaris*	95	4.44	0.99	Berndt, 1939	Germany
European Starling *Sturnus vulgaris*	50	4.82	0.81	Davis, (unpub.)	Maryland

TABLE 2 (Cont.). SIZE OF CLUTCHES

Species	Clutches	Mean	Standard Deviation	References[a]	Place
Ovenbird *Seiurus aurocapillus*	27	4.67	0.68	Hann, 1937	Michigan
Prothonotary Warbler *Protonotaria citrea*	62	5.01	0.85	Walkinshaw, 1941	Michigan
Prothonotary Warbler *Protonotaria citrea*	44	4.55	0.62	Walkinshaw, 1941	Tennessee
Yellow-headed Blackbird *Xanthocephalus xanthocephalus*	118	3.75	0.60	Fautin, 1941	Utah
Bronzed Grackle *Quiscalus quiscula*	55	4.87	0.74	Petersen, 1950	Wisconsin
Black-headed Grosbeak *Pheucticus melanocephalus*	192	3.28	0.67	Weston, 1947	U.S.A.
American Goldfinch *Spinus tristis*	150	4.63	0.90	Stokes, 1950	Wisconsin
Corn Bunting *Emberiza calandra*	92	3.98	0.84	Ryves, 1934	England
Yellowhammer *Emberiza citrinella*	946	3.31	0.77	Parkhurst, 1946	England
Yellowhammer *Emberiza citrinella*	147	4.41	0.58	Haun, 1931	Germany
White-crowned Sparrow *Zonotrichia l. pugetensis*	29	4.00	0.46	Blanchard, 1941	Washington
White-crowned Sparrow *Zonotrichia l. nuttalli*	147	3.25	0.55	Blanchard, 1941	California
Song Sparrow *Melospiza melodia*	210	4.07	0.81	Nice, 1937	Ohio

[a] Only senior author's name given.

CLUTCH-SIZES FOR BIRDS

Minimum standards for inclusion:

1. At least 25 clutches recorded within a few years (less than 10) time within a limited area.
2. Data presented in a frequency distribution.
3. Proof that clutches were complete when counted.
4. Proof that only one female laid in nest.

Obviously some good data have been omitted because the published records do not meet these standards. Also undoubtedly some data have been overlooked.

References give only senior author's name.

Original papers should be consulted for details of division into various years, first and second broods, etc.

April and May for the English Robin, *Erithacus rubecula.* The Pied Flycatcher lays different numbers of eggs in Finland, Germany, and England.

In addition to the complete studies listed in the table there are many contributions that give merely an average number but do not give any measure of variability. Bump *et al.* (1947) gave the average clutch-size (11.5) for 1,473 nests of Ruffed Grouse, *Bonasa umbellus.* Ball (1952) reported that the average clutch-size in 70 pheasant nests in Ontario was 11.2 eggs. Saliger (1952) presented data for clutch-size of pheasants in irrigated lands in Idaho where the mean for two years (152 nests) was 9.8 eggs. Davis (1942a) studied the ovaries of Shiny Cowbirds, *Molothrus bonariensis,* histologically and concluded that this parasitic species lays eggs in clutches of about 5, although not enough ovaries were examined to determine the variability. Nice (1949) confirmed the conclusion that North American Cowbirds lay in clutches but differed on the size of the clutch. Boyd (1936) reported a mean clutch-size for 117 Barn Swallow, *Hirundo rustica,* nests of 4.4 eggs. He further gave the number of young in swallow broods in detail. In 1934, 664 broods averaged 4.0 and in 1935, 596 broods averaged 4.1. Durango (1948) found that the Ortolan Bunting, *Emberiza hortulana,* in Sweden had an average of 4.5 eggs in 89 clutches and 4.1 young in 87 broods. Colquhoun (1951:15 found that 2,095 Wood Pigeon nests had either 2 young or 2 eggs, and only 17 nests had 1, 3, or 4. Allen (1942) found a mean of 2.6 eggs in 87 nests of the Roseate Spoonbill, *Ajaia ajaia.* McCabe and Hawkins (1946) found a mean of 16.5 eggs in 392 nests of Hungarian Partridge in Wisconsin. Kendrick (1940) found a mean of 7.64 for 37 nests of Blue Tits in England. Siivonen (1952) gave voluminous data for Finnish game birds but no means of comparing the averages. Walkinshaw (1953) found that 94 sets of Prothonotary Warbler nests averaged 5.1 eggs.

A few studies of clutch-size in relation to age are available. Von Haartman (1951:33) found no consistent change with age (1-4 years) in 60 clutches of the Pied Flycatcher. Richdale (1949a:95) found that two-year-old Yellow-eyed Penguins, *Megadyptes antipodes,* laid 1.68 eggs per clutch, while older birds laid 2.00. Kluijver (1951:74) found that Great Tits lay slightly larger clutches as adults than as yearlings. Laskey (1943) found no differences in clutch-size of a small number of yearlings and of adult Eastern Bluebirds. Ruiter (1941) reports that the mean clutch for 23 yearling European Redstarts was 6.04 (S.E. = 0.17) and for 61 adults was 6.51 (S.E. = 0.07). The difference is significant at the 5 per cent level.

The problem of seasonal change in clutch-size has been recently noticed and a few authors have adequate data. Stokes (1950:120) presented a model table (reproduced here as Table 3) showing the size of 150 American Goldfinch clutches at two-week intervals. From this table a correlation coefficient of —0.726 was calculated, which is interpreted as significant and as showing that the clutch-size decreases as the season progresses. Randall's (1941:311) data for pheasants give a coefficient of —0.944. Saliger (1952) claimed that his data show a decline but no tests of significance were made and his table is not convincing. Gibb's (1950:535) data on Blue Tits show a correlation of —0.64. These last three papers do not give the full distribution frequency

TABLE 3. VARIATION IN CLUTCH-SIZE WITH SEASON IN THE AMERICAN GOLDFINCH (Stokes, 1950:120)

Date First Egg Laid	Number of Nests by Clutch Size 2	3	4	5	6	7	Mean	Standard Deviation
July 1-15	0	0	0	2	0	0	5.0	—
July 16-31	0	0	8	34	11	1	5.1	0.65
August 1-15	0	1	8	38	5	0	4.8	0.57
August 16-31	3	11	17	6	0	0	3.7	0.90
September 1-15	0	3	2	0	0	0	3.4	0.49
Totals	3	15	35	80	16	1	4.6	0.90

but only the mean for each week and hence are inferior to Stokes' table. Errington (1933) presents data for the average clutch-size of Bobwhite, *Colinus virginianus,* in Wisconsin for semi-monthly periods that show a decline from 19.2 eggs in early May to 11.3 in late July (40 nests). Erickson (1938:288) presented data for Wren-tits, *Chamaea fasciata,* that give a positive coefficient (+0.45) which suggests an increase with season but is of doubtful statistical significance because of the small sample. Putnam (1949:158) found a significant decrease in clutch-size with season in Cedar Waxwings. Walkinshaw (1941:10) presented data for clutch-size according to season for the Prothonotary Warbler in Tennessee (—0.71). Unfortunately his data for Michigan cannot be analyzed for correlation in their published form. Lack (1948:96) also described data indicating a decline in clutch-size for Starlings, *Sturnus vulgaris,* in Holland from 5.2 in April to 4.3 in June. E. Lack (1950:98) presented data showing a seasonal decline in clutch-size of the English Wood Warbler, *Phylloscopus sibilatrix,* from 6.0 in May to 5.6 in June. Lack (1950c:284) presented voluminous data for the Great Tit and the Blue Tit in England and for four species of tits in Holland. In these species the clutch-size is largest at the start of the season and gradually declines. Summers-Smith (1952) provided very detailed data on the clutch-size of the Spotted Flycatcher, *Muscicapa striata,* in England. The means for weekly intervals (total of 309 clutches) show a slight increase in late May from 4.4 to 4.6 and then decline to 2.7 in late July. Von Haartman (1951) shows a regular decline from 7.3 to 5.1 for the Pied Flycatcher in Finland. Laskey (1939) presented the detailed clutch-sizes of Eastern Bluebirds by periods about a month long. The mean clutch-size declined from March to July as follows: 5.00 (34 clutches), 4.65 (35 clutches), and 3.69 (33 clutches). Unfortunately, data recorded at monthly intervals are not as satisfactory for correlation coefficients as data recorded at weekly or semi-monthly intervals.

Apparently clutch-size frequently increases very promptly to a maximum in the early part of the breeding season and then declines slowly as the season advances. However, some exceptions occur. Lack (1947a:99) gave detailed

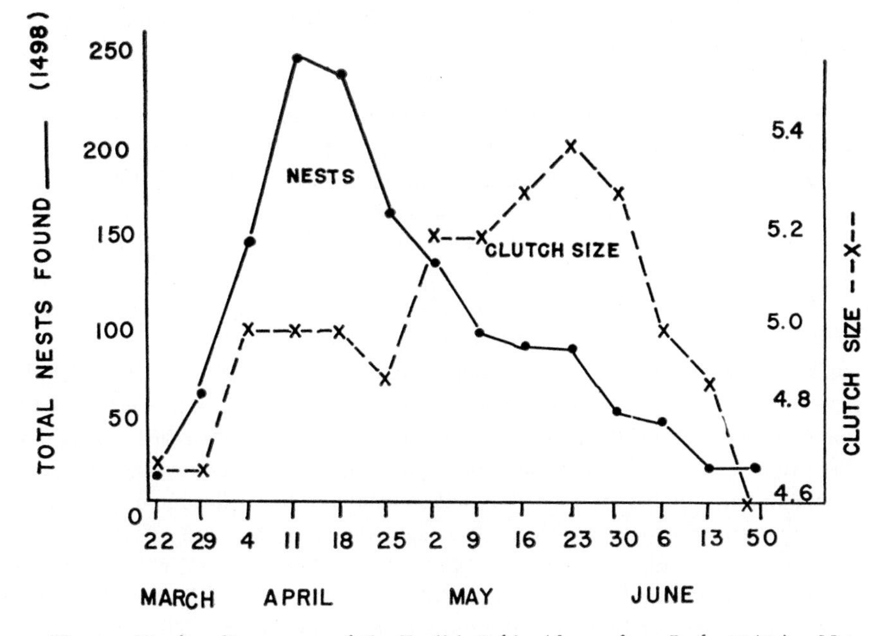

Fig. 1. The breeding season of the English Robin (drawn from Lack, 1947a). Note that about the same numbers of eggs are present during all of April and May because of the inverse relation of clutch-size and frequency.

data for 1,498 clutches of the English Robin (reproduced here as Fig. 1). The clutch-size increases gradually till late May and then declines rapidly during June. Parkhurst and Lack (1946:363) reported that the clutch-size of the Yellowhammer, *Emberiza citrinella,* increases till June and then declines. Haun (1931) gave data also by monthly periods for four species. The clutch-size of the Wood Lark, *Lullula arborea,* increases from April to June while the clutch-size of the Yellowhammer remains the same. In both the English Robin and Yellowhammer the number of clutches reaches a maximum before the clutch-size (see Fig. 1). Lack (1949:61) presented abundant data for two thrushes, *Turdus merula* and *T. ericetorum,* from England and from Holland (Verwey, 1931) that show a maximum in clutch-size in the middle part of the breeding season. Apparently the generalization is that clutch-size increases rapidly to a maximum and then declines, but the actual shape of the curve may vary from place to place or year to year. The straightline negative correlations cited above may be due to an insufficient number of early nests.

As might be expected, local differences in clutch-size occur. Lack (1950c: 286) adequately documented such differences for tits in Holland and von Haartman (1951:34) discusses differences for the Pied Flycatcher in Europe (see

Table 2 also). Siivonen (1952) has voluminous data on regional differences in Finland.

The seasonal decline in clutch-size is in part due to the decrease in numbers of eggs on renesting (nesting after destruction of contents of a nest). The work of Sowls (1949:262) on ducks showed that these birds rarely raise a second brood but will renest, and in the eleven cases observed, the average for first nests was 9.3 eggs and for renests was 7.3 eggs. Bump *et al.* (1947) found that the clutch-size for Ruffed Grouse was 11.5 for 1,473 first nests and 7.5 for 149 renests. For certain species apparently there is no decrease in the number of eggs in renests, as for example the Lapwing (Klomp, 1951).

In second clutches there is also generally a decline. Kluijver (1951:58-71) analyzed the problem of second broods in detail for Great Tits in Holland. He did not present data on clutch-size but he found that older females had more second broods than do yearling females. Habitat had little effect on the proportion of second broods but population density was inversely proportional to the number of second broods. Kluijver here illustrated in a convincing manner with a wealth of data that population size can affect the productivity of a species. Seubert (1952) kept pheasants under semi-captive conditions and found that the first clutches (139) averaged 11.8 eggs, the second (75) averaged 9.8, and the third (10) averaged 9.5. The decline was statistically significant. Schreurs (1941) reported that the number of eggs laid by sixteen female Red-backed Shrikes in the first clutch was 5.0 and in second clutches was 4.6. Nestlings in first broods were found to average 4.25 and in second broods 3.34 in Barn Swallows, *Hirundo rustica* (Mason, 1953). Lack and Arn (1947) found that early season nests of the Alpine Swift averaged 2.30 eggs (970 nests; S. D. = 0.526), while late season nests averaged 2.17 (100 nests; S. D. = 0.459). The difference is significant. It is not known how many of the late season nests were second clutches and how many were renests.

Evolution of Clutch-Size

The factors governing the size of the clutch have received attention in recent years. Some authors have been concerned with what can be called the proximate factors (food, temperature, etc.) of the environment. Thus Gibb (1950: 515) found that the clutch-size of the Great Tit was statistically significantly larger in a year (1948) of abundance of caterpillars than in a year (1949) of scarcity. However, studies of climatic factors are rare and lack meaning because of neglect of microclimatic measurements.

Lack (1947-48) and co-workers have been concerned with the ultimate factor that controls clutch-size. He developed the thesis that clutch-size is determined by a compromise between the ability of the adults to raise young and the likelihood that prolific parents will leave many offspring. Individuals that lay many eggs will tend to replace in the population those that lay few eggs if the number of eggs laid is genetically determined and if survival of young is the same for small clutches as for large clutches. But, if many young need to be fed and brooded the survival may be low in large clutches and result in a low productivity. Thus natural selection ultimately determines clutch-size by favoring survival of individuals that leave the maximum number of descendants. Lack (1947-48) supported his argument by data from several species but Lack and Arn (1947) found that the Alpine Swift fledged 2.4 young per nest, whether three or four eggs were laid. Paynter (1949) found that nests of Herring Gulls with less than three eggs hatched a lower proportion of eggs than did nests with three eggs, perhaps because three eggs in a nest would stimulate the female to incubate more closely than would two eggs. The good survival of young from large clutches is an apparent contradiction of Lack's thesis and may be explained by the nature of the gull's food supply which permits several young to be fed as easily as one. However, an alternative explanation is that, since Herring Gulls lay three eggs in a clutch, nests with less than three eggs have already suffered some loss and hence are not really comparable. Moreau (1947) found that there is less food per young for larger broods but that only in one species of three adequately studied was there a significant increase in nestling period. Moreau (1944) had previously published a splendid critical review and summary of data for African birds. Kendeigh (1952:61) found that the feedings per young House Wren decrease from 115 per day for nests with one young down to 50 per day for nests with six young. The total feedings per nest increased from 115 to 300. The increase is exponential and indicates that 300 is about the maximum. Hence wrens could not feed more than six young. Lack (1947b:23) finds in his voluminous data on clutch-size in the European Partridge no difference in percentage hatched in relation to clutch-size and interprets this result by relying on an assumption that since there are more clutches of medium size than of large size, therefore there must be a higher mortality of the young from large-size broods. Lack (1948: 108) found that the hatching success of Starlings was the same for broods of various sizes but the survival of juveniles (3 months) was less in large broods than in small. Lack (1950c:289) found that larger-sized broods of tits are "not proportionately penalized" because hatching success and survival of nestlings were inadequate to test the thesis.

This thesis of Lack's is intriguing and already has demonstrated great heuristic value. However, the thesis can only be tested by cases in which food is a limiting factor at the time of nesting. For example, in years of scarcity, large broods will not get enough. Thus it is not surprising that the data are equivocal in respect to the thesis because only certain data are suitable for testing the idea.

The keen interest in clutch-size has produced several generalizations (Lack, 1947-48). Clutch-size usually increases with latitude and from west to east in Europe. There is, of course, no causal relation between latitude and clutch-size but only a correlation since latitude itself cannot influence clutch-size. The causal factors have not yet been revealed but may be temperature, survival, or many others. Another set of relations is the slight decrease of clutch-size on islands and the decrease in size of second clutches. Generally the clutch-size increases slightly in early spring and declines toward the end of the breeding season. There is, of course, great annual variation but the causal factors are poorly known. With these generalizations in mind it should be possible to direct attention to the causal relations such as food supply, length of day, and inherent physiology.

The data available about eggs are disappointingly meager. The general outline has been recorded but detailed data that permit comparisons are available for only a few species. Even data for clutch-size are rarely adequate and hence vast opportunities for accumulation of clutch data exist. Groebbels (1937:318-323) summarized much older literature on size, shape, color, etc.

The number of eggs laid can probably be used as an index of biological forces. Lack (1947-48) has explored the evolutionary aspects. Kluijver (1951) has utilized number of eggs laid to measure the role of population size. Other ecological problems can be investigated by using clutch-size as an end point. The role of climatic factors in physiological processes could be studied. Annual variations in clutch-size may be an indication of changes in nutritional requirements or supply. For the purpose of utilizing clutch-size to investigate some biological problems, it is usually necessary to frame the question carefully and then collect the data. Rarely are data from miscellaneous sources adequately controlled to serve special purposes.

INCUBATION

Incubation consists of warming the eggs by the adult. Some tropical birds receive considerable assistance from the environment. The word incubation is used in two senses (Swanberg, 1950; Lohrl, 1951). From the viewpoint of the egg the word refers to the process of warming. Thus there is an incubation time and incubation temperature. From the viewpoint of the adult, the word refers to behavior. Thus a bird incubates an egg, incubates 50 per cent of the time, etc. In this section an attempt will be made to distinguish between these viewpoints. Strictly speaking, the incubation behavior period should be counted from the time the bird starts warming the eggs till it stops brooding the young since brooding behavior is similar to incubation behavior in many species. The incubation time should be the time from laying to hatching of an egg.

Initiation

The adult may begin incubation behavior with the penultimate egg and may begin gradually. Beer and Tibbitts (1950:71) reported considerable variability among Red-winged Blackbirds in the relation between cessation of laying and beginning of incubation behavior but omitted detailed data. Fautin (1941:111) gave an excellent table showing a tendency for the female Yellow-headed Blackbirds to start incubation behavior on the first egg in clutches of three eggs and on the second egg in larger clutches. Gibb (1950:522) presented a table showing the relation between the initiation of incubation behavior and completion of the clutch. For the Great Tit (57 clutches) the females began incubation behavior on the average 0.33 days (S.D. = 1.55) before completion. For 47 nests of the Blue Tit the behavior began 0.62 days (S.D. = 1.25) before completion. The difference is not significant.

Duration

Analysis of the duration of incubation requires a definition of the end points. Moreau (1940) defined the incubation time as the number of days between the laying of the last egg and the hatching of that egg. Obviously this definition suffers from several defects as Moreau was well aware. The last egg laid is not necessarily the last to hatch; also considerable time may be required for the process of hatching (Williamson, 1945:281); incubation may depend on external temperature (Davis, 1940:198). However, as a general, practical definition, Moreau's is as satisfactory as any that can now be formulated. The definition is valuable because it defines the end points in the same unit (the egg) rather than in two units (the adult and the egg). The following discussion will attempt to disentangle "incubation behavior" from "incubation time."

Several studies in recent years give data for the incubation time of various species. Hochbaum (1944:90) summarized data for several species of ducks, incubated artificially, but does not indicate the variability. Roberts (1940) gave data for 9 nests of Wilson's Petrel, *Oceanites oceanicus* (average 43 days). Richdale (1944:34) estimated the incubation time for two species of Prions, *Pachyptila,* to be 55 to 56 days. Barth (1952) found that the incubation time for the Common Gull, *Larus canus,* averaged 26.3 days (S.D. = 2.35) for 61 clutches. Paludan (1951:91) gave an excellent table of incubation times which is presented here because it should be used as a model (Table 4). The Lacks (1951) gave a similar table for the Common Swift, *Apus apus.* The average time till hatching of the second egg (38 nests) was 19.6 days. Nice (1953) found no evidence that any bird has an incubation period as short as ten days.

The duration of incubation behavior is recorded in several recent studies. Gibb (1950:523) presented data for incubation behavior (see Table 5) for 55 clutches of the Great Tit and 46 nests of the Blue Tit. The difference between these two species is significant (p = .05). Nice (1937:122), Noll (1939), and Ryves (1934) gave data (see Table 5). Fautin (1941:111) provided data (Table 6) showing the duration of incubation behavior accord-

TABLE 4. Incubation Times of Gull Eggs (from Paludan, 1951:91)

Days After Last Egg Was Laid	Herring Gull Number of Cases			Lesser Black-backed Gull Number of Cases		
	Egg			Egg		
	A	B	C	A	B	C
22	..	..	..	4	1	..
23	3	..	..	8	3	..
24	6	5	..	28	22	..
25	20	8	1	16	22	9
26	22	34	7	8	11	36
27	12	16	36	1	1	8
28	..	4	23	..	..	2
Total	63	67	67	65	60	55
Average days	25.5	26.1	27.1	24.3	24.7	26.1

ing to the clutch-size for 71 nests. For all clutch-sizes a twelve-day incubation behavior was more frequent than a thirteen-day.

Emlen (1941:216) studied incubation behavior periods experimentally by altering the contents of nests of Tricolored Redwings. He found that the normal eleven-day incubation behavior period can be reduced or eliminated by adding mature young to the nest. Conversely it may be extended by substituting eggs for young.

The duration of incubation time or behavior in relation to environmental factors has rarely been studied. Kluijver *et al.* (1940:15) gave a table of incubation behavior periods by months for forty-three nests of the Wren, *Troglodytes troglodytes.* The duration declines from April to July and the corrrelation coefficient is —.61 indicating that as the year progressed, the duration of incubation behavior decreased. Presumably the causal relation here is an increase in temperature. Note that a decline in duration of incubation behavior does not necessarily mean a decline in incubation time also, although such a decline may occur.

Male

The role of the male in incubation behavior has received some recent attention (Ryves, 1943). In some species the male incubates (Wren-tits, Erickson, 1938:289; Ani, Davis, 1940:193). Koenig (1951) found that the male of *Panurus biarmicus* incubated during the day and the female at night. Odum (1941:527) reported that the male Black-capped Chickadee does not incubate. Fautin (1941:116) described the activity of the male Yellow-headed Blackbird, which does not incubate but guards the territory.

The role of the sexes in incubation behavior may be studied by deter-

TABLE 5. DURATION OF INCUBATION BEHAVIOR IN DAYS

Species	Clutches	Mean	Standard Deviation	Reference[a]	Place
Oystercatcher *Haematopus ostralegus*	49	27.4	0.76	Dircksen, 1932	Germany
Tree Swallow *Iridoprocne bicolor*	66	14.3	0.94	Kuerzi, 1941	Connecticut
Great Tit *Parus major*	55	13.9	0.79	Gibb, 1950	England
Great Tit *Parus major*	20	12.5	1.73	Noll, 1939	Switzerland
Blue Tit *Parus caeruleus*	46	14.2	0.69	Gibb, 1950	England
Spotted Flycatcher *Muscicapa striata*	97	13.2	1.23	Summers-Smith, 1952	England
Wren *Troglodytes troglodytes*	43	16.2	1.42	Kluijver, 1940	Holland
House Wren *Troglodytes aedon*	33	13.9	0.84	Kendeigh, 1952	Ohio
Yellow-headed Blackbird *Xanthocephalus xanthocephalus*	71	12.3	0.43	Fautin, 1941	Utah
Corn Bunting *Emberiza calandria*	21	14.9	0.46	Ryves, 1934	England
Song Sparrow *Melospiza melodia*	32	12.6	0.75	Nice, 1937	Ohio

[a] Only the senior author's name is given.

TABLE 6. LENGTH OF INCUBATION PERIOD IN THE YELLOW-HEADED BLACKBIRD (Fautin, 1941:111)

Size of sets	Duration	Nests	Per Cent
2-egg	12 days	2	100
3-egg	12 days	5	62.5
	13 days	3	37.5
4-egg	12 days	43	75.4
	13 days	14	24.6
5-egg	12 days	3	75.0
	13 days	1	25.0

mining the presence or absence of the incubation patch (Davis, 1945b:188). In this study a patch was never found in a sex known not to incubate, although there are many gaps in our knowledge. For example, the patch was absent in two female tinamous and eleven female cowbirds both known not to incubate. Absence of the patch does not necessarily mean that the sex does not incubate but is suggestive. This method is useful in places where collecting is done but detailed life history studies are impractical.

Attentiveness

The time spent on the nest by a bird in incubation behavior (attentiveness) has received considerable notice in recent years. Unfortunately the data are complex to analyze and laborious to obtain. All too frequently the data are really so meager that little can be deduced. For example, Nice and Thomas (1948:145) obtained excellent data for 92 hours at the nest of a Carolina Wren, *Thryothorus ludovicianus.* But only one nest was observed and the question at once arises, How typical is that nest? However, some papers are based on enough data to permit tentative generalizations. Kluijver (1950:119), using mechanical aids, reported the attentiveness of one pair of the Great Tit in detail. Nice (1937:123) in 92 hours watching at 4 nests of Song Sparrows found that the female incubated (attentive) about 77 per cent of the time. The periods on the nest averaged about 27 minutes; the periods off about 8 minutes. She quoted data from Kendeigh that appear to indicate that the number of periods off the nest are directly proportional to temperature, but it is difficult to analyze the data for significance. Hann (1937:216-217) presented data for 4 Ovenbird nests obtained by an itograph. Apparently the female remains off the nest more in the middle of the day than in the morning. Putnam (1949:163) recorded data for attentiveness at 11 Cedar Waxwing nests during about 400 hours. No significant difference was found in length of attentive period between mornings and afternoons. The length of attentive periods was significantly less during early incubation (3-7 days) than late incubation (13-17 days). He also presented excellent data (Table 7) showing the frequency of attentive intervals. The mean duration was 44.8 minutes (S.D. = 31.1) for 228 periods. Moreau (1940) reported that at 7 nests of Rough-wing Bank-Martins, *Psalidoprocne holomelaena,* the bird incubated 31-66 per cent of the time irrespective of temperature. Richdale (1950:50) found that an Albatross, *Diomedea bulleri,* incubated for 10 days without interruption.

These data are valuable when accumulated in sufficient quantity to test hypotheses. Many physiological problems, such as metabolism or hormone interactions, might be studied with such data. Problems of animal behavior exist in the relation of perception of the contents of the nest to behavior. The duration of incubation time may be used to study climatic factors, and attentiveness may reveal facts about food supply.

THE YOUNG

Hatching

In recent years little attention has been paid to the hatching process since the general outline is well known. Gibb (1950:524), however, gave detailed

TABLE 7. FREQUENCY OF ATTENTION INTERVALS AT ELEVEN NESTS OF THE CEDAR WAXWING (Putnam, 1949)

Time Interval	Frequency	Time Interval	Frequency
minutes		*minutes*	
1-7	12	85-91	6
8-14	21	92-98	6
15-21	23	99-105	1
22-28	26	106-112	5
29-35	26	113-119	3
36-42	30	120-126	1
43-49	14	127-133	0
50-56	18	134-140	2
57-63	14	141-147	1
64-70	8	148-154	0
71-77	11	155-161	1
78-84	6	162-168	1

data on the hatching period of young tits. The mean for 190 clutches of Great and Blue tits was 3.0 days (S.D. = 0.80). Paludan (1951:90) showed in an excellent table that Herring and Lesser Black-backed gulls require about 3.25 days for each egg to hatch. Little of importance concerning the condition of the young at hatching has been reported in recent years and the general descriptions of anatomy and behavior have not been expanded.

Nestling Period

The duration of the nestling period may be difficult to determine because, among other things, of interference by the observer. Gibb (1950:536) gave the duration of nestling period for 412 young Great Tits (mean, 18.9 days; S.D. = 1.16) and for 379 Blue Tits (mean, 19.7 days; S.D. = 1.07). The difference is statistically significant. Summers-Smith (1952) found that the nestling period averaged 13.5 days (S.D. = 1.28) for 110 nests of the Spotted Flycatcher. Kuerzi (1941:31) found that the nestling period for 66 nests of Tree Swallows averaged 19.4 (S.D. = 1.43). Moreau (1947:206) gave some splendid data on duration of nestling period. He compared the duration according to the number of young in the nest. Broods of the Rock-martin, *Ptyonoprogne fuligula,* with three young had a significantly longer nestling period than did broods with two young. But for two species of swifts there was no difference in nestling period for broods of one or of two. Moreau could find little support for the thesis that a large brood has a longer nestling period than a small brood. Since feeding rates per nestling are lower in large broods, nestlings from large broods should weigh less at fledging. Kuerzi (1941:31) also found no indication that the large broods of Tree Swallows had longer nestling periods than did small broods. Koskimies (1950) found that nestling Swifts, *Apus apus*, remained in the nest for 35 to 56 days, depending upon the weather.

Growth

A topic that has received a great deal of effort is the growth of nestlings. Regularly several nestlings are weighed daily and a simple chart made of their growth. Such data are generally worthless for generalizations because too few individuals are measured. A plethora of examples could be cited of measurements of several nestlings, uncorrelated with any factor. Furthermore the data are rarely analyzed to determine the rate of growth or any other constant. However, Lack and Silva (1949) studied the growth of a large number of English Robins. The curve is a typical sigmoid, although no analysis was done. Lack and Lack (1951) analyzed the gain in weight of nestling Swifts, in relation to the weather and found that these young birds gained weight more rapidly in good weather, presumably as a result of a better supply of food. Ornithologists could well follow the example of Brant (1951) in analyzing their data, if and when they have an adequate sample. Brant measured the growth of chicks, analyzed the rates mathematically, and compared the effects of various dietary treatments. Ornithologists could use growth rates to study the effect of temperature on metabolism, the role of nutrition, and many other general problems.

Care of Young

Brooding of young is merely a continuation of incubation behavior, as Emlen (1941:216) pointed out. Few detailed studies are available except for Song Sparrows (Nice, 1937:130). Moreau (1940) found for the first week that young Rough-wing Bank-martins were brooded as much as the eggs had been incubated. Kendeigh (1952) published an analysis of available data in great detail.

Studies of feeding frequency suffer from the same difficulties as those for attentiveness. Richdale (1945:55) called attention to the infrequent feeding of the young Sooty Shearwaters, *Puffinus griseus*. Eight chicks were fed at an interval with a geometric mean of 3.3 days (S.D. = 1.42). Pitelka (1940:11) gave very detailed data but only for twenty-six hours on the Black-throated Green Warbler, *Dendroica virens*. Putnam (1949:168) presented a chart (reproduced here as Fig. 2) showing that the male Cedar Waxwing feeds the young frequently just after hatching but the female feeds them rarely for the first few days while she is brooding. Gibb (1950) presented very detailed tables on feeding frequency by age of nestling for 24 nests of the Great Tit. The number of feeding visits rose till the eighth day and then declined (see Table 8). The greater the number of nestlings, the greater the number of visits but not in proportion to the brood-size. Starlings (Lack,

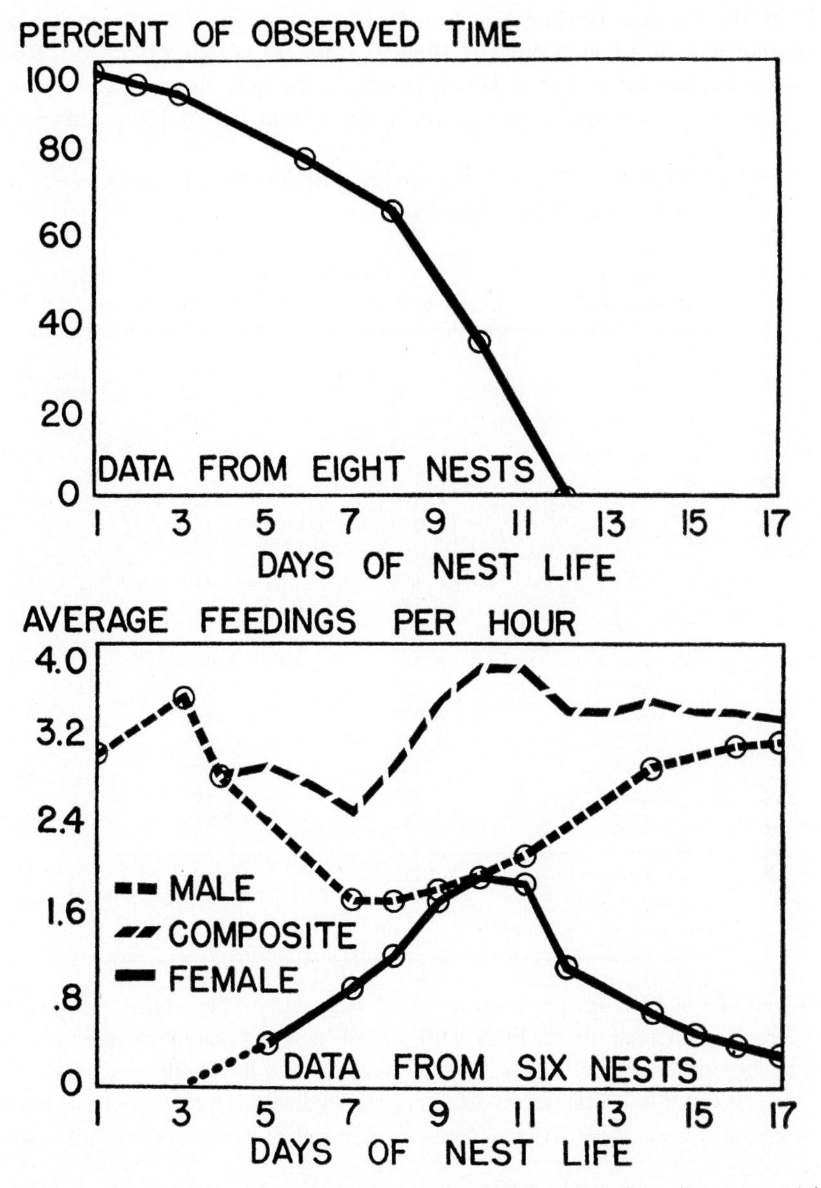

Fig. 2. Brooding time and feeding frequency of Cedar Waxwings (Putnam, 1949). For the first few days the male fed and the female brooded; then the female fed as often as the male but later fed less often.

1948:97) fed each nestling in a brood of 4 an average of 83 times but each nestling in a brood of 6 only 67 times per day. Kendeigh (1952:61) found that as the number of young House Wrens in the nest increased from 1 to 6 the number of feedings increased exponentially from 115 to 300 but obviously

TABLE 8. DAILY VISITS TO THE BROOD IN THE GREAT TIT (from Gibb, 1950:534)

Age of Nestlings	First Broods of: 11 and Over	First Broods of: Up to 10
days		
0.5	85	140
1.5	230	240
2.5	335	270
3.5	370	325
4.5	390	320
5.5	440	365
6.5	463	390
7.5	450	415
8.5	460	410
9.5	490	440
10.5	525	475
11.5	495	455
12.5	490	420
13.5	460	430
14.5	450	410
15.5	435	440
16.5	450	470
Mean daily visits	450	400
Average brood size	11.2	8.5
Daily visits per young	4.0	4.7

the number of feedings per bird decreased from 115 to 50. Nice (1943:231) reported an increase in feedings with age of nestling Song Sparrows but the published data lack any measure of variance or tests of significance.

Sanitation of the nest seems to be rarely studied except from the behavior viewpoint. Data about the frequency of removal of fecal sacs are not readily available.

Emlen (1941:217) found that the "care-of-young" phase could be reduced to four days or extended to seventeen days by substitution of nestlings in nests of Tricolored Redwings.

DURATION OF THE BREEDING SEASON

The recent acquisition of adequate data on nesting has permitted a study of breeding seasons of many species. Care must be taken that the data repre-

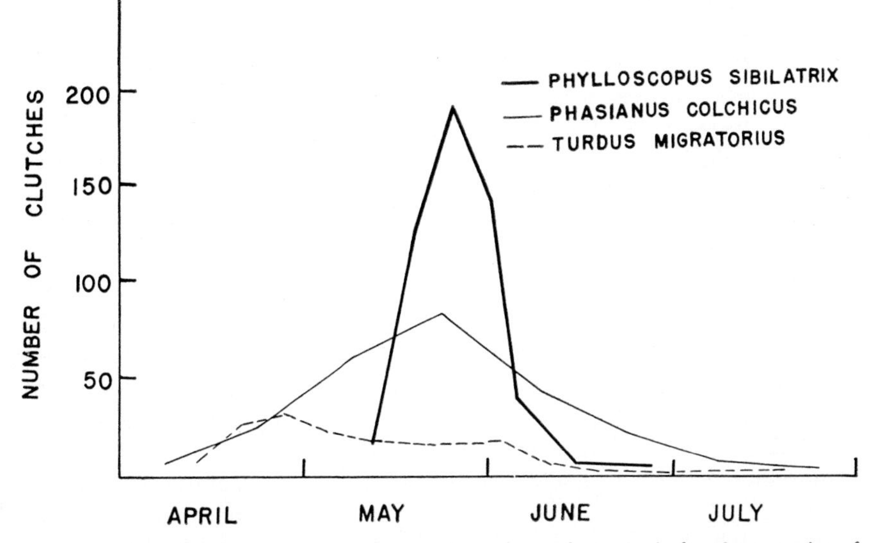

Fig. 3. The breeding season (in terms of numbers of clutches) for three species of birds. The shape of the curves differ in detail but all increase more rapidly than they decline (see text for references).

sent equal effort to find nests in all parts of the season. For example, Lack (1950c:284) apparently did not consider this condition fulfilled for the voluminous data on tits from Holland because he says nothing about duration of breeding season. Nor did he (1949:61) mention duration in thrushes although the data appear to indicate the duration.

Data on the number of nests found according to the period of the season are presented in Figure 3 (also Fig. 1) for 3 representative types. E. Lack (1950:97) presented data for 588 nests of the Wood Warbler found in Devon, England from 1924 to 1931 which show a short season. The breeding season of the Ring-necked Pheasant in Pennsylvania (Randall, 1941:306) is surprisingly symmetrical. The American Robin (Howell, 1942:547) follows the pattern of a rapid increase to a peak and then a slower decline.

Several studies present data and illustrate special points. Vogt (1942) found that on the guano islands of Peru the Guanay, *Phalacrocorax bougainvillii,* nests from August to June with a maximum in November and a gradual decline thereafter. Seubert (1952) kept pheasants under semi-captive conditions and found 16 nests in April, 170 in May, 117 in June, and 33 in July. Saliger (1952) presented a graph showing a rapid increase in pheasant nests and then a decline. Gibb (1950:513) found considerable difference in the nesting season in relation to food (caterpillars) for young tits. In each of three years the number of nests found followed the pattern of a rapid increase to a maximum and a gradual decline, but in 1948 the tits nested earlier than in 1949, presumably because of an earlier appearance of caterpillars in 1948. Merging the data for three years gives a deceptively uniform rate for each week of the season. Stokes (1950:116) presented a graph showing that the American Goldfinch, although a late nester, shows a rapid increase in the number of nests to a maximum in July and a gradual decline till September. Peterson and Young (1950:469) gave graphs showing the nests in use during the breeding season of Bronzed Grackles but do not give the number found by dates. Beer and Tibbits (1950:76) gave the same type of data for Redwings. The season extends from late April to June. Paynter (1949:150) gave the date of hatching of Herring Gulls. The numbers rapidly increase in June and slowly decline in July. Buss *et al.* (1950) showed that in a year when the weather was dry and warm pheasants in Washington hatched about two weeks earlier than in the preceding year which was wet and cold. Yocum (1950) gave data on waterfowl for hatching dates according to weeks. Considerable difference in the dates of the peaks are apparent for Redheads, *Aythya americana,* and Mallards.

Breeding seasons of closely related species may differ greatly even in the same area. Pitelka (1951:199) showed the nesting periods for four kinds of hummingbirds. Two species in the same genus (Anna and Costa hummingbirds, *Calypte anna* and *C. costae*) differ by about two months in the date of maximum breeding. Interspecific competition is not the explanation in this case because these two species live in different habitats.

Colquhoun (1951:2) gave data for the number of nests of Wood Pigeons found according to two-week intervals. The season lasted from March to October although apparently some nests have been found in every month of the year. The peak of reproduction was not pronounced but occurred in June and July. McCabe and Hawkins (1946:20) presented a graph showing the number of first eggs and number of hatchings by dates for the Hungarian Partridge in Wisconsin. Both curves are rather symmetrical. Summers-Smith (1952) presented the numbers of clutches of the Spotted Flycatcher by weekly intervals. The curve is asymmetrical since the peak of the season is reached almost within the first third of the season. Pearson and Rosene (1938) showed that the length of the testes of Mourning Doves, *Zenaidura macroura,* in southern states increases before nest building and decreases before the end of the season. Pearson and Moore (1939) presented data in detail for the number of nests in each month. The curve increases rapidly to a peak from February 15 to May 15 and then declines till October 15. Cowan (1952) in California found a season for doves from March to September with a peak in July. However, his data refer to active nests, not to initiation of nesting. Kozicky and Schmidt (1949:360) gave a table showing the hatching date for 50 nests of Clapper Rails. Half were between June 16 and 20. Girard (1941: 241) gave a graph showing that 28 per cent of 118 Mallard nests hatched between June 11 and 20. Girard (1939) found that the breeding season for Shovellers extended from May to August with the maximum in the middle of

June. White Storks (Schierer, 1952) start arriving at the nest sites in February and continue throughout April but the peak of arrivals is in March. The Adelie Penguin, *Pygoscelis adeliae,* (Sapin-Jaloustre and Bourlière, 1951) begins to lay in the middle of November and completes laying by the middle of December.

The extent of the breeding season has been determined recently for several species by an analysis of the wings of birds shot in the hunting season. The week of hatching may be determined for individual birds and then a graph constructed of the breeding season. For example, Blouch and Eberhardt (1953) compared the breeding season of Ring-necked Pheasants according to habitat.

Apparently Barn Owls, *Tyto alba,* may breed every month of the year because nestlings have been banded in every month in the United States (Stewart, 1952). A long breeding season (10 months) occurs in the Southern House Wren, *Troglodytes musculus* (Skutch, 1953), in contrast to the short season (4 months) in the northern species.

Studies of the correlation of latitude and breeding seasons (Baker, 1939) show that northward from the equator some birds breed later in the year and that southward the breeding seasons are earlier. In other birds, the reverse is true. Studies of the causes of these correlations need to be made.

The general extent of the breeding season in the tropics of Africa has been examined by Moreau (1936). He found a seasonal change in the number of birds nesting but was unable clearly to correlate such changes with any single environmental factor. Lack (1950a) found great variation among the species on the Galapagos. Finches bred only in the rainy season, doves somewhat later, raptors in the cool dry season, and the aquatic birds nearly throughout the year. Moreau (1950) summarized a vast amount of data for African birds. A season of maximum breeding is present everywhere except very near the equator. There may be no distinct season (Congo) or two seasons (East Africa) coinciding with the rains. The "causes" of seasonal breeding are complex and vary from species to species. Davis (1945a) found a definite breeding season for Brazilian birds, coinciding with the warm, rainy season. Lack (1950b) summarized much data for European birds and emphasized the fact that there the magnitude of the seasonal changes in food supply dictate the seasons for breeding. Hutchinson (1950) reviewed the data on breeding seasons of the Sooty Tern, *Sterna fuscata.* The time of year varies greatly from place to place but occurs in the spring in most areas. Chapin (1946) established conclusively the fact that on Ascension Island the species breeds every nine months.

Physiological Breeding Biology

The physiological and anatomical aspects of breeding biology have received attention in recent years. Many of these studies originated from an interest in photoperiodism and included extensive laboratory research. Burger (1949) reviewed the application of such studies to the problem of seasonal reproduction and largely supersedes the excellent review of Marshall (1936).

A number of detailed studies describe the changes in the gonads of wild birds during the year. Blanchard (1941:1949) presented splendid data on the gonadal changes before breeding in three races of White-crowned Sparrows. She interpreted these comparative data to show that an inherent annual rhythm is only slightly modified by environmental conditions. Wright and Wright (1944) described the testicular cycle of Redwings. The testes of both adults and yearlings develop in the spring but those of the adults become larger, develop earlier, and in the regressed phase are larger than those of yearlings. The regression of the testes is correlated with the postbreeding molt. Hiatt and Fisher (1947) presented detailed data on testicular changes during breeding season in Ring-necked Pheasants in Montana and concluded that there is no difference between adults and yearlings in growth or size at maximum. However, the immature testes develop in the fall and then involute slightly.

Wynne-Edwards (1939) presented an interesting study of the ovaries of the Fulmar, *Fulmarus glacialis,* which showed that some individuals bred only intermittently. Bullough (1942) showed that the continental race of the Starling differs from the English race in gonadal size. The testes of the former are more regressed than those of the latter in the nonbreeding season.

EPILOGUE

This chapter has summarized the present status of breeding biology of birds. The observational methods available for studies are reasonably adequate but analysis needs refinement. Although these methods have accumulated a large mass of data, much of it in quantitative form, ornithologists have been reluctant to utilize statistical methods in the analysis. It must be remembered that statistical procedures are not a mysterious way to make bad data good; they merely help the scientist to determine the reliability of the inferences drawn from the sample of data. Some notable examples of the use of statistical methods are provided by European authors (Lack, 1947a; Gibb, 1950; Kluijver, 1950). To be useful for statistical analysis, data must be recorded in quantitative form. The actual number of nests, the number of eggs in each nest, the number of times food was brought in each hour, etc. are essential. Tables 1, 3, 5, 7, and 8 are examples of useful data.

Ornithologists are notably lax in recording detailed data in tabular form. The importance of recording such data is that it frequently may be used by other persons for purposes not thought of by the original investigator. However, caution is necessary in utilizing other persons' data because it is relatively easy to use the data for an unjustified purpose. In this review authors' data have frequently been recalculated and used for purposes not mentioned by the author. We hope that no errors of application have been committed.

The recent development of research teams in science is finding expression in ornithological work. Notable examples in breeding biology are the monograph on Ruffed Grouse (Bump *et al.*, 1947) and other game species and the many splendid papers made possible by the co-operative efforts of the British Trust for Ornithology. Unfortunately the work of teams sometimes deteriorates through lack of cooperation, of training for the task, or of detailed familiarity with the data by the author. Co-operative efforts, however, can contribute significantly in ornithological problems. For example, a team could obtain enough data in one year to compare clutch-size at different latitudes, an impossible task for one individual.

American ornithology could profit from more communication with ornithologists, other zoologists, and especially with poultry scientists. Studies of breeding biology frequently ignore pertinent work by foreign students or in related fields of zoology. Indeed, this review may reflect this isolation by omitting to mention significant foreign work.

Bibliography

ALLEN, A. A.

1934. Sex rhythm in the Ruffed Grouse (*Bonasa umbellus*) and other birds. Auk, 51:180-199.

ALLEN, R. P.

1942. The Roseate Spoonbill. Research Report No. 2, Nat. Audubon Soc., xviii + 142 pp.

ALLEN, R. W., and M. M. NICE

1952. A study of the breeding biology of the Purple Martin (*Progne subis*). Amer. Midl. Nat., 47:605-665.

BAKER, J. R.

1939. The relation between latitude and breeding seasons in birds. Proc. Zool. Soc. London, A., 108:557-582.

BALDWIN, S. P., and S. C. KENDEIGH

1927. Attentiveness and inattentiveness in the nesting behavior of the House Wren. Auk, 44:208-216.

BALL, K. E.

1952. Nesting of the Ring-necked Pheasant on Pelee Island, Ontario. Canad. Field Nat., 66:71-81.

BARTH, E. K.

1952. Incubation period and loss of weight of eggs of the Common Gull, *Larus canus canus,* and of the Lesser Black-backed Gull, *L. fuscus intermedius.* Papers on Game Res., 8:111-121.

BEER, J. R., and D. TIBBITTS

1950. Nesting behavior of the Red-wing Blackbird. Flicker, 22:61-77.

BENT, A. C.

1919-1953. Life histories of North American birds. U.S. Nat. Mus. Bulls.

BERNDT, R.

1939. Untersuchungen uber die zweite Brut beim Star (*Sturnus v. vulgaris* L.) im Braunschweiger Hugelland. Vogelzug, 10:7-16.

BERNDT, R., and F. FRIELING

1939. Siedlungs- und brutbiologische Studien an Hohlenbruter in einem nordwestsachsischen Park. Jour. Ornithol., 87:593-638.

BLANCHARD, B. D.

1941. The White-crowned Sparrows (*Zonotrichia leucophrys*) of the Pacific seaboard: environment and annual cycle. Univ. Calif. Publ. Zool., 46:1-178.

BLOUCH, R. T., and L. L. EBERHARDT

1953. Hatching curves of Michigan pheasants. Jour. Wildlife Mgmt., 17:477-482.

BOYD, A. W.

1936. Report on the swallow enquiry, 1935. Brit. Birds, 30:98-116.

BRANT, J. W. A.

1951. Rate of early growth in domestic fowl. Poult. Sci., 30:343-361.

BULLOUGH, W. S.

1942. The reproductive cycles of the British and continental races of the Starling. Phil. Trans. Royal Soc., London, B231 (580):165-246.

BUMP, G., R. W. DARROW, F. C. EDMINSTER, and W. F. CRISSEY

1947. The Ruffed Grouse. New York State Conservation Dept., Albany, 915 pp.

BURGER, J. W.

1949. A review of experimental investigations on seasonal reproduction in birds. Wilson Bull., 61:211-230.

BUSS, I. O., R. K. MEYER, and C. KABAT

1951. Wisconsin pheasant reproduction studies based on ovulated follicle technique. Jour. Wildlife Mgmt., 15:32-46.

BUSS, I. O., and C. V. SWANSON

1950. Some effects of weather on pheasant reproduction in southeastern Washington. Trans. N. Amer. Wildlife Conf., 15:364-378.

CAMPBELL, B.

1950. Breeding of the Pied Flycatcher. Brit. Birds, 43:13-15.

CHANCE, E. P.

1940. The truth about the cuckoo. Charles Scribner's Sons, New York, 207 pp.

CHAPIN, J. P.

1946. Wideawake fair invaded. Nat. Hist., 55:313-319.

CHAPMAN, F. M.

1935. The courtship of Gould's Manakin. Bull. Amer. Mus. Nat. Hist., 68:471-525.

COLLIAS, N. E.

1950. Hormones and behavior with special reference to birds and the mechanisms of hormone action. In A symposium on steroid hormones, ed. by E. S. Gordon. University of Wisconsin Press, Madison, pp. 277-329.

COLQUHOUN, M. K.

1951. The Wood Pigeon in Britain. Agric. Res. Council. ARC Report Ser., 10:1-69.

COWAN, J. R.

1952. Life history and productivity of a population of Western Mourning Doves in California. Calif. Fish and Game, 38:505-521.

DARLING, F. F.

1938. Bird flocks and the breeding cycle. Cambridge University Press, 124 pp.

DAVIS, D. E.

1940. Social nesting habits of the Smooth-billed Ani. Auk, 57:179-218.

1941. The belligerency of the kingbird. Wilson Bull., 53:157-168.

1942a. The number of eggs laid by cowbirds. Condor, 44:10-12.

1942b. The phylogeny of social nesting habits in the Crotophaginae. Quart. Rev. Biol., 17:115-135.

1942c. Number of eggs laid by Herring Gulls. Auk, 59:549-554.

1945a. The annual cycle of plants, mosquitoes, birds and mammals in two Brazilian forests. Ecol. Monogr., 15:243-295.

1945b. The occurrence of the incubation patch in some Brazilian birds. Wilson Bull., 57:188-190.

DIRCKSEN, R.

1932. Die Biologie des Austernfischers, der Brandseeschwalbe und der Kustenseeschwalbe nach Beobachtungen und Untersuchungen auf Norderbog. Jour. Ornithol., 80:427-521.

DURANGO, S.

1948. Notes sur la reproduction du Bruant Ortolan en Suede. Alauda, 16:1-10.

EMLEN, J. T., JR.

1941. An experimental analysis of the breeding cycle of the Tricolored Redwing. Condor, 43:209-219.

ERICKSON, M. M.

1938. Territory, annual cycle, and numbers in a population of Wren-tits (*Chamaea fasciata*) Univ. Calif. Publ. Zool., 42:247-334.

ERRINGTON, P. L.

1933. The nesting and life equation of the Wisconsin Bob-white. Wilson Bull., 45:122-132.

FAUTIN, R. W.

1941. Incubation studies of the Yellow-headed Blackbird. Wilson Bull., 53:107-122.

GIBB, J.

1950. The breeding biology of the Great and Blue titmice. Ibis, 92:507-539.

GIRARD, G. L.

1939. Notes on the life history of the Shoveller. Trans. N. Amer. Wildlife Conf., 4:364-371.

1941. Mallard: Its management in western Montana. Jour. Wildlife Mgmt., 5:233-259.

GLOVER, F. A.

1953. Nesting ecology of the Pied-billed Grebe in northwestern Iowa. Wilson Bull., 65:32-39.

GRASSÉ, P. - P., ed.

1950. Traité de zoologie. Tome XV. Oiseaux. Masson et Cie, Paris, 1164 pp.

GROEBBELS, F.

1937. Der Vogel; II Geschlsecht and Fortpflanzung. Berlin, pp. 1-478.

GROSS, A. O.

1938. Eider ducks of Kent's Island. Auk, 55:387-400.

HAARTMAN, L. VON

1951. Der Trauerfliegenschnäpper, I. Populationsprobleme. Acta Zool. Fenn., 68:1-60.

HAMMOND, M. C., and C. J. HENRY

1949. Success of Marsh Hawk nests in North Dakota. Auk, 66:271-274.

HANN, H. W.

1937. Life history of the Oven-bird in southern Michigan. Wilson Bull., 49:146-237.

HAUN, M.

1931. Statistische Untersuchungen uber die Eierzahl in den Gelegen der drei Lerchenarten (*Alauda arvensis, Galerida cristata* und *Lullula arborea*) sowie der Goldhammer (*Emberiza citrinella*). Beitr. Fortpfl. Vogel, 7:135-138.

HIATT, R. W., and H. I. FISHER

1947. The reproductive cycle of Ring-necked Pheasants in Montana. Auk, 64:528-548.

HOCHBAUM, H. A.

1944. The Canvasback on a prairie marsh. Amer. Wildlife Inst., Washington, xii + 201 pp.

HOOGERWERF, A.

1937. Uit het leven der witte ibissen, *Threskiornis aethiopicus melanocephalus.* Limosa, 10:137-146.

HOWELL, J. C.

1942. Notes on the nesting habits of the American Robin (*Turdus migratorius*). Amer. Midl. Nat., 28:529-604.

HUTCHINSON, G. E.

1950. Wideawake fair. Amer. Scientist, 38:613-616.

KENDEIGH, S. C.

1941. Territorial and mating behavior of the House Wren. Ill. Biol. Monogr., 18:5-120.

1952. Parental care and its evolution in birds. Ill. Biol. Monogr., 22:1-356.

KENDRICK H.

1940. A study of Blue Tits by colour ringing. Brit. Birds., 33:307-310.

KLOMP, H.

1951. Over de achteruitgang van de Kievit, *Vanellus vanellus* (L.), in Nederland en gegevens over het legmechanisme en het eiproductie-vermogen. Ardea, 39:143-182.

KLUIJVER, H. N.

1950. Daily routines of the Great Tit, *Parus m. major* L. Ardea, 38:99-135.

1951. The population ecology of the Great Tit, *Parus m. major* L. Ardea, 39:1-135.

1952. Notes on body weight and time of breeding in the Great Tit, *Parus m. major* L. Ardea, 40:123-141.

KLUIJVER, H. N., J. LIGTOVOET, C. VAN DEN OUWELANT, and F. ZEGWAARD

1940. De levenswijze van den winterkoning, *Troglodytes tr. troglodytes* (L.). Limosa, 13:1-51.

KOENIG, I. O.

1951. Das aktionssytem der Bartmeise (*Panurus biarmicus* L). Öst. Zool. Zeits., 3:1-82.

KOSKIMIES, J.

1950. The life of the swift, *Micropus apus* (L) in relation to the weather. Ann. Acad. Sci. Fenn., Series A (Biol.), 4:1-151.

KOZICKY, E. L., and F. V. SCHMIDT

1949. Nesting habits of the Clapper Rail in New Jersey. Auk, 66:355-364.

KUERZI, R. G.

1941. Life history studies of the Tree Swallow. Proc. Linn. Soc. N.Y., 52:1-52.

KUUSISTO, P.

1941. Studien uber die Ökologie und Tagesrhytmik von *Phylloscopus trochilus acredula* (L.) Acta. Zool. Fenn., 31:1-120.

LACK, D.

1935. Territory and polygamy in a bishop-bird *Euplectes hordeacea hordeacea* (Linn.). Ibis, Ser. 13, 5:817-836.

1946. Clutch and brood size in the Robin. Brit. Birds, 39:98-109, 130-135.

1947a. Further notes on clutch and brood size in the Robin. Brit. Birds, 41:98-104, 130-137.

1947b. The significance of clutch-size in the Partridge (*Perdix perdix*). Jour. Animal Ecol., 16:19-25.

1947-48. The significance of clutch-size. Ibis, 89:303-352; and 90:25-45.

1948. Natural selection and family-size in the Starling. Evol., 2:95-110.

1949. Family-size in certain thrushes (Turdidae). Evol., 3:57-66.

1950a. Breeding seasons in the Galapagos. Ibis, 92:268-278.

1950b. The breeding seasons of European birds. Ibis, 92:288-316.

1950c. Family-size in titmice of the genus *Parus*. Evol. 4:279-290.

LACK, D., and H. ARN

1947. Die Bedeutung der Gelegegrösse bein Alpensegler. Ornithol. Beobachter, 44:188-210.

LACK, D., and E. LACK

1951. The breeding biology of the Swift *Apus apus*. Ibis, 93:501-546.

LACK, D., and E. T. SILVA

1949. The weight of nestling Robins. Ibis, 91:64-78.

LACK, E.

1950. Breeding season and clutch-size of the Wood Warbler. Ibis, 92:95-98.

LASKEY, A. R.

1939. A study of nesting Eastern Bluebirds. Bird-Banding, 10:23-32.

1943. The nesting of bluebirds banded as nestlings. Bird-Banding, 14:39-43.

1950. Cowbird behavior. Wilson Bull., 62:157-182.

LEWIS, H. F.

1939. Size of sets of eggs of the American Eider. Jour. Wildlife Mgmt., 3:70-73.

LINSDALE, J. M.

1937. Natural history of magpies. Pacific Coast Avifauna, 25:234 pp.

LOHRL, H.

1951. Brutbeginn und Entwicklung im Vogelei. Vogelwelt, 72:1-4.

McATEE, W. L.

1940. An experiment in songbird management. Auk, 57:333-348.

McCABE, R. A., and A. S. HAWKINS

1946. The Hungarian Partridge of Wisconsin. Amer. Midl. Nat., 36:1-75.

McLAUGHIN, C. L., and D. GRICE

1952. The effectiveness of large-scale erection of Wood Duck boxes as a management procedure. Trans. N. Amer. Wildlife Conf., 17:242-259.

MAKATSCH, W.

1936. Der Brutparasitismus der Kuckucksvogel. Quelle Meyer, Leipzig, 152 pp.

MARPLES, G., and A. MARPLES

1934. Sea terns. Country Life Ltd., London, 227 pp.

MARSHALL, F. H. A.

1936. Sexual periodicity and the causes which determine it. Phil. Trans. Roy. Soc. London, B, 226:423-456.

MASON, E. A.

1953. Barn Swallow life history data based on banding records. Bird-Banding, 24:91-100.

MENDALL, H. L., and C. M. ALDOUS

1943. The ecology and management of the American Woodcock. Maine Coop. Wildlife Res. Unit, Orono, Maine, 201 pp.

MOREAU, R. E.

1936. Breeding seasons of birds in East African evergreen forest. Proc. Zool. Soc. London, pp. 631-653.

1939. Numerical data on African birds behaviour at the nest. Proc. Zool. Soc. London, A., 109:109-126.

1940. Numerical data on African birds' behaviour at the nest, II. *Psalidoprocne holomelaena massaica* Neum., the Rough-wing Bank-martin. Ibis, Ser. 14, 4:234-248.

1942. The breeding biology of *Micropus cafer streubelli* Hartlaub, the White-rumped Swift. Ibis, 14th ser., 6:27-49.

1944. Clutch-size: A comparative study with special reference to African birds. Ibis, 86:286-347.

1947. Relations between number in brood, feeding-rates, and nestling period in nine species of birds in Tanganyika Territory. Jour. Animal Ecol., 16:205-209.

1950. The breeding seasons of African birds, I. Land birds. Ibis, 92:223-267.

MOREAU, R. E., and W. M. MOREAU

1940. Incubation and fledging periods of African birds. Auk, 57:313-325.

NERO, R. W., and J. T. EMLEN, JR.

1951. An experimental study of territorial behavior in breeding Red-winged Blackbirds. Condor, 53:105-116.

NICE, M. M.

1937. Studies in life history of the Song Sparrow, I. Trans. Linn. Soc. N.Y., 4:1-242.

1943. Studies in the life history of the Song Sparrow and other passerines. Trans. Linn. Soc. N.Y., 6:1-328.

1949. The laying rhythm of cowbirds. Wilson Bull., 61:231-234.

1953. The question of ten-day incubation periods. Wilson Bull., 65:81-93.

NICE, M. M., and R. H. THOMAS

1948. A nesting of the Carolina Wren. Wilson Bull., 60:139-158.

NOHRING, R.

1943. Ueber Gefangenschaftsbruten des Trauerschnappers (*Muscicapa h. hypoleuca*). Jour. Ornithol., 91:329-340.

NOLL, H.

1939. Die Brutzeiten unserer Vogel und ihre biologische Bedeutung. Arch. suisses d'Ornithol., 1:425-439.

ODUM, E.

1941. Technics in life history study. Oriole, 6:29-35.

1941-42. Annual cycle of the Black-capped Chickadee. Auk, 58:314-333, 518-535; 59:499-531.

1945. The heart rate of small birds. Science, 101:153-154.

PALUDAN, K.

1951. Contributions to the breeding biology of *Larus argentatus* and *Larus fuscus*. Vidensk. Medd. fra Dansk naturh. Foren., 114:1-128.

PARKHURST, R., and D. LACK

1946. The clutch-size of the Yellowhammer. Brit. Birds, 39:358-364.

PAYNTER, R. A., JR.

1949. Clutch-size and the egg and chick mortality of Kent Island Herring Gulls. Ecol., 30:146-166.

1951. Clutch-size and egg mortality of Kent Island Eiders. Ecol., 32:497-507.

PEARSON, A. M., and W. ROSENE, JR.

1938. Observations on the breeding season of the Mourning Dove in the South. Trans. N. Amer. Wildlife Conf., 3:865-868.

PEARSON, A. M., and G. C. MOORE

1939. Nesting habits of the Mourning Dove in Alabama. Trans. N. Amer. Wildlife Conf., 4:468-473.

PETERSEN, A., and H. YOUNG

1950. A nesting study of the Bronzed Grackle. Auk, 67:466-476.

PHILLIPS, W. W. A.

1948-51. Nests and eggs of Ceylon birds. Ceylon Jour. Sci., 23:173-194; 24:143-163.

PITELKA, F. A.

1940. Breeding behavior of the Black-throated Green Warbler. Wilson Bull., 52:3-19.

1951. Breeding seasons of hummingbirds near Santa Barbara, California. Condor, 53:198-201.

PROVOST, M. W.

1947. Nesting of birds in the marshes of northwest Iowa. Amer. Midl. Nat., 38:485-503.

PURCHON, R. D.

1948. The nesting activities of the Swallow. Proc. Zool. Soc. London, 118:146-170.

PUTNAM, L. S.

1949. The life history of the Cedar Waxwing. Wilson Bull., 61:141-182.

RANDALL, P. E.

1941. The life equation of the Ringneck Pheasant in Pennsylvania. Trans. N. Amer. Wildlife Conf., 5:300-320.

RICHDALE, L. E.

1944. The Titi Wainui or Fairy Prion *Pachyptila turtur* (Kuhl). Trans. Roy. Soc. N. Zeal., 74:32-48.

1945. The nesting of the Sooty Shearwater. Condor, 47:45-62.

1949a. A study of a group of penguins of known age. Dunedin, New Zealand, 88 pp. (Published privately.)

1949b. The effect of age on laying dates, size of eggs, and size of clutch in the Yellow-eyed Penguin. Wilson Bull., 61:91-98.

1950. The pre-egg stage in the albatross family. Dunedin, New Zealand, 92 pp. (Published privately.)

1951. Sexual behavior in penguins. University of Kansas Press, Lawrence, 316 pp.

RICHTER, H.

1953. Zur Lebensweise der Wasseramsel I: Der Ortswechsel. Jour. Ornithol., 94:68-82.

RINKEL, G. L.

1940. Waarneminger over het gedrag van de Kievit (*Vanellus vanellus* L.) gedurende de broedtijd. Ardea, 29:108-147.

RITTER, W. E.

1938. The California Woodpecker and I. University of Calif. Press, Berkeley, 340 pp.

ROBERTS, B.

1940. The life cycle of Wilson's Petrel *Oceanites oceanicus* (Kuhl). British Grahamland Expedition, 1934-37. Sci. Rep., 1:141-194.

RUITER, C. J. S.

1941. Waarnemingen omtreut de levenswijze van de gekraagde Roodstart *Phoenicurus ph. phoenicurus* (L.) Ardea, 30:175-214.

RYVES, B. H.

1934. The breeding habits of the Corn Bunting as observed in north Cornwall. Brit. Birds, 28:2-26, 154-164.

1943. An investigation into the roles of males in relation to incubation. Brit. Birds, 37:10-16.

SALIGER, H. E.

1952. A pheasant breeding population study on irrigated lands in southwest Idaho. Jour. Wildlife Mgmt., 16:409-418.

SAPIN-JALOUSTRE, J., and F. BOURLIÈRE

1951. Incubation et development du poussin chez le Manchot Adelie, *Pygoscelis adeliae.* Alauda, 19:65-83.

SCHIERER, A.

1952. Les cigognes en Alsace. Resultats des recensements des années 1950 et 1951. Alauda, 20:129-143.

SCHREURS, T.

1941. Zur Brut und Ernarungsbiologie des Neuntoters (*Lanius collurio*). Jour. Ornithol., 89:182-203.

SCHÜZ, E.

1950. Reifung, Ansiedlung und Bestandswechsel beim Weissen Storch (*C. ciconia*). In Ornithologie als Biologische Wissenschaft, Carl Winter, Heidelberg, pp. 217-228.

SERVENTY, V. N., and S. R. WHITE

1951. The Roseate Tern: notes on the nesting behavior. Emu, 50:145-151.

SEUBERT, J. L.

1952. Observations on the renesting behavior of the Ring-necked Pheasant. Trans. N. Amer. Wildlife Conf., 17:305-329.

SICK, H.

1947. O ninho de "*Panyptila cayennensis*" (Gmelin) e algumas observações compilatórias sôbre a ecologia de outros andorinhões brasileiros. Rev. Brasil Biol., 7:219-246.

SIIVONEN, L.

1939. Zur Ökologie und Verbreitung der Singdrossel (*Turdus ericetorum philomelos* Brehm) Ann. Zool. Soc. Zool.-Bot. Fenn. Vanamo, 7:1-136.

1952. On the reflection of short-term fluctuations in numbers in the reproduction of tetraonids. Papers on Game Research, 9:4-42.

SKUTCH, A. F.

1949. Life history of the Yellow-thighed Manakin. Auk, 66:1-24.

1952. On the hour of laying and hatching of birds' eggs. Ibis, 94:49-62.

1953. Life history of the Southern House Wren. Condor, 55:121-149.

SOWLS, L. K.

1949. A preliminary report on renesting in waterfowl. Trans. N. Amer. Wildlife Conf., 14:260-275.

STEWART, P. A.

1952. Dispersal, breeding, and longevity of banded Barn Owls in North America. Auk, 69:227-245.

STEWART, R. E.

1951. Clapper Rail populations of the middle Atlantic states. Trans. N. Amer. Wildlife Conf., 16:422-430.

STOCKTON, K. L., and A. S. ASMUNDSON

1950. Daily rhythm of egg production in turkeys. Jour. Poult. Sci., 29:477-479.

STOKES, A. W.

1950. Breeding behavior of the goldfinch. Wilson Bull., 62:107-127.

SUMMERS-SMITH, D.

1952. Breeding biology of the Spotted Flycatcher. Brit. Birds, 45:153-166.

SWANBERG, P. O.

1950. On the concept of "incubation period." Vår Fågelvärld, 9:63-80.

VERWEY, J.

1931. Eierzahl der Feldlerche und einiger anderer Vogelarten. Beitr. Fortpfl. Vogel, 7:66-67.

VOGT, W.

1942. Aves guaneras. Boletín, Com. Admin. Guano, 18:3-131.

WAGNER, H. O.

1945. Notes on the life history of the Mexican Violet-ear. Wilson Bull., 57:165-187.

WALKINSHAW, L. H.

1941. The Prothonotary Warbler, a comparison of nesting conditions in Tennessee and Michigan. Wilson Bull., 53:3-21.

1953. Life history of the Prothonotary Warbler. Wilson Bull., 65:152-168.

WESTON, H. G.

1947. Breeding behavior of the Black-headed Grosbeak. Condor, 49:54-73.

WILLIAMSON, K.

1945. The relation between duration of hatching and the incubation period. Ibis, 87:280-282.

WILSON, H.

1946. The life history of the Western Magpie (*Gymnorhina dorsalis*). Emu, 45:233-244, 271-286.

WRIGHT, P. L., AND M. H. WRIGHT

1944. The reproductive cycle of the male Red-winged Blackbird. Condor, 46:46-59.

WYNNE-EDWARDS, V. C.

1939. Intermittent breeding of the Fulmar (*Fulmarus glacialis* (L.)) with some general observations on non-breeding in sea-birds. Proc. Zool. Soc. London, A, 109:127-132.

YOCUM, C. F.

1950. Weather and its effect on hatching of waterfowl in eastern Washington. Trans. N. Amer. Wildlife Conf., 15:309-319.

chapter 10

RECENT ADVANCES IN KNOWLEDGE CONCERNING THE ROLE OF HORMONES IN THE SEX DIFFERENTIATION OF BIRDS . . . L. V. Domm

INTRODUCTION

The role of hormones in the sex differentiation of vertebrates has received increasing attention in recent years, but despite numerous investigations the problem remains a controversial one. We shall attempt to evaluate the current concept that the gonads during their embryonic development secrete hormone-like substances which are responsible for guiding the development of sexual characters. The period in ontogeny at which sex hormones, as we conceive them, first become effective is therefore crucial to our problem, but it should be emphasized that there is no question as to the effectiveness of these agents in postembryonic life, for it has long been known that secondary sex characters and reproductive functions are predominantly controlled by gonad secretions in most vertebrates. However, the presence of these hormones during embryonic development, coincident with or shortly following sex differentiation, has not been so evident.

The suggestion that sex hormones play a role in embryonic life was first made by Bouin and Ancel in 1903. However, the theory received little attention prior to 1916, when the now well-known studies on the freemartin by Lillie first appeared. Lillie advanced the idea that the gonads, following embryonic sex differentiation, begin the secretion of sex hormones, which assume the principal role in guiding the subsequent development of sexual characters. The observed modifications in the reproductive system of the female twin were convincingly interpreted as being the effect of sex hormones. Other interpretations were considered, with the sage warning that the entire concept of embryonic hormone action be experimentally tested before final acceptance. Such was the origin of the concept of embryonic sex hormones which has been widely accepted, has stimulated a significant amount of fruitful research, and has been used as an explanation of a wide variety of experimental results. However, according to some investigators, the freemartin has constituted essentially the only evidence to support this concept in higher vertebrates.

Manuscript received April 1, 1955.

Before submitting the experimental evidence it may be well to review briefly some of the pertinent features respecting normal development of the avian reproductive system, since this is essential for an adequate comprehension of our problem. Regardless of the zygotic sex determination, the embryos of higher vertebrates, including humans, are endowed with the requisite materials for the formation of all parts of either sex system. The gonads arise from a primary proliferation of sex cords destined to form the seminiferous tubules in males, the medulla in females. A second proliferation of sex cords (Pflüger), until recently believed to occur only in females, and in birds, with rare exceptions, confined to the left gonad, gives rise to the ovarian cortex. A transient incipient cortex, readily demonstrable on the testis of lower vertebrates, has also been observed in reptiles, birds, and in some mammals. Likewise, two sets of ducts, the Wolffian and Mullerian, are laid down in each embryo. Normally the Wolffian ducts become functional in males and the Mullerian ducts degenerate, whereas in females the opposite occurs, with the exception that in birds the right Mullerian duct also undergoes involution. We note, therefore, that each embryo is provided with the primordia requisite to the formation of either sex system; and in anomalous cases, in which the characters of one sex are superimposed on the other, there is involved, as Lillie (1927) pointed out, merely the development of dormant pre-existing rudiments laid down in early embryonic life and not the development of any new characters. The recognition that the embryo is potentially bisexual permits us to account for partial or complete inversions of the originally determined sex. Such cases, occurring spontaneously or produced experimentally, are classed as intersexes, hermaphrodites, or sex inversions, depending upon what organs or tissues are actually present. These conditions therefore emphasize the now well-established fact that in the vertebrates sex, which is genetically determined, is not fixed and irreversible, but that regardless of the original zygotic determination, all gradations from a typical female to a typical male are possible.

Before reviewing attempts to modify embryonic development by steroidal substances, let us recall some of the basic concepts relative to hormone action. As stated above, prior to the interpretation of the freemartin by Lillie, little attention had been given to the occurrence of embryonic hormones, although Steinach was responsible for the concept, no longer adhered to by most investigators, of antagonism between the internal secretions of male and female, thus giving hormone action the attributes of stimulating homologous and inhibiting heterologous sex characters. From this, one inferred that hormone secretion was specific for a particular gonad and that tissues responded specifically to a particular secretion, or that ovaries and testes secreted female and male hormones respectively, the former stimulating female and inhibiting male and the latter stimulating male but inhibiting female structures. The vast accumulation of our knowledge concerning hormone action has since necessitated changes in these concepts, though they were generally accepted in 1916, when the first concrete evidence appeared to suggest the occurrence of hormone action during prenatal development.

EXPERIMENTAL DATA

Soon after publication of the observations on the freemartin, investigators began to look about for suitable means of subjecting the theory to experimental tests. The natural presumption was that conditions permitting the circulation of male hormones in the body of a developing female were the essential requisite. In the attempts to modify development in birds by hormones, investigators employed chiefly three types of experimental procedure, namely: (1) transplantation, (2) hormone injection, and (3) castration. Historically, however, these investigations are readily divisible into four periods, and for convenience we have chosen to develop the subject in this manner.

Early Transplantation Experiments

Utilizing living tissues as the source of hormones by grafting them onto growing embryos seemed the most plausible experimental procedure. In birds the developing chick embryo was believed to offer ideal conditions for such experiments since the vascular chorio-allantoic membrane was easily accessible and a successfully incorporated graft should readily discharge secreted substances into the circulating blood.

Minoura (1921), utilizing the procedure of chorio-allantoic grafting, reported positive results in host chick embryos with gonad grafts of either sex. He concluded that growth and differentiation of homologous characters was stimulated and heterologous characters inhibited.

These conclusions were soon discounted by subsequent investigations. Utilizing the same technique, Willier (1927) transplanted undifferentiated gonads from chick embryos (ages four to six days), as well as differentiated gonads (ages seven to thirteen days), onto the chorio-allantoic membranes of embryos of both sexes. Such grafts failed to modify the reproductive system of the host, and differently sexed hosts likewise had no effect on differentiation of grafts. Examination of large numbers of embryos that had been (1) normally incubated, (2) subjected to sham operations, (3) hosts to gonad grafts of both sexes, or (4) hosts of kidney, muscle, spleen, thymus, thyroid, etc. grafts showed no more deviation from normal when these embryos were hosts to gonad grafts than when they were hosts to nongonad grafts or were normally incubated, thus indicating that gonad grafts did not modify the host reproductive system as a consequence of secreted hormones.

Administration of Hormones

The advent of the chemically prepared steroid hormones offered a new and promising approach to the problem, and the influence of these substances on the embryonic avian reproductive system has yielded significant results. Whether the synthetically prepared steroid hormones are similar to those secreted by the adult vertebrate testis or the embryonic testis, if the latter secretes a hormone, is debated, but it should be recalled that the commonly used androgens or estrogens will restore characters lost through castration. Chick embryos furnish ideal conditions for a study of the effects of hormones on the developing reproductive system.

Laulanié (1886) described a thickened germinal epithelium on the left testis of the chick embryo which he characterized as a potential cortex. Burwell (1931) observed a similar condition in duck embryos and later (Lewis, 1946), working in my laboratory at the University of Chicago, she reported its capacity to respond to steroidal hormones. A similar structure has since been observed in other birds. In view of the fact that in females the medullary component of the gonad is a homologue of the tissue which in the testis forms the seminiferous tubules, and since each sex is early endowed with the duct system of the other, it should follow that conditions tending to favor development of one or another of these structures would control sexual differentiation.

The effects of crystalline sex hormones on the sex differentiation of vertebrates were shown for the first time in chick embryos by three groups of investigators, who simultaneously reported essentially similar results, namely, W. Dantchakoff; Willier, Gallagher and Koch; and Wolff and Giglinger (1935). Since then these investigations have been confirmed and extended to all the classes of vertebrates by many investigators.

ANDROGENS

Androgenic hormones administered during early embryonic periods bring about marked changes in sex differentiation, but androgens of somewhat different chemical constitutions yield different results. Thus *testosterone* shows little effect on testes except that they may become somewhat reduced in size, while both ovaries may become testis-like. It stimulates Wolffian ducts in males but has no effect on degenerating Mullerian ducts. Effects on gonoducts in females are similar to those observed in males except that right Mullerian ducts may be more prominent than in normals. *Androsterone,* on the contrary, shows a decidedly feminizing effect. In males the left testis develops into a typical ovotestis, showing a flattened ovary-like structure with characteristic cortex but retaining a testicular medulla. The right testis is usually not modified. Also, unlike testosterone, in males, androsterone inhibits involution of Mullerian ducts, which may in fact show decided hypertrophy, while both have stimulative effects on Wolffian ducts. In females the effects of androsterone differ little from those of testosterone. It is therefore evident that in males certain embryonic characters show masculinizing transformations following the introduction of one androgen and feminization following the introduction of another.

ESTROGENS

When estrogenic hormones are employed in chick embryos we also find substantial modifications in reproductive characters. In developing male embryos these steroidal substances bring about changes in the left testis so that in extreme cases it is indistinguishable from a typical ovary. The right testis is rarely so extensively modified and may in fact remain quite normal. These preparations have no influence on developing Wolffian ducts in males, but they inhibit involution and may cause extreme hypertrophy of Mullerian ducts. In females the commonly employed estrogens have failed to modify ovarian differentiation to any appreciable extent. The effects on gonoducts are similar to those observed in estrogenized males in that no effects are observed in Wolffian ducts, while Mullerian ducts respond. The right Mullerian duct, which normally undergoes involution, persists and both may reveal tremendous hypertrophy.

DEVELOPMENT OF RIGHT OVARIES. In recent experiments, Wolff and Wolff (1949), contrary to previous results, reported the maintenance of the germinal epithelium on the right ovary of the chick embryo and its differentiation into an ovarian cortex under the influence of estrogenic substances injected prior to the fourth day. Among the substances employed, which were soluble in water, was the sodium salt of bisdehydrodoisynolic acid. This substance is particularly favorable because it passes in considerable quantity into the embryo in a minimum of time.

The development of a right ovary is ascribed to a difference in the behavior of the right and left germinal epithelia. The left germinal epithelium develops in the two sexes up to the eighth day, it regresses between the eighth and twelfth day in the male, but it can still react at this stage to estrogens by the proliferation of a thin and aberrant cortex. The right germinal epithelium on the contrary, rarely so voluminous as that on the left, commences to regress at the beginning of the fifth day of incubation and by the end of the sixth is reduced to a thin plate of flattened cells which rarely responds to hormonal stimulation.

This difference in time of involution of right and left germinal epithelia explains why injections must be made early in attempts to provoke the stimulation of the right cortex. It is of interest to note, if these observations are correct, that the action of an estrogenic substance has provoked a supplementary sexual differentiation which is only sporadically encountered arising spontaneously.

Observations in pigeons have shown that treatment of laying females with estrogens may induce differentiation of the incipient cortex on the left testis of males hatched from eggs laid by such females (Riddle and Dunham, 1942). These results are interpreted as being due to the deposition of the injected hormone in the yolk of developing ova in sufficient quantities to modify subsequently developing embryos. The question may be raised whether the substances causing these changes are similar to the estrogens employed in experiments on incubating chick eggs, since in the passage of the administered substances through the mother profound metabolic changes may have taken place.

STABILITY OF INVERTED GONADS. Our observations (unpublished data) indicate that the transformations of the embryonic left testis, invoked by estrogenic hormones, are not stable, since adults have never revealed the complete inversion one may encounter at the time of hatching. Apparently such gonads progressively recover a considerable degree of testicular structure as the individual matures. Since the gonad of the adult is many times larger than that of the embryo and the distinction between cortical and medullary tissue not easily made at this time, it becomes difficult to determine the relative proportions of testicular and ovarian tissues. We do not know whether the greater preponderance of testicular tissue in such ovotestes is the result of a greater capacity to hypertrophy on the part of the medulla or to a partial involution of the induced cortex. It may of course be more difficult to suppress a gonadal component like the ovarian medulla, normally persisting in both sexes, than one like the incipient ovarian cortex on the left gonad which normally undergoes retrogression in the male.

It is evident from our experiments that the induced cortex on the left testis does not regress completely, since estrogens injected between the third and fifth days of incubation produced, after hatching, intersexual males revealing varying degrees of femininity as indicated by the ovotesticular composition of the gonads, character of head furnishings, amount of female plumage, and grades of sex behavior exhibited. The testicular component in adult ovotestes has usually been significantly more voluminous than the cortical component. When the latter is relatively prominent the plumage may be entirely female; when smaller it may be either a mixture of male and female or entirely male in character. Whether a gonad which is partly or completely inverted by the action of sex hormones can revert to its original genetic sex has not been determined in the fowl. It has also not been established whether such inverted gonads in the bird can actually function even though well-developed follicles and apparently normal oviducts may be encountered.

EMBRYONIC GONAD EXTRACTS

Leroy (1948) extracted from chick embryos, ages fourteen to nineteen days, a preparation active on the comb of the capon, at least twenty embryos being required to derive enough extract to produce an effect. Since estrogens have been recovered from egg yolks, it is conceivable that yolks also contain appreciable amounts of androgenic substances. These could be taken up by the embryo in subthreshold quantities during incubation, as the estrogens are, and recovered by chemical extraction. If the observations of Leroy are verified, and if we find no evidence that the extracted embryonic androgenic substances are exogenous or produced by other embryonic organs, then we would obviously be justified in regarding their source as gonadal.

PITUITARY HORMONES

Attempts to modify or enhance the hormonal secretions of the embryonic gonad were first attempted by the writer (Domm, 1937). Chick embryos (ages four to eighteen days) were treated with an extract of pituitary gland tissue which caused marked hypertrophy of gonadal elements in both sexes. However, despite these pronounced changes in gonad morphology, no evidence of significant growth or differentiation in gonoducts was evident. Earlier observations by the writer had shown that precisely the same type of treatment begun on the second or fourth day after hatching will stimulate androgenic secretions which bring about a response, first noticeable in head furnishings, within forty-eight to sixty hours and very conspicuous in these characters as well as in behavior and gonoducts by the seventh to tenth day. Since our observations and those of others have shown that embryonic combs and gonoducts are sufficiently differentiated to respond to exogenous steroidal hormones, this evidence was believed to indicate insufficient differentiation of embryonic gonads prior to hatching to secrete sex hormones even when precociously developed to the extent observed in these experiments.

New Transplantation Experiments

In recent experiments having an important bearing on our problem, Wolff (1947) succeeded in obtaining what he described as a freemartin effect in chick embryos by the introduction of gonad grafts. Although this is not the first time such a result was reported, Bradley (1941) having observed a similar effect in several chick and duck embryos, Wolff's results have the distinction of much greater constancy.

In Wolff's experiments, donors incubated for six to eleven days provided gonad tissue which was placed in the somatopleure or the coelomic cavity of forty-eight- to fifty-two-hour hosts near the host gonad site. Donor tissues were invariably unmodified; host tissues were modified in heterosexual graft combinations only.

In the case of a female donor and a male host, the left testis was converted to ovary or ovotestis, if the donor ovary was on the left side. The right testis was inhibited if the ovarian graft was on the right side, unchanged if the graft was on the left side. Modifications in the gonads of the host depended on proximity to the graft. Occasional development of a short anterior segment of the left oviduct occurred.

A result which merits emphasis, although it has been observed only in a small number of cases, is the feminizing action of the right rudimentary gonad of female embryos, which when transplanted to male hosts provoked transformations as pronounced as those induced by the left ovary.

In the case of a male donor and a female host, no effects on the gonads were observed, but regression or suppression of Mullerian ducts was noted.

The type of transformation described here is comparable to that obtained in chick embryos following the administration of steroidal hormones. Unlike the latter, however, the changes here are localized and manifest themselves more intensely nearer the graft. The influence of ovarian grafts therefore diminishes with distance, as in some of the effects observed in amphibian parabiosis. The earlier negative results of other investigators are believed to be due to the relatively great distance between host and transplant.

Ablations

HYPOPHYSECTOMY

Hypophysectomy of chick embryos performed by X-rays or surgery does not alter sex differentiation. However, Fugo (1940) claims, contrary to other authors, that during the second half of incubation hypophysectomized embryos are smaller and their gonads subnormal in size. If the subnormal gonad size in these experiments is a consequence of the absence of pituitary secretions, then according to the Moore-Price theory of reciprocal pituitary-gonad relationship, it may be reasonable to infer that the embryonic gonads secrete hormone-like substances in normal embryos.

EMBRYONIC CASTRATION

If sex hormones play a role in embryonic sex differentiation, then removal or destruction of gonad primordia prior to sex differentiation should give some clue as to the presence of hormones during embryonic life. Castration of a vertebrate embryo was obtained for the first time by de Beaumont (1933), who operated on the tadpole. This operation has since been performed on the embryos of other vertebrates, particularly mammals, and more recently was reported for the first time in avian embryos.

Wolff and Wolff (1949, 1951) reported successful castrations on chicken and duck embryos by means of localized irradiations. In these studies the genital ridges were irradiated between the third and fifth days of incubation, the dosage of X-rays administered ranged from 3,300 to 7,000 roentgens as measured without localizers. This technique was successful at two stages of incubation, namely, (1) at the 28- to 32-somite stage (fiftieth to sixtieth hour in the chick, sixtieth to seventieth hour in the duck) and (2) at the 35-somite stage. The method yielded complete, partial, and unilateral castrates. Many of the embryos lived beyond the twelfth day and most of them were removed for study between the thirteenth and sixteenth day of incubation. The tests employed for hormonal activity of embryonic gonads were development of the syrinx and of the genital tubercle in duck embryos and development of Mullerian ducts in chick and duck embryos. Each of these characters reveals a precocious sexual dimorphism, and embryos can readily be sexed by examination of these structures soon after sexual differentiation of gonads. Since the syrinx and the genital tubercle are found some distance from the gonad region, they furnish a valuable criterion in castration experiments of the distant action of the embryonic gonads.

THE SYRINX IN DUCKS. The syrinx or "osseus bulla", which is the organ of voice production in birds, reveals a conspicuous dimorphism in embryos by the thirteenth day of incubation (Lewis and Domm, 1948). It is the first known sex difference to appear after differentiation of the gonads. Located at the bifurcation of the trachea, this structure is symmetrical and little developed in the female. It is voluminous and very asymmetrical in the male, where the three cartilaginous rings situated at the bifurcation of the confluent bronchial tubes are expanded and present a considerable dilation on the left side and along the median line.

Injections. In treating duck embryos with estrogenic hormone Lewis and Domm (1948) observed that the syrinx was strikingly modified in the female direction. Thus when incubating eggs were injected with the estrogen, hexestrol, between the fourth and tenth days of incubation, sexes could not be distinguished at the time of hatching on the basis of this character. When injections were made between the twelfth and sixteenth days, males could be distinguished from females, though the osseus bulla was not typically male but intersexual in character. Injections on or after the eighteenth day had no effect.

Castration. Embryos that had been totally castrated between the third and fifth days of incubation, when autopsied between the thirteenth and eighteenth day, revealed a male-type syrinx. In incompletely castrated females, the syrinx was intermediate between the male and female type, whereas incompletely castrated males revealed no modifications.

These results are in accord with the effects of hormone administration. They show that the asexual form of the syrinx corresponds to the male type and that the ovary is responsible for the sexual dimorphism observed in normal development. That is, it inhibits development of the male-type syrinx in the female.

THE GENITAL TUBERCLE IN DUCKS. The development of the genital tubercle in the normal and castrated duck embryo parallels that of the syrinx. As in the case of the syrinx, it is also at the beginning of the thirteenth day of incubation that this character begins its divergent development in the two sexes, and by the sixteenth day sexual dimorphism is well established. The genital tubercle continues its development into a prominent penis or organ of intromission in males, whereas in females it regresses and forms a rudimentary clitoris.

Injections. We observed (unpublished data) that under the influence of the estrogen, hexestrol, administered between the fourth and tenth days of incubation, the genital tubercle undergoes involution in the male so that at the time of hatching it approximates that of normal females. These observations were recently confirmed by Wolff (1949), who also reported that under the influence of the male hormone, testosterone propionate, the genital tubercle of female embryos develops into a penile organ comparable to that of the male.

Castration. Embryos that had been totally castrated by localized X-rays between the third and fifth days of incubation, when examined on the seventeenth day, revealed a genital tubercle of the male type. It is interesting to note Wolff's observation that partially castrated embryos, in which the syrinx was intermediate between the male and female types, also revealed genital tubercles of intermediate type. These followed the same gradations as observed in the syrinx.

The asexual type in the case of the genital tubercle, as was also observed with respect to the syrinx, therefore corresponds to the male type. In both instances it is obviously the ovary which in some way determines the qualitative difference between the sexes by inhibiting the development of the syrinx and of the genital tubercle.

DISCUSSION

In comparing the results of embryonic gonad transplantations with those on the injections of steroid hormones one cannot fail to note the similarity in results obtained in the two types of experiments. The steroid hormones as well as the association of heterosexual gonads provoke phenomena in the host which are characteristic of intersexuality.

The left gonad of a male host is feminized in the presence of an ovarian graft. Most of the transformations thus obtained correspond to the weaker types acquired by the injection of low dosages of estrogenic hormones.

However, contrary to the hormonal intersexes, the transformations obtained following transplantations are localized. They manifest themselves more intensely on the side where the transplant occurs. The ovarian transplant exerts its influence on the zone of the host gonad nearest it, and the intensity of the effect diminishes with distance, as in the experiments on amphibian parabiosis. The conclusion that this effect is a consequence of the diffusion of a substance through the embryonic tissues seems warranted, since we know of no instance where such localized effects occur as a consequence of hormones conveyed by the circulatory system. Experiments by Greenwood and Blyth (1935) support this interpretation. They observed that oestrone injected intradermally, in amounts (0.0125 mg.) considerably below those known to produce a general feminizing effect on plumage when injected subcutaneously, will nevertheless feminize growing feathers adjacent to the site of injection. The effect was greatest near the point of injection and diminished with distance. Regardless of how it is conveyed, or what it may be, it is evident that a substance passes from the gonad transplant to the host and has effects of the same nature as those of the injected estrogenic hormones. We believe the evidence clearly indicates that these substances are hormones which, because of the nature of their effects, are similar to or the same as those of the adult.

It is obvious from the results we have discussed that, in general, androgenic and estrogenic hormones, regardless of their source, provoke respectively the male and female components of the bisexual embryonic reproductive system. The male hormones tend to stimulate only male characters in embryos of either sex and inhibit female characters, whereas female hormones, on the contrary, stimulate female and inhibit male characters. It is therefore evident that it is the specific physiological organization of the sex component which determines whether or not it is activated or inhibited and not the genetic constitution of the embryo. An exception to this generalization, not observed in transplantation experiments, is found in the investigations of Willier, Gallagher, and Koch (1935), who observed that androsterone and dehydroandrosterone had both masculinizing and feminizing effects in male embryos.

The asymmetrical differences in response of the male gonad primordia are especially important in this particular. The left testicular primordium under the influence of injected estrogens or ovarian transplants transforms into ovary or ovotestis, while the right remains essentially normal. The left testicular primordia possess an incipient ovarian cortex usually lacking on the right. However, the latter occasionally shows scattered traces of this structure which is correlated with the finding of right ovotestes.

It is also of interest to note that the investigations on embryonic injections and ovarian transplantations indicate that once the potential cortex is undergoing involution, or has disappeared, estrogens can no longer stimulate the production of an ovarian cortex in the male. This observation confirms the conclusion of Lillie (1927) that hormones never initiate the formation of any new structure, but that they only activate or inhibit primordia already laid down. In other words, there is no response on the part of any structure in the absence of a specific cell or tissue potentiality which is genic in origin.

Wolff (1947) described the occurrence of a labile intersexuality in cases of weak transformations, where cortex is in process of regression and new testicular tubules are formed from germinal epithelium maintained beyond the stage of its normal involution. Does this indicate that the feminizing substance emanating from the graft early ceased to exercise its effects or that it is only secreted during a very brief period? Indications are that the latter is not the case. Since the condition was observed only in the presence of small grafts, or in cases where grafts were farthest from the gonads of the host embryo, one may conclude that the quantity of hormone, initially sufficient to induce a cortex, is at a later time no longer able to insure its development. It is in fact necessary to take into account the growth of the host gonad primordia which rapidly exceeds in volume that of the smaller grafts. The latter either do not elaborate sufficient hormone to maintain the cortex or else the hormone becomes too dilute in the rapidly enlarging embryo to assure continuity of the initial effect. Wolff (1947) compared the phenomena of cortical regression and the formation of testicular tubules with those observed in hormonal intersexes after hatching when the latter are no longer subjected to hormone injections.

It is necessary here to take into account the role of genetic factors, though it is not entirely clear just how they operate in sex differentiation, when they are subordinated by hormonic factors, or what the total consequences of the interactions of these two factors are. The actual mechanisms whereby one sex component predominates over the other in differentiation of the gonad appears to be endocrine in nature. This is clearly indicated by the sex inversion effects produced by the injected hormones. What the genes actually control physiologically, therefore, is intensity of hormone secretion. The gonad component with the relatively greater intensity of hormone secretion determines the direction of sex differentiation.

The fact that testicular transplants produce no noteworthy modifications in the gonads of female host embryos, whereas they do modify the Mullerian ducts is of interest. Testicular nodules, little developed at autopsy, that had been grafts in the left or right splanchnopleure caused regression of the Mullerian ducts, and in the majority of cases, the complete suppression of the oviduct of the host. When we compare these results with those of hormone injections in female embryos, we find that they are essentially concordant. The transplants had no notable effect on the gonads of genetic females, while only the higher dosages of male hormone modified the shape and structure of ovaries (Willier, 1939). However, both revealed an inhibitory action on Mullerian ducts.

It is noteworthy that in the previous series (testis transplants to female hosts) the effect of embryonic testis grafts is shown to be more powerful than that of injected androgens. In fact, although high dosages of androgen such as androsterone and testosterone cause regression of Mullerian ducts, except for a short proximal segment which almost invariably persists, the testicular transplants may cause complete suppression of the Mullerian ducts. This result contrasts with that observed in the reverse experiment, ovarian transplants to male hosts, in which the effect of grafts was observed to be less pronounced than that of injected estrogenic hormones.

The androgenic hormones utilized in the experiments on intersexuality may be grouped into two categories. In the one belong the sterols such as androsterone, which reveal masculinizing actions in females and feminizing in males, the so-called paradoxical effects described by many investigators. In the other category belong the sterols like testosterone which have an exclusively masculinizing action in females. It is to the effects of the latter category of substances that those of the male grafts may be compared. However, the androgens emanating from the embryonic gonads have a much stronger effect than the preparations of crystalline hormones corresponding to the male hormones of the adult. The results indicate that they are probably effective in much lower dosage. This quantitative difference poses several questions, the answers for which must await further exploration. Do the known hormones, or their unknown derivatives, contain a substance with the same quantitative and qualitative effect as the hormones of the embryonic testis? Do the testes of the adult secrete this substance, and if so is this the true male hormone of the adult? It is probable that endogenous sterols do not act in a pure state in the organism but in various combinations with other substances and that such substances may act as synergists under specific conditions.

Finally, how can we visualize the course of sexual differentiation in the light of these results? Let us recall first that in birds the female sex is heterogametic, while in amphibians it is the male sex that is heterogametic. It is rather remarkable that, in the experiments on injections and on transplantations as in those on castrations, the female hormone in birds but the male hormone in amphibians manifests the most pronounced effects.

In birds, the medullary primordium is the first to differentiate in both sexes. The cortical primordium develops in the female and regresses in the male beginning on the eighth day. In the experiments on transplants as in those on injections, the female hormone stimulates the incipient ovarian cortex and causes the medulla to regress, whereas the male hormone has no notable action on the gonadic primordia of the two sexes. We may, therefore, explain differentiation of the sexes by the intervention of the female hormone; we may also assert that the male hormone, present in both sexes, is dominated by the female hormone.

Concerning the genital ducts, the female hormone stabilizes and stimulates the left Mullerian duct, the male hormone inhibits and causes its involution. Embryonic castrations have shown that the female hormone is not necessary to obtain differentiation of the oviducts, but that the male hormone is necessary to provoke its suppression. Both androgenic and estrogenic hormones are therefore necessary to explain differentiation of the genital ducts. The fact that testicular transplants secrete a very potent hormone inhibiting the Mullerian ducts is additional evidence that the testicular primordium is not deprived of hormone either. We may, therefore, conclude that the embryos of each sex secrete their own hormone, that estrogenic hormone is indispensable to the differentiation of the ovary, and that probably the two antagonistic hormones intervene respectively in the differentiation of the ducts. This conclusion was recently confirmed in a brilliant study by Wolff (1953) on the in vitro regression of the Mullerian ducts. Wolff showed that maintenance of the Mullerian ducts in male embryos may also be brought about by explantation in vitro before the beginning of sex differentiation and, on the other hand, that association of testes with undifferentiated ducts in vitro, or the addition of androgens to the culture medium, caused the regression of these ducts. It may be logically assumed therefore that embryonic hormones are responsible for the normal atrophy of the Mullerian ducts.

It is difficult to determine whether one or two hormones are necessary for sexual differentiation, since in the experiments on injections the introduced hormones interfere with those of the host, adding their effects to the latter, so that one never operates in a hormone-free environment. The experiments on embryonic castration have not furnished proof of a hormone-free differentiation of the genital tract but instead have established the role of sexual hormones in this differentiation.

The experimental evidence seems to indicate that in birds at least one hormone intervenes in the differentiation of the gonads. It is probable that the hormone appropriate to each sex intervenes in the differentiation of the genital ducts. However, as the endogenous hormone always interferes with those introduced experimentally, and as the same effect can be produced by a stimulating or an inhibiting hormone, it is difficult to conclude definitely whether two sex hormones necessarily act on the same primordium, one stimulating in one of the sexes, the other inhibiting in the opposite sex.

The experiments on sinistral ovariectomy in the hen (Benoit, 1923; Domm, 1927; and others) contribute an element to our discussion. Removal of the left ovary disposes of the inhibitor of the right medulla, or of both right and left medulla, if only the left cortical component is removed. Following removal of the ovary, the rudimentary right gonad differentiates into a testis. This result agrees with the observations on Bidder's organ following castration in the toad and shows that the estrogenic hormone inhibits the development of the primordia of the opposite sex. However, it also reveals the capacity of the female to produce the hormones of both sexes and that the heterogametic sex has a bisexual hormone potential.

Since the gonadal primordia of male and female secrete their own hormone, we would agree with the conclusion of Wolff (1947) that the two processes coexist in nature and that there is stimulation in one of the sexes and inhibition in the other.

Bibliography

BEAUMONT, J. DE

1933. La différenciation sexuelle de l'appareil urogénital du Triton et son déterminisme. Arch. Entwickl. Mech., 129:120-178.

BENOIT, J.

1923. Transformation expérimentale du sexe par ovariotomie précoce chez la poule domestique. C. R. Acad. Sci., 177:1074-1077.

BOUIN, P., and P. ANCEL

1903. Sur la signification de la glande interstitielle du testicule embryonnaire. C. R. Soc. Biol., 55:1682-1684.

BRADLEY, E. M.

1941. Sex differentiation of chick and duck gonads as studied in homoplastic and heteroplastic host-graft combinations. Anat. Rec., 79:507-528.

BURNS, R. K.

1949. Hormones and the differentiation of sex. Survey of biological progress, ed. by G. S. Avery, Jr., Vol. I. Academic Press, Inc., New York, pp. 233-266.

BURWELL, L. L.

1931. Early differentiation of the duck gonad. Master's dissertation, Harper Library, University of Chicago.

DANTCHAKOFF, V.

1935. Sur les différences de sensibilité des récepteurs tissulaires envers la folliculine à divers stades embryonnaires. C. R. Acad. Sci., 201:161-163.

DOMM, L. V.

1927. New experiments on ovariotomy and the problem of sex inversion in the fowl. Jour. Exper. Zool., 48:32-119.

1937. Observations concerning anterior pituitary-gonadal inter-relations in the fowl. Cold Spring Harbor Symposia in Quant. Biol., 5:241-257.

1939. Modifications in sex and secondary sexual characters in birds. Sex and internal secretions, ed. by Allen, Danforth and Doisy, 2nd edit. Williams and Wilkins Co., Baltimore, pp. 227-327.

FUGO, N. W.

1940. Effects of hypophysectomy in the chick embryo. Jour. Exper. Zool., 85:271-297.

GREENWOOD, A. W., and J. S. S. BLYTH

1935. Variation in plumage response of brown leghorn capons to oestrone, II. Intradermal injections. Proc. Roy. Soc. London, 118:122-132.

JOST, A.

1948. Le contrôle hormonal de la différenciation du sexe. Biol. Rev., 23:201-236.

LAULANIÉ, M.

1886. Sur le mode d'évolution et la valeur de l'épithelium germinatif dans le testicule embryonnaire du poulet. C. R. Soc. Biol., 38:87-89.

LEROY, P.

1948. Effet androgène d'extraits embryonnaires de poulet sur la crête du chapon. C. R. Acad. Sci., 226:520-522.

1949. Permanence des canaux de Müller dans l'embryon de poulet et action possible du cortex surrénalien. C. R. Soc. Biol., 143:1350-1352.

LEWIS, L. B.

1946. A study of some effects of sex hormones upon the embryonic reproductive system of the white Pekin duck. Physiol. Zool., 19:282-329.

LEWIS, L. B., and L. V. DOMM

1948. Sexual transformation of the osseus bulla in the duck embryo following administration of estrogens. Physiol. Zool., 31:65-69.

LILLIE, F. R.

1917. The free-martin: a study of the action of sex hormones in the foetal life of cattle. Jour. Exper. Zool., 23:371-452.

1927. The present status of the problem of "sex-inversion" in the hen: comments on Dr. Domm's paper. Jour. Exper. Zool., 48:175-196.

MINOURA, T.

1921. A study of testis and ovary grafts on the hen's egg and their effects on the embryo. Jour. Exper. Zool., 33:1-61.

MOORE, C. R.

1947. Embryonic sex hormones and sexual differentiation. A monograph in American lectures in endocrinology, ed. by W. O. Thompson. Charles C. Thomas, Springfield.

1950. The role of the fetal endocrine glands in development. Jour. Clinical Endocr., 10:942-985.

PRICE, D.

1947. An analysis of the factors influencing growth and development of the mammalian reproductive tract. Physiol. Zool., 20:213-247.

RIDDLE, O.

1931. Factors in the development of sex and secondary sexual characteristics. Physiol. Rev., 11:63-106.

RIDDLE, O., and H. H. DUNHAM

1942. Transformation of males to intersexes by estrogen passed from blood of Ring Doves to their ovarian eggs. Endocr., 30:959-968.

WELLS, L. J.

1946. Effects of androgen upon reproductive organs of normal and castrated fetuses with note on adrenalectomy. Proc. Soc. Exper. Biol. and Med., 63: 417-419.

WILLIER, B. H.

1927. The specificity of sex, of organization and of differentiation of embryonic chick gonads as shown by grafting experiments. Jour. Exper. Zool., 46:409-465.

1939. Embryonic development of sex. Sex and internal secretions, ed. by Allen, Danforth, and Doisy, 2nd edit. Williams and Wilkins Co., Baltimore, pp. 64-144.

WILLIER, B. H., T. F. GALLAGHER, and F. C. KOCH

1935. Sex modification in the chick embryo resulting from injections of male and female hormones. Proc. Nat. Acad. Sci., 21:625-631.

WILLIER, B. H., and E. C. YUH

1928. The problem of sex differentiation in the chick embryo with reference to the effects of gonad and non-gonad grafts. Jour. Exper. Zool., 52:65-125.

WOLFF, Et.

1947. Recherches sur l'intersexualité expérimentale produite par la méthode des greffes de gonades à l'embryon de poulet. Arch. Anat. Micros. Morph. Exper., 36:69-90.

WOLFF, Et.

1953. Le déterminisme de l'atrophie d'un organe rudimentaire: le canal de Müller des embryons mâles d'oiseaux. Exp. IX, 4:121-133.

WOLFF, Et., and A. GIGLINGER

1935. Sur la transformation des poulets mâles en intersexués par injection d'hormone femelle (folliculine) aux embryons. Arch. Anat. Hist. Embry., 20:219-278.

WOLFF, Et., and B. SALZGEBER

1949. Sur un nouveau procédé permetettant d'obtenir l'intersexualité expérimentale chez l'embryon d'oiseau: l'irradiation des gonades embryonnaires à l'aide de rayons X. C. R. Soc. Biol., 143:532-533.

WOLFF, Et., and R. STOLL

1937. Le rôle de l'hypophyse dans le développement embryonnaire du poulet, d'après l'étude des cyclocéphales expérimentaux. C. R. Soc. Biol., 126:1215-1217.

WOLFF, Et., and Em. WOLFF

1949. Application de la méthode de castration à l'embryon de canard: sur deux tests de l'activité précoce des gonades embryonnaires, la syrinx et le tubercule genital. C. R. Soc. Biol., 143:529-531.

1951. The effects of castration on bird embryos. Jour. Exper. Zool., 116:59-98.

chapter 11

SOME AMERICAN POPULATION RESEARCH ON GALLINACEOUS BIRDS . . . Joseph J. Hickey

This review is an attempt to picture the progress of American population research on gallinaceous birds during the 1940's and to learn what principles have emerged from these investigations.[1] To some extent, work outside this period and this country will also be noticed. Within the limits of my own ability, time, and experience, I have also attempted to review our progress in this field critically.

Scientific names of the species and subspecies mentioned in this review have been taken from Peters (1934); the grouping into two families is that recommended by Mayr and Amadon (1951):

PHASIANIDAE

PHASIANINAE (Pheasants, Quail, etc)
Oreortyx picta: Mountain Quail
Lophortyx californica: California Quail
Lophortyx gambelii: Gambel's Quail
Colinus virginianus: Bobwhite Quail
Alectoris graeca: Indian Hill or Chukar Partridge
Perdix perdix: European (or Hungarian) Partridge
Phasianus colchicus: Ring-necked Pheasant

TETRAONINAE (Grouse and Ptarmigan)
Tetrao urogallus: Capercaillie
Lyrurus tetrix: Blackgame
Lagopus scoticus: Red Grouse (also regarded as a race of *L. lagopus*)
Lagopus lagopus: Willow Grouse or Ptarmigan
Lagopus mutus: Rock Grouse or Ptarmigan
Canachites canadensis: Spruce Grouse
Bonasa umbellus: Ruffed Grouse
Pedioecetes phasianellus: Sharp-tailed Grouse
Tympanuchus cupido ssp.: Prairie Chicken
Tympanuchus cupido cupido: Heath Hen
Tympanuchus pallidicinctus: Lesser Prairie Chicken
Centrocercus urophasianus: Sage Grouse

MELEAGRIDIDAE (Turkeys)
Meleagris gallopavo: Turkey

[1] This review is by no means a complete one. For a body of fugitive literature some of which was not included in this chapter, see the check-list of technical game bulletins subsequently prepared by Hickey and Wagner and published in Wildlife Review No. 72.

Manuscript received January 18, 1952.

Among the colleagues who have helped in this review, I am indebted to Messrs. F. N. Hamerstrom, Jr., Cyril Kabat, and D. R. Thompson of the Wisconsin Conservation Department, F. A. Pitelka of the University of California, and Messrs. R. A. McCabe, J. C. Neess, A. W. Schorger, and A. W. Stokes of the University of Wisconsin for advice and criticism; and to Messrs. R. N. Bach, J. T. Emlen, Jr., J. B. Hale, and J. P. Linduska for bibliographical assistance. The individual help of others is acknowledged in appropriate passages later. In any critical review, it is of course exceedingly difficult to credit the sources of one's own ideas most of which—when good—are scarcely original. This acknowledgment is becoming more and more impossible as the field of biology expands and formal scientific meetings encourage the free and unwritten exchange of criticisms and appraisals.

In the present paper, I have attempted to avoid quoting from the Pittman Robertson Quarterly and other similar periodicals which today record the unofficial progress of contemporary research on game species in America. It seems to me unethical to quote extensively from such materials, even with permission, in a review of this kind; yet the very scanning of such reports by a reviewer is bound to temper his judgment of other work that is published in the formal and conventional channels of science.

THE DEVELOPMENT OF TECHNIQUES

The early 1940's impress one particularly with the attention given to technique both by game managers and game biologists. This was a time when more and more concern was being attached to the biology of game populations. The complacency about game management in the 1930's was gone. The new approach demanded new methods not only in censusing populations but also in learning something of their structure and composition.

Inventories and Indices of Population Levels

The principal census problem during the decade was the determination of population indices applicable to regions as large as a state. While the political boundaries of these encompass as much as 263,000 square miles, in practice the area to be surveyed is normally about 25,000 to 50,000 square miles. Methods that work well on small study areas are often totally inadequate for state-wide use, and at present most state officials are interested only in learning if the population is going up or down and in what parts of their state this is taking place. Solutions to the problem vary according to the importance of each species in the hunting economy of the region, the availability and ingenuity of technical manpower, and the field difficulties that vary from species to species and from habitat to habitat. For economically important game species, the trend is toward regional indices covering separate soil types and with a predictable limit of sampling error in the final estimate. Up to the present, this latter goal has rarely been approached.

ROADSIDE COUNTS

These are used principally for pheasants and were first developed by Bennett and Hendrickson (1938). The term is generally understood to mean that biologists are carrying out the work. Counts, as used in Nebraska (Mohler, 1948), begin at sunrise and cover a twenty-mile rural route that is driven by a single person in a motor car and without interruption at twenty to twenty-five miles per hour on mornings of good road condition and weather. In North Dakota, about 100 transects each twenty-four miles long and twenty-four miles apart are spread over the state, the cruising speed is fifteen miles per hour, and only birds on the roadside right of way are counted (Blomquist, 1951). Cocks, hens, and young are tallied separately. Each route is annually covered on three mornings at the same period in the reproductive cycle of the pheasant and late enough so that most broods will be off the nest. Elsewhere, early efforts (Bennett and Hendrickson, 1938; Randall and Bennett, 1939) to relate the results of these transects to actual densities have not been accepted. Thus one pheasant seen per mile was alleged to represent about six birds per 100 acres, two per mile about twelve per 100 acres. Today Nebraska regards such results as indicating fair hunting or excellent hunting (Mohler, 1948). In all these more or less treeless states, roads tend to run north-south and east-west. In states where roads are relatively scarce, the roadside count seems to have been difficult to utilize (Einarsen, 1945a).

RURAL MAIL CARRIER SURVEYS

In this variant of the roadside count by biologists, rural mail carriers are asked to report the numbers of pheasants they see while delivering mail throughout a three- or six-day period. For the most part, these routes are covered in midday, and smaller numbers of birds are recorded then than right after sunrise. Nebraska inaugurated this system in 1945 in an effort to obtain data on sex ratios in pheasants. It now has over 600 carriers reporting each time (Mohler, 1948). North Dakota has about 350 (Blomquist, 1951) and has used them to obtain indices on pheasants, European Partridges, Sharp-tailed Grouse, and Prairie Chickens (Bach, 1951b). The data are summarized as numbers seen per 100 miles of driving. Mohler (1948) believes this is the quickest way to obtain a population survey blanketing an entire state and that the results represent a reliable index of relative abundance from one year to another. Summer and winter indices are also obtained in this way in Nebraska where, in four successive summers, the total has run 24.5, 17.6, 10.4, and 16.1 (pheasants seen per 100 miles of driving). In North Dakota, the survey is run in July, September, January, and April (Blomquist, 1951). Michigan has also used rural mail carrier indices. In one December test, the carriers reported about 10 per cent fewer pheasants than did conservation officers (game wardens), but the sex-ratio data of the two groups were identical (Linduska, 1947).

CALLING-MALE TRANSECTS

Crowing by pheasants, "bobwhite" calls by quail, drumming by Ruffed Grouse, and booming by Prairie Chickens have all been used in varying degrees as regional indices of population levels each spring. As much as five-years of study preceded the formal use of crowing counts on a state-wide basis (Mohler, 1948). Kimball (1949) regards this census of pheasants as more accurate than the roadside one; it is also completed at one-third the cost. In North Dakota, pheasants are censused along eighteen- to twenty-mile transects on cruises starting fifteen minutes before sunrise. The observer stops every two miles and listens for two minutes. Sometimes two to three runs are made, mostly in April and May, and an average taken (Blomquist, 1951). Detonation of a small aerial bomb has been used to excite male birds and cause them to crow. It is not an improvement over simple listening during the breeding season (McClure, 1945). Kimball (1949) has reported no significant variation between the work of different investigators, but winds of eight or more miles per hour do mar the results for pheasants.

For Bobwhite Quail, a call index has been carefully worked out by Bennitt (1951). The number of males giving the bobwhite call varies very little between June 1 and July 20 (the count is now taken between July 13 and 19). Nor is there much variation between the first half-hour after sunrise and the second; they therefore use this full hour. On the other hand, crowing by cock pheasants tends to decrease throughout the sunrise period, and it displays important seasonal variations as well (E. H. Smith, 1950). Bobwhite Quail routes in Missouri encompass each of twenty-five soil types and are laid out proportionately to their respective areas. The number of birds (not the number of calls) are counted at one-mile intervals until all "whistling cocks within earshot" are recorded, usually two to three minutes. Adjustments are made for variations in temperature, but were found to be unnecessary for wind velocity or type of road. In ten years, this state-wide index has predicted hunting success within a mean accuracy of 89 per cent (Bennitt, 1951).

For the Ruffed Grouse, North Dakota technicians use fourteen-mile transects, stopping each mile and recording all drumming heard in four minutes (Blomquist, 1951). For species like the pheasant, this type of census requires that a midwinter sex ratio be obtained if an index to the whole population is wanted. A modification of this technique involves the location of the communal courtship grounds of birds like the Prairie Chicken. Davison (1940), whose results are remarkably uniform and convincing, found he could census three such grounds in a morning and 4 x 4-mile tracts in Oklahoma every five or six days.

QUADRAT INVENTORIES

A system used for pheasants in Oregon for a number of years involves the selection of quadrats, preferably one mile long by one-fourth mile wide, as study areas (Einarsen, 1945a). The investigator traverses the boundaries walking at a slow gait and counting only birds in a 100-foot strip on each side of his line of travel. The results are expressed in terms of birds per acre. According to Einarsen (1945a), field work cannot be undertaken before 8 A.M. (when birds may be still at their night roosts), nor should it be pursued between 11 A.M. and 2 P.M. on cloudy, windy days, nor in Oregon on the first wet and stormy days of autumn. Einarsen's tests for accuracy made on 800 quadrats indicated that this technique gets about 8 per cent less birds than direct drive methods. Since a field man can daily cover four or five of the quadrats described above, this method means censusing 240 to 300 acres per man per day. As practiced in Oregon, the deliberate use of quadrats of favorable habitat by the observer clearly prevents calculation of sampling error in population estimates based upon randomly selected areas.

Variants of this method include intensive searches for nests on a quadrat basis. Patterson (1949) has described one in which thirty-five plots, each forty acres in extent, were thoroughly searched for Sage Grouse nests, their total acreage (1,400 acres) representing 1 per cent of the total area under study. A similar technique has been used by Stokes (unpublished) for pheasants on 10,000-acre Pelee Island, Ontario. With selection of the plots properly randomized and all nests found (or almost certainly found), reliable estimates of the nesting population can thus be computed. However, nest searching can scarcely be carried out on much larger areas, and this technique will probably remain restricted to intensive studies.

FARMERS' REPORTS

Game-bird records by farmers have been used to show pheasant population trends in Vermont (Foote, 1942), in Michigan (Linduska, 1947), in Nebraska (Mohler, 1948), and Ohio (Leedy, 1949), as well as for Bobwhite Quail in Wisconsin (D. R. Thompson, personal communication). Such records are not true surveys of populations on an acreage basis. The questionnaires are brief, issued in early spring (for wintering populations) and in late summer (for nesting success). With more than 600 persons co-operating in Nebraska, the reports are believed to indicate general changes over the state.

AERIAL CENSUSES

Light low-flying airplanes carrying two persons have proven satisfactory in censusing upland game birds in North Dakota when snow is on the ground. According to Blomquist (1951), this method is cheap and efficient when conditions are right. Although two to three runs of the plane may be needed to get a count of a given flock of pheasants, Sharp-tailed Grouse flush easily and are readily counted. This technique is said also to give trends for European Partridge populations. Its usefulness in the study of gallinaceous species would seem to be restricted to snow-covered open country like the plains or the tundra. South Dakota currently is using a plane to work with a ground crew in censusing pheasants during the winter (J. W. Kimball, personal communication). Census blocks of eighty square miles are used each winter to study losses after severe storms (Kirsch, 1951).

INDICES DERIVED FROM POPULATION STRUCTURE

D. L. Allen (1942b) has pointed out that pheasant population levels can be determined from a few basic figures that eliminate the necessity of taking a census. In regions where the total hunting kill has been accurately established from areas of known size, sex-ratio statistics taken in the field can be used to compute the population level either before (P_1) or after (P_2) the hunting season. Convenient summaries of these relationships, patterned after those of Petrides (1949), follow

$$P_1 = \frac{(f_2 K_T) - K_f}{f_2 - f_1} \qquad P_2 = \frac{(f_1 K_T) - K_f}{f_2 - f_1}$$

where f_1 and f_2 are the proportions of females in the population before and after the hunting season (expressed as decimals), K_T is the total number of males killed, and K_f is the number of females (if any) killed. These relationships are sometimes referred to as Kelker ratios, after G. H. Kelker (1940), who originally proposed their use for the estimation of deer populations.

A number of technicalities have prevented these formulas from coming into general usage. As Allen (1942b) has pointed out, the difficulty of establishing bona fide sex ratios makes for the greatest potential source of error in this analysis. In the field, behavior differences of cocks and hens during the fall and early winter considerably increase the variance in sex ratios obtained by transect methods. Thus sex ratios accumulated for successive semimonthly periods starting February 1 may run 6.1, 7.3, 5.6, 3.8, and 2.1 females per male (Linduska, 1947). These data were compiled by conservation officers as they drove over 100,000 miles in Michigan. Other sources of error in Kelker ratios are unreported illegal kills of hens and the often unknown numbers of cocks that are knocked down and left to die.

POPULATION ESTIMATES FROM BANDED BIRDS: PETERSEN'S METHOD

The ratio of banded to unbanded birds in a given area has, up to the present, found little usage in the estimation of galliform populations. This technique was first developed for fish by Petersen (1896) and is known among mammalogists as the Lincoln index. The well-known necessity of having the tagged animals randomly dispersed throughout the population to be sampled virtually precludes the possibility of using this index on a state-wide basis. Inability to control egress and ingress likewise has prevented ornithologists from using the technique on most study areas. Island or islandlike populations offer the greatest potentialities. Thus Glading, Selleck, and Ross (1945) banded California Quail on 450 acres that represented an oasis in the center of "almost a biologic desert." Using the ratio $M(T/R)$, where M was the number of quail marked (771), T the total number (594) bagged by hunters, and R the number of marked quail bagged (188), they obtained an estimate of 2,436 birds, against field surveys indicating about 2,240 wild birds present plus 265 known to have been hand-reared and released. The similarity of the two estimates is quite convincing, but the estimate from banded birds seems to have been slightly biased by including hand-reared birds in the calculations.

As these authors demonstrate elsewhere in their paper, hand-reared California Quail are potentially more vulnerable to hunting than wild native stock. Thus the birds bagged contained 22 per cent of 506 banded wild birds and 28 per cent of 265 that were banded and hand-reared. Natural mortality among the wild birds as well as sampling errors might account for some of this difference. An estimate of the population based only on wild birds would be 2,660 as against 2,436 by the authors' method.

In other cases where juveniles are more vulnerable than adults to the gun, the Petersen method will likewise contain a similar source of bias in the estimate of populations based on samples furnished by hunters. This bias can possibly be removed with the use of correction factors involving the percentage of adults and of juveniles shot on the study area. With these sources of bias removed, the convenient charts of Clopper and Pearson (1934) provide ready estimates of the confidence limits in sampling results obtained by Petersen's method.

STATE-WIDE KILL RECORDS

A number of states and provinces require that hunters and/or trappers annually report the number of animals they harvest. The fraction of hunters co-operating has varied in certain years from 10 per cent (for Massachusetts) to 98 (for Pennsylvania) and 100 per cent (for Northwest Territory) (Gordon, 1940). These reports are generally corrected to represent 100 per cent of all the known license holders, on the assumption that hunters who do not report are as successful as those who do. Sondrini (1950) has demonstrated that this assumption is unwarranted. As a result, state-wide kill records tend to be too high. Although also influenced in varying degrees by changing hunting regulations, they have, however, the great merit of screening out local variation and, despite their crude form, are useful indices of major changes in the population levels of large regions. In some states they go back for two or more decades. Sondrini's elaborate adjustment of these reports has made the Connecticut records by far the most interesting thus far published, but the problem of removing all bias in such statistics still remains unsolved (Hayne, 1951).

MISCELLANEOUS TECHNIQUES

McClure (1945) has tried fecal counts as an index of pheasant populations. The method seems to be of limited effectiveness and more applicable to nocturnal species.

Drive censuses probably have a very ancient origin and scarcely need any description. In brief, a crew of beaters forces the birds past lines of enumerators. About 7 to 10 per cent more accurate than the quadrat method for pheasants (Einarsen, 1945a), this technique is costly in terms of manpower. Buss (1947) mentions two winter censuses when pheasant drive results, as checked by banding, were 13 to 55 per cent too low. Here excessively low temperatures (–5° F.) "encourage" the birds to lie close and let the beaters pass right over them (McCabe, personal communication). Drive censuses are particularly useful for species which congregate at some season. Rope censuses (in which a rope is dragged across fields and meadows) are well known to most ornithologists. Lehmann (1941) has introduced an interesting variation of this by having motor cars drag a long and heavy rope. In this way a small crew can census thousands of acres in treeless country.

Glading (1941) has described a variant of this technique in which the driving is done by three men riding horseback on parallel strips slightly more than 200 feet apart. This census is said to be about 90 per cent accurate and adaptable to birds that form coveys and flush at 25 or 30 yards. It is inaccurate on very hot, windy, or rainy days, and in terrain covered by heavy brush or uniformly tall grass. The three men census 750 acres in an eight-hour day (Glading, 1941).

Strip flushing, a technique which converts transect census data into densities, has not been widely used. Also known as King's method, it consists of walking a series of transect lines and recording the distances at which birds are flushed. The mean distance of these flushing points (at a 90° angle to the transect) is then multiplied by the length of the transect. Trippensee (1948:281-283), who has given a full description of this method, has pointed out that the results for Ruffed Grouse are impaired by winds, rain, snow, temperatures below –10° F., scarcity of grouse, vertical diversification of vegetation, and by any local conditions that group food supplies in a limited part of the range. This technique requires a man to be on foot, and this has tended to restrict its usage to study areas. Keller, Shepherd, and Randall (1941) have applied this method to Sage Hens and found the results highly variable from one month to another.

Hayne (1949) has pointed out that the flushing distances observed do not constitute a good sample of the flushing distances of all animals throughout the population studied and that the numbers of each class of animal with regard to flushing distance should be separately estimated. Hayne's working formula sums up these several subpopulation estimates as follows:

$$N_t = \frac{C}{2L}\left(\frac{F_1}{d_1} + \frac{F_2}{d_2} + \frac{F_3}{d_3} \ldots + \frac{F_n}{d_n}\right)$$

where N_t = the estimate of the total population per unit area; L = the length of the observer's path or census strip; $d_1, d_2, d_3, \ldots d_n$ = the various flushing distances observed; $F_1, F_2, F_3, \ldots F_n$ = the numbers of animals observed to flush at the corresponding flushing distances; and C = a conversion factor such as 43,500 when L and values of d are given in feet and N_t is to be expressed as animals per acre. It is obvious that this technique can also be applied to other birds beside the Galliformes. Nothing is yet known about sampling errors that govern the final estimate of the population.

DEGREES OF PRECISION

With but few exceptions these techniques have been designed to sample state-wide populations. During the 1940's, only the biological variables in these sampling methods were studied. Yet the roadside counts, mail carrier surveys, and calling-male transects are in a very real sense sampling problems that require statistical analysis. It is easy to see now that this point was frequently being overlooked. The unreliability of the roadside census has, for instance, been pointed out by McClure (1945) and conclusively demonstrated by Fisher, Hiatt, and Bergeson (1947). Yet the annual trends of pheasant populations in six states as shown by this index (Kimball, 1948) are remarkably well synchronized. Extensive replication of the roadside count during a narrow interval of time has apparently produced a statistical index of some reliability in which the day-to-day biological variables have been averaged out. (A highly valuable statistical analysis of crowing counts and roadside counts in Iowa was published in 1952 by E. L. Kozicky after this review was completed.)

In North Dakota, transects are arbitrarily set twenty-four miles apart and spread right across the state (Blomquist, 1951). This eliminates any bias that might be introduced in the selection of routes by the observer. Descriptions emanating from other states generally avoid mention of this crucial point. In the quadrat inventory described by Einarsen (1945a), the observer actually picks the better pheasant areas. The results then are probably typical of the better pheasant coverts in Oregon, but they cannot be considered typical of pheasant range in Oregon as a whole. Although the subject has never been fully explored, there is some likelihood that population declines take place first in submarginal habitat; hence an index set up only for optimal habitat could be biased as a result.

Among the peculiar statistics of hunting are those involving hunter success, such as birds killed per gun hour, or birds taken per man-day. These all describe decreasing returns per unit of hunting effort. DeLury (1947) has outlined the procedures by means of which "catch-effort" records can be converted into estimates of population size and certain important parameters. While his examples involve lobsters and fish, it would seem that the same approach should be explored in the study of hunted galliform populations.

It is also possible to estimate the size of state-wide populations of birds by means of randomly selected study areas which can be annually censused, usually during the breeding season. Some stratification of such samples according to important soil types or regional blocks of vegetation would also be necessary. I have seen an unpublished manuscript by Atwood (1951) showing the design of such a study for waterfowl in eastern Canada. The same approach might well be explored for its applicability to gallinaceous birds. It would appear that, in general, methods of inventorying regional populations of galliform birds have been markedly perfected during the past decade, and that the years immediately ahead should witness continued refinement and verification.

Age and Dating Criteria

The 1940's witnessed a tremendous attempt to determine the age of American game birds. Many of the techniques were by no means new, like the presence of pointed primaries in certain juvenal birds, but all of them were carefully evaluated for their accuracy throughout the fall and winter season. The movement really began with papers by Gower (1939) and A. S. Leopold (1939) calling attention to the bursa of Fabricius and juvenal feathers as age criteria in gallinaceous birds. The great value of these techniques was immediately demonstrated by Emlen (1940) in California Quail and by Hochbaum (1944) in waterfowl. Linduska (1943, 1945), Kirkpatrick (1944), Buss (1946), and McCabe (1949) have all refined the use of the bursa. Petrides and Nestler (1943), McCabe and Hawkins (1946), Bump *et al.* (1947:80-90), Thompson and Taber (1948), Thompson and Kabat (1950), and Kabat, Thompson, and Kozlik (1950) increased the accuracy and use of wing molt as an aging technique. Among the incidental but useful results of this work has been the accumulation of evidence that Bobwhite Quail raise only one brood in a season (Thompson, 1949; Thompson and Kabat, 1949).

Pointed primaries offer a quick clue to juvenal galliforms, but Janson (1951) has reported that their accuracy for Sharp-tailed Grouse and Prairie Chickens dropped from 95 per cent in the last week of September (1948) to only about 80 per cent in the latter half of October.

Spurs are, of course, another age criterion (Linduska, 1943) in pheasants. To increase the speed of sampling, Kimball (1944) developed an age gauge to separate the old from young during the hunting season. This gauge appears to have an over-all accuracy of 96.9 per cent in a fairly even-aged population (Nelson, 1948), but early or late nesting seasons mar its validity and necessitate the use of correction factors (Kimball, personal communication, Dec., 1950). The gauge loses somewhat in accuracy as the proportion of young in the population increases (Petrides, 1949).

European workers have long known that the strength of the (lower) mandible distinguishes adult from juvenal gallinaceous birds. Girard (1937) has reported that young Sage Grouse can be identified in this way until about eight months of age. In pheasants, adult and juvenal males can similarly be separated (Linduska, 1945). When juvenal birds that have been shot are held by the lower mandible (with thumb on top and index finger below), the mandible breaks. This test has an over-all accuracy of 94.5 per cent for males in the fall hunting season; for females it is quite imperfect (Linduska, 1945).

A number of interesting techniques have been devised in order to utilize all observations in fixing the dates eggs were laid or hatched. Back of these developments lies the hope that the timing of weather or other adverse factors can be successfully narrowed down and recognized in determining the general success or failure of a nesting season. Westerskov (1950a) has, for instance, explained the limitations and advantages of candling, measuring weight loss, determining specific gravity, and using egg position in water as indices of embryo growth in the pheasant. McCabe and Hawkins (1946) have worked out the embryological development of the European Partridge, for use on nests broken up by predators. Bureau's (1911) early work on the aging of young European Partridges has been extended to Bobwhite Quail by Petrides and Nestler (1943), to Prairie Chickens and Sharp-tailed Grouse by Ammann (1944), and to the pheasant by Buss (1946).

The impetus given to population research by these developments is tremendous, but many of the results are not yet available for review. Thus, as this is written, fall or winter age ratios for Ruffed Grouse have been published only on 2,495 birds (by Bezdek, 1944; and Hale and Wendt, 1950). Yet in a single year, James B. Hale tells me, nine state groups working on this species recently aged 5,961 individuals. The fruits of this work are yet to come.

THE VITAL PROCESSES

Bird populations have a field reality and a paper existence. Productivity and mortality rates can be ascertained for a real population on a given area in a given year. These usually vary annually. When we combine such statistics from several areas or for many years, they hold only for theoretical populations which have a paper existence only. Thus, mean nesting success or mean annual mortality rates are true of paper populations but rarely of real ones. They do, however, form convenient yardsticks for the interpretation of population behavior and therefore have a place in this review.

Reproductive Success

EGG-LAYING

Lack (1947) has presented evidence to show that there are annual differences in the average size of first clutches of the European Partridge in Britain. He regards the reasons as unknown, although changes in the age-distributions of the populations might account for some of the differences, which ranged from 13.2 to 16.2 (Lack, 1947). Some interesting corroborative evidence on the existence of this phenomenon in the pheasant has been provided by Buss, Meyer, and Kabat (1951), who show that the number of ovulated follicles varies significantly between years as well as between areas in the same years. Of especial interest is their finding that the number of ovulated follicles far exceeds the number of eggs reported in first and second clutches. Three phenomena seem certain to complicate differences in clutch size observed annually: (1) the proportion of renests, (2) the number of eggs laid at random by the hens, and (3) the number of eggs laid in nests and promptly deserted. From an ecological point of view, observed clutch size now looks like a statistic that needs to be computed from carefully randomized searching throughout the full period of the laying season.

NESTING SUCCESS

Examples of nesting success in gallinaceous birds are listed in Table 1.

TABLE 1. REPRESENTATIVE EXAMPLES OF NESTING SUCCESS
(Other examples will be found in Table 3.)

Species	Place	Number Nests	Per Cent Success	Reference
Phasianinae				
California Quail	Calif.	96	18%	Glading, 1938
Bobwhite Quail	Ga.-Fla.	602	36	Stoddard, 1931
Bobwhite Quail	Tex.	189	46	Lehmann, 1946a
European Partridge	Mich.	143	32	Yeatter, 1934
European Partridge	Britain	18,890	80.0[a]	Middleton, 1935-37; 1936
European Partridge	Wis.	435	32	McCabe and Hawkins, 1946
Pheasant	Iowa	445	23	Hamerstrom, 1936
Pheasant	Pa.	310	20	Randall, 1940b
Pheasant	Ohio	563	58	Leedy and Hicks, 1945
Pheasant	Utah	149	36	Rasmussen and McKean, 1945
Pheasant	Iowa	527	26	Baskett, 1947
Pheasant -weighted mean		1,834	36.2	5 studies above
Tetraoninae				
Willow Ptarmigan	Norway	125	63	Olstad, 1932
Willow Ptarmigan	Norway	107	80	Kristoffersen, 1937
Ruffed Grouse	N.Y.	1,431	61.4	Darrow, 1947:311
Prairie Chicken	Wis.	100	50	Hamerstrom, 1939
Sage Grouse	Utah	161	60	Rasmussen and Griner, 1938
Sage Grouse	Colo.	238	35	Keller, Shepherd, Randall, 1941
Sage Grouse	Wyo.	134	34	Patterson, 1949

[a] My calculation; from Middleton's four papers.

Exclusive of Middleton's work on the European Partridge and the New York State work on the Ruffed Grouse, we have 35.5 per cent of 3,299 Phasianinae nests and 51 per cent of 865 nests of the Tetraoninae hatching. For all 2,296 grouse nests, this figure is 57.5. These percentages may be contrasted with 46 per cent of 814 open nests in which Nice (1937:143) reports passerine young to be successfully fledged. Nice's figure is in fact almost matched by 44.5 per cent for 5,597 galliform nests exclusive of the highly managed Partridge nests reported by Middleton. As a general and rather well-recognized principle, it appears likely that the larger clutch size of the single-brooded gallinaceous birds at least is in part counterbalanced by the multibroodedness of passerine species, at least in the north temperate zone. Comparative nesting success here is complicated by the inclusion of records of nests in which perhaps only a single-egg nest was broken up or abandoned.

Some attention in America has been given to the search for the "best" type of nesting cover for the pheasant. Mowing has been a universally serious factor, accounting for 57 per cent of the known losses in 1,160 hayfield nests found throughout the country (Buss, 1946). The destructiveness of this to females averages 32 per 100 nests mowed over in hayfields, but this varies from year to year, according to Leedy and Hicks (1945:74-75). Indeed this hen mortality in Ohio is said to be almost as great as that sustained by cocks during the hunting season (Leedy and Hicks, 1945:75). In Wisconsin, where about 35 of every 100 pheasant nests are in hay, Buss (1946:38) was led to conclude that in hayfields the mower is eleven times more destructive than predators. In Iowa, Baskett (1947) found nesting success intermediate in hay (20-35 per cent), low in fencerows (5-20 per cent) and high in small grains (40-80 per cent).

JUVENILE MORTALITY

Some grasp of the sweep of mortality among the very young galliform birds can be obtained by perusal of Table 2. Many of the results

TABLE 2. MORTALITY IN THE FIRST WEEKS OF LIFE

Family or Subfamily	Species	Approx. Per Cent Dying	Reference
Phasianinae	Bobwhite Quail	29% to 8 weeks of age	Klimstra, 1950
	European Partridge	52% hatching to mid-August	Middleton, 1936
	Pheasant	12% in first 8 weeks	Randall, 1940b
	Pheasant	at least 30% in 8 weeks	Leedy and Hicks, 1945
	Pheasant	20% after ¼ grown	Linduska, 1947
Tetraoninae	Ruffed Grouse	slightly less than 40%	Darrow, 1947:527
	Prairie Chicken	50% first 4 wks.; 12% thereafter	Lehmann, 1941:60
	Prairie Chicken	46%; mostly in first days	Yeatter, 1943
	Sage Grouse	32% to August 1	Girard, 1937
	Sage Grouse	54% in 9 weeks	Keller, *et al.*, 1941
	Sage Grouse	50% following hatching	Patterson, 1949
Meleagrididae	Turkey	20% June to September	Dalke, *et al.*, 1946

have been obtained in relatively short-term studies and must be interpreted with caution. In very general terms, 20 to 50 per cent mortality in the first two months of life can be expected. This is in contrast to about 30 per cent that I would expect in young waterfowl. The shrinkage of broods in these gallinaceous birds also varies much more widely from year to year than it does in the Anatidae. Randall (1940a) has had pheasant broods shrinking from 9.7 to 8.5 in about eight weeks, while Leedy and Hicks (1945:66) have reported 2,229 observations in which the drop went from 8.8 to 6.1 in a similar period. According to Yeatter (1943), the heaviest losses among Prairie Chickens probably occurred on his area when the young were either a few hours or a few days old. Among pheasants this early mortality seems to be more spread out. Brood shrinkage offers a wealth of observational material, but the data are complicated in some species by the appearance of small and late broods emerging from renests. Up to the present time, separate observations are not available on the shrinkage of broods according to the time they were hatched each season.

NET PRODUCTIVITY

Darrow (1947:539) has tabulated the productivity of Ruffed Grouse populations by comparing the number of birds present on September 1 against the number of breeders found in April. Over a thirteen-year period, the September population was 1.73 times that of the April population on one study area and 2.04 times this breeding group on another. On another area, these productivity ratios varied from 0.96 to as high as 2.27. Ingress of some birds marred the results during at least one summer (Darrow, 1947: 531).

Errington and Hamerstrom (1937) have pointed out that nesting success for pheasants may be low, but renesting will frequently permit many females to raise a brood. A few appropriate statistics along these lines are given in Table 3. Darrow (1947) is quite certain that there is little or no renesting

TABLE 3. IMPLICATIONS OF RENESTING IN GALLIFORM POPULATIONS

The number of females that successfully raise at least one young can be expressed as (*A*) a percentage of all the females that are alive at the start of the nesting season, or as (*B*) a percentage of those females still alive at or near the end of the nesting season. The latter statistic is a somewhat easier one to obtain in the field, but it may not be as meaningful as (*A*).

Species	Nesting Success	Successful ♀♀ (A)	(B)	Reference
	per cent	*per cent*	*per cent*	
Pheasant	33–41	70–80	—	Errington and Hamerstrom, 1937
Pheasant	25	45	52–55	Randall, 1940b[a]
Pheasant	23–36	—	71.3	Leedy and Hicks, 1945
Pheasant	58	73	—	Baskett, 1947
Sage Grouse	39	—	37	Patterson, 1949
Turkey	—	—	<27	Wheeler, 1948

[a] This is based on a sample of 181 nests and hence differs from the figures quoted for 310 nests in Table 1.

in the Ruffed Grouse. This is not surprising in view of a 61 per cent nesting success for this species. Patterson (1949) has found only 10 per cent of his female Sage Grouse renesting following nest destruction or desertion. It is startling, however, to obtain preliminary reports that compensatory productivity is displayed neither by the Sage Grouse nor the Turkey. (My own suspicion is that the ecological compensation in these two species has evolved through much greater natural longevity, but no statistics on this point are available at this time.)

Cartwright (1944), who has seemed to imply that compensatory reproduction is common in the Sharp-tailed Grouse of the Prairie Provinces, has pointed out that the spreading out of the nesting season by predatory action on nests represents insurance against local extirpation by weather factors operating within a short period. In effect, preyed-upon populations can be expected to fluctuate less violently than predator-free populations. Leedy and Hicks (1945) believe that only about 58 per cent of the pheasant hens in Ohio survive to the end of the nesting season. For these survivors they find differences in the percentage seen with young in September. On good range little variation from 73.5 per cent was seen in a three-year period. But on poor range it dropped to 14.5. To detect annual differences in productivity during the summer, two other sets of statistics seem more promising. One of these is a midsummer age ratio of the number of young per adult hen. According to Mohler (1948), it now seems well established in Nebraska that fall pheasant populations will decline if this ratio drops much below three young per hen. A second approach is to obtain roadside counts of the number of broods seen per 100 miles traversed. MacMullan (1950) has used this technique on pheasants in Michigan and found the results to be positively correlated with indices of hunting success.

Adult Survival and Mortality Rates

CALIFORNIA QUAIL

Sumner (1935) has conducted intensive trapping observations on an area of approximately sixty acres and concluded that the adult survival rate was about 27 per cent per year. His observations covered a single year's span of time. The mortality rate of young birds was high in the months following hatching and appeared to have dropped to that of the adults by November 1.

In a much more extensive study, Emlen (1940) has found young birds to represent 56 per cent among 983 in museum collections, 58 per cent among 985 in hunters' bags, and 60 per cent among 2,052 trapped at twelve banding stations. One of the most remarkable results of this fine paper was the picture of a steady shrinkage in the frequency of young birds in the population (Table 4). These were identified by the arrested development of their wing molt. From these data one can construct either one of two hypotheses: these young birds continued to molt their juvenal wing coverts throughout the winter; or their rate of survival is less than that of the adults until the time of the breeding season. Because there seems to be no evidence that molt continues throughout the fall and winter in the Phasianinae, the phenomenon of

TABLE 4. REPORTED CHANGES IN AGE COMPOSITION OF CALIFORNIA QUAIL (after Emlen, 1940)

Age statistics are often given as a ratio of the number of young per 1 or 100 adults. They may also be expressed as the percentage of young in the population. Each such statistic is subject to sampling errors, the limits of which we could predict if we knew the actual age composition of the population. Since this is never known, the potential sampling limits (column *d* below) can be explored on the tentative assumption that the percentage actually found in a sample (as in column *c*) is indeed the percentage in the population. On this basis, sampling limits in column *d* will not be exceeded 95 times out of 100.

Month	(a) Size of Sample	(b) Ratio Young per 100 Adults	(c) Per Cent Young in Population	(d)
			As sampled	Potential sampling limits
October	440	228	70	66-74
November	1,042	165	62	59.1-64.9
December	1,004	160	62	59.0-65.0
January	482	136	58	54-62
February	436	127	56	51-61
March	229	116	54	48-60
April	207	107	52	45-59
May	222	109	52	45-59
June	195	82	45	38-52
	4,252	146	59	

differential survival between the two age groups seems to be a more plausible explanation of Emlen's results. This difference extends over a much longer period of time here than in the passerine species thus far studied. In the Blackbird, *Turdus merula,* Song Thrush, *Turdus ericetorum,* and the Starling, *Sturnus vulgaris,* young birds attain the same survival rate as adults by January 1 (Lack, 1946). A steadily increasing survival rate throughout the winter seems likely for some of the larger birds like the Cormorant, *Phalacrocorax carbo* (Kortlandt, 1942), and Herring Gulls, *Larus argentatus* (Marshall, 1947; and Paynter, 1947).

Among 622 quail sampled during the April-June breeding season, Emlen has (1940) found that young from the previous year represented 50 per cent of the population. It is thus fairly safe to conclude that the adult mortality rate in this species averages about 50 per cent per year. This rate differs for the two sexes and is discussed further under sex ratios in this review.

Some interesting data on the survival of banded California Quail have also been provided by Richardson (1941), who has summarized the recoveries reported (95 per cent of them by hunters) following the liberation of 64,688

TABLE 5. ABRIDGED LIFE TABLE FOR LIBERATED CALIFORNIA QUAIL (after Richardson, 1941)

Life-table statistics involve a mortality series (d_x), a survivorship series (l_x), and mortality rate (q_x) that often can be readily obtained from banding data. Both game-farm and wild-trapped birds are included in this table; the age of each was not reported as of the time of liberation.

Interval After Liberation	No. of Birds Liberated[a]	Actual No. Recovered Dead	(d_x) No. Dead Per 10,000 Liberated	(l_x) Alive at Start of Each Year	(q_x) Mort. Rate (Per Cent Per Year)
0-1 years	50,578	537	106.2	150.7	70
1-2 years	55,293	188	34.0	44.5	76
2-3 years	58,208	38	6.5	10.5	
3-4 years	53,170	17	3.2	4.0	
4-5 years	47,295	4	0.8	0.8	—
Totals and Mean Mortality Rate per Year			150.7	210.5	72
Totals and Mean Mort. Rate Less First Year			44.5	59.8	74

[a] The numbers in this column vary peculiarly because closed hunting seasons affected the numbers that could be shot by hunters and hence were available for study.

wild-trapped and game-farm birds in southern California. Using a method developed by Hanson and Smith (1950:173) and others, I have placed these in the form of an abridged life table (Table 5) after making due allowance for the absence of reports in certain years due to closed hunting seasons or the short lapse of time between liberation of the birds and compilation of the data.

It is unfortunate that no breakdown is available to permit separate analyses of the survival of wild-trapped and game-farm birds in this species. According to Richardson (1941), the latter were almost without exception liberated on refuges. The safest and most striking statistic emerging from the figures in Table 5 is the mean mortality rate of birds recovered after one year of liberation: 74 per cent per year. This closely approaches that found by Sumner (1935) for wild birds during one year on a study area but is importantly higher than the 50 per cent per year rate derived by Emlen (1940). Because Richardson's data cover a span of nine years, they are more directly comparable to the extensive data compiled by Emlen than Sumner's which hold only for a single year and a single study area. Unless Emlen's results are biased by continued molting of this species throughout the winter (an alternative we have already rejected), we must conclude that the birds liberated by the California Fish and Game Commission had a markedly higher adult mortality rate than the native stock. For a species adjusted to a 50 per cent adult mortality rate, consistent adult mortality at 74 per cent per year for some segment of the population can only mean its extirpation.

BOBWHITE QUAIL

Survival data on this species of quail have been among the most remarkable to emerge in the literature of vital statistics for birds. The first clues appeared in two tables published by Stoddard (1931:175-176) on the "returns" of banded birds. Designed to show movement of mature birds, these data lend themselves to at least a preliminary analysis of survival and mortality rates (Table 6).

TABLE 6. SOME EARLY DATA ON SURVIVAL IN BOBWHITE QUAIL (after Stoddard, 1931:175-176)

Time Interval (Nesting Seasons)	Number of Returns			(l_x) Alive at Start of Interval	(d'_x) Disappearing in Interval	(q'_x) Disappearance Rate[a]	Minimum Survival Rate[a]
	Fla.	Ga.	Total				
Betw. 1st and 2nd	98	56	154	154	119	77	23
Betw. 2nd and 3rd	29	6	35	35	24	69	31
Betw. 3rd and 4th	8	3	11	..	..	..	..
	135	65	200	189	143	76	24

[a] Per cent per interval.

Stoddard's "returns" include dead birds obtained from hunters' bags and recaptures obtained from retrapping. Because retrapping seldom represents an efficient or randomized method of sampling a population, no significance has ever been attached to the high mortality rates implied in Stoddard's study. One can, however, conclude from this early work that this small game bird possessed an adult survival of at least 24 per cent per year in the southeastern United States. This is the region of reputed maximum Bobwhite density; it is also a region where quail shooting is widely practiced.

Additional clues to the survival rates in this species have come from age ratios, which are discussed more fully in a subsequent section. The percentage of young in Missouri fall populations has been given as 76.8 per cent over a five-year period by A. S. Leopold (1945) and as 82.3 per cent over seven years by Bennitt (1951). Similar figures for winter have been given as 84 and 83 per cent in two years in Wisconsin (Buss, Mattison, and Kozlik, 1947) and as 80 per cent over a six-year period in Virginia (Mosby and Overton, 1950). It seems to me fairly safe to assume that stable populations of Bobwhite do in fact involve an age ratio of the order of eighty young to twenty adults. This in turn must mean that adult survival rates average about 20 per cent per year. The mortality rate for the Bobwhite is among the highest thus far calculated for any species of bird. It is particularly interesting to notice that the implied mortality rates in optimum range (Florida and Georgia) are not very much different than those suggested in submarginal and peripheral range like Wisconsin.

Reports of seasonal mortalities in the Bobwhite tend to support the impression of a high annual rate. Especially severe and atypical rates are cited by Sanders (1943) for three severe winters on Iowa study areas where calculated losses of this quail ran 88, 75, and 55 per cent. On two Missouri areas, the mean fall-to-spring loss was 66 per cent (Murray, 1948). On a Texas area it was at least 72 per cent (Lehmann, 1946b). In Virginia over a six-year period, it averaged 55 per cent and varied importantly with the amount of snow (Mosby and Overton, 1950). From fourteen years' data given by Errington (1945) for a Wisconsin area, it is evident that the mean winter mortality there was 47 per cent. In contrast to this picture of heavy winter losses is Wilson and Vaughn's (1944) report of the disappearance of only 7 per cent of 233 birds on a Maryland area, and a report by Buss, Mattison, and Kozlik (1947) that there was little evidence of winter mortality among coveys they were artificially feeding at the northern edge of the Bobwhite's range. These last two results now seem to be atypical and in need of further explanation. It is obvious that especially severe losses tend to be better reported than normal ones in the literature. There is no doubt, however, that the Bobwhite's mortality rate is high and that some of it is importantly operative in the winter season. Reeves (1951), in a recent and preliminary report, has stated that in Indiana the percentage of adults among cock birds drops from a high of 18 per cent in the fall to 15 per cent in midwinter and 8 per cent by early summer. The full implications of this observation are not as yet evident, but a picture only slightly similar to that given for California Quail by Emlen (1940) seems to be shaping up.

EUROPEAN PARTRIDGE

There was no American work on the survival of the Partridge during the 1940's. A Danish sample of fifty-two banded birds reported by Westerskov (1951) displayed a mean survival rate of 20 per cent per year. Among 6,065 wings secured from Danish sportsmen in 1949, 19.7 per cent were from adult birds. This preliminary evidence clearly suggests that the high mortality rate for Bobwhite Quail is by no means an exclusive one.

PHEASANT

The survival rate of a Wisconsin pheasant population has been calculated by Leopold, Sperry, Feeney, and Catenhusen (1943) and more recently by Buss (1946), whose data cover a six-year period of retrapping. A survival series worked out by Buss runs 100 — 26 — 9 — 4 — 0.4. Based on arithmetical means, this might more properly be weighted to read 100 — 32 — 12 — 5 — 0.6. The real accuracy of any result here depends importantly upon the validity of a correction factor introduced by the authors to compensate for the trapping inefficiency of their program. In a ten-year review of this project, McCabe (1949) has concluded that at least 46 per cent of the adult birds survive during an average year. This figure is also an adjusted one, since the trapped birds averaged 66.3 per cent of the total number censused on the study area. McCabe (1949) has also calculated an annual survival rate of 20 per cent for birds of the year and has determined that some egress of the banded birds must have occurred from the study area. This bias would tend to make the survival rate calculations too low. Leedy and Hicks (1945) have reported that the average life span of pheasants in Ohio is 9.85 months (from October 1) for males and 20.83 months for females. As far as I know, the proof of this statement has not yet been offered. It is obvious that we have only a rough estimate of the adult survival rates sustained by this species in the United States. These very probably are much lower for cocks in regions where the legal hunting kill is restricted to birds of this sex.

The loss of pheasants due to winter storms in the North Central states has been severe enough to encourage careful studies of the actual mortality. Using three census methods, South Dakota biologists have charted the losses since 1945. One two-day blizzard in 1950 is said to have wiped out ten to fifty per cent of the pheasants over much of the eastern part of the state (Kirsch, 1951).

GROUSE AND PTARMIGAN

The grouse are poorly represented in the literature on vital statistics. From some Norwegian data on Willow Ptarmigan published by Hagen (1935), one can calculate a mean survival rate of about 22 to 23 per cent per year for this species. This preliminary estimate arises from a very small sample but checks well with age ratios obtained for this species from different sources. The percentage of old "barren" birds in such a population, must, as Westerskov (1950b) has pointed out, be very, very small.

Darrow (1947:531-532) has attempted to calculate adult survival rates for Ruffed Grouse, apparently by a combination of census figures and age ratios. The result actually holds for both adults and young as of September 1. From this date, the mean survival rate was 49.8 per cent per year on one study area and 42.1 per cent on another. Most of the mortality occurred prior to April, when 58.4 and 47.4 per cent of the September birds were known to be surviving. In each area egress during at least one summer is said to have marred the results. This type of indirect calculation seems to be potentially quite hazardous. The future publication of age ratios in this species for several years and for many states may give us more reliable estimates of mortality rates in this species.

Ammann (1946) in a preliminary report has listed the survival of fifty near-adult Sharp-tails transplanted and released in Michigan. A minimum survival rate of 40 per cent per year is indicated for these birds. A rather similar rate for Prairie Chickens can be deduced from a small sample described by Hamerstrom and Hamerstrom (1949). Ammann (1947) in another preliminary report has obtained two estimates of 30 per cent winter mortality in the Sharp-tail. This would fit in fairly well with an annual mortality rate of 60 per cent. As far as I know, this sums up our meager published evidence of annual mortality rates in the Tetraoninae at this time.

GENERAL REMARKS

Our knowledge of adult survival rates in this group can now be briefly summarized in Table 7. One is immediately impressed in this review with the

TABLE 7. MEAN ANNUAL SURVIVAL RATES FOR ADULTS (Some of which are inferred from hunting- or winter-age ratios)

Species	Preliminary or Intensive Data		Extensive Data	
	per cent		*per cent*	
California Quail	27	(Sumner, 1935)	50	(Emlen, 1940)
California Quail		——	26	(Table 5)
Bobwhite Quail	24	(Table 6)	15.9	(Bennitt, 1951)
Bobwhite Quail	17	(A. S. Leopold, 1945)	23	(A. S. Leopold, 1945)
Bobwhite Quail	17	(Buss *et al.*, 1947)		——
European Partridge	20	(Westerskov, 1951)		——
Pheasant	30	(Leopold *et al.*, 1943)	46	(McCabe, 1949)
Willow Ptarmigan	22-23	(Hagen, 1935)		——
Ruffed Grouse	42-50	(Darrow, 1947)		——
Sharp-tailed Grouse	40	(Ammann, 1946)		——

scarcity of banding data on gallinaceous birds in North America. The sheer difficulty of trapping adequate samples of these birds and the poor co-operation of hunters in reporting upland-game-bird bands have apparently discouraged many investigators. It would seem highly desirable that the U. S. Fish and Wildlife Service extend its banding scheme to include all these species so that all recovery data can be centrally filed and permanently recorded. It might also be helpful to encourage amateur ornithologists to trap galliform birds as time and opportunity permit.

Age ratios represent satisfactory circumstantial evidence of adult mortality rates only if (1) they span a period of years and can thus be assumed to hold for stable populations, (2) they are not biased by extra vulnerability of juveniles to the gun, and (3) they are taken at a date past which the overall mortality rate for juveniles is identical to that of the adults. Thus the various age ratios reported by A. S. Leopold (1945), Buss, Mattison, and Kozlik (1947), and Bennitt (1951) can be taken together as an approximation of the probable average survival rates in Bobwhite Quail.

The literature of this group and the conversation of biologists studying it are frequently studded with the terms "turnover rate" and "turnover period." Leopold, Sperry, Feeney, and Catenhusen (1943) introduced these with reference to the time 100 birds shrink to zero, that is, completely succumb to mortality. Other workers use the terms more loosely, as in speaking of say 253 birds instead of 100. This is quite a different thing, especially if one is handling age-specific mortality rates for adults. Since these rates are generally constant in birds for all adult ages, a group of 253 birds will have a longer turnover period than 100. Some dissatisfaction is also attached to the end points in a survivorship series that are so considered. My own preference is for 1 per cent as the end point. Davis (1948) has used 5 per cent in mammals, this representing a point when a given age class ceased to be significant in the entire population in his opinion.

The preliminary picture emerging from these statistics is this. Some adult gallinaceous birds seem to have the same annual survival rates (40 to 60 per cent per year) as those thus far reported for the passerines. Others are somewhat lower, the Bobwhite having the lowest adult rate ever calculated for any species of bird.

THE STRUCTURE OF POPULATIONS

Sex Ratios

Sex ratios favoring females at hatching have been reported for both the European Partridge and pheasants (see Table 8). Only in the former is the result statistically different from a 50-50 ratio. In the domestic chicken, Landauer and Landauer (1931) have also reported males to be less than females: 48.77 $\pm$ 0.13 per cent in a sample of 67,993. In another large sample, Byerly and Jull (1935) have found the sex ratio at hatching perfectly even, there being 50.1 $\pm$ 0.23 per cent males. The poultry evidence in fact points to significant differences between strains at hatching time. Equally significant differences between galliform species in the wild due to sex-linked lethal genes probably can be expected.

Quails studied by Emlen (1940) and A. S. Leopold (1945) have an evenly balanced sex ratio in their first autumn. Possible distortions of this ratio are less clear cut in other species but are particularly noticeable in samples of Sharp-tailed Grouse and Sage Grouse obtained from hunters; these may or may not be biased (Table 8). From thence on, the trend is toward a shrinkage of the females in the population except, of course, in species in which the males are selectively shot by hunters.

This shrinkage in the number of females is thought to reflect the extra vulnerability of this sex to predators during the nesting season. As a factor affecting the population, the effect of this distorted ratio may be of limited importance. Thus in a Bobwhite population of 1,000 birds coming up to the breeding season, we can expect 80 per cent to be birds of the year and the sex ratio to be nearly equal. Of the 200 adults, about 64 per cent (or 128) will be males and 36 per cent (or 72) females. The 128 minus 72 leaves 56

TABLE 8. SOME CHANGING SEX RATIOS IN GALLIFORM BIRDS

Autumnal sex-ratio data originating from the bags of hunters may be biased if any tendency exists to shoot male birds on their communal courtship grounds. This is probably true of the Sharp-tailed Grouse reports below.

Species	At Hatching % ♂	At Hatching (Sample)	In First Fall or Winter % ♂	In First Fall or Winter (Sample)	Adults % ♂	Adults (Sample)	References
Phasianinae							
California Quail	—	—	50	(814)	58	(511)	Emlen, 1940
Bobwhite Quail	—	—	50.5	(1,254)	62	(579)	A. S. Leopold, 1945
Bobwhite Quail	—	—	48	(622)	61	(442)	Lehmann, 1946a
Bobwhite Quail	—	—	54	(494)	63	(99)	Buss *et al.*, 1947
Bobwhite Quail	—	—	52	(628)	66	(169)	Jackson, 1951
Bobwhite Quail	—	—	50.5	(34,989)	59.0	(7,521)	Bennitt, 1951
European Partridge	—	—	47	(461)	62	(273)	Middleton, 1935
European Partridge	43	(331)	—	—	58	(115)	McCabe and Hawkins, 1946
Pheasant	50	(532)	—	—	—	—	Latham, 1942
Pheasant	—	—	30[b]	(543)	26	(606)	McCabe, 1949, *in litt.*
Tetraoninae							
Ruffed Grouse	—	—	43	(225)	61	(192)	Bezdek, 1944
Ruffed Grouse	(52)[a]	(464)	56	(274)	42.5[c]	(2,266)	Darrow, 1947
Sharp-tailed Grouse	—	—	61	(163)	63	(103)	Ammann, 1947
Lesser Prairie Chicken	—	—	53	(491)	47	(432)	Lee, 1950
Sage Grouse	—	—	—	—	50.2	(1,881)	Girard, 1937
Sage Grouse	—	—	46	(1,485)	32	(1,114)	Patterson, 1949

[a] Birds collected during first three months after hatching.
[b] Winter sample obtained by trapping.
[c] Based on the identification of birds as they flushed in summer. This seems to be a somewhat risky technique, and the thirteen-year result quoted here should be regarded with caution. An eleven-year check on another study area yielded 49 per cent males in a sample of 236.

surplus males that presumably will be nonbreeding. This is 5.6 per cent of our hypothetical population of 1,000 individuals. In other species with lower adult mortality rates, this statistic will tend to have a higher value.

While an unbalanced sex ratio appears to be fairly typical of the adult segments of galliform populations, Yocum (1943) got an even sex ratio among 137 unaged Hungarian Partridges obtained mostly from fall hunters, and Gorsuch (1934) found a 51-49 ratio among 304 unaged Gambel's Quail trapped during the winter.

When cock birds receive all or a major part of local hunting pressure, the percentage of males in the population may drop considerably. This explains in part the 16 to 23 per cent drop for Sage Grouse in Wyoming reported by Patterson (1949). Among 112,024 unaged pheasants in Wisconsin, this percentage was 19.0 (Buss, 1946). Among 64,337 similarly sexed in Ohio, it was 28 per cent (Leedy and Hicks, 1945). Among 9,772 in North Dakota, it ran from 40 to 49 per cent (Bach, 1951b).

Buss (1946) has reported that a winter pheasant ratio of 1 male to 4.4 females changed to 1 to 3.5 in spring, "indicating differential mortality as the winter advanced." A more conservative interpretation is that this change is due to the onset of more conspicuous behavior of the males. This is well brought out by Linduska's (1947) work in Michigan.

How far can the sex ratio be safely unbalanced in polygamous species like the pheasant? On a Michigan study area with a nearly even sex ratio, D. L. Allen (1938) has found more than one-half of the males unmated. In Wisconsin where state-wide sex ratios run about three or four females per male, Taber (1949) has reported nonterritorial cocks on an intensively watched study area. At least under some field conditions in America, this work suggests that surplus males exist in Ring-necked Pheasant populations.

Bach (1948), whose contributions to our understanding of population phenomena in this group extend well beyond his own writings, has endeavored to formulate how harvests of higher and higher proportions of the males simply change the sex ratio and do not affect the number of young produced by the females. These relationships seem to me to be complicated by the density of the breeding population. In artificially dense populations, as on game farms, a ratio of one cock to fifty hens results in close to normal fertility of pheasant eggs (Twining, Hjersman, and MacGregor, 1948). In very sparse populations, a strongly unbalanced sex ratio might be associated with poor reproductive success either because the hens fail to find cocks as mates, or because the formation of a harem makes for a density of hens in excess of the locally available and safe nesting niches. Although one servicing by a cock pheasant lasts on an average about twenty-two days (Shick, 1947), it seems doubtful that hens would spread out very far from the cock with which they are associated. This close association of the sexes seems to be the case in northern Wisconsin where a sparse population of pheasants inhabits a series of pockets in country that is largely unsuitable for this species (R. A. McCabe, personal communication). The upper limit of an unbalanced sex ratio in a sparse population of pheasants is unknown at this time.

In the Meleagrididae, distribution of the sexes is not clear-cut. Of 392 Turkeys shot in Virginia, hunters reported 42 per cent to be males, but it is not certain how many immature males were overlooked in their sample (Mosby and Handley, 1943). Winter observations on 21 flocks in West Virginia, where hunting is also allowed, revealed 34 per cent to be males (Glover, 1948). Among 36 winter (unshot) flocks observed in Missouri, 52 per cent of the 351 birds were males (Dalke, Leopold, and Spencer, 1946). The unbalanced ratio in Virginia and West Virginia is quite evidently due to shooting pressure. Breakdowns of the sexes by age classes lack sufficient sample size, but run as expected. Among trapped birds in Wyoming, Crump and Sanderson (1951) have reported six immature males, seven immature females, ten adult males, and twenty-four adult females. It is interesting to see this familiar pattern of a sex ratio that is even among young birds and unbalanced among adults existing in the Turkey as it does in the Sage Grouse and probably in the pheasant. The pertinent ecological point here is that male wild Turkeys are physiologically unable to breed until their second year. In pheasants this condition may be ecologically either approached or realized by nonterritorial males which, Taber has (1949) pointed out, have little or no access to the females. In effect, such cocks are ecological but not anatomical "castrates". In the Turkey, the sterility of the young males obviously has no depressing effect upon the population.

An extraordinary case of unbalanced sex ratios in a protected pheasant population will be noted in the section on population behavior that follows shortly.

Age Ratios

Hagen (1935) has been among the first to report age ratios in a gallinaceous bird population. In small samples of Norwegian Willow Ptarmigan he found a ratio of 83 per cent young to 17 per cent adults among birds that were taken by hunters and a 76 per cent to 24 per cent ratio among birds that were trapped. Although the differences are not statistically significant, we do have here our first hint as to the age structure of a gallinaceous bird population. These two samples total only seventy-six birds. The age ratio of 79-21 which they yield in the aggregate compares quite favorably with a mean mortality rate of 77-78 per cent computed from different data in an earlier section of this review.

During the 1940's, a tremendous attempt was made to age American game birds before, during, or after the fall hunting season. This is slow work when hunters are individually interviewed in the field, or when winter populations are laboriously trapped. When, however, wings are mailed to a central research station, or bagged birds are examined in a cold-storage plant (where they are often cleaned and dressed), the size of a given sample may run as high as 10,000 specimens. Despite the quantity of data, interpretation has been labored and sometimes confused. This is inevitable when observations may be carried out during the very period when the ratio of young to old birds is rapidly changing in the fall population (that is, during the hunting season). The scope of these changes can be understood by study of a hypothetical case (Table 9) in which 65 per cent of the young are shot as against 48 per cent of the adults.

The principle emerging here is this: Whenever age ratios are steadily

TABLE 9. AGE RATIOS IN A HYPOTHETICAL POPULATION

Hunted populations of gallinaceous birds sometimes display rather rapid changes in the ratio of young per adult. This table explores potential discrepancies between ratios for the living and the dead. The values for young per adult shot or dying in each week during the hunting season (Column 9) are in actual practice much lower than those cited here.

	No. Alive at Start			Per Cent Dying Each Week			No. Dying in Each Week		
	(1) Yng.	(2) Adults	(3) Yng. per Ad.	(4) Yng.	(5) Adults	(6) Yng. per Ad.	(7) Yng.	(8) Adults	(9) Yng. per Ad.
1st week	1,000	250	4	30	15	2	300	38	7.9
2nd week	700	212	3.3	25	15	1.7	175	32	5.5
3rd week	525	180	2.9	20	15	1.3	110	27	4.1
4th week	415	153	2.7	15	15	1.0	62	23	2.7
5th week	353	130	2.7	—	—	—	—	—	—
Totals				65[a]	48[a]		647	120	5.4

[a] A percentage of the number alive at the start of the first week.

shrinking during the period of observation, the ratio of young to adults among the dead will always be higher than that among the living. It is also clear from this table that several different types of age ratios may be available for study:

(1) *Time-specific age ratios* refer to some brief interval of time such as a day or a week. The specimens or subjects for study may be living or dead.

(a) Age ratios of the living may be obtained by trapping, by field observations during the late breeding season (when the young are noticeably smaller than adults), or by inferences drawn from life tables. Any of the values in column 3 of Table 9 are time-specific age ratios for the living.

(b) Age ratios of the dead may be obtained from inspections of hunters' bags or from reports of banded birds that are shot or found dead. Any of the first four values in column 9 of Table 9 are examples of this type, as are Emlen's (1940) monthly breakdowns of California Quail in museums.

(2) *Cumulative age ratios* refer to some long period of time, such as a hunting or autumnal season. These ratios usually are restricted to mortality data. Illustrations are provided in the last line of Table 9 and in hunters' kill data reported for South Dakota by Nelson (1948). Kimball (1948) believes that such ratios at least indicate annual trends in the productivity of pheasants. Thus the ratio of young per adult in that state ran 1.06, 1.53, and 2.98 from 1945 to 1947. This is supposed to indicate steady improvement in productivity during this period. While this is probably

correct, Kimball has correctly stressed that age-ratio data of this sort can be very misleading. This is especially true if a particularly late hatching season makes the young birds more vulnerable to the gun. These South Dakota age ratios clearly need to be re-evaluated and compared to population indices. They are not comparable to other age ratios referable to a specific time. Cumulative age ratios for California Quail are also among those mentioned by Emlen (1940), who has broken down such data according to their source (hunters' bags, museum collections, and banders' traps).

Bennitt (1951) has continued the Missouri collection of quail wings which in a seven-year period totaled 51,378 specimens and now represents the finest collection of its kind in existence. The percentage of young here varied from 79.2 to 84.1 and averaged 82.1 [their arithmetic mean; geometric mean, 82.3]. Thus in good quail range, there seems to be remarkably little variation in annual productivity. This is probably to be expected, since this species is believed to be a persistent renester (Errington, 1933; Davison, 1949). Predation on eggs therefore has a minimal effect upon productivity. Because Bobwhite flush before the hunter usually as a covey, the young would seem to be almost as wary as adults. One test of this possibility has been made by Bennitt who, after breaking down his data over an eight-week hunting season, has reported that the percentage of young does drop about 0.6 per cent for each week of the season. This strongly suggests that the percentage of young in hunters' bags is—for Bobwhites in Missouri—very close to what is actually in the population. In other states and at other times, late nesting seasons may possibly increase the vulnerability of young birds to the gun and thus bias age ratios in hunters' bags as a picture of the internal structure of a galliform population.

The age information brought together in Table 10 has some striking peculiarities. Although young birds seem to represent 50 to 60 per cent of fall populations among several members of the Tetraoninae, the number of young varies from two to four per adult female. At least some of these differences are actually brought about by unbalanced sex ratios among the adult birds, as one can see by reviewing Table 8. The percentage of young in a population happens to be a statistic about which one may recall some confidence limits that govern the sampling; but, as an expression of productivity in a galliform population, it must be used with caution. Young per adult female would appear to be a less distorted figure.

The enormous productivity implied here for Bobwhite Quail, 8.1-12.0 young per surviving adult female in most studies, has not been fully documented by other methods. Lehmann (1946a) has found juvenal birds to represent as low as 49 per cent of a sample trapped in the fall. This fall population was, however, only 18 per cent higher than the spring population,

TABLE 10. Some Autumnal and Winter Age Ratios Reported for Gallinaceous Birds

Species	Place	Years of Data	Source of Data	No. in Sample	Per Cent Young	Young Per Adult ♀	Reference
Mountain Quail	—	—	Museum	193	48	—	A. S. Leopold, 1939[b]
California Quail	—	—	Museum	389	58	—	A. S. Leopold, 1939[b]
California Quail	—	—	Museum	983	57.0	—	Emlen, 1940
California Quail	Calif.	3	Census	2,566	68.7	—	Emlen, 1940
California Quail	Calif.	3	Traps	2,052	60.0	—	Emlen, 1940
California Quail	Calif.	3	Hunters	985	56.6	—	Emlen, 1940
California Quail	Calif.	2	Hunters	1,016	72-78	—	Glading *et al.,* 1945
California Quail	Hawaii	1	Hunters	239	72	—	Smith, 1948
Gambel's Quail	—	—	Museum	111	56	—	A. S. Leopold, 1939
Bobwhite Quail	—	—	Museum	78	77	—	A. S. Leopold, 1939
Bobwhite Quail	Mo.	5	Hunters	1,633	76.8	8.6	A. S. Leopold, 1945
Bobwhite Quail	Tex.	2	Traps	1,109	49-72	2.3-8.1	Lehmann, 1946a
Bobwhite Quail	Wis.	3	Traps	593	83	13.4	Buss *et al.,* 1947
Bobwhite Quail	Mo.	7	Hunters	51,178	82.3	10.6-12.0	Bennitt, 1951
Bobwhite Quail	Tex.	2	Hunters	797	79	11.0	Jackson, 1951
Pheasant	Mont.	1	Census	1,014	83.2	—	Hiatt and Fisher, 1947
Pheasant	S.D.	1	Hunters	723 ♀	48	1.82[a]	Nelson, 1948
Pheasant	S.D.	1	Hunters	2,016 ♀	61.1	3.14[a]	Nelson, 1948
Pheasant	Wis.	6	Traps	1,177	47.3	1.2	McCabe, 1949, *in litt.*
European Partridge	Britain	4	Census	—	72-78	—	Middleton, 1935-37
European Partridge	Denmark	1	Hunters	6,065	80.3	8.9	Westerskov, 1951
Ruffed Grouse	Canada	3	Traps	417	54	3.0	Bezdek, 1944
Ruffed Grouse	Wis.	1	Hunters	2,078	82	—	Hale and Wendt, 1950
Sharp-tailed Grouse	Mich.	3	Hunters	292	61	3.9	Ammann, 1947
Prairie Chicken	Tex.	1	Census	274	50	—	Lehmann, 1941
Lesser Prairie Chicken	N.M.	1	Hunters	923	53.2	2.13	Lee, 1950
Sage Grouse	Wyo.	1	Hunters	2,599	57.1	1.95	Patterson, 1950

[a] Estimated by the reviewer as twice the number of juvenal females per adult female reported.
[b] Leopold's museum data were not originally collected for a summary of this sort; they offer, however, a revealing comparison with statistics taken from other sources.

in contrast to a 58 per cent increase a year previously when young made up 72 per cent of the population. A nearly even fall age ratio in this species thus seems to be atypical of stable populations. This species apparently is a persistent renester, but the percentage of successful females in a late-summer population has never been determined. Because the number of young per adult is roughly twice that of any other galliform species thus far reported, speculation always seems to arise that this species may raise two broods. This possibility ought to be settled by close observation of marked birds under semi-captive conditions. The available explanation for this high autumnal ratio of young to adults in the Bobwhite seems to rest on (1) the very large clutches laid by this species (averages of 19.2 have been reported in early May, and even in late July mean clutch seems to be 11 or higher [Errington, 1933]), and (2) an intense renesting drive that persists over a five-month period (Davison, 1949). At the present time, it is difficult to determine the effect of the adults' high annual mortality rate upon this amazing age ratio, but it must be quite considerable.

The identification of age ratios representing a Malthusian or growing population of gallinaceous birds has not yet been achieved. In East Texas, Lay (1950) has reported that the young per adult Bobwhite hen in hunters' bags increased from 5.3 (70 per cent young) to 11.8 (82 per cent young) when the population was growing. In a poor year for Bobwhite in western Texas, A. S. Jackson found 75 per cent young, 8.1 young per adult hen, and the extremely distorted adult sex ratio of 69 males to 31 females in a sample of 306 (Lay, 1950).

Some comparisons between British and American game management are useful. A recapitulation of Middleton's (1935-37) several papers on the Partridge reveals a higher nesting success, 82.0 per cent, than any thus far reported in America (Table 1). Middleton's papers show that the young in August populations in four years varied from 71.7 to 78.1 per cent. There were no comparable figures for Partridge in America during the 1940's, but many other reports on galliform birds here (Table 10) equal or top these British figures. What is especially striking in this review is our general failure to use a wide variety of materials in compiling age-ratio statistics and to determine beyond any shadow of a doubt the reliability of these as measures of the internal structure of galliform populations. The randomly collected specimens in museum collections usually span a great many decades and can often be taken as a working approximation of the age ratio in stable populations. Birds trapped for banding purposes are usually free of bias associated with the vulnerability of young birds to the gun. The use of bait to attract birds to a banding station may of course have the opposite effect: it may encourage adults in a disproportionate ratio to the number of young locally present. Thus far, A. S. Leopold (1939) and Emlen (1940) have been the only ones to combine age data from banders, museum collectors, and hunters.

BEHAVIOR OF POPULATIONS

General Phenomena

GROWTH CURVES

Einarsen (1945b) has described the introduction of two male and eight female pheasants on 394-acre Protection Island in Oregon. Two male cats were

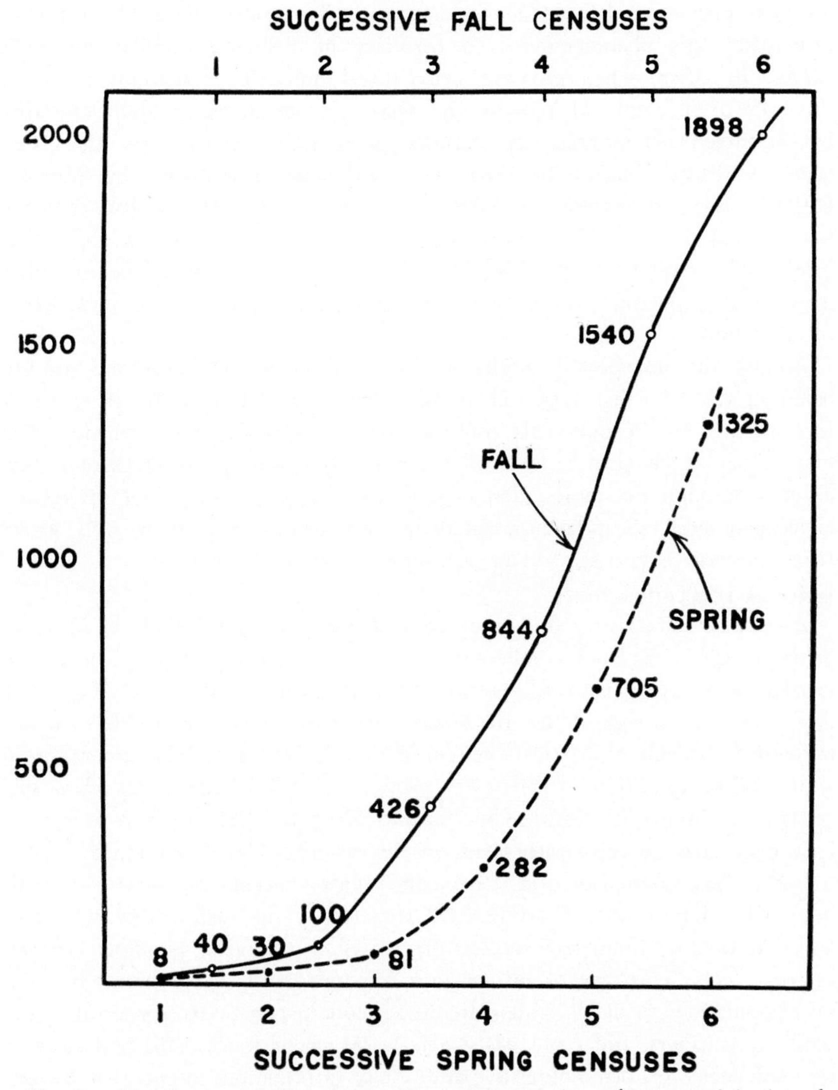

Fig. 1. Annual growth of an insular Pheasant population subject to minimal predation pressure and no hunting (after Einarsen, 1945b).

also placed on the island as the equivalent of mammalian predator pressure on the mainland. The sigmoid growth curve of this pheasant population, illustrated in Figure 1, is typical of growth curves reported for animals in other phyla and classes.

Errington's (1945) review of galliform population responses stresses the principle that the percentage of summer reproductive gain by a population is inversely proportional to its density in spring. Sometimes called "the inversity principle," this phenomenon is a corollary of S-shaped population-growth curves. In effect, when growing avian (and human) populations begin to slow down their rate of growth, the reason is not increased adult mortality but restricted net productivity. Similar population behavior has also been found in Ruffed Grouse by Darrow (1947) and in Bobwhite by Klimstra (1950). In a re-analysis of Errington's data, Lack (1951) has correctly stressed that the depressed rates of summer gain accompanying high population levels must result from increased juvenile mortality rates. A number of other interesting population curves are illustrated in the section on cycles that follows shortly.

Among the unexpected results of Einarsen's (1945b) study was an unbalanced sex ratio that appeared in this unshot population. After three years, for instance, the spring birds consisted of 185 males and 97 females. The first evident mechanism to level off the population was egg or chick mortality, induced through the molestation of the hens by the cocks. This interesting experiment was abruptly terminated by war conditions. It is well worth repeating, especially if sex and age ratios can be obtained regularly.

MINIMUM POPULATION UNITS

Almost no statistics for this group of birds exist on the threshold of numbers below which an isolated population can no longer maintain itself against the usual type of emergency and routine losses. An inspection of Gross's (1928) data leads one to suspect that the Heath Hen was several times able to maintain itself at levels of 75-100 when fires kept the Martha's Vineyard range in a prairie-like condition. [Today fire protection in Wisconsin, plus plant succession, is eliminating Prairie Chicken and Sharp-tail habitat much as it must have once done so for Heath Hens on the eastern seaboard.] Grange (1950: 230-231) has reported that, in Wisconsin, Prairie Chickens can survive in small detached colonies, that Sharp-tailed Grouse have no such ability whatever, and that Ruffed Grouse can successfully persist in ungrazed woodlots as small as forty acres. This type of information, expanded into actual counts of local bird populations, is of particular interest to modern geneticists, conservationists, wildlife managers, and ecologists generally. Much of it may still be buried in the notebooks of ornithologists. Additional information might also be uncovered in the files of governmental agencies that have successfully transplanted game birds into new range or old range from which they had been extirpated. According to Ligon (1946), the minimum number for a transplant of Turkeys is twelve to twenty.

Sporadic Fluctuations

GENERAL STATISTICS

Actual census data on gallinaceous birds are still quite scarce, and the normal magnitude of population fluctuations is little understood. Seasonal and average daily bags for Bobwhites reported by Stoddard (1931:345-346) have annual maxima that run 150 to 200 per cent higher than some annual minima. In Iowa, calculated densities have shown annual increases as high as 74 and 166 per cent for the same species on a study area of 7,713 acres (Sanders, 1943).

Two difficulties beset the investigator in studies of this sort. First of all, gallinaceous birds often present especially difficult problems of observation in the field. Then, intensive watching cannot always detect normal ingress to and egress from a study area.

Results of rural mail carrier surveys do seem to provide some materials for the study of fluctuations. According to a progress report by Bach (1951a), North Dakota carrier observations have been as follows (in terms of the average number of birds seen per mile):

TIME	PHEASANT	PARTRIDGE	SHARP-TAIL	PRAIRIE CHICKEN
Dec. 1946	0.300	0.120	0.040	0.040
Dec. 1947	0.770	0.310	0.093	0.087
Dec. 1948	0.622	0.218	0.065	0.071
Jan. 1950	0.550	0.330	0.144	0.048
Jan. 1951	0.256	0.373	0.063	0.036

Although these data provide an interesting degree of synchronized changes in 1947 and 1948, I feel unable to evaluate the validity of the figures. As one would expect, the state-wide indices tend to fluctuate much less violently than do the results from study areas.

State-wide hunting-kill statistics represent another index bearing on this point. As far as I can determine, such data for Wisconsin similarly suggest that for most galliforms annual increases in state-wide populations are usually less than 100 per cent. In some years, these crude statistics picture a decline of more than 50 per cent.

The picture tentatively emerging from these heterogeneous statistics (some of which are of admittedly doubtful value) is that on good range gallinaceous populations fluctuate with annual increases of less than 100 per cent and with annual decreases of less than 50 per cent. What sometimes happens on poor range is discussed in the paragraphs that follow.

DIE-OFFS

Schorger (1942) has found that the Turkey in early Wisconsin was sporadically wiped out at the northern periphery of its range and that it systematically reinvaded this state from better range in Illinois to the south. This replenishment of marginal range from a "reservoir" is also said to have taken place in Prairie Chickens and Bobwhite Quail (Schorger, 1942), but the evidence for the latter two species is less clear-cut (see Schorger, 1944, 1946).

A virtually complete mortality of Bobwhite was reported in a belt several counties wide in Wisconsin during the winter of 1935-36 (Leopold, 1937). Almost equally severe mortality amounting to 80 per cent among Ring-necked Pheasants in South Dakota has been reported by Beed (1938). The impression persists that animal populations in optimum range are controlled by density-dependent factors, and that in submarginal (peripheral) range they are more subject to density-independent factors.

EMIGRATIONS AND IRRUPTIONS

Mass movements of galliform birds in North America are now quite rare, although nineteenth-century records of such phenomena among Prairie Chickens and Sharp-tails are fairly common (Schorger, 1944; Hamerstrom and Hamerstrom, 1949). Emigrations of Sharp-tailed Grouse appear to have taken place in 1865, 1896, and 1932. Snyder (1935), who reviewed these phenomena, has described the great Sharp-tail emigration from the area south of James Bay in October and November, 1932. Another southern invasion of the Willow Ptarmigan took place over a three-year period, 1931-32 to 1933-34, and represents a more orderly southward extension of range from the Rockies east to the Gulf of St. Lawrence (Snyder and Shortt, 1936). These movements seem to be responses to population pressure occurring at the time of "cyclic" highs. (Table 11 will offer a pertinent comparison in the section on cycles that follows.) It would be interesting to know the age composition of such invading populations in the future.

Spectacular overpopulation ("irruptions") of galliform birds are rarely described in the literature of ornithology. Some extremely interesting Bobwhite Quail evidence along these lines during the nineteenth century has been brought together by Schorger (1946). The combination of factors producing these remarkable irruptions in Wisconsin was cessation of the Indians' burning of the prairie (which had previously reduced brush and presumably quail cover) and an apparently optimal ratio of wild to cultivated land just after the early settlers moved in. An equally interesting irruption has recently been described by Jackson (1947) for Bobwhite Quail throughout the lower plains of Texas. Here at the periphery of this species' range, the biological background for the population explosion lay in drought and overgrazing which had destroyed the grass turf. Abnormally high rainfall then produced an extensive growth of weeds in 1941 and 1942. The build-up to large numbers (50-100 birds per 100 acres) occurred following the second of these two breeding seasons. The population's collapse was importantly confined to an eight-day period in January, 1943, and seems to have culminated in a spectacular display of predation. The evidence here seems to point to wholesale movement of the birds which thereupon developed a great vulnerability to predators. According to a Pittman-Robertson Quarterly progress report by Jackson (Vol. 4, No. 4, p. 168), the ratio of young to old was 4 to 1 in the fall of 1942. To me it appears that the birds had reached the irruptive stage by purely normal reproductive success. One year later this ratio was

0.5 young per adult—the most distorted age ratio in this species thus far reported.

An equally extraordinary irruption of Ring-necked Pheasants apparently took place in South Dakota during recent years. Estimates of the number of birds there in 1944 and 1945 range up to 50,000,000 (Nelson, 1946), but during these war years little technical information on this population was available. Apparently the birds reached a density of about a bird per acre. The sequence of events that permitted this phenomenon seems to be as follows (Nelson, personal communication). Drought in the 1930's led to abandonment of many farms. During the 1940's, adequate rainfall made for luxuriant cover, and the land was gradually put back into cultivation. The pheasants now enjoyed an optimal ratio of tame land to wild land. As late as 1945, entire quarter sections of land (each 160 acres) remained densely choked with sunflowers. Winters appear to have been relatively mild, and the population sky-rocketed.

A substantially similar picture to this for North Dakota has also been described by Stuart (1951), who has indicated that, here at the northern edge of their range, pheasants went through a somewhat more modestly proportioned population irruption. The scope of this is apparent in Stuart's listing of the hunting kill of pheasants in his state (for total harvest each year, add three ciphers).

	1940	'41	'42	'43	'44	'45	'46	'47	'48	'49	'50
Average kill per hunter	13.1	16.7	34.1	37.2	48.9	38.3	8.7	4.7	6.6	5.9	1.1
Total harvest	525	920	1,825	1,390	2,690	2,220	590	280	460	420	60

One is at once reminded that combinations of factors (like logging, predator control, buck-laws, and forest-fire protection) are known to produce overpopulations of White-tailed Deer, *Odocoileus virginianus*. Population irruptions in noncyclic species evidently result from unusual combinations of environmental factors, hence their relative rarity. Time factors seem to be important.

Periodic Fluctuations

By 1950, two important periodic fluctuations were being reported for gallinaceous bird populations: a three- to four-year cycle that seems to average out to about three and one-third years (Siivonen, 1948a) and a so-called ten-year cycle that roughly averages out to about nine and one-half years. This long-term fluctuation has been the subject of much speculation. There is no doubt that galliform birds markedly fluctuate in numbers at more or less regular times in many parts of southern Canada and the northern United States. The degree of this regularity and the presence or absence of minor peaks in the fluctuations apparently cannot, however, be fixed at this time. The literature on mammals has long been known to demonstrate a nine- to ten-year cycle in Canadian predators. Lynx, *Lynx canadensis,* Red Fox, *Vulpes fulva,* and Mink, *Mustela vison,* are surely involved, but the century-old pelt collection records of the Hudson's Bay Company unfortunately have no counterpart in regional population indices for North American gallinaceous birds. The few that do exist for grouse cover a relatively brief period, or arise from subjective estimates, or refer to areas outside the general region where long-term cycles are known to occur.

It now seems apparent that three- to four-year fluctuations of animals could well arise from environmental factors which vary randomly in a local and/or annual sense (Palmgren, 1949; Cole, 1951). A generally acceptable explanation of the ten-year cycle seems to await the publication of more detailed population indices for such prey species as the Varying (Snowshoe) Hare, *Lepus americanus,* and the Muskrat, *Ondatra zibethica.* Cole (1951) has argued that true ten-year population cycles do not exist. This hypothesis does not hold, I think, for such predators as the Lynx; but in the absence of better indices at the present time, it is hard to prove or disprove its applicability to North American population fluctuations in gallinaceous birds. Until the exact periodicity of these fluctuations as well as their exact geographical extent has been cleared up, only a preliminary and tentative analysis of them seems to be possible.

LATITUDINAL GRADIENTS

At the present time, there seems to be some evidence that the three- to four-year periodicity of gallinaceous birds in the North changes gradually into a longer one toward the South and then (apparently) disappears below 40° north latitude. Thus grouse, *Lagopus* sp., in Greenland are said to have a three-and-one-third-year cycle (Siivonen, 1950), while in Labrador and Newfoundland, their cycle is about ten years (Clarke, 1936). For grouse in southern Canada and the northern part of the United States, a ten-year cycle has been regarded as exclusive. In Quebec, peak pelt collections of Red Fox have a three- to four-year periodicity in the northern parts of the province and an eight- to ten-year periodicity in the south (Butler, 1951). (According to Airaksinen (1946), ten-year fluctuations of grouse in Finland are most noticeable in the northern part of that country, are still evident in the central part, and are progressively less evident in the south.)

It is in the general area between the 55th and 70th parallels that Siivonen (1950) finds much evidence for the short-term cycle. In North America, reports of ten-year-cycle data originate mostly between 40° and 55° north latitude. For areas below 40°, reports of cycles in gallinaceous birds and fur bearers are generally absent. These three regions are the great biomes—the tundra, the northern coniferous forest, and the deciduous forest. The three possess increasing degrees of complexity in their animal pyramids and, as Lack (1951) has pointed out, the ecologist is impressed with the probability that food relationships basically govern the behavior of populations in each region.

INTERSPECIFIC SYNCHRONISM

The North American grouse cycle is popularly supposed to include the Ruffed Grouse, Sharp-tailed Grouse, and the Prairie Chicken. Population fluctuations of the Varying Hare are often considered to coincide with these species, and the term North American game cycle is frequently used to include these four species.

One of the most interesting developments of the 1940's was the coincidence of a high in Ring-necked Pheasants with that of grouse in 1942. This high in pheasants was widespread, from Alberta (Rowan, 1948) to Connecticut (Sondrini, 1950), the peak in some states occurring perhaps a year or two later (Kimball, 1948). It was followed by a spectacular widespread decline which stands out as one of the most notable population phenomena displayed by North American birds during the 1940's. (An equally striking decline of bird populations in northwestern Europe took place a few years earlier, according to Siivonen, 1948b). Roadside-census data, assembled for various states by Kimball (1948), show a prominent pheasant peak in 1942, a conspicuous drop in 1943, and a consistently downward trend from 1945 to 1947. Kimball (1948) emphasizes that this decline was not accompanied by noticeably increased adult mortality rates. The evidence points to reproductive failures, and there is a strong implication that rainy spring weather was the causative agent. This peak and decline seem to have led some writers (like Grange, 1950:89) to include the pheasant in the ten-year game cycle.

In much of its present North American range the successful introduction of the pheasant was not accomplished until the 1920's or the 1930's. In Alberta, where the European Partridge preceded the pheasant by about two decades, this partridge is now said to have reached three population highs coinciding with the last three peaks of the ten-year cycle, and Rowan (1948) is convinced that its populations there are now governed by the same factors. MacLulich's (1937) fine study of Varying Hares and sunspots is ample warning of the impossibility of using a few decades' observations to prove that two periodic phenomena are coincident. Despite three decades of coincidence, the evidence must still be regarded as suggestive and not conclusive. In a North Dakota mail carrier index which we have already noticed in this review, four species of gallinaceous birds peaked in three different years out of a possible four (Bach, 1951a). In Wisconsin hunters' reports, there is some similarity between the pheasant and partridge curves, but one peaked in 1939, the other in 1942 (Bersing, 1951).

An interesting test of interspecific synchronism in the ten-year game cycle is provided by hunters' reports of game taken in three of the Lake states. Although these statistics can only be regarded as extremely crude population indices, they do represent some of the best available quantitative data on cycles in gallinaceous birds in North America. From the reports of the Michigan, Minnesota, and Wisconsin conservation departments, one notices that Varying

Hares in Michigan were evidently out of phase with those in Wisconsin as well as with Ruffed Grouse at the close of the 1930's. A somewhat better agreement in hare and bird indices appeared a decade later. All three states showed moderately good agreement in Ruffed Grouse peaks in 1942, but the pheasant kill exhibited various peaks from 1941 to 1942 and 1944. Although some of these differences are not necessarily significant ones, the evidence from these crude population indices seems to suggest only a very rough type of interspecific synchronization in fluctuations of hares, grouse, and pheasants in this region during the past two decades.

Schorger (1944, 1947), who has scanned (for wildlife news) every page of every newspaper published in Wisconsin prior to 1900, has uncovered an invaluable series of historical pictures of game populations in the Lake states. He has pointed out that the available evidence of a ten-year periodicity during the nineteenth century in Wisconsin is admittedly rather crude but still quite appreciable. Airaksinen (1946) has also found a ten-year fluctuation going back nearly 100 years in the early statistics of gallinaceous birds exported from Finland. The two series are compared in Table 11. Surprisingly enough, the

TABLE 11. THE "TEN-YEAR CYCLE" IN NORTH AMERICA AND EUROPE

"Peaks" are here defined as values immediately preceded and followed by somewhat lower values. "Highs" are taken as the last year of generally high numbers immediately before a three-year decline. Very high peaks are indicated as "climax years." Periods not covered in these studies are marked by XX below.

Wisconsin		Finland	Hudson Bay
Prairie Chicken Lows	Ruffed Grouse Peaks	General Galliform Climax Years	Varying Hare Highs
1857	1857	XX	1856
1867	1866	1867-68	1864
1878	1877	—	1875
1887	1887	1886-87	1886
1897	1898	1896-97	1895
XX	1906	1905-06	1904
XX	1914	1913	1914
1927	1924	1923	1924
1937	1932-33	—	1934
1947	1942	XX	XX

References:
Schorger (1947), Airaksinen (1946:88), MacLulich (1937:16), Grange (1950:91), Darrow (1947:566)

Ruffed Grouse peaks in Wisconsin show some similarity to the climax years reported for gallinaceous birds in Finland. In contrast to this is Schorger's conclusion that in Wisconsin the Ruffed Grouse and Prairie Chicken cycles were definitely not synchronized within the period of his study. In recent years, however, the two seem to be more aligned.

British galliforms do not fit into such a table. Siivonen (1950) has claimed a three-and-one-third-year cycle for Red Grouse, Blackgame, and the European Partridge in Britain, but some of the data he cites appear to be the result of random fluctuations in the environment. In one nineteen-year period, for instance, ten different peaks are given for the partridge. Somewhat longer cycles for these species have been reported by Leopold and Ball (1931) and by Middleton (1934). It seems to me more likely that the reported fluctuations of these British grouse are sporadic rather than rhythmic. One should notice that, up to 1952, the British data have always been reported on an estate or local basis, while the Finnish and North American data which we have here considered refer to much larger regions.

Siivonen (1948b) has called attention to a widespread and exceptionally long decline of Ring-necked Pheasant, Blackgame, Capercaillie, and European Partridge in northwestern Europe near the end of the 1930's. This change in numbers, locally equivalent to population crashes, is said to have been brought on by falling winter temperatures and increasing amounts of snow. The decline was quite manifest in 1939 and thus was four years ahead of the decrease in gallinaceous birds that began in North America about 1943. During the 1940's, the galliform populations of these two continents were obviously not displaying the same oscillation.

GEOGRAPHIC HETEROGENEITY

In a given species, some lack of harmony between the fluctuations of regional populations on the same continent has long been evident. The heterogeneity of local population changes of a so-called cyclic species was thoroughly demonstrated in Wisconsin by Leopold (1931:137-144). It has also been abundantly confirmed for Varying Hares by the fur studies of the Bureau of Animal Populations. In the Ruffed Grouse, Clarke (1936) has reported the existence of fluctuations slightly out of phase for different parts of Ontario, and Darrow (1947:565-571) has shown similar deviations between the dates of high populations in the states as well as the provinces. Their data attempt to summarize population behavior of Ruffed Grouse for nearly twenty different states and provinces. Peak and near-peak populations in these regions are said to have occurred in 1903-06, 1913-16, 1922-25, 1930-34, and 1940-42. A Newfoundland peak in 1928 mars the series. The difference between Ruffed Grouse peaks in Wisconsin and general galliform climax years in Finland (Table 11) are no more than what Clarke (1936) has reported between Ruffed Grouse peaks in different parts of Ontario.

Cross (1940) after reviewing the fluctuations of Red Foxes in Ontario has concluded, "It is probable that the cycles demonstrated by Seton and Hewitt . . . are in the main arithmetic periodicities and not inherent continent-wide biological periodicities of Canadian fur-bearers." What Cross tried to stress was this: the picture derived from Hudson's Bay Company data represents the pooling of information from almost half a continent; the reality of what is taking place on small areas is lost. Something of this same feeling against the reality of the ten-year cycle in Canada is expressed (on quite different grounds) by Siivonen (1948a).

Does the ten-year cycle have reality on small areas? The answer to this important question might well depend of course on how small an area we wish to consider. Ten available examples of the fluctuations of grouse populations on small areas are illustrated in Figures 2 and 3. The two fall censuses of Ruffed Grouse in New York and the spring censuses of Prairie Chickens in Illinois give no hint of periodic phenomena; the others do. For the most part, the censuses either (1) cover too few years to permit a critical comparison with the behavior of random numbers along lines recommended by Palmgren (1949) and Cole (1951) or (2) originate in southerly parts of grouse range where the ten-year cycle has never been said to occur.

While it is quite clear that North American research sadly lacks long-term censuses of cyclic grouse on sample areas, the fact remains that clear-cut ten-year cycles have rarely been demonstrated on small areas.

CHRONOLOGICAL REGULARITY

Considering lows, Grange (1950:91) has made an interesting case for the reality of a nearly perfect ten-year grouse cycle in Wisconsin and Manitoba. By taking Schorger's (1944) Prairie Chicken lows in Wisconsin (1857, 1867, 1878, 1887, and 1897), Criddle's (1930) Sharp-tail lows in Manitoba (1897, 1907, and 1918), and his own observations on recent lows among all Wisconsin grouse (1927, 1937, and 1947), Grange has found that "in eight out of ten years the periodicity indicated was exactly ten years." To combine Manitoba and Wisconsin data in this fashion seems to me to be statistically indefensible. At times grouse peaks in these regions have differed by as much as three years. On its own, the Prairie Chicken picture in Wisconsin does show lows with six out of seven years ending in the digit 7. On the other hand, reported Ruffed Grouse highs in Wisconsin show only two out of seven peaks exactly ten years apart (Table 11). Some refutation of a straight ten-year cycle also lies in tabulations by Clarke (1936) and Darrow (1947), where the intervals between highs represented show this distribution:

17 years once	10 years 20 times	7 years once
12 years 6 times	9 years 18 times	6 years once
	8 years 10 times	

These fifty-seven examples average out to 9.5 years. This is fairly similar to the 9.6-year cycle reported for the Lynx by Elton and Nicholson (1942) and the 9.7-year periodicity reported by MacLulich (1937:112) as holding for major peaks of the Varying Hare. The reported long-term grouse and fur cycles would appear to be of the same magnitude.

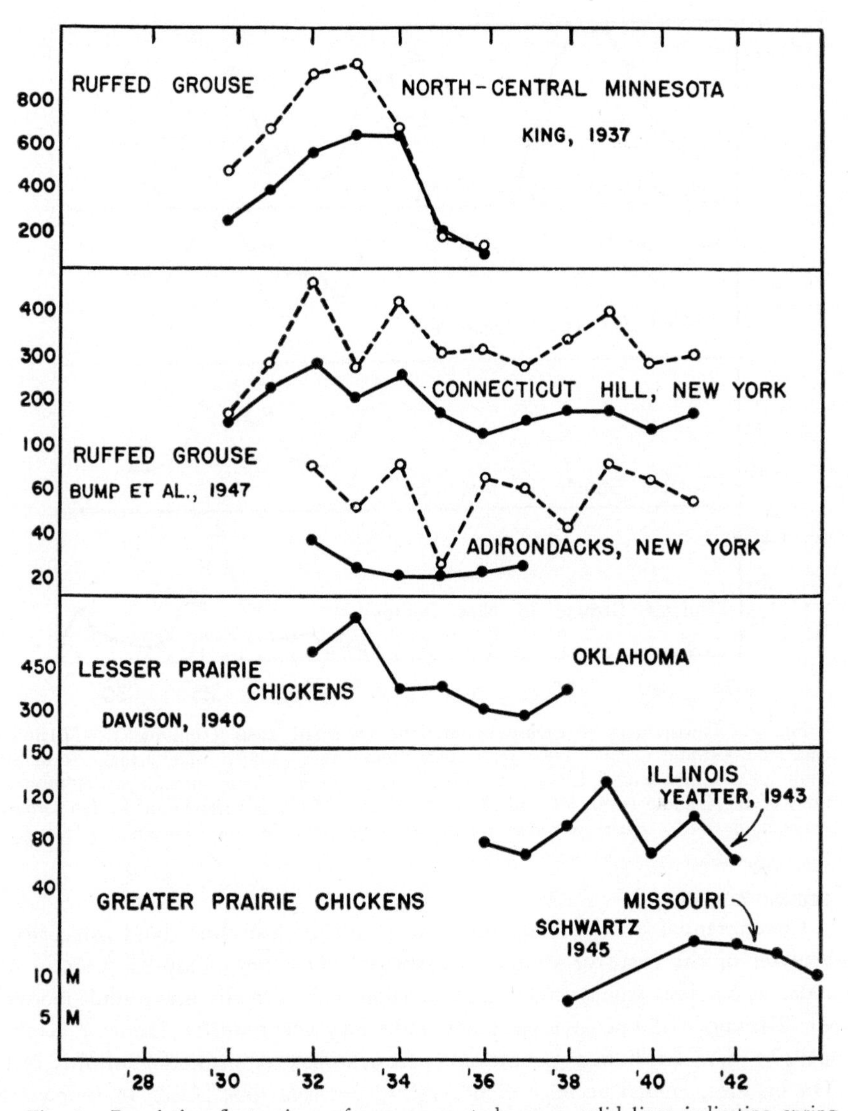

Fig. 2. Population fluctuations of grouse on study areas, solid lines indicating spring censuses, and broken lines fall counts. The size of tracts was about 2,500 square miles in Missouri, 16 square miles in Oklahoma, and 1½ to 4 square miles elsewhere. No cycle is evident in the fall counts for New York nor in the spring counts for Illinois. In the other censuses, peaks in 1932, 1933, or 1934 are quite evident as well as a Missouri peak in 1941.

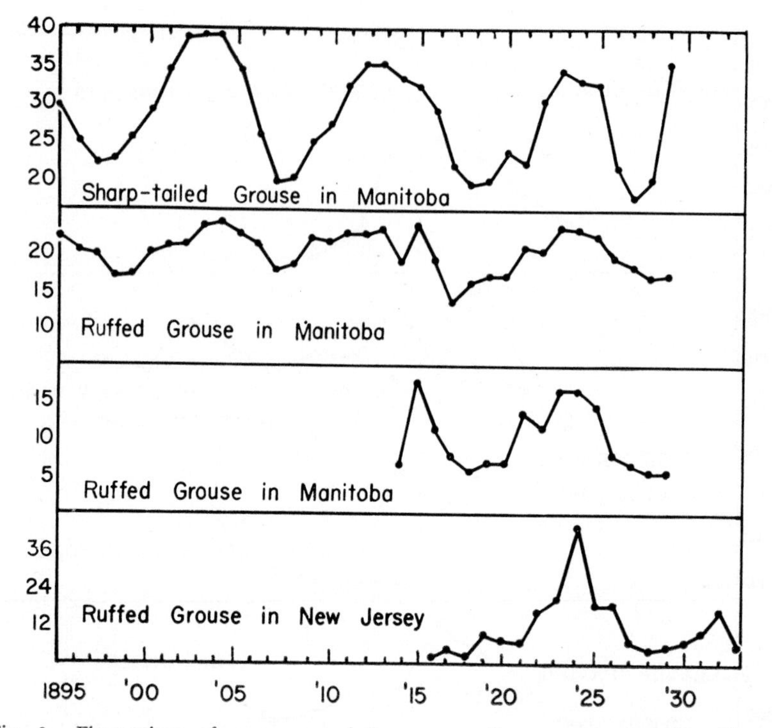

Fig. 3. Fluctuations of grouse populations on small areas (continued). Manitoba data from Criddle (1930), New Jersey data from Eaton (1934). The actual size of the study areas is not known for the two upper graphs here. These summarize the observations of the Criddle family on and about their farm. Criddle's short-term Ruffed Grouse curve holds for a 26-acre woodlot and in part duplicates the curve immediately above it.

DECLINE CURVES

Circumstantial evidence regarding the nature of a decline could come from analyses of the curve of spring populations. (Declines of say 85 per cent or more in one year would almost certainly signify abnormally heavy adult mortality. Declines of 50 per cent per year could typify a reproductive failure.) King's (1937) data on Ruffed Grouse are pertinent for an inspection of this sort. On his area, annual declines of 66 and 45 per cent took place. In four years of rising population, October birds were 1.66 times more numerous than spring birds; in three years of population decline they actually averaged slightly less. Failure to reproduce is clearly implied. Population curves given by Criddle (1930) and Eaton (1934) refer to such small samples that one hesitates to infer much from their slopes. No abnormal adult mortality is indicated. It is of interest to note that mortality among young animals was stressed by Green and Evans (1940) as a controlling factor in the decline of the Varying Hare population in Minnesota in the 1930's.

A number of writers seem to regard the decline of grouse populations as consisting of rather pronounced "crashes." The available census data illustrate that declines usually require several years to take place. Population curves of this sort are evident in the work of Eaton (1934), King (1937), Fisher (1939), Davison (1940), and Buss and Buss (1947) on small areas. This is equally true of population indices for large areas like Minnesota and Wisconsin. Rowan (1948) has reported that the crash of hares in Alberta is much more abrupt than that of birds. The decline of galliform species there in the 1940's appears to have been spread over a two-year period.

Darrow (1947:571-572) has concluded that in Ruffed Grouse the decline generally represents a reproductive failure, presumably in terms of brood losses. While early reports of a lack of young among birds bagged by hunters now seem to have a doubtful authenticity, summer observations of such veteran ornithologists as Brewster and Forbush must be accepted. In Ontario, Clarke (1936) did determine that losses involved young Ruffed Grouse in the summer. Extensive determinations of age ratios in this species are now being carried out and should help settle this point more conclusively. We can, I think, conclude that population crashes among the gallinaceous birds are relatively rare, even among the so-called cyclic species. Crashes may occur, but reproductive failure seems to be the commonest mechanism by which significant population declines are said to be effected.

THE CYCLIC MECHANISM

The actual mechanism of the ten-year "cycle" still remains something of a mystery. Darrow (1947:573) has reviewed the reasons ascribed by various writers as causing periodic scarcity in Ruffed Grouse. A wide variety has been suggested. Janson's (1948) speculations on the decline of South Dakota grouse are typical. The 1915 decline is ascribed to heavy rainfall in June and July. The 1926 decline followed two years of heavy rainfall in June and coincided with outbreaks of tularemia in both rabbits and grouse. The 1935-36 decline was probably due to drought. Clarke's (1936) observations on Ruffed Grouse in Ontario suggest that a blood protozoon may have been associated with the decline there in the 1930's. This diversity of causes, real or alleged, is also instructively illustrated in the Varying Hare, which during one important widespread decline in Minnesota exhibited symptoms of hypoglycemia (Green, Larson, and Mather, 1938). This interesting condition, popularly known as "shock disease," did not reappear apparently in the 1940's. On the other hand, MacLulich (1937) has found a number of other pathological factors, at least one of which, *Staphylococcus apreus,* undoubtedly causes important epidemics in this species. Grange (1949) has seemed to consider starvation as the hares' mortality factor in Wisconsin. Variation in the nutritional properties of newly grown browse has long been suspected as a causative agent. Kalela (1944) has suggested that short-term meteorological cycles (viz. 74.54 days) could influence the growth and metabolism of plants and so affect herbivores during those critical periods when their young are growing rapidly.

Hutchinson and Deevey (1949) also have pointed to the possibility of sodium fluctuating in the mineral content of plants. Amid this welter of suggestion and conjecture, one fact is crystal clear: no single recurring mortality factor has ever been found to cause periodic population declines among mammalian or avian prey species.

In a helpful review of ecological studies of animal populations, Hutchinson and Deevey (1949) have pertinently classified animal cycles as *extrinsic* or *intrinsic*. The former involve controls exercised by some inconspicuous cyclic changes, real or alleged, in the environment. Among the controls that have been suggested are the well-known sunspots (recently resurrected by Grange, 1949), changes in ozone content of the atmosphere (Huntington, 1945), and variations in the nutritional content of vegetation mentioned above.

Intrinsic cycles involve population oscillations produced solely by the life-history properties of a species in an environment that is entirely or at least essentially static. Nearly all writers (*viz.* Dymond, 1947) agree that the growth of a population toward the peak of its cycle could be simply explained as a function of its high breeding potential. In intrinsic cycles, the decline could be caused by an epidemic or by a predator-prey oscillation of the sort pictured by Volterra, Lotka, and others. The spread of rabies through a dense fox population (Gier, 1948; Cowan, 1949) or of a *Leucocytozoon* through grouse (Clarke, 1936) are cases in point. Another example would be oscillations produced by the tension existing between an animal population and the plant community it depends upon for food.

Grange (1949) has attempted to explain the game cycle by a combination of these ideas. His model is pictured as a hare population that suddenly is favored by the shrub stage in a new plant succession. For some years, food and shelter exist in optimal quantities. The hares reach peak numbers. Their food resources now grow up out of reach, predation increases greatly, and the population crashes. The sunspot cycle then increases the incidence of forest fires. New hare (and grouse) range is opened up. Plant successions start all over again. The cycle repeats itself. Ecologically speaking, this is a very ingenious picture. The 9.7-year average of the hare cycle seems to me to offer an irreconcilable difference from the 11.4-year mean of the sunspot cycle, and I therefore believe Grange's hypothesis for an extrinsic control is fundamentally implausible.

Continued failure to find any environmental factor fluctuating in a nine- to ten-year rhythm has more and more set the stage for an intrinsic explanation of the ten-year cycle. Suspicions that the three- to four-year cycle might be a basic component of the longer one go back a quarter of a century. In recent years, Siivonen (1948a) has attempted to demonstrate that the ten-year animal cycle actually is based on a three-and-one-third-year cycle and that this short-term fluctuation is characteristic of a wide series of birds and mammals in the northern parts of the Northern Hemisphere. Siivonen's efforts to fit so many species in both North America and Europe into a single pattern are labored and hard to follow. It is Siivonen's belief that as one goes South (where cyclic phenomena are less spectacular) the minor peaks of the three-and-one-third-year cycle drop out, leaving only a ten-year cycle clearly visible. Blackgame, Capercaillie, Red Grouse, Willow Ptarmigan, and the European Partridge are among the species and subspecies said to fluctuate in this manner.

In a review of this important paper, Palmgren (1949) has used a series of simple mathematical models to suggest that this short-term cycle may well be due to random fluctuations in the environmental factors controlling such populations. The appearance of this analysis coincided with an independent warning by Hutchinson and Deevey (1949) against the over-enthusiastic search for obscure periodicities.

More recently, Cole (1951) has sought to demonstrate the validity of Palmgren's postulate. Cole initially concentrated his attention on cycles to those found in two kinds of plants, four kinds of mammals, and one bird (the European Partridge); but he has obviously regarded his remarks as applying to animal population cycles in general. His tests of significance were largely confined to examinations of the mean length of a species' cycle and the calculation of a coefficient of variation for each such statistic. None of the North American data on gallinaceous birds provide population indices sufficiently long to be analyzed in this fashion.

It seems certain that any fundamental understanding of the cyclic mechanism must consider the heterogeneity of population data arising from small study areas. This diversity seems to be characteristic of data arising from questionnaires on grouse (see Leopold, 1931:144) and on hares (Chitty and co-workers). It has also been reported by Cross (1940) who has found great discrepancies in the numbers of Hudson's Bay Company posts reporting maxima in the collections of pelts of the Red Fox in Ontario. If randomly fluctuating environmental factors can produce population cycles, it follows that heterogeneity must logically be expected in the population curves reported from small areas. Indeed the lack of uniformity in hunters' reports in neighboring states can then be expected.

Siivonen (1950) has attempted to reject randomized factors as a satisfactory explanation for short-term cycles on the ground that the high frequency of two-year peaks in Palmgren's models is atypical of those found in natural population phenomena. Yet Cole (1951) in redefining the peaks to be identified has subsequently obtained a number of such distributions in species like the Lynx, the Partridge, and the Red Fox. He even has managed to produce a Lynx cycle with a mean period of 5.8 years. The result is technically true of 134 years in a Hudson's Bay Company pelt series, but it can scarcely serve as a full explanation of a remarkably clear nine- to ten-year cycle in other fur collection records for this species. Cole's concentration on the average period between rigidly defined cyclic population peaks has markedly advanced our understanding of cycles, but reasons for the general synchronism of major peak phenomena in Lynx pelt reports are not yet understood. Lack (1951) has suggested that predator densities rise as hare populations increase, and that, following the decline of the rodents (due to starvation), predation upon galliform populations might not be negligible. This at least would account for the near synchronization of cycles in populations of such widely unrelated groups. In six Lake states cases that I know of, hare population declines actually have preceded those of gallinaceous birds. Lack's hypothesis thus has some factual basis; it should be studied further.

According to Selye's (1947) concept of the general adaptation syndrome, animals undergoing adreno-pituitary exhaustion may easily succumb to a variety of otherwise insignificant stress factors. Upon this hypothesis, which has awakened wide interest in the medical world, Christian (1950) has suggested that such exhaustion may be typical of cyclic populations in the North where severe climatic conditions and the demands of food shortages could easily set the stage for exhausted adreno-pituitary systems in many mammals. The idea has equal applicability for birds, especially when one recalls the wide variety of things that are said to have caused populations to decline during the past three decades.

This explanation simply accounts for the variety of factors bringing about the decline of "cyclic" populations. The hypothesis fails to attack the core of the problem. As Dymond (1947) has said, "It is the regularity of the events producing a decline in populations that must be accounted for." This regularity has expressed itself in Red Fox and Lynx fur reports that demonstrate regional "ten-year" cycles across the length and breadth of Canada. As far as I know, these cycles do not go out of phase by more than two years from a mean in any given decade. If ten-year cycles are governed by random fluctuations of environmental factors, it is strange that diverging cycles in Ruffed Grouse and Prairie Chicken should be so rare (Table 11; Schorger, 1947) and that the near-alignment of regional grouse cycles should be so commonly reported. Some may regard this latter phenomenon as the result of a natural bias prejudicing the judgment of the investigator. This is not an impossibility, but the scarcity of long-term census data on small areas and of regional population indices (especially in southern Canada) prevents any objective reanalysis at this time.

Moran (1949) has pointed out that the ordinary methods for testing correlation do not apply when we attempt to compare two such series as Lynx trapping data and sunspot numbers. In effect, if we did discover the existence of an environmental factor that controlled a ten-year cycle, we would at the present time lack a mathematical technique that would establish the validity of our hypothesis. Prospects for an immediate solution to the biological enigma of the ten-year cycle seem to me to offer greater promise if attention can be concentrated on intensive long-term population studies in a series of Canadian localities where hares, Lynx, and grouse occur together in numbers. Certainly a study of local phenomena must be worked out if we are ever to understand the regional population indices already existing in the pelt-collection records of Canada.

POPULATION FACTORS AND CONTROLS

The factors controlling galliform populations deserve a much fuller treatment than I can allocate to them in this already long chapter. Smith (1935) has helpfully classified such controls as those that operate on a population irrespective of its density (such as sleet storms) and those that are density-dependent. This arrangement is not always clear-cut, and what holds for one species may not hold for another.

Density-dependent Factors

FOOD

The basic idea of food as the controlling factor in Bobwhite populations has been eloquently argued by Davison (1949). However one may be ecologically drawn to this idea, there are as yet few facts to support the hypothesis. Errington and Hamerstrom (1936:380-382) have characterized the food situation for wintering Iowa and Wisconsin quail as typically either a vast abundance or just not enough. They emphasize, however, that tremendous quantities of food may exist in fields but be available to few if any Bobwhites.

One experiment, in which a wild population of California Quail was systematically and artificially fed, failed to increase the subjects to any important degree (Glading, Enderlin, and Hjersman, 1945). This test deserves to be repeated elsewhere and especially in the area that Davison (1949) discusses.

Nestler (1946) has suggested that vitamin A deficiency may possibly act as a limiting factor on gallinaceous bird populations. This situation has not been found to exist among Ohio Bobwhites (Schultz, 1948) nor among Bobwhites and Ring-necked Pheasants in Wisconsin (Thompson and Baumann, 1950). Actually, the amount of vitamin A carried in the livers of these wild birds was far in excess of their estimated requirements.

PREDATION

The effect of predation on galliform populations has been reviewed by Errington (1946), who minimizes the effects of predators because of automatic adjustments ("intercompensatory trends") exhibited by the prey in their rates of reproductive gain. In effect, the heavier the predation, the more young the population will produce. Stoddard (1939), whose years of experience rank him at the top of game managers in America, has put it quite clearly: "It is evident, other things being equal, that were wholesale killing of all hawks and owls advantageous on quail lands, those preserves that have controlled these birds most closely should have the most quail. *This, however, has not been the case,* and the most productive preserves appear to be those that wage no campaign against birds of prey other than the [Accipitrine] 'blue darters.' "

Several short-term experiments on predator control have been reported by Edminster (1939). Control appears to have halved the mortality in Ruffed Grouse nests. It had, however, no effect on brood mortality and was ultimately offset by increased losses among adults on the uncontrolled areas. This work indicated that, at least in years of grouse abundance, predator control has no effect on fall populations of this species. A five-year experiment on predator control has also been reported by Robeson, Crissey, and Darrow (1949). Removal of 1,240 predators from a 1,050-acre island was followed by an autumnal increase of Ruffed Grouse from 17 to 98 and then a crash to 31. On a nearby check area, the fall population fluctuated moderately between 63 and 50. These New York workers concluded that the high cost of control operations was not balanced by a commensurate improvement in hunting opportunity.

Horn (1939) has described how California Quail populations increased following poisoning operations that destroyed "great numbers" of California Ground Squirrels, *Citellus beecheyi.* The increase was promptly followed by a population crash on one study area where only 30 birds could be found in December after 300 had been counted eight months earlier. In Texas, intensive elimination of 524 fur bearers over a thirteen-month period had no measurable effect on reproductive success of quail on the area (Jackson, 1951). These studies thus form a considerable body of evidence that predator control is not a reliable technique in increasing gallinaceous bird populations.

Intensive management of California Quail on about 450 acres has been reported by Glading, Selleck, and Ross (1945). Two principal techniques were used: complete predator control and artificial feeding. Release of 400 artificially raised and 186 wild-trapped birds appears to have been incidental to the main program. The unique character of this project lay in the distribution of 6 to 12 sacks of grain per week. These totaled 500 per year, which presumably represents about 25 to 30 tons. This food was scattered three times a week throughout the year from a blowing device mounted on a truck. Elimination of predators involved about 500-550 birds and 150 mammals annually. Attempts at cover improvement were not very effective, but grazing was eliminated. In November, 1941, separate field estimates by three California Fish and Game field men averaged 2,240 quail for the 450 acres. This density of close to 500 per 100 acres stands in contrast to about 10 to 20 birds per 100 acres on a nearby check area and represents about the highest ever reported in the fall for a gallinaceous bird population in America. Glading, Selleck, and Ross have attributed it largely to the intensive predator control practiced. The practical extension of this Dune Lakes experiment has never been advocated by Californians for reasons that have not been clearly set forth in the literature. According to J. T. Emlen, Jr. (personal communication), the management program radically altered the whole animal pyramid on the area. As one would expect, mice reached incredible densities. Flocks of wintering sparrows grew to enormous numbers. Almost inevitably, poison set out for mice killed these harmless sparrows seemingly by the thousands. The price of a wrecked biota is not one that American hunters have insisted upon paying for an overflowing game bag.

In a Wisconsin study of the Bobwhite, Errington (1945) has concluded that rates of nonemergency losses (especially predation) remain low when the population is below some level of security provided by the cover. As soon as populations exceed this threshold, the loss rates mount in a characteristically sigmoid curve.

The role of rodents in serving as buffers for gallinaceous birds has been studied in the New York State Grouse Investigation. According to Darrow (1947:314-315, 325-329), the predation of foxes upon nests of Ruffed Grouse was, in a seven-year period, inversely proportional to the numbers of mice, rabbits, and shrews present. Similarly, hares and rabbits buffered adult Ruffed Grouse against the depredations of Horned Owls, *Bubo virginianus* (*ibid.*: 322).

HUNTING

Hunting is essentially a type of predation that affects a prey species according to its density. At the present time, it does not appear to exert a generally depressive effect on most galliform populations in America. This has been best brought out in studies of the Bobwhite Quail. Thus Errington and Hamerstrom (1935) have reported that winter losses on an unshot population of quail in Iowa amounted to 28 per cent, as against 10 per cent for a shot population. A quite similar situation has been reported from Oklahoma, where Baumgartner (1944) found hunting-season losses to amount to 44 per cent on a study area, as against 6 per cent on an unshot area; winter losses on the two areas were 9 and 25 per cent, respectively. Mosby and Overton (1950) have begun managed shooting on a study area. Even when 38 per cent of the population was harvested, the experimental population had virtually the same spring numbers as that of a controlled unshot area. It must be remembered that the Bobwhite has an extremely high annual mortality rate, and that even without hunting its seasonal losses are considerable. A somewhat intermediate ecological picture has been presented for the California Quail by Glading and Saarni (1944). Censuses each March showed the hunted population to be consistently below that of the refuge population. Yet by the following autumn the two groups were nearly equal. In fact, during the latter part of this study, the hunted area showed a few more birds than the unhunted one. At the opposite pole is the Turkey. This species is extremely vulnerable to excessive hunting pressure, and upon it hunting operates critically in many regions regardless of the Turkey's local density. Thus, on a Texas study area of 8,150 acres, hunting pressure on gobblers in one year resulted in a sex ratio of one male to twenty-one females (Walker, 1949).

The percentage of the fall population that can on the average be harvested by hunters has not been fixed with any precision. A number of game biologists believe that the numbers now taken each fall are too small for many gallinaceous game species. A higher kill by man would lower the numbers taken by other predatory animals (compensatory predation) and increase the probability of higher rates of reproductive gain.

According to Glading and Saarni (1944), California Quail were apparently able to withstand an annual kill of 25 per cent, an additional 10 per cent of the birds being crippled and unrecovered. Baumgartner (1944) has found that, at least in some years, the hunting kill of Oklahoma Bobwhites could be as high as 55 per cent. For Bobwhites on a Virginia study area, Mosby and Overton (1950) have tentatively set this figure at 40 per cent. Davison (1949:135) has recommended leaving 50 per cent of each fall covey intact at the end of the hunting season. Middleton (1936) has estimated a 55 per cent harvest as typical of densely stocked British estates where European Partridges are the principal game crop.

Ohio has for some decades set itself up as a refuge for Bobwhite Quail. Quail population trends there have apparently fluctuated in about the same manner as in nearby Indiana where hunting is permitted (Leedy, 1950). Despite the elimination of hunting over such a wide area, no reports of unusual quail abundance in Ohio are available. Grange's (1949) statement that "it is impossible to stockpile game" seems to hold well for galliform birds with their high mortality rates.

Crudely stated, it seems probable that monogamous gallinaceous birds can safely withstand a hunting kill equivalent to about one-half of their annual mortality rate. In some species like the Ruffed Grouse, where the annual take in New York is said to average about 17 per cent (Edminster, 1947:369), the annual harvest almost certainly underutilizes the available crop.

The ecological mechanism controlling these situations in the North Central states has been previously stated by Errington and Hamerstrom (1935). The carrying capacity of early fall environment tends to be high, with plant growth green, dense, and fairly well distributed. The drying up of the herbaceous cover and the loss of deciduous leaves accelerate the mortality from predators. Gallinaceous birds shot prior to this date tend to represent birds that would otherwise be taken by predators.

A somewhat more complex problem has been discussed by Edminster (1937), who has analyzed the effect of a refuge on a cyclic species like the Ruffed Grouse. In a three-year study, a hunted area maintained a higher population than the protected area. A much longer comparison is available in the Lake states. Here, Ammann (1949) has pointed out, Minnesota closed its hunting of Ruffed Grouse for four years during the cyclic low of the 1940's, and Wisconsin did so for three years. Yet by 1948, Michigan, with a consistently open fall hunting season throughout this period, estimated a higher hunters' kill than its two neighbors did following their closed period. At least during this relatively short period, the protected populations were oscillating in about the same manner as the unprotected one.

The probable existence of a principle governing the harvest of cock birds in polygamous galliform birds has already been discussed under sex ratios in this review. In the Lake states, there is still some conflict in opinion on the effect of hunting pressure on the pheasant. To Kozlik and Kabat (1949), who have reported the autumnal disappearance of 602 out of 652 hen pheasants on a Wisconsin study area, illegal hunting looms as a population factor of possibly large importance. In Michigan, D. L. Allen (1942a, 1947) has stressed the application of the law of diminishing returns to the activities of pheasant hunters on two study areas with good escape cover. Apparently the harder pheasants are hunted, the more wary they become. This makes for greater discouragement among hunters who, even on areas moderately close to big cities, have failed to unbalance the sex ratio beyond one cock to four hens.

Density-independent Factors

LAND-USE

During the 1940's, a widespread decrease in the United States population of Bobwhite Quail was noticed (Goodrum, 1949). Increases in clean farming, in livestock, and in dairying are said to have been mainly responsible for this deterioration from 1939 to 1948 (*ibid.*). On a well-censused study area in Wisconsin, Kabat and Thompson (1950) have traced the deterioration in cover which has led to a 60 per cent reduction of the quail population in a period of about fifteen years. Among the land-use changes associated with this was a 47 per cent elimination of fence rows and roadside hedges.

The effects of land-use on other species are so numerous as to be outside the spatial limitations of this review. In the United States, much of this has taken the form of destruction of wildlife cover, and Swift and Scott (1951) have presented a very dramatic picture of this in a single state. Lumbering and its ensuing plant succession have also made for some of the more interesting changes that have taken place. Thus in the Lake states, brush-loving Sharp-tailed Grouse have moved eastward with the cutting off of the forest. They entered the upper peninsula of Michigan by 1922 (Douglass, 1941) and crossed into Ontario about 1925 (Baillie, 1947). This range expansion involved about 200 miles and took about twenty-five years to accomplish (Hamerstrom and Hamerstrom, 1951). With the regrowth of a new forest, this range extension of thousands of birds is probably doomed, although some extremely interesting population islands of this species now persist.

Faber (1948) has attempted to demonstrate the effect of land-use practices upon pheasants in Iowa. While I find it difficult to follow his graphs, his report of rapidly changing farm practices in Iowa is impressive. In a five-year period, 2,600,000 acres more were planted to corn and soybeans; woodlands in the state shrank some 120,000 acres, and 132,000 acres of "waste land" shifted to some other category. According to Faber, pheasant numbers in Iowa (from 1937 to 1946) vary directly with the number of acres in small grains and hay, and inversely with the number of acres in corn and soybeans. Other workers have related gallinaceous bird densities indirectly to soil fertility. Thus Missouri Prairie Chickens have been driven from the best to medium- and low-grade prairie soils (Bennitt, 1939; Schwartz, 1945). In Wisconsin, they have been pushed principally onto sandy soils and into marshlands (Schorger, 1944). In each of these cases, intensive agriculture seems to have reduced the amount of permanent grassland below the minimum niche requirements of this species. In Missouri the Turkey has likewise been driven to the lowest grade forest soil by protracted lumbering operations which it will not tolerate (Leopold and Dalke, 1943).

In Ohio, an intensive study of 1,344 acres of hayfields revealed nineteen adult and nine juvenal pheasants killed for each 100 acres (Dustman, 1950). Here the use of high-speed mowing machines to cut alfalfa at night is especially lethal. Every development of new farming machinery is now studied by astute game managers for its effect on upland game birds. In dairy states like Wisconsin, the use of manure spreaders throughout the winter has been a boon to pheasants, European Partridges, and Bobwhites, which become pressed for food because of the deep snow in winter. The recent trend of farm machines to save labor has been accompanied by increasing wastage of grain that is left in the fields. In a temporary sense, this helps the galliform species below the region of deep winter snows, but the increased ability of a farmer to cultivate more acreage tends to decrease the amount of wild land left in the country, and declining wildlife populations can be expected. This is especially true of the Prairie Chicken, which has already lost one race (the Heath Hen) in the East, has another occupying only 7 per cent of its former range in Texas (Lehmann, 1941), and now has a third race thinly and dangerously scattered in the North Central states.

CLIMATE

The failure of released pheasants to survive as a population in the southern part of the United States has inevitably focused attention on the factor which keeps this species from that part of the continent. Studies of climatographs have led Graham and Hesterberg (1948) to suggest that heat from direct rays of the sun may well be able to raise the temperatures of exposed eggs to lethal levels prior to incubation and thus serve as the factor marking the limits of this species' distribution toward the south. This indeed seems to be the period of a pheasant's particular vulnerability to a warm climate, but Yeatter (1950) has been able to supply a clear hypothesis to account for the known facts. Among the galliforms, reports of egg hatchability have been rather consistently high: 86 to 92 per cent (Leedy and Hicks, 1945; Baskett, 1947; Lack, 1947). Yeatter (1950) has observed a sharp decrease of successful hatches and the number of young per brood in central Illinois. This decrease has proved to involve a decline in the hatchability of the eggs; dead embryos were found in 43 per cent of the fertile eggs in nests that hatched after July 1. Simultaneous exposure of eggs of Bobwhite and the pheasant to a variety of experimental conditions demonstrated that the viability of quail eggs is not destroyed by high pre-incubation temperatures that are followed by lower (night) temperatures, but pheasant embryos are. It thus seems that the vulnerability of pheasant embryos to air temperatures during the laying period importantly limits the southern distribution of this species in the Middle West. Additional experiments appear necessary in order to determine the exact role played by relative humidity in this wholesale failure of pheasant eggs to hatch at the southern limit of their range.

The detection of the actual climatic factors keeping a species from the South has long been a baffling problem to ornithologists. Yeatter's (1950) work therefore represents a notable step forward in this field. Studies of the hatchability of eggs in other species will now form a promising area of research, especially at the southern boundaries of their ranges.

Twomey (1936), Cahn (1938), and McCabe and Hawkins (1946) have all used climatographs to explore climatic barriers to the introduction of exotic gallinaceous birds into North America. This technique is a rather crude analytical tool because of the difficulty of establishing a single set of reference figures for the climate of each species in its native range. Twomey (1936) and McCabe and Hawkins (1946) in their study of the European Partridge point out that the North Central states are too warm in the breeding and brood season of this species and that the low winter temperatures of Alberta do not affect partridge survival.

Shelford (1951) has compared Bobwhite Quail population reports in Ohio and Wisconsin with optimal intensities of solar ultraviolet in April when "quail-nesting operations begin." Although a relationship between the two is claimed, it is difficult to establish this statistically, particularly in time series of fifteen to thirty years' duration, as Moran (1949) has pointed out. To say that "quail-nesting operations" begin at this time in the northern part of the United States is technically correct but hardly valid for an ecological test of this kind. Hatching dates in this region, as determined from wing molt of autumn birds, actually begin in June and peak in July (Thompson, 1949; Thompson and Kabat, 1949; Reeves, 1951).

Shifts in range boundaries, in centers of maximum abundance, and in general population level have been frequently laid to the weather, although this factor is little understood. Generally speaking, the dry years of the 1930's witnessed the spread of European Partridges in Wisconsin (Leopold, 1940) and their increase in Michigan until 1936 (Dale, 1943). The wet period that followed was accompanied by a shift westward (toward the rain shadow of the Rockies) of the center of pheasant density in the Dakotas (Kimball, 1948). At about the same time, partridge populations were declining in Michigan (Dale, 1942) and in Wisconsin (McCabe and Hawkins, 1946; Bersing, 1951). On light-textured soils and on uneven terrain, drainage tended to counteract the effect of high summer rainfall (Dale, 1943).

Important shifts in the northern boundaries of galliform birds have not been noticed in North America. These presumably would be due to an amelioration of the climate in the last fifty years. At least in the Lake states, these could have been readily masked by the changes in plant cover that followed the northward march of the sawmill operator and the farmer. These boundaries obviously are pulsating ones for species, like the Bobwhite Quail, that are quite vulnerable to severe winter weather. According to Trautman, Bills, and Wickliff (1939), average stress periods (in Ohio) take only those birds that are weakened by diseases, parasites, and the like. In a particularly severe winter, range contraction of Bobwhites may amount to as much as 100 miles in Wisconsin (Aldo Leopold, personal communication).

Kabat, Thompson, and Kozlik (1950) have found that weight gains in hen pheasants are importantly delayed following late nesting or renesting. They point out that climatic factors may work quite indirectly on such populations. When adverse weather prolongs the nesting season and delays the hatching-date schedule, the abnormal stress may increase the hen's susceptibility to mortality factors of all types, including such diseases as those of the avian leucosis-complex type.

PLANT SUCCESSIONS

Very little quantitative work has been done on the effect of plant successions on gallinaceous bird densities. In Texas, Lay (1940) reported that Bobwhite densities run about ten per 100 acres in the first four years following the cutting off of timber. The birds reach their maximum density, eighteen per 100 acres, eight years later and then drop to fifteen and later to three per 100 acres. Grange (1949) has helpfully emphasized the role of succession in his stimulating book *The Way to Game Abundance.* In the Lake states, he has reported, four different grouse occupy different stages of a plant succession: Prairie Chickens in the early grassland; Sharp-tailed Grouse in the preforest stage of grass, shrubs, and open forest; Ruffed Grouse in the next stages of broad-leaved woodland; and finally Spruce Grouse in the climax forest of narrow-leaved conifers. Grange (1949:135) goes on to formulate a number of ecological principles, one of which we may notice here. This he calls the "Law of Ideal Succession Stage." In any plant succession, Grange holds, there is usually only one successional stage (or combination of several) which in the entire sequence up to climax will support real abundance for a given species of animal. Elsewhere, Grange (1950:206-224) has outlined the fascinating ecological changes that took place in a central Wisconsin township over a 100-year period. In a temporary sense, the food, cover, and nesting niches in a given block of plant succession would appear to act as density-dependent factors on animal populations. Although high population levels of hares, rabbits, cattle, and deer can even control the course of plant successions, those of gallinaceous birds cannot. In the long-term sense, plant successions can radically alter their population densities and even replace one species with another. In this way, plant successions are density-independent factors.

SUMMARY

In this review, great progress is shown to have been made during the past decade in setting up regional indices and inventories of galliform populations: roadside counts by biologists, rural mail carrier surveys, calling-male transects, quadrat inventories, questionnaires to farmers, aerial censuses, and indices derived from population structure. The biological variables are being studied, but the statistical designs for many of these indices have rarely been described; and the reliability of most of the results remains to be determined. Techniques fixing the age and hatching schedule of fall populations are well worked out, but the results are only now becoming available.

Productivity seems to involve many more eggs than those of a single clutch. For 5,597 nests of gallinaceous birds, 44.5 per cent hatched, compared to 46 per cent for open-nesting passerines. Renesting tendencies vary interspecifically and permit as many as 70 to 80 per cent of the females in some populations to raise at least one young.

Mortality rates run 20 to 50 per cent in the first two months of life. For adults they range rather widely: California Quail, 50 per cent per year (74 for liberated birds); Bobwhite Quail, 77 to 84; and Ring-necked Pheasant, about 50. Preliminary data from Europe place adult European Partridges and Willow Ptarmigan close to the Bobwhite. Ruffed and Sharp-tailed grouse seem to have much lower rates. Sex ratios probably vary at hatching, tend to be even by the first fall, and are markedly skewed toward the males by the second fall in monogamous species. Physiological sterility is present in one-year-old male Turkeys; ecological sterility may occur in Ring-necked Pheasants when otherwise capable males are prevented from holding territories.

Autumnal ratios of young to adults offer valuable clues to adult mortality rates and annual productivity, but biases may occur in hunting data when young are sometimes more vulnerable than adults are to the gun. Age ratios are reported to be nearly even in some galliform species (Mountain Quail, pheasants, and Prairie Chickens) and to involve as much as 80.3 to 84.1 per cent young in others (European Partridge and Bobwhite).

Population growth curves of a sigmoid shape are reported. In general, the percentage of summer gain is inversely proportional to the density in spring. Annual fluctuations usually involve increases of less than 100 per cent and decreases of less than 50 per cent. Severe winters may cause range shrinkage of as much as 100 miles in some species (Bobwhite) and mortalities as high as 80 per cent in others (pheasant). Emigrations of Sharp-tailed Grouse were marked in 1865, 1896, and 1932, apparently in response to population pressure. Spectacular overpopulations of Bobwhite occurred in Wisconsin in the 1850's and in Texas in 1943. As in similar irruptions of pheasants in the Dakotas during the 1940's, these phenomena are due to a multiplicity of factors compounded by time.

The typical population fluctuations of North American grouse exhibit a three-and-one-third-year cycle in regions of 55° to 70° N. latitude. A frequently reported nine-and-one-half-year cycle at 40° to 50° N. rests upon incomplete indices and short-term censuses. While these demonstrate the existence of considerable fluctuations from year to year, there was no complete evidence at the end of the 1940's that grouse actually followed the nine- to ten-year cycles of Lynx, Mink, and Red Fox. Whatever the exact oscillation, both the pheasant and European Partridge are now fitting into it in some regions. Synchronism reported in population changes of grouse seems to involve a two-year spread of regional population peaks on either side of a continental mean; but Prairie Chicken and Ruffed Grouse fluctuations are reported to have been completely out of phase in Wisconsin in the nineteenth century. Elsewhere, regional highs fit well within the two-year limit, with general galliform climax years in Finland approximating Ruffed Grouse peak years in Wisconsin.

Declining population curves for grouse generally imply reproductive failure, but a wide variety of factors have been suggested to bring this about. A useful hypothesis has been offered by Palmgren that random fluctuations of such factors may actually force a population to oscillate with peaks three to four years apart. Future research will have to provide census data and population indices to clarify the exact periodicity which grouse populations exhibit in both Canada and the United States.

Predator control has been found to result only in temporary increases of gallinaceous bird populations (being followed by epidemic diseases in three cases), to have no effect in one instance, and to wreck the biotic pyramid in another. Losses to predators apparently remain low as long as the population is below some level of security provided by the cover. They may, however, become inversely proportional to the availability of other prey species that serve as buffers. Autumnal hunting has had no effect on spring populations of Bobwhite or on subsequent fall populations of California Quail. It can, however, wipe out Turkeys. California Quail can stand a 25 per cent hunting kill and Bobwhites 40 to 55 per cent. New York could probably harvest more than 17 per cent of its Ruffed Grouse annually. Refuges and closed seasons on cyclic species did not help grouse during the past two decades.

Land-use activities have importantly affected many gallinaceous species. Lumbering and the ensuing plant succession permitted Sharp-tailed Grouse to expand their range 200 miles in some twenty-five years. Intensive agriculture seems to have depressed populations of Bobwhites. The effect of new farm machinery varies widely.

Responses to climatic factors are still poorly understood. Pheasants are restricted in the South by mortality among their embryos between oviposition and hatching. Increased precipitation during the early 1940's was accompanied by a widespread decline of pheasant numbers, and their actually shifting somewhat farther west. The dry years of the 1930's witnessed the spread of European Partridges in Wisconsin and their increase in Michigan; these subsequently declined during the wet period that followed. This shift from drought to rainy years was fundamentally responsible for spectacular overpopulations of Bobwhites in Texas and Ring-necked Pheasants in the Dakotas.

Bibliography

ADAMS, L.

1951. Confidence limits for the Petersen or Lincoln index used in animal population studies. Jour. Wildlife Mgmt., 15:13-19.

AIRAKSINEN, K.

1946. Kanalintujen runsaudenvaihtelusta Suomessa. Suomen Riista, 1:75-92.

ALLEN, D. L.

1938. Ecological studies on the vertebrate fauna of a 500-acre farm in Kalamazoo County, Michigan. Ecol. Monogr., 8:347-436.

1942a. That season limit. Mich. Conservation, 11(2):4-5.

1942b. A pheasant inventory method based upon kill records and sex ratios. Trans. Seventh N. Amer. Wildlife Conf., pp. 329-333.

1947. Hunting as a limitation to Michigan pheasant populations. Jour. Wildlife Mgmt., 11:232-243.

AMMANN, G. A.

1944. Determining the age of Pinnated and Sharp-tailed grouses. Jour. Wildlife Mgmt., 8:170-171.

1946. "Chicken" management in the lower peninsula of Michigan. Mich. Dept. of Conservation, 45 pp. (mimeo.).

1947. Summary of Sharptail population data for Drummond Island, Michigan. Mich. Dept. of Conservation, 3 pp.

1949. Grouse prospects. Mich. Conservation, 18(5):14-19.

ATWOOD, E. L.

1951. A sample design for aerial estimation of breeding and total summer populations of game ducks and Canada Geese in Quebec, Newfoundland, New Brunswick and Anticosti Island. Unpublished MS filed at Waterfowl Biometry Office, Section of Waterfowl Management Investigations, U.S. Fish and Wildlife Service, Laurel, Maryland.

BACH, R. N.

1948. The effect of sexidiscriminate harvest on the coefficient of reproduction in pheasants. N.D. Outdoors, 10(10):4-5. Reprinted in Trans. Thirteenth N. Amer. Wildlife Conf., pp. 521-526.

1951a. Pittman-Robertson Division, rural letter carrier upland game survey. N.D. Outdoors, 13(10):12.

1951b. Pheasant cock-hen ratios high in state. N.D. Outdoors, 13(10):12.

BAILLIE, J. L., JR.

1947. Prairie Chickens in Ontario. Sylva (Ont. Dept. Lands and Forests), 3(1):49-51.

BASKETT, T. S.

1947. Nesting and production of the Ring-necked Pheasant in north-central Iowa. Ecol. Monogr., 17:1-30.

BAUMGARTNER, F. M.

1944. Bobwhite Quail populations on hunted vs. protected areas. Jour. Wildlife Mgmt., 8:259-260.

BEED, W. E.

1938. Do fur bearers affect upland game birds in winter? Trans. Third N. Amer. Wildlife Conf., pp. 508-510.

BENNETT, L. J., and G. O. HENDRICKSON

1938. Censu[s]ing the Ringneck Pheasant in Iowa. Trans. Third N. Amer. Wildlife Conf., pp. 719-723.

BENNITT, R.

1939. Some agricultural characteristics of the Missouri Prairie Chicken range. Trans. Fourth N. Amer. Wildlife Conf., pp. 491-500.

1951. Some aspects of Missouri quail and quail hunting. Mo. Conservation Comm. Tech. Bull. No. 2, 51 pp.

[BERSING, O.]

1951. Wisconsin game kill and license sales charts (revised 1951). Wis. Conservation Dept., Madison, 20 pp.

BEZDEK, H.

1944. Sex ratios and color phases in two races of Ruffed Grouse. Jour. Wildlife Mgmt., 8:85-88.

BLOMQUIST, W.

1951. Census techniques. N.D. Outdoors, 13(10):6-8,15.

BUMP, G., R. W. DARROW, F. C. EDMINSTER, and W. F. CRISSEY

1947. The Ruffed Grouse: life history, propagation, management. N.Y. State Conservation Dept., Albany, xl + 915 pp.

BUREAU, L.

1911. L'age des perdrix. 1. Le perdrix grise. Bull. de la Soc. des Sci. Nat. de l'Ouest de la France. 3e Serie, Tome 1, 124 pp.

BUSS, I. O.

[1946]. Wisconsin pheasant populations. Wis. Conservation Dept., Publ. 326, A-46, pp. 1-148.

1947. Review of new techniques—gallinaceous birds. Trans. Twelfth N. Amer. Wildlife Conf., pp. 330-336.

BUSS, I. O., and H. E. BUSS

1947. Deer hunting records from central Bayfield County, 1930-1946. Wis. Conservation Bull., 12(1):5-11.

BUSS, I. O., H. MATTISON, and F. M. KOZLIK

1947. The Bobwhite Quail in Dunn County, Wisconsin. Wis. Conservation Bull., 12(7):6-13.

BUSS, I. O., R. K. MEYER, and C. KABAT

1951. Wisconsin pheasant reproduction studies based on ovulated follicle technique. Jour. Wildlife Mgmt., 15:32-46.

BUTLER, L.

1951. Population cycles and color phase genetics of the Colored Fox in Quebec. Canad. Jour. Zool., 29:24-41.

BYERLY, T. C., and M. A. JULL

1935. Sex ratio and embryonic mortality in domestic fowl. Poult. Sci., 14:217-220.

CAHN, A. R.

1938. A climographic analysis of the problem of introducing three exotic game birds into the Tennessee Valley and vicinity. Trans. Third N. Amer. Wildlife Conf., pp. 807-817.

CARTWRIGHT, B. W.

1944. The "crash" decline in Sharp-tailed Grouse and Hungarian Partridge in western Canada and the role of the predator. Trans. Ninth N. Amer. Wildlife Conf., pp. 324-330.

CHRISTIAN, J. J.

1950. The adreno-pituitary system and population cycles in mammals. Jour. Mammal., 31:247-259.

CLARKE, C. H. D.

1936. Fluctuations in the numbers of Ruffed Grouse, *Bonasa umbellus* (Linne), with special reference to Ontario. Univ. Toronto Studies (Biol. Series) No. 41, 118 pp.

CLOPPER, C. J., and E. S. PEARSON

1934. The use of confidence or fiducial limits illustrated in the use of the binomial. Biometrika, 26:404-413.

COLE, L. C.

1951. Population cycles and random oscillations. Jour. Wildlife Mgmt., 15:233-252.

COWAN, I. McT.

1949. Rabies as a possible population control of arctic Canidae. Jour. Mammal., 30:396-398.

CRIDDLE, N.

1930. Some natural factors governing the fluctuations of grouse in Manitoba. Canad. Field Nat., 44:77-80.

CROSS, E. C.

1940. Periodic fluctuations in numbers of the Red Fox in Ontario. Jour. Mammal., 21:294-306.

CRUMP, W. I., and H. B. SANDERSON

1951. Wild Turkey trapping and transplanting. Wyoming Wild Life, 15(4):4-11, 36-37.

DALE, F. H.

1942. Influence of rainfall and soil on Hungarian Partridges and pheasants in southeastern Michigan. Jour. Wildlife Mgmt., 6:17-18.

1943. History and status of the Hungarian Partridge in Michigan. Jour. Wildlife Mgmt., 7:368-377.

DALKE, P. D., A. S. LEOPOLD, and D. L. SPENCER

1946. The ecology and management of the Wild Turkey in Missouri. Mo. Conservation Comm., Tech. Bull. No. 1, 86 pp.

DARROW, R. W.

1947. Chapters 7, 12, and 13 in The Ruffed Grouse: life history, propagation, management, by G. Bump, R. W. Darrow, F. C. Edminster, and W. F. Crissey. N.Y. State Conservation Dept., Albany, pp. 307-352, 511-580.

DAVIS, D. E.

1948. The survival of wild brown rats on a Maryland farm. Ecology, 29:437-448.

DAVISON, V. E.

1940. An 8-year census of Lesser Prairie Chickens. Jour. Wildlife Mgmt., 4:55-62.

1949. Bobwhites on the rise. Charles Scribner's Sons, New York, 150 pp.

DeLURY, D. B.

1947. On the estimation of biological populations. Biometrics, 3:145-167.

DOUGLASS, D. W.

1941. Sharptailed Grouse in Michigan. Mich. Conservation, 10(9):4,11.

DUSTMAN, E. H.

1950. Effects of alfalfa mill cutting on pheasants and other wildlife in Wood County, Ohio, 1946-1947. Jour. Wildlife Mgmt., 14:225-234.

DYMOND, J. R.

1947. Fluctuations in animal populations with special reference to those of Canada. Trans. Roy. Soc. Can., 41(Sec. 5):1-34.

EATON, W. F.

1934. Eighteen years of Wyanokie (1916-1933). Abst. Proc. Linn. Soc. N.Y., No. 43-44:14-26.

EDMINSTER, F. C.

1937. An analysis of the value of refuges for cyclic game species. Jour. Wildlife Mgmt., 1:37-41.

1939. The effect of predator control on Ruffed Grouse populations in New York. Jour. Wildlife Mgmt., 3:345-352.

1947. Influence of man [on the Ruffed Grouse]. Chapter 9 in The Ruffed Grouse: life history, propagation, management, by G. Bump *et al.* N.Y. State Conservation Dept., Albany, pp. 369-400.

EINARSEN, A. S.

1945a. Quadrat inventory of pheasant trends in Oregon. Jour. Wildlife Mgmt., 9:121-131.

1945b. Some factors affecting Ring-necked Pheasant population density. The Murrelet, 26:29, 39-44.

ELTON, C.

1931. The study of epidemic diseases among wild animals. Jour. Hygiene, 31:435-456.

1942. Voles, mice and lemmings: problems in population dynamics. Oxford University Press, 496 pp.

ELTON, C., and M. NICHOLSON

1942. The ten-year cycle in numbers of the Lynx in Canada. Jour. Animal Ecol., 11:215-244.

EMLEN, J. T., JR.

1940. Sex and age ratios in survival of the California Quail. Jour. Wildlife Mgmt., 4:92-99.

ERRINGTON, P. L.

1933. The nesting and the life equation of the Wisconsin Bob-white. Wilson Bull., 45:122-132.

1945. Some contributions of a fifteen-year local study of the Northern Bob-white to a knowledge of population phenomena. Ecol. Monogr., 15:1-34.

1946. Predation and vertebrate populations. Quart. Rev. Biol., 21:144-177, 221-245.

ERRINGTON, P. L., and F. N. HAMERSTROM, JR.

1935. Bob-white winter survival on experimentally shot and unshot areas. Iowa State College Jour. Sci., 9:625-639.

1936. The Northern Bob-white's winter territory. Agric. Exper. Station, Iowa State College, Res. Bull. 201, pp. 301-443.

1937. The evaluation of nesting losses and juvenile mortality of the Ring-necked Pheasant. Jour. Wildlife Mgmt., 1:3-20.

FABER, L. F.

1948. The effect of farm crops on the production of the Ring-necked Pheasant in Iowa. Proc. Iowa Acad. Sci., 55:109-113.

FISHER, H. I., R. W. HIATT, and W. BERGESON

1947. The validity of the roadside census as applied to pheasants. Jour. Wildlife Mgmt., 11:205-226.

FISHER, L. W.

1939. Studies of the Eastern Ruffed Grouse (*Bonasa umbellus umbellus*) in Michigan. Mich. State College Agric. Exper. Station Tech. Bull. 166, 46 pp.

[FOOTE, L. E.]

1942. Vermont pheasant investigation, yearly summary October 20, 1941, to December 1, 1942. Vermont Fish and Game Service State Bull. No. 8 (Pittman-Robertson Series), 64 pp.

GIER, H. T.

1948. Rabies in the wild. Jour. Wildlife Mgmt., 12:142-153.

GIRARD, G. L.

1937. Life history, habits and food of the Sage Grouse, *Centrocercus urophasianus* Bonaparte. Univ. Wyoming Publ., 3:1-56.

GLADING, B.

1938. Studies on the nesting cycle of the California Valley Quail in 1937. Calif. Fish and Game, 24:318-340.

1941. Valley Quail census methods and populations at the San Joaquin Experimental Range. Calif. Fish and Game, 27:33-38.

GLADING, B., R. W. ENDERLIN, and H. A. HJERSMAN

1945. The Kettleman Hills quail project. Calif. Fish and Game, 31:139-156.

GLADING, B., and R. W. SAARNI

1944. Effect of hunting on a Valley Quail population. Calif. Fish and Game, 30:71-79.

GLADING, B., D. M. SELLECK, and F. T. ROSS

1945. Valley Quail under private management at the Dune Lakes club. Calif. Fish and Game, 31:166-183.

GLOVER, F. A.

1948. Winter activities of Wild Turkey in West Virginia. Jour. Wildlife Mgmt., 12:416-427.

GOODRUM, P.

1949. Status of Bobwhite Quail in the United States. Trans. Fourteenth N. Amer. Wildlife Conf., pp. 359-369.

GORDON, S.

1940. An analysis of methods used to collect game kill statistics. Pennsylvania Game News, 11(8):4-5, 22-23, 30-31.

GORSUCH, D. M.

1934. Life history of the Gambel Quail in Arizona. Univ. Ariz. Biol. Sci. Bull. No. 2 (Univ. Ariz. Bull. 5, No. 4), 89 pp.

GOWER, W. C.

1939. The use of the bursa of Fabricius as an indication of age in game birds. Trans. Fourth N. Amer. Wildlife Conf., pp. 426-430.

GRAHAM, S. A., and G. HESTERBERG

1948. The influence of climate on the Ring-necked Pheasant. Jour. Wildlife Mgmt., 12:9-14.

GRANGE, W. B.

1949. The way to game abundance, with an explanation of game cycles. Charles Scribner's Sons, New York and London, 365 pp.

1950. Wisconsin grouse problems. Wis. Conservation Dept., Madison, 318 pp.

GREEN, R. G., and C. A. EVANS

1940. Studies on a population cycle of Snowshoe Hares on the Lake Alexandria Area, III. Effect of reproduction and mortality of young hares on the cycle. Jour. Wildlife Mgmt., 4:347-358.

GREEN, R. G., C. L. LARSON, and D. W. MATHER

1938. The natural occurrence of shock disease in hares. Trans. Third N. Amer. Wildlife Conf., pp. 877-881.

GROSS, A. O.

1928. The Heath Hen. Memoirs Boston Soc. Nat. Hist., 6:491-588.

HAGEN, Y.

1935. Ringmerking av lirype i Rauland og Tinn. Nytt Mag. Naturv., 75:243-288.

HALE, J. B., and R. F. WENDT

1950. Reports on the 1949 Ruffed Grouse season. Wis. Conservation Bull., 15(3):11-14.

HAMERSTROM, F. N., JR.

1936. A study of the nesting habits of the Ring-necked Pheasant in northwest Iowa. Iowa State College Jour. Sci., 10:173-203.

1939. A study of Wisconsin Prairie Chicken and Sharp-tailed Grouse. Wilson Bull., 51:105-120.

HAMERSTROM, F. N., JR., and F. HAMERSTROM

1949. Daily and seasonal movements of Wisconsin Prairie Chickens. Auk, 66:313-337.

1951. Mobility of the Sharp-tailed Grouse in relation to its ecology and distribution. Amer. Midl. Nat., 46:174-226.

HANSON, H. C., and R. H. SMITH

1950. Canada Geese of the Mississippi Flyway with special reference to an Illinois flock. Bull. Ill. Nat. Hist. Surv., 25:67-210.

HAYNE, D. W.

1949. An examination of the strip census method for estimating animal populations. Jour. Wildlife Mgmt., 13:145-157.

1951. [Review] Estimating game from licensee reports. Jour. Wildlife Mgmt., 15:325-327.

HIATT, R. W., and H. I. FISHER

1947. The reproductive cycle of Ring-necked Pheasants in Montana. Auk, 64:528-548.

HOCHBAUM, H. A.

1944. The Canvasback on a prairie marsh. The Amer. Wildlife Inst., Washington, 201 pp.

HORN, E. E.

1939. Factors in nesting losses of the California Valley Quail. U.S. Dept. Interior, Bur. Biol. Surv., Wildlife Res. & Mgmt. Leaflet BS-124 (7-pp. mimeographed revision of paper in Trans. Third N. Amer. Wildlife Conf., pp. 741-746).

HUNTINGTON, E.

1945. Mainsprings of civilization. John Wiley & Sons, Inc., New York, 600 pp.

HUTCHINSON, G. E., and E. S. DEEVEY, JR.

1949. Ecological studies on animal populations. In Survey of Biological Progress, Vol. I. Academic Press, Inc., New York, pp. 325-359.

JACKSON, A. S.

1947. A Bobwhite Quail irruption in northwest Texas L[o]wer Plains terminated by predation. Trans. Twelfth N. Amer. Wildlife Conf., pp. 511-519.

1951. The Bobwhite Quail in relation to land management in the Western Cross Timbers. Texas Game, Fish and Oyster Comm., FA Rept. Series, No. 7, 47 pp.

JANSON, R. G.

1948. Grouse cycles. S. D. Conservation Digest, 15(5)10,13,16.

1951. Determining age and sex of—grouse! S.D. Conservation Digest, 18(1): 8-10.

KABAT, C., and D. R. THOMPSON

1950. Game and cover changes in southern Wisconsin, 1929-51. In Report to the people of Wisconsin on cover destruction, habitat improvement and watershed problems of the state in 1950. Wis. Conservation Bull., 16(2):45-47.

KABAT, C., D. R. THOMPSON, and F. M. KOZLIK

1950. Pheasant weights and wing molt in relation to reproduction with survival implications. Wis. Conservation Dept., Tech. Wildlife Bull. No. 2.

KALELA, O.

1944. Uber den 10jährigen Massenwechsel bei pflanzenfressenden Vögeln und Säugetieren nebst einigen Gesichtspunkten zu seiner Erklärung. Ornis Fennica, 21:42-62.

KELKER, G. H.

1940. Estimating deer populations by a differential hunting loss in the sexes. Proc. Utah Acad. Sci., Arts and Letters, 17:65-69.

KELLER, R. J., H. R. SHEPHERD, and R. N. RANDALL

1941. Report of the Sage Grouse survey: Pittman-Robertson Project, Colorado 4-R, Season 1941, with comparative data of previous seasons. Sage Grouse Survey Colorado, 3:31 pp.

KIMBALL, J. W.

1944. Age gauge for pheasants. Jour. Wildlife Mgmt., 8:263-264.

1948. Pheasant population characteristics and trends in the Dakotas. Trans. Thirteenth N. Amer. Wildlife Conf., pp. 291-314.

1949. The crowing count pheasant census. Jour. Wildlife Mgmt., 13:101-120.

KING, R.

1937. Ruffed Grouse management. Jour. Forestry, 35:523-532.

KIRKPATRICK, C. M.

1944. The bursa of Fabricius in Ring-necked Pheasants. Jour. Wildlife Mgmt., 8:118-129.

KIRSCH, L.

1951. Our winter storm losses. S.D. Conservation Digest, 18(4):2-3, 7, 12.

KLIMSTRA, W. D.

1950. Bob-white Quail nesting and production in southeastern Iowa. Iowa State College Jour. Sci., 24:385-395.

KORTLANDT, A.

1942. Levensloop, samenstelling en structur der Nederlandse aalscholverbevolking: Een deersociologisch—geographisch onderzolk. Ardea, 31:175-280.

KOZLIK, F., and C. KABAT

1949. Why do pheasant populations remain low? Wis. Conservation Bull., 14(10):1-4.

KRISTOFFERSEN, S.

1937. Undersökelser over lirypens forplantningsforhold. Tromsö Museums rypeundersökelser. Nytt Mag. Naturv., 77:141-194.

LACK, D.

1946. Do juvenile birds survive less well than adults? Brit. Birds, 13:258-264.

1947. The significance of clutch-size in the Partridge (*Perdix perdix*). Jour. Animal Ecol., 16:19-25.

1951. Population ecology in birds: a review. Proc. Tenth Internat. Ornithol. Cong., pp. 409-448.

LANDAUER, W., and A. B. LANDAUER

1931. Chick mortality and sex-ratio in the domestic fowl. Amer. Nat., 65:492-501.

LATHAM, R. M.

1942. A simple method of sexing day-old Ringneck Pheasant chicks. Pennsylvania Game Comm., Res. Circ. No. 2.

LAY, D. W.

1940. Bob-white populations as affected by woodland management in eastern Texas. Tex. Agric. Exper. Station, Bull. 592, 37 pp.

1950. Facts from quail wings. Texas Game and Fish, 9(1):26.

LEE, L.

1950. Kill analyses for the Lesser Prairie Chicken in New Mexico, 1949. Jour. Wildlife Mgmt., 14:475-477.

LEEDY, D. L.

1949. Ohio pheasant nesting surveys based on farmer interviews. Jour. Wildlife Mgmt., 13:274-286.

1950. Ohio's status as a game and fur producing state. Ohio Jour. Sci., 50:80-94.

LEEDY, D. L., and L. E. HICKS

1945. The pheasant in Ohio. In The Ring-necked Pheasant and its management in North America, ed. by W. L. McAtee. The Amer. Wildlife Inst., Washington, pp. 57-130.

LEHMANN, V. W.

1941. Attwater's Prairie Chicken: its life history and management. N. Amer. Fauna No. 57, 65 pp.

1946a. Bobwhite Quail reproduction in southwestern Texas. Jour. Wildlife Mgmt., 10:111-123.

1946b. Mobility of Bobwhite Quail in southwestern Texas. Jour. Wildlife Mgmt., 10:124-136.

LEOPOLD, A.

1931. Report on a game survey of the North Central states. Amer. Game Assn., Washington, 299 pp.

1937. The effect of the winter of 1935-36 on Wisconsin quail. Amer. Midl. Nat., 18:408-416.

1940. Spread of the Hungarian Partridge in Wisconsin. Trans. Wis. Acad. Sci., Arts and Letters, 32:5-28.

LEOPOLD, A., and J. N. BALL

1931. British and American grouse cycles. Canad. Field Nat., 45:162-167.

LEOPOLD, A., T. M. SPERRY, W. S. FEENEY, and J. A. CATENHUSEN

1943. Population turnover on a Wisconsin pheasant refuge. Jour. Wildlife Mgmt., 7:383-394.

LEOPOLD, A. S.

1939. Age determination in quail. Jour. Wildlife Mgmt., 3:261-265.

1945. Sex and age ratios among Bobwhite Quail in southern Missouri. Jour. Wildlife Mgmt., 9:30-34.

LEOPOLD, A. S., and P. D. DALKE

1943. The 1942 status of Wild Turkeys in Missouri. Jour. Forestry, 41:428-435.

LIGON, J. S.

1946. History and management of Merriam's Wild Turkey. New Mexico Game and Fish Comm., Albuquerque, x + 84 pp.

LINDUSKA, J. P.

1943. A gross study of the bursa of Fabricius and cock spurs as age indicators in the Ring-necked Pheasant. Auk, 60:426-437.

1945. Age determination in the Ring-necked Pheasant. Jour. Wildlife Mgmt., 9:152-154.

1947. Keeping tab on pheasants. Mich. Conservation, 16(7):6-7, 10; (8):8-9, 14.

McCABE, R. A.

1949. A ten-year study of a refuge population of Ring-necked Pheasants. Summaries of doctoral dissertations, University of Wisconsin . . ., Vol. X. University of Wisconsin Press, Madison, pp. 231-233.

McCABE, R. A., and A. S. HAWKINS

1946. The Hungarian Partridge in Wisconsin. Amer. Midl. Nat., 36:1-75.

McCLURE, H. E.

1945. Comparison of census methods for pheasants in Nebraska. Jour. Wildlife Mgmt., 9:38-45.

MacLULICH, D. A.

1937. Fluctuations in the numbers of the Varying Hare (*Lepus americanus*). Univ. Toronto Studies (Biol. Series) No. 43.

MacMULLAN, R. A.

1950. Anticipating fall pheasant kill from summer brood surveys. Paper presented at Twelfth Midwest Wildlife Conf., Columbus, Ohio, Dec. 15, 1950.

MARSHALL, H.

1947. Longevity of the American Herring Gull. Auk, 64:188-198.

MAYR, E., and D. AMADON

1951. A classification of recent birds. Amer. Mus. Novit., No. 1496, 42 pp.

MIDDLETON, A. D.

1934. Periodic fluctuations in British game populations. Jour. Animal Ecol., 3:231-249.

1935-37. The population of Partridges (*Perdix perdix*) . . . in Great Britain. Jour. Animal Ecol., 4:137-145; 5:252-261; 6:318-321.

1936. Factors controlling the population of the Partridge (*Perdix perdix*) in Great Britain. Proc. Zool. Soc. London, 1935, pp. 795-815.

MOHLER, L. L.

1948. Nebraska's Pheasant inventory. [Nebraska Game, Forestation and Parks Comm.] Wildlife Mgmt. Notes, 1:7-10, 11-14.

MORAN, P. A. P.

1949. The statistical analysis of the sunspot and Lynx cycles. Jour. Animal Ecol., 18:115-116.

MOSBY, H. S., and C. O. HANDLEY

1943. The Wild Turkey in Virginia: its status, life history and management. Commission of Game and Inland Fisheries, Richmond, Va., 281 pp.

MOSBY, H. S., and W. S. OVERTON

1950. Fluctuations in the quail population on the Virginia Polytechnic Institute Farms, Montgomery County, Virginia. Trans. Fifteenth N. Amer. Wildlife Conf., pp. 347-355.

MURRAY, R. W.

1948. Wintering Bobwhite in Boone County, Missouri. Jour. Wildlife Mgmt., 12:37-45.

NELSON, B. A.

1946. Population characteristics of South Dakota pheasants. Mimeographed paper presented at Eighth Midwest Wildlife Conf., Dec., 1946, Columbia, Mo. 3 pp.

1948. Pheasant data from a two-year bag study in South Dakota. Jour. Wildlife Mgmt., 12:20-31.

NESTLER, R. B.

1946. Vitamin A, vital factor in the survival of Bobwhites. Trans. Eleventh N. Amer. Wildlife Conf., pp. 176-195.

NICE, M. M.

1937. Studies in the life history of the Song Sparrow, I. A population study of the Song Sparrow. Trans. Linn. Soc. N.Y., 4:1-247.

OLSTAD, O.

1932. Undersøkelser over Lirypens Fortplantningsforhold. Nytt Mag. Naturv., 71. Reprint, 71 pp.

PALMGREN, P.

1949. Some remarks on the short-term fluctuations in the numbers of northern birds and mammals. Oikos, 1:114-121.

PATTERSON, R. L.

1949. Sage Grouse along the Oregon Trail. Wyoming Wild Life, 13(8):1-16.

1950. The 1950 Sage Grouse season. Wyoming Wild Life, 14(10):18-23, 38.

PAYNTER, R. A., JR.

1947. The fate of banded Kent Island Herring Gulls. Bird-Banding, 18:156-170.

PETERS, J. L.

1934. Check-list of birds of the world. Vol. II. Harvard University Press, Cambridge, 401 pp.

PETERSEN, C. G. J.

1896. The yearly immigration of young plaice into the Limfjord from the German Sea, etc. Rept. Danish Biological Station for 1895, 6:1-77.

PETRIDES, G. A.

1949. Viewpoints on the analysis of open season sex and age ratios. Trans. Fourteenth N. Amer. Wildlife Conf., pp. 391-410.

PETRIDES, G. A., and R. B. NESTLER

1943. Age determination in juvenal Bobwhite Quail. Amer. Midl. Nat., 30: 774-872.

RANDALL, P. W.

1940a. Causes of juvenile mortality of the Ringneck Pheasant. Pennsylvania Game News, 11(3):10-11, 28.

1940b. The life equation of the Ring-neck Pheasant in Pennsylvania. Trans. Fifth N. Amer. Wildlife Conf., pp. 300-320.

RANDALL, P. E., and L. J. BENNETT

1939. Censusing Ringneck Pheasants in Pennsylvania. Trans. Fourth N. Amer. Wildlife Conf., pp. 431-436.

RASMUSSEN, D. I., and L. A. GRINER

1938. Life history and management of the Sage Grouse in Utah, with special reference to nesting and feeding habits. Trans. Third N. Amer. Wildlife Conf., pp. 852-864.

RASMUSSEN, D. I., and W. T. McKEAN

1945. The pheasant in the Intermountain Irrigated Region. In The Ring-necked Pheasant and its management in North America, ed. by W. L. McAtee. The Amer. Wildlife Inst., Washington, pp. 234-253.

REEVES, M. C.

1951. Sex, age, and weight studies of Indiana Bobwhite Quail. Outdoor Indiana, 18(8):10-11.

RICHARDSON, F.

1941. Results of the southern California quail banding program. Calif. Fish and Game, 27:234-249.

[ROBESON, S. B., W. F. CRISSEY, and R. W. DARROW]

1949. A study of predator control on Valcour Island. N.Y. State Conservation Dept. Research Series (Div. of Fish and Game) No. 1, 28 pp.

ROWAN, W.

1948. The ten-year cycle: outstanding problem of Canadian conservation. Univ. Alberta Dept. Extension, Edmonton, 15 pp.

SANDERS, E.

1943. Development of a Bob-white management area in southern Iowa. Iowa State College Agric. Exper. Station Res. Bull. 317, pp. 698-726.

SCHORGER, A. W.

1942. The Wild Turkey in Wisconsin. Wilson Bull., 54:173-182.

1944. The Prairie Chicken and Sharp-tailed Grouse in early Wisconsin. Trans. Wis. Acad. Sci., Arts and Letters, 35:1-59.

1946. The quail in early Wisconsin. Trans. Wis. Acad. Sci., Arts and Letters, 36:77-103.

1947. The Ruffed Grouse in early Wisconsin. Trans. Wis. Acad Sci., Arts and Letters, 37:35-90.

SCHULTZ, V.

1948. Vitamin A as a survival factor of the Bobwhite Quail (*Colinus v. virginianus*) in Ohio during the winter of 1946-47. Jour. Wildlife Mgmt., 12:251-263.

SCHWARTZ, C. W.

1945. The ecology of the Prairie Chicken in Missouri. Univ. Mo. Studies, 20: 1-99.

SCHWARTZ, C. W., and E. R. SCHWARTZ

1950. The California Quail in Hawaii. Auk, 67:1-38.

SCOTT, W. E.

1946. Graphs showing game kill in Wisconsin, with license sales charts. Wis. Conservation Dept., Madison, 20 pp.

SELYE, H.

1947. The general-adaptation-syndrome and the diseases of adaptation. In Textbook of endocrinology. Acta Endocrinologica, Montreal Univ., Montreal, pp. 837-867.

SHELFORD, V. E.

1951. Fluctuation of non-forest animal populations in the Upper Mississippi Basin. Ecol. Monogr., 21:149-181.

SHICK, C.

1947. Sex ratio—egg fertility relationships in the Ring-necked Pheasant. Jour. Wildlife Mgmt., 11:302-306.

SIIVONEN, L.

1948a. Structure of short-cycle fluctuations in numbers of mammals and birds in the northern parts of the northern hemisphere. Finnish Fdn. Game Preserv., Papers on Game-Research 1, 166 pp.

1948b. Decline in numerous mammal and bird populations in northwestern Europe during the 1940's. Finnish Fdn. Game Preserv., Papers on Game-Research 2, 26 pp.

1950. Some observations on the short-term fluctuations in numbers of birds and mammals in the sphere of the northernmost Atlantic. Finnish Fdn. Game Preserv., Papers on Game-Research 4, 31 pp.

SMITH, E. H.

1950. Refinement and practical application of the crowing count census. Paper presented at Eleventh Midwest Wildlife Conf., Dec. 15-17, 1949. Mimeographed by Wis. Conservation Dept.

SMITH, H. S.

1935. The role of biotic factors in the determination of population densities. Jour. Econ. Ent., 28:873-898.

SMITH, J. D.

1948. [Unpublished report to Territorial Board of Commissioners of Agriculture and Forestry, Honolulu; as quoted by C. W. and E. R. Schwartz, (1950)].

SNYDER, L. L.

1935. A study of the Sharp-tailed Grouse. Contr. Royal Ont. Mus. Zool., No. 6, 66 pp. (reprinted from Univ. Toronto Studies, Biol. Series, No. 40).

SNYDER, L. L., and T. M. SHORTT

1936. A summary of data relative to a recent invasion of Willow Ptarmigan. Royal Ont. Mus. Zool. Occ. Papers No. 3, 4 pp.

SONDRINI, W. J.

1950. Estimating game from license reports. Connecticut State Bd. Fisheries and Game, Pittman-Robertson Bull. No. 3, 50 pp.

STODDARD, H. L.

1931. The Bobwhite Quail: its habits, preservation and increase. Charles Scribner's Sons, New York, 559 pp.

1939. Cooperative Quail Study Association, seventh annual report, 1937-38. Thomasville, Ga., 31 pp.

STUART, R. W.

1951. The pheasant in the forties! N.D. Outdoors, 13(11):4-6.

SUMNER, E. L., JR.

1935. A life history study of the California Quail, with recommendations for conservation and management. Calif. Fish and Game, 21:167-256, 277-342.

SWIFT, E., and W. E. SCOTT

1951. Report to the people of Wisconsin on cover destruction, habitat improvement and watershed problems of the state in 1950. Wis. Conservation Bull., 16(2):3-78.

TABER, R. D.

1949. Observations on the breeding behavior of the Ring-necked Pheasant. Condor, 51:153-175.

THOMPSON, D. R.

1949. Bobs away. Wisconsin Conservation Bull., 14(5):17-20.

THOMPSON, D. R., and C. A. BAUMANN

1950. Vitamin A in pheasants, quail and muskrats. Jour. Wildlife Mgmt., 14:42-49.

THOMPSON, D. R., and C. KABAT

1949. Hatching dates of quail in Wisconsin. Jour. Wildlife Mgmt., 13:231-233.

1950. The wing molt of the Bob-white. Wilson Bull., 62:20-31.

THOMPSON, D. R., and R. D. TABER

1948. Reference tables for dating events in nesting of Ring-necked Pheasant, Bobwhite Quail, and Hungarian Partridge by aging of broods. Jour. Wildlife Mgmt., 12:14-19.

TRAUTMAN, M. B., W. E. BILLS, and E. L. WICKLIFF

1939. Winter losses from starvation and exposure of waterfowl and upland game birds in Ohio and other northern states. Wilson Bull., 51:86-104.

TRIPPENSEE, R. E.

1948. Wildlife management: upland game and general principles. McGraw-Hill Company, Inc., New York, 479 pp.

TWINING, H., H. A. HJERSMAN, and W. MacGREGOR

1948. Fertility of eggs of the Ring-necked Pheasant. Calif. Fish and Game, 34:209-216.

TWOMEY, A. C.

1936. Climographic studies of certain introduced and migratory birds. Ecology, 17:122-132.

WALKER, E. A.

1949. Factors influencing Wild Turkey. Texas Game, Fish and Oyster Comm., FA Rept. Series No. 4, 20 pp.

WESTERSKOV, K.

1950a. Methods for determining the age of game bird eggs. Jour. Wildlife Mgmt., 14:56-67.

1950b. Bestandsskifte-perioden og levealderen hos lirypen. Naturen, nr. 11, pp. 321-328.

1951. Om Aldersfordeling og Goldhed i Agerhønsebestanden. Vildtbiol. Station Kalö, medd. nr. 4. Rept. from Dansk Jagt., 68(3):26-28.

WHEELER, R. J.

1948. The Wild Turkey in Alabama. Alabama Dept. Conservation, 92 pp.

WILSON, K. A., and E. A. VAUGHN

1944. The Bobwhite Quail in eastern Maryland. Game and Inland Fish Comm. of Md., Baltimore, 138 pp.

YEATTER, R.

1934. The Hungarian Partridge in the Great Lakes region. Univ. Mich. School Forestry and Conservation Bull. 5, 92 pp.

1943. The Prairie Chicken in Illinois. Bull. Ill. Nat. Hist. Surv., 22:375-416.

1950. Effects of different preincubation temperatures on the hatchability of pheasant eggs. Science, 112:529-530.

YOCUM, C. F.

1943. The Hungarian Partridge *Perdix perdix* Linn. in the Palouse region, Washington. Ecol. Monogr., 13:167-202.

chapter 12

BIRDBANDING IN THE STUDY OF POPULATION DYNAMICS[1]

. . . Donald S. Farner

INTRODUCTION

A population of a species may be regarded as an open system to which new individuals are being added by reproduction and from which individuals are being removed by death. Further additions and losses may be effected by immigration and emigration. Populations display properties of a self-compensating steady state in which positive and negative fluctuations in size or density may be rather promptly eliminated by compensating devices. To note the over-simplified analogy with a water reservoir with continual, but variable, inflow and outflow and a variable volume is inescapable. As open systems these have obvious properties in common. Mathematically a population is a system involving many parameters. Among the variable factors operating in an avian population are rate of egg production, rate of hatching, mortality rates for various periods of the life span, rates of addition and loss by emigration and immigration, etc. None of these is a simple independent variable. Rather each is a result of the interaction of other variables, for example, the role of environmental, genetic, and density variables in mortality rates. Not only is the population dynamic with respect to its *composition* and *size* or *density,* it is also dynamic *geographically* as evidenced by migration, irruptive and nomadic movements, and changes in geographic range.

Certain aspects of the dynamics of avian populations can be described and perhaps partially explained by analyses of banding data. However, it is likewise patent that banding studies alone cannot develop a total elucidation of the population dynamics of any species but rather must be regarded as a virtually indispensable element in the battery of research tools which must be employed.

With respect to the geographic aspects of avian population dynamics, the contribution of banding to the description of migratory movements is classical and of profound importance. It has been less important with respect to irruptive and nomadic movements and of very little importance with respect to studies of changes in geographic range. Since the contributions of birdbanding to the

[1] The procurement of a part of the data on which this chapter is based was made possible by a grant from the Committee on Research of The State College of Washington.

Manuscript received December 26, 1952.

study of the movements of birds are well known and adequately described in many treatises, they will not be included in the ensuing discussion. The primary function of this treatise, then, is to assemble the results of banding studies which contribute to an understanding of those aspects of avian population dynamics which have a bearing on the size or density and the composition of populations, to suggest ways in which this type of study can be integrated with other research tools, and to indicate additional related problems which appear worthy of attention. Considerations of space prohibit the very desirable introduction of material from investigations on other groups of animals and, conversely, the projection of conclusions derived from investigations on birds into principles of general application. The reader interested in these ramifications may be aided and guided by the excellent discussion of Deevey (1947).

Since the inception of systematic birdbanding with the activities of Mortensen (Jespersen and Tåning, 1950) in Denmark in 1899, approximately nine million birds have been banded by the birdbanding systems and organizations in countries of three continents (von Haartman, 1948). There are currently at least thirty-nine systems in operation in at least twenty-six countries (Rydzewski, 1951). In each of these, birds are marked with leg bands on which are engraved an identification number and an indication of the address to which the recovered band should be sent. Each system maintains a file of records of banded birds and a file of recovered birds, with the pertinent data for each record. The rather extensive quantity of data which has been accumulated from the recovery of these banded birds can, with careful analysis, be a rich source of information concerning the above-mentioned aspects of the population dynamics of many species. Included are age-group structure, mean natural longevity, annual mortality and survival rates, and life expectancy.

Among the earlier studies on population dynamics employing data from banded birds were those of Burkitt (1926) on the European Robin, *Erithacus rubecula;* Magee (1928, 1936) and Whittle (1929) on the Purple Finch, *Carpodacus purpureus;* Hoffman (1929) on the Blue Jay, *Cyanocitta cristata;* Kendeigh (1937) on the House Wren, *Troglodytes aëdon;* and Nice (1937) on the Song Sparrow, *Melospiza melodia.* However, only in the last two is there a clear conception of the relation of mortality and survival rates to age-group structure of populations and to the mean natural longevity of the individuals of a population. These studies and the excellent analysis by Kraak, Rinkel, and Hoogerheide (1940) of banding data on the Lapwing, *Vanellus vanellus,* actually represent the pioneer efforts in this field. The major contributor has been Lack who has published several important studies on British species. The methods and philosophy of this approach have been reviewed critically in Hickey's (1952) important monograph.

TERMINOLOGY

A small body of terminology has been developed in relation to the utilization of banding data in the study of population dynamics. In respect to individual and mean longevity, three concepts may be recognized (Farner, 1945:56). *Potential longevity* is the maximum life span possible for an individual of a species under optimal conditions. Since the attainment of potential longevity by an individual of a species requires the maximization of the simultaneous functions of a large number of variables mostly unknown and uncontrollable, no accurate numerical value can be assigned. However, values above which the numerical value of potential longevity must lie can be obtained from the data on longevity of birds kept in zoological parks and aviaries. *Potential natural longevity* is the maximum life span possible for an individual of the species under natural conditions. Like the previous concept, the assignment of a definite value is not possible. Similarly, values above which the numerical value of potential natural longevity must lie can be obtained from records of the maximum survival of banded birds. *Mean natural longevity* is the mean age attained by individuals of a population at the time of death. Logically and ideally this value should represent true mean age, i.e., from the date of hatching. For reasons discussed subsequently herein, it is frequently not possible to calculate, from banding data, mean natural longevity as of the date of hatching. Consequently, it frequently is necessary to express mean natural longevity (or life expectancy) *as of a prescribed initial date.* From this it is sometimes possible, however, to estimate mean longevity as of the date of hatching. Mean longevity as of a prescribed initial date is obviously synonymous with *mean after lifetime* as of that particular date.

Mortality is usually expressed as an *annual mortality rate* (M) which is obtained by dividing the number in a group or sample which die during the course of a year by the number alive at the beginning of the year. Similarly, the *annual survival rate* (S) is obtained from the number in a group or sample which survive to the end of the year divided by the number alive at the beginning of the year. Obviously, $S = 1 - M$. Davis (1952:316) has correctly indicated that *mortality rate,* as a term, has been a matter of considerable confusion and suggests that its usage should be discontinued. In part, the reason for the confusion lies in the fact that a mortality rate is fundamentally more rational if it is obtained by dividing the number of deaths for the designated period by the number (which decreases with time) exposed to death during the period. However this is obviously rather impractical. The discussion presented by Davis (1952) is of fundamental importance and should be studied by everyone interested in avian population dynamics. However, *annual mortality rate,* as defined above, does have extensive currency in the literature on mortality in birds, and I am consequently of the opinion that abandonment of it, and similar terms such as monthly mortality rate, annual survival rate, etc., is unnecessary. Nevertheless it is obvious that such terms must be carefully defined whenever they are employed.

An *age group* or *age class* consists of birds whose ages lie in a specified year after the prescribed initial date, i.e., first year, second year, etc. *A year group* or *year class* consists of those individuals hatched during a particular year, e.g., 1927 year group and 1943 year group. A *cohort* is a group of individuals, real or theoretical, which begin life together. In work on birds, "beginning life together" frequently is interpreted as being hatched during the same breeding season. In actual practice, the cohort is frequently composite, being composed of individuals hatched during different breeding seasons but treated as though they were hatched at the same time. The theoretical cohort is frequently assigned an initial size of 1,000 with proportional conversion of its strength in subsequent years to this scale. The survival series in Tables 2*a* and 3*a,* when multiplied by ten, give the survival histories for theoretical cohorts of 1,000.

The *life table,* in one form or another, has proved to be most useful in the concise presentation of certain vital statistics of populations. In studies on avian populations it has been used in a more traditional form by Deevey (1947), Paynter (1949), Paludan (1951), and Hickey (1949, 1952). These tables give, for each year interval of life, the *number of deaths,* the *number of survivors,* the *rate of mortality,* and *expectation of further life* (mean after lifetime) for a real or theoretical cohort. Deevey (1947) and Hickey (1949, 1952), following, at least in part, an unpublished paper by Margaret Merrell in 1946, have crystallized the essential basic differences in life tables. Hickey (1949, 1952:7) recognizes three types. *Dynamic life tables* are based on a cohort of a specific year group. This is the "horizontal life table" of Deevey (1947:287); it has found some limited use in investigations of avian populations. *Time-specific life tables,* "the vertical life tables" of Deevey, are based on data obtained during a restricted period of observation. In essence the primary data constitute a record of the age-group structure of a population at a given time or for a given period. Frequently it is assumed that the age-group structure may be similar to the survival history of a cohort of that population, a condition which obviously would hold only under ideal conditions of constant population size and a constant temporal pattern of mortality (Deevey, 1947:287). Its usefulness in studies of avian populations is obviously limited. A *composite life table* involves treatment of the records of individuals born or hatched in different breeding seasons as though they were members of the same year group. This is the most frequently employed type of life table in investigations on birds (Lack, 1943a-c, 1946a, 1948b; Farner, 1945, 1952; Paludan, 1951; Hickey, 1949, 1952; and others). The data in such a life table can be treated *dynamically* as in the dynamic life table or *time-specifically* as in the time-specific table. The former has been used most frequently and is preferable on theoretical grounds. Hickey (1949, 1952) has made the acceptable proposal that this be known as *Lack's method.* Time-specific analyses have been used in the investigations of Kraak, Rinkel, and Hoogerheide (1940), Tinbergen (1946), Magnusson and Svärdson (1948), and others. By extension, this is the basis of the prediction of gross adult mortality rates by use of adult-juvenile ratios. This method can be used only with considerable caution since it is dependent on the stability in size of the population and its temporal mortality pattern. Comparative results with actual samples have been presented by Farner (1945) and Hickey (1949, 1952).

BASIC PREMISES

In the use of records of birds banded as young and recovered dead beyond a *selected initial* date in the life of the bird, there are several fundamental assumptions. It is assumed that the sample used is sufficiently random and unbiased to allow the calculation of a mortality rate and the construction of an average pattern of mortality about which the annual mortality rates and the patterns of mortality in the total population over successive years should fall in approximately normal-frequency distributions. Ideally, this should entail the annual banding of a constant fraction of the young in uniform geographic distribution. That there may be geographic differences in mortality rates is apparent from the studies of Lack and Schifferli (1948) on the Starling, *Sturnus vulgaris*. Hickey (1949, 1952:27) has summarized in more detail the validity of the assumption of a random sample in the use of banding data and has suggested tests which can be employed as an indication of the degree of randomness.

For certain types of considerations it is necessary to assume that the population of the species involved is relatively stable, i.e., that its number is approximately the same on the same date each year or, at least, that fluctuations occur randomly. In other words, the mortality of birds surviving the initial date is, on the average, equivalent to the annual reproductive increment less losses up to the prescribed initial date.

It is assumed that there is no appreciable loss of bands, or if there is, that it operates randomly and independently of age. Although there is some evidence that this is not strictly true, it appears that errors thus introduced are, except in long-lived species, probably of no greater magnitude than others inherent to the sizes of the samples employed. The problem of band loss is discussed in greater detail later.

A further assumption, unless the sexes can be treated separately, is that there is no appreciable sex difference in longevity, or that the sexes occur in approximately equal numbers in the sample. The latter appears to be valid in most studies in which data on the sex distribution in the sample are available.

Further, it must be assumed that banding operations and the wearing of bands has no effect on mortality and longevity or that any such effects can be ascertained quantitatively so that adequate corrections can be made.

In using the records of birds banded as young and subsequently recorded as dead, it is necessary to allow for, or correct for, the death of *all* birds banded during the period embraced by the study in order to give the proper natural balance. This may be done with reasonable accuracy by admitting to the sample after a prescribed date no records of birds banded beyond this date: if the period of collecting records beyond this date is sufficiently long, four to six years in passerine and galliform birds, no appreciable error is introduced. (See, for example, Lack, 1943a:167; and Farner, 1945:58.) If the number banded each year does not vary appreciably, a more precise correction is that which Paynter (1949:162) has applied to Herring Gulls, *Larus argentatus*. This correction, slightly revised, may be expressed as

$$N_{cz} = \frac{N_{az}b}{b + 1 - z} \tag{1}$$

where N_{cz} is the corrected number of recoveries during the *z*th year of life; N_{az} is the actual number of recoveries during the *z*th year of life; z is a year of life after the selected initial date; and b is the period in years during which bandings were made and recoveries accumulated.

Obviously equation (1) assumes that banding and recoveries were made through precisely the same period b. In many investigations, this is not necessarily the case. Consequently, a more general formula is desirable:

$$N_{cz} = \frac{N_{az}b}{r - z + 1} \qquad (2)^{2}$$

where r is the period during which recoveries were made presuming r and b to begin on the same initial date. This calculation of N_{cz} obviously must be applied only to those cases where $b \,/\, (r - z + 1) > 1$.

The use of the corrections represented by (1) and (2), however, requires the assumption that equal numbers of birds are banded, or actually survive the selected initial date, for each year during b. If this assumption cannot be made, the method of Paludan (1951:107), which corrects also for members of the older age groups still living and in addition with regard to the numbers of individuals banded annually, may be used. This correction may be formulized as

$$N_{cz} = \frac{N_{az}N_{b}}{N_{b} - N_{q}} \tag{3}$$

where N_b is the total number of birds banded during b and N_q is the total banded during years too recent to allow attainment of age-group z. The values of N_{cz} constitute an *adjusted survival series*. Similarly, Magnusson and Svärdson (1948), Hanson and Smith (1950), and Hickey (1949, 1952) have prepared *adjusted survival series* by weighting actual survivors, or deaths, for a particular age in terms of the number of banded individuals theoretically (from banding records) available to attain that age. Actually, as Hickey (1949, 1952) has indicated, this philosophy may be traced back to the *recovery rate* (number recovered during a given year after banding divided by the number of the particular year group banded) and the *returning ratio* (number retrapped during a given year divided by the number of the particular year group

[2] In the original review paper the final term in the denominator was inadvertently omitted (Farner, 1952:44, formula 1*a*).

banded) of the earlier banders in this country (Whittle, 1929), for it is obvious (Hickey, 1949, 1952:43) that when the numbers of birds found dead or reported shot are expressed, according to the year of death, as percentages of the cohort originally banded, the survival series thus constructed is also the same *adjusted survival series.* Theoretically this could also be done from returning ratios, although obtaining returning ratios which are similar or identical to actual survival in the population is obviously difficult. As early as 1935 Low (1935:62) applied the returning ratios of banded Mourning Doves, *Zenaidura macroura,* to the construction of an adjusted survival series. Although the *adjusted survival series* is the soundest basic treatment of a series of data on recovered banded birds, it still involves at least two statistical difficulties inherent also to other treatments. In the first place, changes in banding and recovery operations, as well as other conditions, from year to year may alter the probabilities of recovery of banded individuals. Secondly such series still involve the decreasing statistical reliability of the small samples of the older age groups.

When data are obtained by retrapping or observation of survivors, corrections are necessary for survivors which are not retrapped or observed. Such corrections have been employed by Ruiter (1941:204), Leopold *et al.* (1943: 386), Magnusson and Svärdson (1948:132), Buss (1946:103, 111), and von Haartman (1951:18). These involve several approaches all of which have an element of uncertainty.

Ordinarily, the use of data on birds banded as young and recovered dead requires selection of an initial date before which recoveries are not used and on which the values of mean longevity or mean after lifetime are based. The selection of such a date is necessitated first by the fact that not all young are banded at comparable dates thus making it difficult to compare data based on banding dates. Of greater importance, however, is the necessity of allowing a period following the banding for adequate dispersal. Failure to allow such a period is very apt to yield a biased sample with too high a proportion of the birds which die soon after banding. This initial date is probably best placed after the beginning of fall migration; the problem is more complex for non-migratory species. Experience has shown that in many species there is a stabilization of *annual mortality rate* at a value apparently independent of age after an initial juvenile period of higher mortality. It is consequently advantageous for some purposes to select an initial date which is at least coincident with the stabilization of annual mortality rate. The selection of an initial date has been discussed at length by Farner (1949:68), who has summarized the experience and suggestions of others including those of Lack (1943a, 1946b). Lack and Farner agree that the first January 1 is satisfactory for passerine species in the north temperate zone; this date appears likewise to be satisfactory for at least certain galliform, charadriiform, and apodiform species. Hickey (1952) does not accept the first January 1 initial date of Lack and Farner, stressing the desirability of beginning calculations from as near the date of hatching as possible. The desirability of beginning calculations as early as possible is, of course, obvious. However, the possibility of bias in recovery during the period after banding on one hand, and the advantages for comparative purposes on the other, in my opinion make the use of the first January 1, or some similar initial date, desirable at this stage of development of the field. The development of data on mortality and survival for the period from hatching to the selected initial date probably may be attained most accurately by direct observation as in Paludan's (1951) investigation of a colony of Herring Gulls, or Ruiter's (1941) investigation of the European Redstart, *Phoenicurus phoenicurus,* or more indirectly estimated as in the case of Farner's (1945) study of the American Robin, *Turdus migratorius.* Davis (1952) has critically examined and formulized the relationships involved in such calculations.

Studies of mortality and survival in birds, employing data from birds banded as young and subsequently recovered, dead or alive, fall generally in two groups. The first includes those in which the data are obtained from an extensive birdbanding system and consequently involve a wide geographic range and a considerable span of years. Examples of this type are the studies of Lack (1943a-c, 1948b, 1949a, b) on several British species; Lack and Schifferli (1948) on the Starling in Switzerland; Plattner and Sutter (1946, 1947) on several species of *Parus* in Switzerland; Marshall (1947) on the Herring Gull in North America; Bourlière (1947) on the Rook, *Corvus frugilegus,* and the Common Heron, *Ardea cinerea,* in France; Kraak *et al.* (1940) on the Lapwing in western Europe, and Hickey (1949, 1952) on a series of North American species. If a case can be made for randomness with respect to the area of banding operations such studies may give a theoretical picture of the mortality and survival situation for the population of that area.

The second type of study is that involving a restricted population which can be observed directly by the investigator. Information on population dynamics may be obtained as a primary objective or incidental to other objectives. Studies of this type include those of Nice (1937) on the Song Sparrow at Columbus, Ohio; Erickson (1938) on the Wren-tit, *Chamaea fasciata,* at Berkeley, California; Ruiter (1941) on the European Redstart, at Wageningen in the Netherlands; Buss *et al.* (1947) on the Bobwhite Quail, *Colinus virginianus,* near Menomonie, Wisconsin; Paynter (1947, 1949) on Herring Gulls on Kent Island, New Brunswick; Drost and Hartmann (1949) on the Oystercatcher, *Haematopus ostralegus,* on Mellum Island of the North Sea coast of Germany; Austin (1951) on the Mourning Dove at North Eastham, Massachusetts; and Kluijver (1951) on the Great Tit, *Parus major,* near Wageningen, Netherlands. In such studies caution must be exercised in projecting the results beyond the population studied.

GENERAL MORTALITY AND SURVIVAL RATES

Most investigators have included in their calculations some expression of annual mortality or survival rates for individual age groups; several have attempted to present rates which are characteristic for the population or species from which the samples have been drawn. For this purpose Plattner and Sutter (1947:21) have employed simple unweighted arithmetic means of the mortality rates of the age groups for which there are adequate data. Bellrose and Chase (1950:8 *et seq.*) have used the unweighted arithmetic mean of the annual mortality rates for the first five years after banding. A similar expression was employed by Hanson and Smith (1950:172) whose "survival index"[3] is the simple unweighted arithmetic mean of the annual survival rates for the first three years of life after banding. The apparent disadvantage of these mean rates is that they weigh *equally* the mortality or survival rates for age groups of *different* strengths and with consequently different influences on the general mortality or survival rate for the population concerned. To avoid this disproportionate emphasis, Farner (1945:62), Lack (1948b:266), Hickey (1949, 1952) and others have calculated weighted annual mortality rates, in which the annual rate for each group is weighted proportionately to the strength of the group, so that

$$M_w = \frac{D_1 + D_2 + D_3 \ldots D_n}{D_1 + 2D_2 + 3D_3 \ldots nD_n} = \frac{\sum_{i=1}^{n} D_i}{\sum_{i=1}^{n} iD_i} \quad (4)$$

where D_1, D_2, D_3 . . . D_n are the deaths during the 1st, 2nd, 3rd . . . nth years of life respectively and M_w is the weighted mean annual mortality rate. If the assumptions enumerated in an earlier section of this paper are valid, M_w should be the actual over-all mean annual mortality rate for that portion of the population which has passed the selected initial date. I am indebted to Dr. J. R. Vatnsdal for verification, on the basis of Fisher's method of maximum likelihood, that this formula gives the most probable mean annual mortality rate.

If the population is relatively stable, the fraction of first-year individuals in the total population on the selected initial date should be equivalent to M_w, since these first-year birds are the replacements which restore the population (actually the number which have survived the selected initial date) to that of the corresponding date of the previous year. This method has been con-

[3] Unfortunately, *survival index* was applied almost simultaneously by Hickey (1949, 1952:37) to a different concept, namely, the ratio of deaths in one year in a cohort to the number of deaths during the preceding year in the same cohort. It is my opinion that the *survival index of* Hanson and Smith should be abandoned since it is better replaced by an *annual survival rate* derived from M_w of equation (4) or, if the annual mortality rates fluctuate appreciably, by a simple statement of the *annual survival rates* as defined on p. 399.

sidered by Emlen (1940:95), Farner (1945:59, 62; 1949:78), and Marshall (1947:194) and has been shown to be basically feasible. However, it has, as noted above and as shown extensively by Hickey (1949, 1952), the inherent difficulties of a time-specific life table or the time-specific treatment of a composite life table. Nonuniform mortality rates, bias in sampling with respect to age groups, annual fluctuations in the size of the population, and differential migration present rather serious difficulties. It has the advantage, however, of being applicable in situations where the samples, live or dead, show only young-adult ratios.

Retrapping as a source of the sample bias in favor of young is demonstrated by the data of Plattner and Sutter (1947:21) and Farner (1949:74).

It must always be remembered that the annual mortality rates obtained by the procedures discussed above can be considered as characteristic of the species or population concerned only if they are based on samples which are random both with respect to space and time. Such a calculated rate also must be thought of only as a mean annual rate which is identical with few, if any, of the rates for the individual years for the period concerned. However, the annual mortality rates for the individual years during this period should fall about this mean in a normal frequency distribution. For species which are cyclic, or which have marked irregular fluctuations in population, the standard deviation from this mean may be great if these fluctuations are the result of variations in adult mortality rate. From a variety of sources it becomes increasingly apparent that the various causes of death may vary extensively from year to year in their contribution to the total mortality without great effect on the annual mortality rate. Also, it becomes increasingly apparent (Errington, 1946; Tinbergen, 1946, 1948; Solomon, 1949) that decreases resulting from an increased mortality during the course of one year, or a period of years, are rectified by compensating factors. This tends to maintain a characteristic mean annual mortality rate for a species or population.

The mean annual mortality rates characteristic of particular populations may also be obtained from direct observations of the banded and unbanded fractions of the population with proper regard for changes in size of the population and for the living banded individuals who fail to remain in, or to return to, the area. There are actually several possible approaches in this type of method. In one form or another, it has been employed by Nice (1937), Kendeigh (1937), Laven (1940), Ruiter (1941), Buss (1946), and in part by Kortlandt (1942). If the calculation of mortality rate involves the estimation of population size from the ratio of banded to unbanded individuals in a sample (Davis, 1951:103), careful consideration must be given to the validity of the sample, particularly in terms of immigration and emigration, but also in other respects (see, for example, Adams, 1951), as well as to the general properties of hypergeometric distribution (Chapman, 1951). This method has been used in estimating populations of waterfowl by the U. S. Fish and Wildlife Service

(Lincoln, 1930). It has been critically analyzed recently by Adams (1951) and particularly by Chapman (1951). Methods of this type are of importance because direct observations may yield data on productivity and also may allow possibilities for the circumvention of the difficulties incident to the selection of an initial date for calculations.

A crude estimation of the validity of the sample and the conformance to the basic assumptions cited earlier in the paper may be obtained by consideration of the reasonableness of the calculated mortality and survival rates, i.e., whether or not the annual loss as indicated by the calculated rates can reasonably be replaced by the known productivity (as established by field studies) of the species, taking into consideration the mortality from hatching to the selected initial date (Davis, 1952). Such a test may indicate whether the calculated rates are impossible or of a reasonable order. If it indicates that they are of a reasonable order, it does not follow, because of possible sampling error and other variables, that the calculations are necessarily correct but rather that they can be correct. For example, considerations of this type apparently indicate a reasonable order for the mortality rates established by Nice (1937) for the Song Sparrow; Kendeigh (1937) for the House Wren; Lack (1948b) for the European Robin, (1943a) the European Blackbird, *Turdus merula,* (1943b) the Song Thrush, *Turdus ericetorum,* and (1943c) the Lapwing; and Farner (1945) for the American Robin. On the other hand, such an evaluation has shown the mortality and survival rates to be inaccurate for data on the Black-headed Gull, *Larus ridibundus,* by Lack (1943c); Cormorant, *Phalacrocorax carbo,* by Lack (1943c) and Stuart (1948); and Herring Gull by Paynter (1949). This test is an integral part of the analyses of Hickey (1949, 1952) on a series of North American species. Certainly any investigator who uses banding data in the calculation of survival and mortality rates should attempt to establish the reasonableness of his calculations in relation to the known productivity of the population or species under consideration.

The use of banding data in developing, and contributing to, concepts of population dynamics is obviously in its infancy. There is a great need for intensive sustained programs concentrating on individual species or groups of species with carefully integrated field studies to establish the plausibility of the calculations. Such studies will provide a better insight into the matter of normal fluctuations in annual mortality rates. Although no criticism is intended with respect to the currently operating banding systems, it must be recognized that there is a definite and unsatisfactory limit to the accuracy of the results obtained by the somewhat desultory efforts on which, for the most part, the present systems must depend.

Two interesting and important ramifications of mortality studies have recently been developed by Lack (1948a) and Lack and Schifferli (1948). In the case of Swiss Starlings (Lack and Schifferli, 1948:108), there are apparently more eggs per clutch and slightly more broods per pair per season than in

British Starlings, the ratio of productivity being 1.0:0.8; correspondingly, British Starlings banded as young show an annual adult mortality rate of 52 per cent compared to 62 per cent for the Swiss population. Although these data are very impressive, the innate variability of this type of material makes it advisable that the conclusions be regarded as suggestive rather than conclusive until so demonstrated by adequate statistical analysis. The authors have pointed out also that similar differences in mortality rate exist between Dutch and British Lapwings without, however, differences in clutch size. Lack (1948a) has concluded further that natural selection apparently operates with respect to clutch size. In the case of Starlings, birds from normal clutches appear to survive better than those from larger clutches, presumably because of limitations of the feeding ability of the parents. Lack (1948a:104) has suggested that the normally larger clutches of Swiss Starlings may be possible because of better feeding conditions. Thus Swiss Starlings can replace this greater mortality and maintain a constant population. Lack and Arn (1947) have shown that a similar situation may exist with respect to Swiss and British Common Swifts, *Apus apus.*

Although they have not been used extensively thus far in practical wildlife management, the value therein of mortality studies based on banding data is amply apparent in the investigations of Kraak *et al.* (1940), Klomp (1946, 1951), Buss (1946), Bellrose and Chase (1950), Hanson and Smith (1950), and particularly Hickey (1949, 1952). It is equally apparent that such studies must be carefully integrated with other types of investigation.

RELATION BETWEEN MORTALITY RATE AND MEAN LONGEVITY OF THE INDIVIDUALS OF A POPULATION

A reciprocal relation between general mortality rate and mean longevity was apparently discussed first with respect to birds by Burkitt (1926:97; also 1936:337), whose equation, however, was impractical in its original form. Furthermore, the assumed values used in the solutions now appear to be incorrect. The equation was used also by Erickson (1938:309) in her studies on Wren-tits, and in a modified form by Kluijver (1935) in studies on Starlings, and Ruiter (1941:210) on the European Redstart. The simplified equation employed by Nice (1937:191), Odum (1942:157), Farner (1945:65), Marshall (1947:194), Hann (1948:10), and Petrides (1949:404) assumes relatively uniform mortality rates in the constituent age groups of a population and gives an approximate mean longevity from the date of hatching for those birds which survive the selected initial date, *providing* that the period between the selected initial date and the mean date of hatching does not deviate appreciably from 0.5 years. Because of this limitation, Farner (1949:72) has recommended that the use of this simple equation be abandoned.

If a general mean annual mortality rate, such as M_w of the previous section, for a population is known, and if the mean annual mortality rates for the constituent age groups do not deviate appreciably from the general mean mortality rate, the following relationship may be employed:

$$Y = \frac{1}{M} - (1 - p) \qquad (5)$$

where Y is the *mean after lifetime* (Hickey, 1952:7), in years, as of the selected initial date[4] for those individuals which survive the selected initial date; p is the mean period, in years, survived during the year of death; and M is the general annual mortality rate, such as M_w of the previous section, for the population.

When there is reason to believe that the annual temporal pattern of recovery of bands is different from that of the actual total temporal mortality pattern, an assumption of a uniform mortality pattern throughout the year may be less misleading. Thus Lack (1948b:266) in his treatment of mortality data of the European Robin has assumed p to be 0.5 years. Farner (1949:71) has pointed out that this is actually an approximation, although sufficiently accurate for annual mortality rates which are not appreciably in excess of 50 per cent. This has been accepted by von Haartman (1951). If a uniform mortality rate through the course of the year is to be assumed, p is more precisely obtained as follows (Farner, 1949:71):

$$p = - \frac{0.4343}{\log_{10} S} - \frac{S}{M} \qquad (6)$$

where S is a general annual survival rate, beyond the selected initial date; $S = 1 - M$.

Substituting in (5) gives an equation for direct calculation of Y,

$$Y = - \frac{0.4343}{\log_{10} S} \quad . \qquad (7)$$

That the relation expressed in (7) is at least useful as an approximation is evident from the data recorded in Table 1. The fact that the actual values of Y are usually smaller than the calculated values may possibly be a simple indication of higher mortality in winter in passerine species and is doubtless the effect of fall shooting in the case of Mallards, *Anas platyrhynchos.* As more evidence is accumulated it is most likely, however, that the application of the mortality pattern resulting from a uniform mortality rate within the year will be abandoned in favor of empirically established p-values which reflect periods of higher mortality within the year. There is reason to suspect the existence of such periods in Farner's (1949:80) tabulation of annual mortality patterns for the American Robin and in Austin's (1951:166) data on Mourning Doves. However, bias in recovery of bands, as suspected by Lack (1948b:264-266), can by no means be precluded. This type of bias is almost certain to develop if p is calculated from band recoveries alone in a species which migrates into an area where recovery of bands is infrequent, as in the

[4] This is the same as *mean longevity as of the selected initial date* (Farner, 1945, 1949, 1952), *expectation of life* (Deevey, 1947:295) as of the selected initial date, and life expectancy as of the prescribed date of many authors.

TABLE 1. Comparison of Y Values Obtained Directly and by Calculation

Species	Area	Reference	Selected Initial Date	Banded as	S[a]	Y[b] in Yrs. Actual	Y[c] in Yrs. Calculated
Turdus migratorius	Eastern North America	Farner (1949:78)	1st Jan. 1	juv.	0.48	1.3	1.4
Sturnus vulgaris	England	Lack and Schifferli (1948:109)	1st Jan. 1	juv.	0.48	1.4	1.4
Sturnus vulgaris	Switzerland	Lack and Schifferli (1948:109)	1st Jan. 1	juv.	0.37	1.1	1.05
Parus major	Switzerland	Plattner (1947:22)	1st Nov. 1	?	0.54[d]	1.4	1.6
Richmondena cardinalis	Eastern U.S.A.	Farner (1952:126)	1st Jan. 1	juv.	0.52	1.45	1.6
Richmondena cardinalis	Eastern U.S.A.	Farner (1952:126)	1st Jan. 1	ad.	0.52	1.4	1.6
Anas platyrhynchos ♂♂	Illinois	Bellrose and Chase (1950:9)	banding date	ad.	0.60	1.8	1.95
Anas platyrhynchos ♀♀	Illinois	Bellrose and Chase (1950:11)	banding date	?	0.53	1.4	1.5
Anas platyrhynchos ♂♂	Illinois	Bellrose and Chase (1950:8)	banding date	juv.	0.50	1.3	1.5

[a] $S = 1 - M$

[b] Mean period of survival beyond selected initial date according to actual band recoveries.

[c] $Y = -\frac{0.4343}{\log_{10} S}$

[d] Recalculated using equation (4)

case of Lack's (1949b:147) Swallows, *Hirundo rustica.* Certainly in anseriform species, in which shooting is now an important cause of death, apparently having replaced partially some of the "natural causes" (Bellrose and Chase, 1950:23), there must be a shift in the distribution of deaths towards the fall months with the consequence that p and Y may be somewhat smaller than would be predicted by equations (5) and (6).

Obviously an estimate of mean longevity or mean after lifetime can best be obtained from a sample of birds banded as nestlings or juveniles and recovered dead after the selected initial date, providing that there is no bias in the temporal pattern of recovery. Equation (7) is useful primarily where the annual adult mortality rate has been obtained by adult-juvenile ratios, from birds of unknown ages, from retrapped samples, or where there is reason to believe that the recovery pattern is biased with respect to the true mortality pattern. Obviously, in the United States, if our knowledge of mean longevity is to be well-founded, it is necessary that encouragement be given to the banding of nestlings and juveniles in general.

If mean longevity *from the hatching date* for those birds surviving the selected initial date is desired, it is necessary to establish a mean hatching date from field observations and add this to Y *obtained* in equations (5) or (7), or to Y established directly from the recovered bands. The calculation of mean longevity from hatching for all birds is quite difficult because of bias in recoveries when a period for dispersion is not allowed; judicious combination of field observations and calculations from recoveries of bands such as employed by Nice (1937) and Paludan (1951) can circumvent the difficulties, however. The same is applicable to mortality rates beginning with the hatching date or date of banding.

It should be noted here that there has been a tendency to overlook the importance of mean natural longevity. For example, Bellrose and Chase (1950: 17) have stated that longevity research does not provide information essential for population dynamics. On the other hand, Deevey (1947) has already amply demonstrated the value, for comparative purposes, of showing survivorship in terms of percentage deviation from mean adult longevity. Furthermore, as longevity data become more refined there may be other important implications. For example, the difference between the actual longevity as ascertained by recovery of bands and that calculated by equation (7) could be an indication of the number of birds which die during the year but which nevertheless survive the breeding season; certainly this kind of information would be important in the understanding of population dynamics.

MORTALITY AND SURVIVAL RATES AS FUNCTIONS OF TIME

The tendency of adult mortality rate to remain relatively constant in birds was considered by Nice (1937) with respect to Song Sparrows and was apparently first formulized by Kraak *et al.* (1940:165, 167) in their analysis of

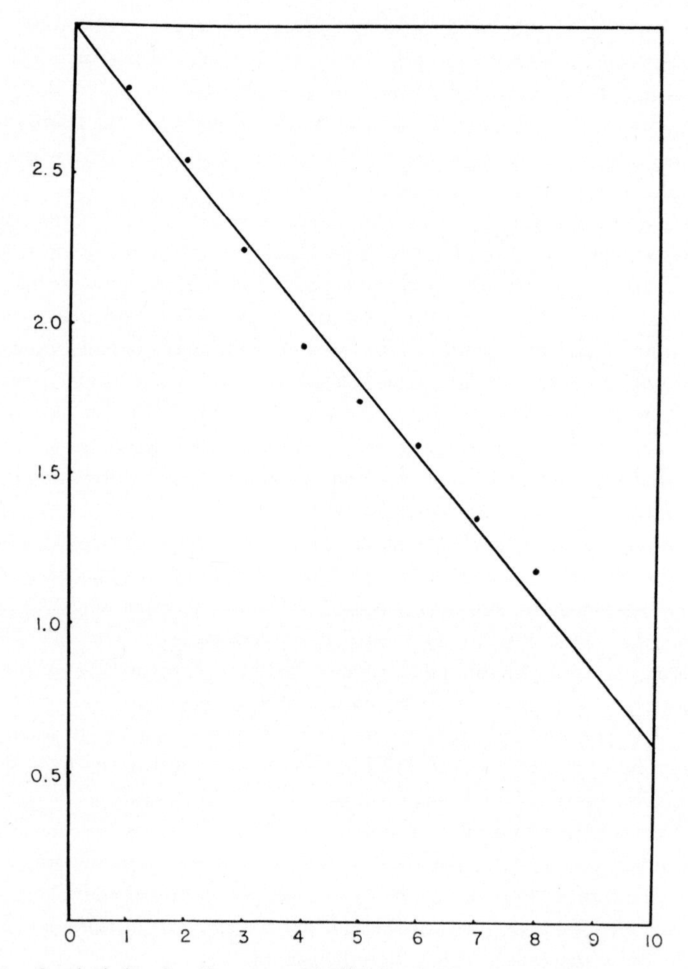

Fig. 1. Survival in the European Blackbird, *Turdus merula* Linnaeus. Ordinate: logarithms of numbers surviving per thousand alive on the first January first. Abscissa: anniversaries of first January first of life. Plotted points represent actual survival data. Solid line represents hypothetical survival curve, $N_x = N_0 e^{-kx}$. (Courtesy, *Northwest Science.)* Original data are from Lack (1946b).

data on Lapwings. This relationship has been emphasized by Lack (1943a) for the European Blackbird and later for other species. An examination of Tables 2 to 3*a* indicates that this tendency may be quite general for passerine, galliform, and possibly certain anseriform and charadriiform species. Figure 1 shows an example of the type of survival curve resulting from a uniform mortality rate. The zero point on the abscissa corresponds to the selected initial date. The actual data from band recoveries are plotted for comparison.

If the mortality pattern conforms with such a logarithmic regression curve, it means that the probability of death, beyond the selected initial date, is without relation to age; as a corollary, it means that life expectancy does not change with age and that experience and senescence are unimportant in survival curves or at least that they are mutually counteractive. The number of deaths in a given year group would then be a function of the time elapsed beyond the initial date and the mortality rate to which, in some cases at least, a constant value may be assigned. Hence,

$$N_z = N_0 e^{-kz} \tag{8}$$

where N_0 is the number alive at the selected initial date, N_z is the number alive at z years after the selected initial date, and k is equal to ln $(1 - M)$. This formula has been employed in a different form by Petrides (1949:405) for estimating the sizes of older age groups.

Examination of Figure 1 shows that there is not a strict conformance between the line represented by equation (8) and the actual data. This is of course true for any set of survival data. The problem of establishing the probability that such a logarithmic regression curve represents the true relation and the selection of the theoretical curve with which the actual data should be compared is a matter of considerable complexity. Of the several possible ways of establishing the theoretical curve to represent the effect of a constant age-independent annual adult mortality rate it would appear, on the basis of Fisher's principle of maximum likelihood, that the curve represented by equation (8) using M_w from equation (4) is most logical. If this is acceptable, there is then the problem of a test to ascertain the probability that this curve may be a good representation of the actual data on survival. Because of the important implications of a near-constant adult mortality rate in theoretical ecology and in practical game management, a careful study of the theoretical statistical aspects of this problem would be of great value. It should be emphasized that any statistical test, however, can obviously do no more than to indicate the level of probability at which the hypothesis of constant adult mortality rate need not be excluded.

Provisionally, it appears that the available data may be interpreted to indicate that, for several species, whose populations are reasonably stable on a long-term basis, there is a tendency to approach a characteristic adult mortality rate which does not vary extensively with age. If one considers the vast complexities, both physiologic and ecologic, which are involved in the natural determination of annual mortality rate, it is very apparent that the probability of the operation of a strictly constant age-independent annual adult mortality rate is extremely remote. It therefore seems most appropriate to interpret the tendency towards a constant adult mortality rate, where it exists, as an indication that the various mortality factors operate independently of age in adult birds and that there are intercompensating relations among these factors. With respect to the effects of predation and certain other mortality factors, the excellent studies of Errington (1945, 1946, 1951) and Tinbergen (1946, 1948),

TABLE 2. MORTALITY AND SURVIVAL IN SELECTED NON-PASSERINE SPECIES AS INDICATED PRIMARILY BY ANALYSES OF BANDING DATA

Species	Area	Size of Sample	Age at Banding	Initial Date for Calculations	M %	S %	Reference
Anas platyrhynchos ♂♂	Illinois	3,245	adult	banding date	40	60	Bellrose and Chase (1950)[a]
♂♂	Illinois	2,361	1st fall	banding date	49.5	50.5	Bellrose and Chase (1950)[a]
♀♀	Illinois	1,609	unknown	banding date	47	53	Bellrose and Chase (1950)[a]
♂♂	Pacific Northwest	1,762	unknown	1st Sept. 1 after banding	48	52	Hickey (1952)[a]
	Britain	305	adult	banding date	64.5	35.5	Höhn (1948)
	Britain	271	young	banding date	83	17	Höhn (1948)
Anas rubripes	Illinois	939	varies	banding date	50	50	Bellrose and Chase (1950)[a]
Anas discors	Illinois	307	varies	banding date	53	47	Bellrose and Chase (1950)[a]
Branta canadensis	Ontario	302	unknown	1st yr. after banding	39	61	Hanson and Smith (1950)[a]
Phasianus colchicus	Wisconsin	562	unknown	banding date (winter)	71	29	Leopold *et al.* (1943)
	Wisconsin	834	unknown	banding date (winter)	72	28	Buss (1946)
	Wisconsin	349	unknown	banding date (winter)	81	19	Buss (1946)
Colinus virginianus	Wisconsin	1,188	unknown	banding date (fall and winter)	87	13	Buss (unpublished)
Vanellus vanellus	Britain	460	juvenile	1st Aug. 1	35	65	Lack (1943*c*)
	Western Europe	978	juvenile	1st Jan. 1	40	60	Kraak *et al.* (1940)[b]
Scolopax rusticola	Britain	203	juvenile	1st Aug. 1	45	55	Lack (1943*c*)
Larus argentatus	North America	504	young in nesting colony	1st Sept. 1	—	—	Hickey (1952)
	Eastern North America	1,252	young in nesting colony	date fledged	—	—	Paynter (1949)
	Denmark	966	young in nesting colony	1st Sept. 1	15[c]	85[c]	Paludan (1951)
Zenaidura macroura	Massachusetts	105	unknown	1st Nov. 1 after banding	69[d]	31[d]	Austin (1951)

[a] Adapted from the data of the authors.
[b] Adapted from the author's Figures 6 and 7 (pp. 165, 166) in which the data are presented on a time specific basis. Here a dynamic analysis has been applied to the composite sample.
[c] For 2nd through 10th years.
[d] These rates are 55 and 45, respectively, when calculated from the 2nd Nov. 1 after banding.

TABLE 2a. MORTALITY AND SURVIVAL IN SELECTED NON-PASSERINE SPECIES AS INDICATED PRIMARILY BY ANALYSES OF BANDING DATA

Species	Survival in % of N of Initial Date on Successive Anniversaries of Initial Date																Y[a] as of Initial Date	
	0	1	2	3	4	5	6	7	8	9	10	11	12	13	14	15	Years	How Obtained
Anas platyrhynchos ♂ ♂	100	64	39	24.5	14	7.8	2.8	0.3	0	—	—	—	—	—	—	—	1.8	actual
♂ ♂	100	45	25	14	8.8	5.1	2.5	0.6	0	—	—	—	—	—	—	—	1.3	actual
♀ ♀	100	54	28	15	8.8	4.3	2.2	1.1	0	—	—	—	—	—	—	—	1.4	actual
♂ ♂	100	46	25	15	8.9	5.2	2.8	1.8	1.0	0.6	0.2	0	—	—	—	—	1.5	calculated
	100	35	11	4.3	2.0	1.0	0.7	0.3	0.3	0.3	0	—	—	—	—	—	1.2	actual
	100	12	4.4	2.6	1.5	0	—	—	—	—	—	—	—	—	—	—	0.4	actual
Anas rubripes	100	52	26	13	5.8	2.0	0.6	—	—	—	—	—	—	—	—	—	1.4	calculated
Anas discors	100	50	23	10	4.2	1.4	0	—	—	—	—	—	—	—	—	—	1.3	calculated
Branta canadensis	100	58	34	22.5	13	9.3	8.3	6.3	2.6	2.0	1.0	0	—	—	—	—	2.0	calculated
Phasianus colchicus	100	30	9	1.8	0	—	—	—	—	—	—	—	—	—	—	—	0.8	calculated
	100	26	9	4	0.4	0	—	—	—	—	—	—	—	—	—	—	0.8	calculated
	100	19	5	0	—	—	—	—	—	—	—	—	—	—	—	—	0.6	calculated
Colinus virginianus	100	13	1	0	—	—	—	—	—	—	—	—	—	—	—	—	—	—
Vanellus vanellus	100	62	41	28	20	13	7.6	5.2	3.3	2.6	1.7	1.1	0	—	—	—	2.4	actual
	100[b]	59	35	22	14	7.7	4.9	2.7	1.8	1.4	0.7	0.4	0.2	0.1	0.1	0	2.0	calculated
Scolopax rusticola	100	44	28	17	9.9	6.4	3.4	2.5	2.5	2.0	2.0	1.5	0.5	0	—	—	1.7	actual
Larus argentatus	100	40	28	22	16	12	7.5	6.0	5.1	4.0	3.0	2.4	1.4	1.0	0.8	0	—	—
	100	58	40	30.5	24	17	11	6.6	4.5	1.9	0	—	—	—	—	—	2.4	actual
	100	38	29.5	24	20	17	14	13	10.5	8.8	7.4	6.8	5.3	4.9	4.3	3.6		
							16	17	18	19	20	21	22	23	24	25		
							3.0	2.2	2.0	1.8	1.5	1.5	1.2	0.5	0.5	0.5	2.7	actual
Zenaidura macroura	100	25	10.5	5.7	2.9	0.9	0	—	—	—	—	—	—	—	—	—	0.5[c]	calculated

[a] When Y is obtained directly as the mean survival beyond the selected date, with or without correction, it is indicated as "actual." When Y is indicated as "calculated," it has been obtained by use of the formula, $Y = \frac{-0.4343}{\log_{10} S}$ (Farner, 1949:76).

[b] The data for this series were adapted from the time specific presentation in the authors' Figures 6 and 7 (pp. 165, 166). This series is an approximation since the authors' figures do not give the exact numbers of deaths in each age group. Here a dynamic analysis is applied to the composite sample.

[c] Y = 0.9 years as of the 2nd Nov. 1 of life.

TABLE 3. Mortality and Survival in Selected Passerine Species as Indicated Primarily by Analyses of Banding Data

Species	Area	Size of Sample	Age at Banding	Initial Date for Calculations	M %	S %	Reference
Phoenicurus phoenicurus	Netherlands	383	breeding adults	banding date	62	38	Ruiter (1941)
Erithacus rubecula	Britain	130	nestling	1st Aug. 1	66	34	Lack (1948b)
	Britain	129	unknown	1st Aug. 1	62	38	Lack (1948b)
Turdus merula	Britain	258	nestling	1st Jan. 1	42	58	Lack (1946b)
Turdus ericetorum	Britain	262	nestling	1st Jan. 1	47	53	Lack (1946b)
Turdus migratorius	Eastern N. A.	597	juvenile	1st Jan. 1	52	48	Farner (1949)
Troglodytes aëdon	Ohio	907	1st breeding season	1st breeding season	68	32	Kendeigh (1937)
Sturnus vulgaris	Britain	197	juvenile	1st Jan. 1	52	48	Lack and Schifferli (1948)
	Switzerland	306	juvenile	1st Jan. 1	63	37	Lack and Schifferli (1948)
	Switzerland	139	unknown	1st Jan. 1	58	42	Lack and Schifferli (1948)
Parus major	Switzerland	64	unknown	1st Nov. 1	46	54	Plattner and Sutter (1947)
	Switzerland	520[a]	unknown	1st Nov. 1	53	47	Plattner and Sutter (1947)
	Switzerland	225[a]	nestling	1st Nov. 1	61	39	Plattner and Sutter (1947)
Parus caeruleus	Switzerland	69[a]	unknown	1st Nov. 1	54	46	Plattner and Sutter (1947)
Parus palustris	Switzerland	89[a]	unknown	1st Nov. 1	47	53	Plattner and Sutter (1947)
Corvus frugilegus	France	121	nestling	date of fledging	—	—	Bourlière (1947)
Cyanocitta cristata	Eastern N. A.	636	unknown	1st Jan. 1	45	55	Hickey (1952)
Richmondena cardinalis	Eastern U.S.A.	46	nestling	1st Jan. 1	48	52	Farner (1952)
	Eastern U.S.A.	212	unknown	1st Jan. 1	48	52	Farner (1952)
Melospiza melodia	Ohio	54	breeding	1st breeding season	40	60	Nice (1937)[b]
Hirundo rustica	Britain	99	nestling	1st Jan. 1	63	37	Lack (1949b)

[a] Sample includes birds recovered dead as well as retrapped birds.
[b] Adapted from author's data. See Farner (1949:79).

TABLE 3a. MORTALITY AND SURVIVAL IN SELECTED PASSERINE SPECIES AS INDICATED PRIMARILY BY ANALYSES OF BANDING DATA

Species	Survival in % of N of Initial Date on Successive Anniversaries										Y[a] as of Initial Date	
	0	1	2	3	4	5	6	7	8	9+	Years	How Obtained
Phoenicurus phoenicurus	—	—	—	—	—	—	—	—	—	—	1.0	calculated
Erithacus rubecula	100	28	15	3.9	1.5	0.8	0	—	—	—	1.0	actual
	100	38	16	6.2	1.6	0	—	—	—	—	1.1	actual
Turdus merula	100	60	36	18	11	7.0	4.3	2.3	1.5	0.4	1.9	actual
Turdus ericetorum	100	55	33	14	4.6	3.4	1.5	0.4	0	—	1.55	actual
Turdus migratorius	100	51	25	9.7	3.0	1.5	0.8	0.2	0.2	0.2	1.3	actual
Troglodytes aëdon	100	29	12	4.4	0.9	0.2	—	—	—	—	1.5[b]	actual[b]
Sturnus vulgaris	100	51	24	13	3.6	2.0	0.5	0.5	0	—	1.4	actual
	100	39	11	4.2	1.6	0.3	0.3	0.3	0.3	0.3	1.1	actual
	100	42	21	8.6	0.7	0	—	—	—	—	1.2	actual
Parus major	100	58	33	12.5	7.8	3.1	1.6	0	—	—	1.7	actual
	100	52	20	9.4	4.8	1.2	0.2	0	—	—	—	——
	100	42	14	0	—	—	—	—	—	—	—	——
Parus caeruleus	—	—	—	—	—	—	—	—	—	—	1.4	actual
Parus palustris	—	—	—	—	—	—	—	—	—	—	1.6	actual
Corvus frugilegus	—	—	—	—	—	—	—	—	—	—	1.4[c]	actual
Cyanocitta cristata	100	57	32	17	8.7	4.4	2.5	0.9	0.5	0	1.7	calculated
Richmondena cardinalis	100	43	30	20	8.7	6.5	0	—	—	—	1.45	actual
	100	49	25	13	7.1	4.7	2.4	1.9	0	—	1.4	actual
Melospiza melodia	—	—	—	—	—	—	—	—	—	—	1.9[d]	actual
Hirundo rustica	100	32	13	6.1	4.0	1.0	1.0	1.0	1.0	1.0	1.1	actual

[a] When Y is obtained directly as the mean survival beyond the selected date, with or without correction, it is indicated as "actual." When Y is indicated as "calculated" it has been obtained by use of the formula, $Y = \frac{-0.4343}{\log_{10} S}$ (Farner, 1949:76).

[b] Calculated value for Y is 0.9 years.

[c] See text.

[d] Adapted from the author's data. See Farner (1949:79).

and the similarly excellent critical review of Solomon (1949) lend a basis for possible understanding of such intercompensating relations. Bearing in mind further the basically instinctive nature of avian behavior and the well-established fact (Bourlière, 1946:261) that mean longevity is usually a small fraction of potential longevity thereby probably mitigating or even largely eliminating senescence as an important factor in mortality, the possibility of an approximately constant age-independent annual adult mortality rate appears plausible.

On the other hand, it is not entirely improbable that additional studies with more adequate data for the older age groups, particularly in species of greater longevity, may show that some species deviate, within these older age groups, from this random adult mortality pattern towards an improved survival rate. In the words of Deevey (1947:312) this would involve the evolution of mechanisms which tend to extend the mean life span toward the maximum potential span. Buss (1946:112) has suggested that this may occur in the Ring-necked Pheasant, *Phasianus colchicus;* Hanson and Smith (1950:186) have made the same suggestion for Canada Geese, *Branta canadensis.* Although the data in each instance are suggestive, the statistical probability that this is actually the case appears to be quite low. On the other hand it seems quite possible that survival may improve with age in the population of Oyster-catchers described by Drost and Hartmann (1949:102) as well as in the Yellow-eyed Penguins, *Megadyptes antipodes,* which have been studied by Richdale (1949). Paynter's (1949) analysis of data on Herring Gulls indicates a possible situation of this type; should band loss among the older age groups prove to be appreciable, improvement in survival among the older groups would certainly be evident. Paludan's (1951:110) data on the same species appear to indicate an improvement in survival up to about the fifth year. Although it is considerably a matter of aspect, it would appear best to regard this as a type of prolonged period of juvenile mortality, since there is no reason to believe that there is any improvement in survival beyond this point. The Cormorant population studied by Kortlandt (1942:279) obviously shows an improvement in survival as ages increases; however, this population was one whose size was gradually increasing; whether this relation will persist when the population becomes stable is conjectural.

It is likewise very possible that there may be an accelerated mortality rate in the oldest age groups. However, the detection of this would require vastly larger samples than are now available. Furthermore, since it would affect such a small portion of the population, its role in the population dynamics would be negligible.

Thus far the discussion has been based predominately on the assumption of a constant population. This does not necessarily mean that the population on the selected initial date each year must be the same. It does mean, however, that the population sizes on these initial dates must show a normal-frequency distribution around a mean population size. The smaller the standard deviation the more accurate the calculated mortality and survival rates are likely to be. Although, with some notable exceptions, it is probable, within the order of accuracy of the currently available data, that most species thus far studied have sufficiently constant populations, this is basically very difficult to establish. A long-term study, which demonstrates such a constancy, is that of Alexander (1946) on the Common Heron. This invaluable study (Lack, 1946a:205) has produced data which show how an increased mortality rate imposed by severe winter conditions is almost immediately compensated by a decreased mortality rate so that the population quickly returns to normal equilibrium with the environment and to stability in numbers. A study of similar duration by Errington (1945) on Bobwhite Quail indicates similar compensations, although the basic population levels are influenced by "depression phases" of unknown etiology, thus involving a situation more complex than that observed in herons.

For a population such as Alexander's herons, and probably even for Errington's Bobwhite Quail, despite these irregular fluctuations, there can be a meaningful mean annual mortality rate, providing that cognizance is given to the nature and extent of variations from it. With the accumulation of more data the degree of deviation from means can be represented by standard statistical expressions. It seems very likely that the situation represented by Alexander's herons may be characteristic of many species.

The restriction of consideration of mortality and survival rates with respect to age and other time-dependent factors to stable populations or to populations with irregular random fluctuations about a mean is rather severe. It precludes consideration of many interesting problems in population dynamics. Unfortunately, the available banding data as well as the available data on changes in population size, even for the more intensely studied game species, allow, at best, only speculation concerning other situations. For this reason only the briefest consideration will be included herein. Although categorization with respect to such situations is both dangerous and irrational, it is perhaps useful to recognize three types of populations with respect to variation in size, excepting annual cycles:

1. *Stable populations or populations with random fluctuations.* This is the type to which principal consideration has been given thus far. Positive fluctuations can be produced by increased productivity, decreased adult mortality rate, or immigration. Negative fluctuations may be the result correspondingly of decreased productivity, increased adult mortality rate, or emigration. Productivity, because of the considerations incident to the use of the selected initial date, is used here to designate the rate of production of new individuals alive on the selected initial date.

2. *Populations undergoing gradual long-term increases or decreases in size.* These gradual changes may or may not be accompanied by random fluctuations

of the type discussed in the previous category or by cyclic fluctuations. These gradual changes in population size may be incident to the establishment of new populations in favorable areas previously unavailable to the species and may not actually involve, therefore, a change in environmental conditions. It should not be assumed that such changes in population size have a linear relation to time. This type of situation has been discussed by Davis (1950) with respect to the growth of Starling populations in the United States. A good case is presented for the development of a sigmoid population curve and the "inversity effects" of increased population size on the annual increments in population. The increase in Gannets, *Sula bassana,* on Noss, Shetland Islands, as described by Fisher and Venables (1938), may be a more complex example of this type of increase in population. The general population of this species appears still to be increasing, with protection against human depredation an important factor. Fisher and Vevers (1951:466) feel that the upper limit, which is fixed by available food, has not been reached. A further case of interest is that of the steady increase in population and distribution of the Atlantic Fulmar, *Fulmarus glacialis,* in the north Atlantic area as described by Fisher (1951). In Britain from 1878 to 1914 the increase was geometric at the rate of about 18 per cent per year. Thereafter the increase has been at the rate of 7 per cent per annum. Fisher (1951:454) suggests that immigration was a factor until 1914 and very possibly thereafter. Improved feeding associated with increased trawling for fish appears to be very important. Populations may also show gradual changes in size as the result of environmental changes. Among the causal factors may be changes in climate, adverse or favorable, as in the cases of the several populations studied in northern Europe by Kalela (1946, 1949, 1950, 1952) and those in Greenland noted by Salomonsen (1948); frequently changes in range are involved also. Culture-linked changes likewise may be causative as noted, for example, by Kalela (1942) for several species and by Curry-Lindahl (1950) for the Eagle Owl, *Bubo bubo;* in each of these situations changes in range may also be involved. Regardless of the basic etiology of these changes in size of populations, in every case the normal equilibrium between loss and replacement, characteristic of the stable population, does not exist. Basically the changes must be caused in the same way as the fluctuations discussed under category 1. The principal difference lies in the persistent inbalance between loss and replacement.

3. *Cyclic populations.* The phenomenon of cyclic populations has been the subject of a vast quantity of literature of varied quality. A critical analysis of this literature is obviously totally beyond the scope of this treatise. The subject is introduced here only to provide a basis for suggestions with respect to banding as a tool in the investigation of cyclic behavior of populations. Siivonen (1948) has reviewed the empirical data on population cycles and has discussed the probable periodicities for several avian species. The possible

causal factors have been ably reviewed by Franz (1950). Particularly noteworthy among recent contributions are the ingenious suggestions of Braestrup (1942) in reference to the operation of cycles through the effect of physical (possibly climatic) cycles on the availability of nutrient materials for plants and consequent nutritional effects on animals, and the suggestion of Kalela (1944) of the possibility that short-term physical cycles may actually cause longer-term population cycles, with slightly shifting periodicity, by being able to exert a "depressing" effect only during a restricted "critical period" in the life of the susceptible organism. Obviously, with the possible exception of immigration and emigration, any one or combination of the basic principles operative in the fluctuations discussed under category 1 could, if operating with a definite periodicity, be involved in cyclic population phenomena. A discussion of the possible physical cycles, together with the probable avenues through which they ultimately reach expression in altered productivity or mortality, is likewise beyond the scope of this discussion. Recently Palmgren (1949) has presented logical arguments which indicate that population cycles may be caused by random variables. He has shown that the cycles tabulated by Siivonen (1948) can be simulated closely by models in which the population is determined by the level of the previous year and a random variable such as some climatic factor. Cole (1951), employing somewhat different mathematical approaches, has also concluded that the basis of "cycles" may be random variables in the environment. These conclusions are worthy of careful study; all cyclic population phenomena should be carefully re-examined from this aspect. Obviously much research needs to be accomplished with respect to the basic etiology of population cycles and the physiologic and ecologic mechanisms through which they reach expression in the animals involved. Banding studies will be among the important tools in ascertaining the extent of the modification of the equilibrium between mortality and replacement during the various phases of the cycle.

With respect to categories 2 and 3 it should be observed that there are, of course, obvious differences among species in regard to "susceptibility" towards fluctuations in population, cyclic or noncyclic. Actually little is known concerning the basis of these differences in "susceptibilities."

It must be emphasized again that the three categories erected here are almost hopelessly arbitrary, even though they provide a convenient basis for thinking about fluctuations in populations. Although there are possibly many populations, if restricted to relatively short periods, which fall into category 1, few, if any, pure examples of 2 and 3 occur. For example, many of the cyclic species described by Siivonen (1948) also appear to show basic long-term changes. Errington's quail populations illustrate the hazards of categorization. Certainly they display elements characteristic of 1 and 3; the threshold changes, discussed by Errington, could be of the same nature, although shorter in duration, as some of the environmental changes which may be operative in 2.

The population of Great Tits studied by Kluijver (1951) in general shows the random fluctuations described in 1, but also shows a slight long-term tendency towards an increase in size. Obviously the assignment of a particular case to one of these categories is to a considerable degree a matter of aspect and perspective. The discussions of Errington (1945, 1951) and Kluijver (1951) illustrate much better the extreme complexities involved.

It should be obvious now even to the most casual reader that an ultimate comprehension of the population mechanics of any species will require a well-integrated combination of planned banding studies (Davis, 1951) and other field techniques. Data on mortality and survival rates and, to some extent on immigration and emigration may be obtained by banding techniques. However, these data alone give an incomplete picture without information on the size of the population from year to year and productivity. Banding may be one of the tools employed in obtaining this information. With respect to banding studies, many refinements will be necessary in basic techniques and more particularly in the development of statistical and other mathematical procedures. Since mathematical techniques will vary from species to species and project to project, it is beyond the scope of this discussion to attempt generalizations on their nature. Excellent examples of techniques developed to conform to a particular species and a particular set of conditions are those of Kortlandt (1942), Ruiter (1941), Bellrose and Chase (1950), Hanson and Smith (1950), Paludan (1951), Kluijver (1951), and von Haartman (1951). In terms of basic techniques particular attention must be given to the banding of nestling and juvenal birds, despite the lower percentages of recoveries, in order to accumulate a greater mass of data on birds of known age.

LOSS OF BANDS

Loss of bands can occur from forcible removal by the bird or as the result of wearing. Replacement of worn bands is not an uncommon procedure in the operation of a banding station. Because of this, Linsdale (1949:91) has stressed the possibility of errors from this source when banding data are used to study mortality and longevity. Loss of bands and loss of legibility of numbers and directions printed on bands have been discussed carefully by Hickey (1949, 1952:23) on the basis of material obtained with respect to several species from the files of the Fish and Wildlife Service.

If bands are lost before or shortly after the selected initial date, obviously there is little or no effect on the validity of the sample of recovered birds. It is possible or even probable that most forcible removals occur relatively soon after banding, before the bird has become accustomed to the band, and hence fall into this category. The four Cardinals, *Richmondena cardinalis,* which Lovell (1948:71) described as successful in removing bands accomplished the removal in each case within sixty days of banding. However, the Cardinal described by Young (1941) apparently attempted, at least sporadically, for two years to remove its band; twice the band was badly mutilated; once it was removed entirely. Laskey (1944:39) has replaced numerous mutilated bands on Cardinals. However, she has been unable, by means of tail marking, to demonstrate actual removal. Further, it should be noted that Cardinals with five-year or older bands are not uncommon (Lovell, 1951:33; Laskey, 1944:39; Table 3, Farner, 1949). Parks (1947:62) has reported mutilation of bands by tail-marked Evening Grosbeaks, *Hesperiphona vespertina,* but found no cases of actual removal.

More serious from the standpoint of statistical studies dealing with population dynamics is loss which results from wearing. Since wearing is a time-dependent variable, it means that such losses will be reflected in terms of biased samples in which the older age groups are represented by disproportionately smaller numbers of recoveries; mortality rates calculated from such samples will be exaggerated. The difficulties appear to be associated primarily with larger and longer-lived birds, although it should not be assumed that they are necessarily unimportant in smaller shorter-lived species. Exposure to salt water appears to be important in deterioration. Kortlandt (1942:178, 201, 205) observed the loss of bands from European Cormorants in Holland and calculated indirectly that this loss, together with loss accountable to "accidents" incidental to banding and bearing of bands, could be as high as 10 per cent. Stuart (1948) is of the opinion that similar losses occur among British Cormorants; this could account, at least in part, for the discrepancies noted by Lack (1943c:219) between his calculations of mortality rate and the reproductive capacity of this species. In his considerations of the discrepancies between mortality as indicated by banding data for his Herring Gulls and the observed productivity, Paynter (1949:163) has raised the possibility of band loss; since many bands on birds of this species survive ten years in good condition, it is his opinion that loss up to this age is not great. Paludan (1951) also apparently regards band loss to be unimportant in this species. Austin (1942:163) has found band loss to occur in the Common Tern, *Sterna hirundo;* the average period of wearing appears to be about ten years. Lockley (1942) has reported the loss of bands from Manx Shearwaters, *Puffinus puffinus.* Also Richdale (1949:2) has had similar difficulties in the banding of Yellow-eyed Penguins and has been compelled to continue to rely primarily on foot marking. It is consequently obvious that any study of mortality and survival in populations of relatively long-lived species must consider very carefully the possible occurrence and effect of band loss; this is particularly important for marine species.

On the other hand, for passerine and near-passerine species with lower longevities it appears that the possible error from this source is of much smaller magnitude. This supposition is substantiated by the general plausibility of the calculated mortality rates in relation to productivity and also by the experience that bands usually do not wear thin in less than three or four years; many, perhaps most, require considerably greater time. In view of other errors presently inherent in the methods, it does not appear that band loss is of great importance at this time. As greater refinement in methods is developed it may, however, prove to be important. In general, it would appear that the situation with respect to band loss from anseriform and galliform species may be similar to that for passerine birds, although Buss (1942) has described difficulties that occurred with Ring-necked Pheasants when aluminum bands of poor quality were used.

The remarks in the paragraph above are by no means to be construed as a dismissal of the problem of band loss for passerine, near-passerine, anseriform, and galliform species. There is a pressing need for controlled studies on the wearing and loss of bands. I can think of no more fundamental contribution than a well-conceived and well-executed investigation of this problem. Attention should be directed also toward the quality, width, and gauge of the metal. Field and aviary studies should be integrated. Data on wear and replacement from large operations concentrating on one or a few species should be carefully analyzed. Blake's (1951) suggestion of measuring wear by reduction of weight should certainly be employed. He has suggested that a loss of two-thirds of the weight may represent the maximum permissible wear. Also it would be profitable to investigate the qualities of various light alloys with respect to their potentialities as materials for durable bands. I think that there may be merit in my earlier suggestion (Farner, 1949:75) of an index of band loss from double-banded birds.

Band loss may be a variable of unknown magnitude in calculating mortality and survival rates as well as in ascertaining the age-group structure. Until it can be accurately estimated, the determination of these properties of populations involves an element of uncertainty.

SYSTEMATIC RÉSUMÉ OF DATA ON POPULATION DYNAMICS BASED ON THE RECOVERIES OF BANDED BIRDS

In this section an attempt is made to review systematically the results of important recent studies on mortality, survival, longevity, and age-group composition. It must be borne in mind that methods and conditions vary tremendously in the various studies. Whenever feasible, effort has been extended to make the data as nearly comparable as possible. In general, however, this can be accomplished only to a limited extent without access to the original data. Consequently, the reader must constantly remember that similarities and differences may be regarded only as suggestive. Definite conclusions, except in a few instances, must be formed with the greatest of caution.

Spheniscidae

In the course of his excellent studies on the Yellow-eyed Penguin on the Otago Peninsula in New Zealand, Richdale (1949:10) has accumulated survival data for 460 individuals of known age. The actual survival may be higher than that indicated in his tables because of the possibility of displacement of individuals away from the colony where they would not be recorded. Since foot marks were employed in addition to bands, distortion because of loss of bands is eliminated. Accepting the data in Richdale's tables as representing minimum survival and employing a system of calculation similar to that of Magnusson and Svärdson (1948), it is possible to estimate a minimum survival rate for this population.

For a group of 162 locally hatched birds this minimum annual survival rate beginning with the time of entry into the sea is about 80 per cent per year, with the highest rates from the fifth through the eighth years (86 to 93 per cent). For a group of 298 penguins whose hatching places were unknown the apparent annual survival rate is about 70 per cent. However, the apparent survival during the first year is only about 50 per cent compared to 84 per cent for locally hatched birds. The author suggests that there may be a greater tendency towards displacement in the second group. If this apparently low survival for the first year is disregarded, the survival rate is likewise 80 per cent, with the highest rates from the fourth through the eighth years. At least superficially it would therefore appear that the mean annual survival rate for these penguins must be at least 80 per cent and that it is probable that survival rate improves through the eighth year. It would indicate that the mean after lifetime from the first entry into the sea must be at least 4.5 years.

Phalacrocoracidae

Two studies involving analyses of banding data on the European Cormorant have been published. The more extensive is the remarkable investigation of Kortlandt (1942) in the Netherlands. Of interest for comparative purposes is the briefer study of Stuart (1948) on a colony of the nominate race in Wigtownshire, Scotland. According to Kortlandt, the Dutch populations were increasing at the rate of 10 per cent based on actual counts of colonies. In 1940 it was estimated that there were 4,000 breeding nests, 4,000 females of three years or older, and 4,300 males of three years of age or older (i.e., birds of breeding age); 4,500 to 5,500 young able to fly were reared. According to Kortlandt's calculations, there is a 10 per cent extra apparent loss due to mortality incident to banding operation and to band loss. Allowing for this and further for the greater probability of recovery of young birds, he estimated annual mortality rates for females as 36 per cent for the first year ("from flying out"), 22 per cent for the second year, 16 per cent for the third year, and 9 to 14 per cent for older females; for males the corresponding values are similar except that the rate for mature birds is 7 to 12 per cent. More than half of the deaths are the result of human activities. According to Kortlandt's calculations, this species, then, is one in which there is a definite improvement in survival in the older age groups.

The analysis of Stuart (1948) is based solely on 172 recoveries of Cormorants banded at a single stable colony. If this sample were accepted as representative, a first-year mortality rate of 70 per cent and a mean survival of 2.2 years from the first March 1 would be indicated. Stuart's calculations show this could not allow the maintenance of a constant population. It is suggested that the discrepancies occur because of loss of bands, particularly from older birds, and because the banding of juvenal birds causes them to leave earlier and to be more susceptible to death. In view of the fact that most of the birds were obtained by shooting, it is possible that simple bias resulting from the greater susceptibility of first-year birds to shooting may contribute to the discrepancy. This has been suggested by Lack (1943c:219) in reference to a similar series of data. It seems clear that Cormorant recoveries obtained by shooting do not give a reliable insight to the population dynamics of the species.

Hickey (1949, 1952:46) has analyzed the available recoveries of the Double-crested Cormorant, *Phalacrocorax auritus.* His analysis of marine-banded individuals indicates an annual mortality rate of 80 per cent during the first year of life and 39 per cent thereafter. For inland-banded individuals the annual mortality rates are 68 per cent for the first year, 30 per cent for the second year, and 24 per cent thereafter. Rationalization of the two sets of data is difficult because of the apparently poorer rate of recovery and the greater loss of bands as a result of obliteration or disintegration under marine conditions. The observed first-year mortality rates (Hickey, 1952:53), as in the case of European Cormorants, are not consistent with the known productivity, indicating bias in the recovery of birds which die during the first year. Despite these uncertainties Hickey's (1952:55) conclusion that the Double-crested Cormorant populations are characterized by high mortality and high productivity in contrast to low productivity and low mortality in the European Cormorant is certainly reasonable.

Ardeidae

Hickey (1949, 1952:59) has prepared an abridged life table for the Black-crowned Night Heron, *Nycticorax nycticorax,* based on 141 recoveries of birds banded in North America. This table indicates a first-year mortality rate of 61 per cent and a mean adult mortality rate of 31 per cent per year. These rates appear to be provisionally consistent with the available information on productivity. Hickey's calculations do not contain estimates of longevity or mean after lifetime. However, if the adult mortality rate is relatively constant, it must be of the order of 2.5 to 2.9 years as of the second August 1 of life.

Bourlière (1947:180) has analyzed the records of 177 Common Herons banded as young in France and subsequently recovered, mostly by shooting. The mean longevity for this sample is less than one year, possibly as the result of the greater susceptibility to shooting among young birds. However, for those which survived the first January 1 of life, the mean longevity or mean after lifetime as of the first January 1, was about 2.9 years.

Lack (1949a) has analyzed 195 records of Common Herons banded as nestlings in England and subsequently recovered largely by shooting. From this sample, a first-year mortality rate (June 1–May 31) of 69 per cent is indicated. Lack is justifiably of the opinion that this is probably too high, since it would be inconsistent with the available information on reproduction. From the beginning of the second year, however, the annual mortality rate appears to be about 31 per cent, which appears to be reasonable. Quite possibly the difficulties with the first-year data are the result of bias from shooting, although additional sources of error are indicated by Lack. The mean longevity as of the beginning of the second year was found to be 2.8 years, which is quite consistent with Bourlière's calculation.

The analysis by Verheyen and le Grelle (1952:217) of 247 records of Common Herons banded as young in Belgium leads them to the conclusion that the observed mortality rates, which indicate that only 22 per cent survive to the assumed minimum breeding age, are inconsistent with the maintenance of a stable population. These data appear, therefore, to be very similar to those of Lack (1949a). Verheyen and le Grelle (1952:218) have suggested that immigration from heronries in France may be important in the maintenance of the Belgian heronries. Apparently consideration is not given to possible bias in the sample, nor does it appear that consideration is given to the shorter period available for recovery of older birds.

Unfortunately the studies of Bourlière (1947), Lack (1949a), Hickey (1952), and Verheyen and le Grelle (1952) involve sufficient uncertainties with respect to mortality rates and productivity to prevent precise comparisons. Superficially, however, it does appear that the Black-crowned Night Heron and the Common Heron may be quite similar with respect to mortality rates and age-group structure.

It could be of very substantial interest to compare this information on herons with similar information for the White Stork, *Ciconia ciconia,* which has been banded extensively in Europe. Although extensive data on recoveries have been published by Hornberger (1943), Libbert *et al.* (1937), Skovgaard (1937), Schüz and Böhringer (1950), and others, an analysis of these is beyond the scope of this paper.

Anatidae

The calculations of mortality rates and longevity in anseriform species are difficult because of fluctuations in populations, hunting pressure, changes in habitat, and possible bias in sample since most records come from shooting. The most extensive studies are those of Bellrose and Chase (1950) on several species of ducks in Illinois; Hanson and Smith (1950) on Canada Geese; Van Den Akker and Wilson (1949) on several species in Utah; Höhn (1948) on

Mallards in England; and Hickey (1949, 1952) on Mallards and Redheads, *Aythya americana,* in North America. Selected data from these studies are summarized in Tables 2 and 2*a*. Whereas these are doubtless indicative of the general order and trend of mortality and survival rates, they must, for the reasons cited above, be accepted as provisional until more studies have been accomplished.

The mortality rates for the data of Bellrose and Chase (Table 2) have been calculated for this study as more useful for comparative purposes than the arithmetic means of mortality rates given by the authors. The investigation of Hanson and Smith is based on two samples. The first consists of geese banded at Horseshoe Lake, Illinois, and subsequently retrapped there. Retrapped banded birds were assumed to represent a sample of the entire population and hence representative of its population dynamics. Because of the short period involved in the investigation (1940-1947), the annual variation in numbers banded (143–1,379) and the necessity of weighting very small samples to equivalence with much larger samples, the calculations can be regarded, as noted by the senior author, as only suggestive. The "survival index" (i.e., the *unweighted* arithmetic mean of the survival rates for the first, second, and third years) of 43 per cent may be an approximation of actual survival rate. The "survival index" for geese of all ages is given as 48 per cent. The second group of data consists of records of birds banded at Kingsville, Ontario (1925–1944), and recovered dead in the Mississippi Valley. An analysis of the data in Hanson and Smith's (1950:186) Table 41 according to the methods of Lack and Farner indicates a mortality rate of about 38 per cent for 1925–1932. A total approximate survival curve (Hanson and Smith, 1950:186) indicates the possibility of improved survival at about the fifth or sixth year of life. The data of Van Den Akker and Wilson include recoveries of many ducks which had recuperated from botulism before banding and release. To what extent, if any, this has modified the mortality rates and patterns is not apparent.

Hickey (1949, 1952) has presented an extensive series of interesting data on mortality in Mallards. There is an indication that annual mortality rates for males on the Pacific coast may have declined from 65 per cent in the late 1920's to less than 50 per cent in the 1940's. Hickey suggests that this is the result of reduced hunting pressure. It is quite probable that this is true, although in considerations of this kind there are at least four variables which are difficult to evaluate because the samples involved are obtained largely by shooting. These variables are: (1) the fraction of the total mortality which is the result of shooting, (2) the extent to which shooting replaces natural mortality and the extent to which it is additive with respect to natural mortality, (3) the deviation of the survival curve of a cohort in which all deaths occur by shooting from a survival curve based on natural causes of death, and (4) differential migration with respect to age. These variables must be borne in mind when using the data tabulated in Tables 2 and 2*a,* particularly with respect to anseriform and galliform species. With respect to the first variable there can be no question that shooting has become an important mortality factor but its magnitude is difficult to ascertain with any degree of certainty. Farner (1952:123), on the basis of population and kill estimates of the Fish and Wildlife Service, has suggested that at least half of the deaths could be the result of shooting. However, as Hickey (1949, 1952:125) has correctly indicated, these estimates by the Fish and Wildlife Service are very crude approximations at the best and Farner's estimate is consequently of a similar nature. Earlier Bellrose and Chase (1950:22) estimated that shooting losses for Mallards of the Mississippi flyway for 1939 to 1947 amounted to about 41 per cent per year. Assuming a total annual mortality rate which could scarcely be in excess of 60 per cent, this estimate would indicate that about two-thirds of the mortality was the result of shooting. Hickey (1952:154) is of the opinion that the estimates of Bellrose and Chase are "quite possibly too high." The second of the variables is associated with the nature and magnitude of the so-called "harvestable surplus." At just what level removal by shooting ceases to replace natural mortality and begins to add to it has never been established satisfactorily. With respect to the third variable there is little doubt that samples obtained by shooting are biased with regard to first-year birds (Höhn, 1948:234; Hochbaum, 1944:133; Hanson and Smith, 1950:185; Bellrose and Chase, 1950:22). The extent of this bias is not clear although Hickey (1952:160) has suggested that young may be 1.6 to 3.1 times as vulnerable to shooting as adults. If this is an appreciable tendency, the development of shooting as an important mortality factor probably has had the effect of increasing the mean age of the birds of a stable breeding population. Hickey's (1949, 1952) data, however, suggest that a sample of adult Mallards obtained by shooting is sufficiently "normal" with respect to age-group composition for calculation of mortality rates. The fourth variable, differential migration with respect to age, is known to occur in many species of birds and probably occurs in anseriform species, although this remains to be demonstrated (Hickey, 1952:160).

Hickey's (1952:73) statistics on the Redhead, based on a sample obtained by shooting, indicate that the first year mortality rate beginning on the first of September is in excess of 70 per cent compared to an adult mortality rate of about 55 per cent. Hickey (1952:82) concludes that this high first-year vulnerability is a very real and important problem in the conservation of this species.

Hickey's (1952:125-163) very interesting discussion of certain aspects of the dynamics of Mallard populations, employing data from banding, is eloquent testimony of the great potentiality of this tool. It is equally eloquent evidence of the need for a much greater degree of intelligent planning and integration of banding programs than has been possible up to this time.

Accipitridae

A life table for the Marsh Hawk, *Circus cyaneus,* has been prepared by Hickey (1949, 1952:85) on the basis of the records of ninety-nine individuals banded in North America as nestlings and recovered by shooting. The first-year mortality rate is 59 per cent and the mean adult mortality rate is 30 per cent. Since there is no basis for evaluation of bias due to shooting, these data must be regarded as strictly provisional.

Galliformes

Calculations of mortality rates and longevity in this order are confronted with difficulties similar to those encountered with anseriform species, with the consequence that the few available data are not sufficiently adequate to give more than a suggestion concerning the nature of the population dynamics. Interpretations are frequently difficult because of gross annual fluctuations in population densities. In general it appears that galliform species may have annual mortality rates in the range of 60 to 90 per cent. The data, in the main, appear to indicate a constant annual mortality rate regardless of age. However, Buss (1946:107) suggests that the data on Ring-necked Pheasants at the University Arboretum (1937–1943), and at the Fish Hatchery, Madison, Wisconsin, indicate that there may be an improvement in survival with age; because of the small numbers the data are certainly suggestive rather than conclusive. Certainly, unless substantial band loss is involved, the improvement in survival is not very great. The data from the Wisconsin pheasant studies are summarized in Tables 2 and 2*a*.

The data obtained in the study of a population of Bobwhite Quail in northern Wisconsin (Buss *et al.*, 1947, and unpublished data) suggest an annual mortality rate which may be of the order of 80 per cent, which would be very near the maximum replacement potential. Mean after lifetime, as of the end of the first summer, could be as low as 0.5 years. The data obtained by Leopold (1945:30) on age ratios of Bobwhite Quail in Howell County, Missouri, indicate that, in samples obtained by shooting, "immatures" represent 73 to 82 per cent of the individuals; other data from Missouri give 75 to 88 per cent with the higher percentages in the more agricultural areas. Assuming reasonably constant populations and reasonably unbiased sampling by shooting, this would indicate annual mortality rates of 73 to 82 and 75 to 88 per cent since the immatures as replacements must equal the loss for the previous year. If, however, "immatures" are shot more easily than adults and/or the "immatures" have not reached adult mortality rate by the hunting season and/or there has been a large production of young which has not been reduced to replacement numbers by the hunting season, these inferred mortality rates would be too high. Tentatively, it appears that mortality rates for Bobwhite Quail in northern Wisconsin may be higher than those in Missouri.

The data on California Quail, *Lophortyx californica,* obtained by Sumner

(1935), Emlen (1940), and Richardson (1941) suggest annual mortality rates in the order of 60 to 75 per cent.

Bump *et al.* (1947:548) and Middleton (1935) have presented estimates, from nonbanding techniques, indicating annual mortality rates of the order of 60 to 70 per cent for the Ruffed Grouse, *Bonasa umbellus,* and the Partridge, *Perdix perdix.*

Charadriiformes

With respect to population dynamics, this order is obviously one of considerable diversity. In view of the large numbers of recoveries of gulls, terns, and shorebirds available in the files of the various birdbanding systems, it is to be hoped that additional significant studies will be forthcoming.

Of particular note is the pioneer investigation of Kraak *et al.* (1940) on the Lapwing in western Europe. Their data, analyzed on a time-specific basis, show a remarkable tendency towards a 40 per cent annual mortality rate which does not change with age (Tables 2 and 2*a*). A similar rate was found later by Klomp (1946). The investigations of Klomp (1951) and Verheyen and le Grelle (1952) suggest that either land-use practices or shooting, or both, are holding this population below its natural level. Since most of the recoveries were by shooting it seems that younger Lapwings are no more susceptible to shooting than older birds. Similar results were obtained by Lack (1943c) in England, where the mean annual mortality rate was found to be 35 per cent (Table 2). Lack's (1943c) data on the European Woodcock, *Scolopax rusticola,* also consist almost entirely of recoveries which were obtained by shooting. Laven's (1940) investigation of a limited population of Ringed Plovers, *Charadrius hiaticula,* in East Prussia indicates an annual mortality rate of about 50 per cent. Bergman (1946:49) concluded that his data on the European Turnstone, *Arenaria interpres,* suggest a mean longevity of 6 to 7 years for breeding birds.

Of interest also are the data of Drost and Hartmann (1949) for the Oystercatchers on the Island Mellum. This population has been under observation for a quarter of a century. The mean age for those (22) with bands was 12.55 years; assigning to the unbanded breeding birds the minimum age of 3 years, the mean age would be 9.56 years. This conforms with Dircksen's (1932) calculations which indicate a loss of 90 per cent from hatching to breeding age (3 years) and, consequently, a mean age of 8.5 years for breeding birds. Mean ages of this order probably can be regarded as indicative of annual mortality rates of the order of 10 per cent.

There have been several investigations concerning mortality and longevity in gulls. Marshall (1947) analyzed the records of 3,806 Herring Gulls banded as young and recovered dead in North America. He concluded that the annual mortality rate must be about 47 per cent and that the mean after lifetime beginning with the first September 1 must be about 1.5 years, and 2.3 years beginning with breeding age. Paynter (1949:161) has shown that Marshall's conclusions are untenable in terms of the maintenance of a constant population level. In analyzing his own data for Kent Island, Paynter (1947:168, 1949:162) has corrected the actual number of recoveries in light of the progressively smaller number of years during which the older-aged birds could be recovered; these calculations would indicate a mean expectancy of about 3 years for those which survive to breed and an annual mortality rate of about 31 per cent after the first year. However, these calculations also would indicate a failure of the population to maintain itself. Paynter suggests three possible explanations: (1) studies have covered periods which are too brief to obtain adequate data on long-lived birds, (2) an abnormally high mortality for the period of Paynter's investigation (1936–1947), or (3) loss of bands by older birds. According to him, if 1 per cent of the birds were to survive to 20 years or if the first-year mortality were 26 per cent instead of 42 per cent, a stable population could be rationalized. The first assumption is certainly very possible since recoveries of banded Herring Gulls of this age are not uncommon; also there is certainly some band loss before this age which would reduce the probability of recovery. The possibility that first-year mortality is as low as 26 per cent appears unlikely, however. There is a further possible source of error in terms of possibly biased recovery caused by different geographic distribution and habits of the nonbreeding age group.

Hickey (1952:90) has criticized the treatment of data by Paynter (1949) and Marshall (1947) and has presented an abridged life table which indicates a first-year mortality rate of 60 per cent followed by 29, 21, and 27 per cent per year for the second, third, and fourth to sixteenth years. However, these also cannot be reconciled with the available data on productivity.

Paludan (1951) has recently published an excellent analysis of recoveries of Herring Gulls banded as chicks in Denmark. His calculations indicate a first-year (after the first September 1) mortality of 62 per cent, which, because of biased recovery of first-year birds, he believes to be too high. Thereafter, from the second through the twentieth year, the annual mortality rate deviates little from 15 per cent. In the opinion of Paludan, this rate can be rationalized with his observations of productivity by the colony on Christiansø and, therefore, an age-independent annual adult mortality rate (beyond the second year) is actually characteristic of the population involved. Paludan has also recalculated Marshall's (1947) data to allow for lesser opportunity to recover birds of the older age groups. With this correction, Paludan found in Marshall's series also evidence of an age-independent mortality rate after the first year. However, in this case, the rate was 29 per cent which is similar to Paynter's calculation of 31 per cent. Paludan is convinced from his statistical analysis that the difference between the American and Danish series cannot be attributed either to band loss or to the fact that the Danish series involves more age groups. It is rather tempting then to assume that there is a true difference in mortality rate between the nominate race as studied by Paludan in Denmark and *Larus argentatus smithsonianus* of North America. Caution is necessary, however, since it is not possible to rationalize the calculated mortality rates for *smithsonianus* with its productivity as observed by Paynter. Hickey (1952:92) has suggested that the differences between the Danish and American data may be the result of the use of bands of inferior quality in America. Although the data of Wilmann (1948:40), Välikangas and Siivonen (1949:231), and Välikangas and Koskimies (1950:153) are somewhat fragmentary, they appear to fall in the pattern of the above-cited detailed studies.

Of interest also are Lack's (1943c:217) data on Black-headed Gulls. His sample of 252 recoveries not reported as shot indicate a weighted mean mortality rate of about 42 per cent as of the first August 1. The mortality rate for the first year is 52 per cent; for subsequent years, 36 per cent. In the sample of 203 obtained by shooting, 78 per cent were first-year birds, indicating that shooting samples first-year birds disproportionately. Verheyen and le Grelle (1952:220) have considered this in respect to their data from Belgium which appear to be similarily biased (78 per cent mortality during the first year). The percentage of recoveries by shooting is not given. However, Verheyen and le Grelle (1952:222) are convinced that the Belgian population of this species is maintained only by substantial immigration of breeding adults.

The only extensive study on terns has been that of Austin (1942) on the Common Tern on Cape Cod. His data consist primarily of returns of Common Terns banded as either young or adults. Because the tendency to return to the birthplace to breed is much less pronounced than the persistent tendency to return to the breeding place of the previous year, only returns of terns banded as adults can be used as a basis for estimating mortality rate. Using Austin's data (p. 165) and considering the progressively smaller number of years for recovery of older birds and the possible errors because of band loss, it seems certain that the annual adult mortality rate must be under 30 per cent and that the mean survival beyond the banding date must be in excess of three years. Austin (1949:38) suggests that the mortality rate is only 17.2 per cent. The ultimate analysis of Austin's extensive data on this species will constitute a highly significant contribution to the study of avian population dynamics.

Hickey (1949, 1952:90) has presented a preliminary life table for the Caspian Tern, *Hydroprogne caspia,* which is based on 106 individuals banded as nestlings in North America. These data indicate a first-year mortality rate of 44 per cent, a second-year rate of 26, and 18 per cent for subsequent years. If the adult mortality rate were actually about 15 per cent, which is reasonable, the maintenance of a stable population can be rationalized with the available data on productivity.

Columbidae

Hickey (1949, 1952:102) has compiled an abridged life table for the Mourning Dove based on the recovery, mostly by shooting, of 297 doves originally banded as juveniles. This table indicates a first-year (beginning the first September 1) mortality rate of 64 per cent compared to an adult rate of 56 per cent per year. A series of 263 recoveries of doves unaged at banding indicates a mean annual mortality rate of 58 per cent.

Austin (1951) has recently analyzed the data on Mourning Doves banded during the course of twenty years at North Eastham, Massachusetts. Field studies indicate that the population has remained reasonably constant throughout this period. Using samples of birds recovered dead, largely by shooting, and samples obtained by retrapping, it is concluded that the first-year mortality rate is about 80 per cent, and that the adult annual mortality rate, attained at about the end of the first year, is about 55 per cent. These rates are apparently compatible with the potential replacement rate, although the margin is rather slight.

Strigiformes

Schifferli (1949) has analyzed the records of 81 Barn Owls, *Tyto alba,* which were banded as young in Switzerland and subsequently recovered. His calculations indicate a mean after lifetime from the banding date of 11 months; as of the end of the first year it was 2.25 years; the corresponding annual mortality rates were 71 and 57.5 per cent with a rate of 76 per cent for the first year alone. Although these rates are rather surprisingly high, the author shows them to be compatible with the known productivity of the species, presuming that all birds breed during the first year. The calculations of von Haartman (1951:25), based on the data of Schneider (1937), indicate a mean mortality rate of 47 per cent and a mean longevity of 1.6 years. In view of the assumptions made by von Haartman and the small size of the samples, the discrepancy is not surprising. Hickey (1949, 1952:111) has prepared an abridged life table for this species on the basis of 98 recoveries of individuals that were banded as young in North America. His data suggest a first-year mortality rate of 58 per cent, a mean adult mortality rate of 28 per cent per year, and an over-all mean annual mortality rate of about 40 per cent. These are rather substantially lower than the rates suggested by Schifferli. Further, the available data on productivity suggest that replacement is at a definitely greater rate than would be required for maintaining a stable population with mortality rates of the order suggested by Hickey's data. Consistent with these differences between the Swiss and American data is Stewart's (1952:243) calculation of a mean longevity of 1.5 years from the time of banding as nestlings for 220 North American Barn Owls. With a correction for the lesser chance of recovery for older individuals this mean longevity would be still higher; likewise, however, such a correction was not included in Schifferli's calculations. With respect to the mortality rate, a recalculation of Schifferli's data to correct for the lower chance of recovery of older birds does not eliminate the major difference in adult annual mortality rate. The available data do not suggest an explanation of these differences and discrepancies. However, it does seem possible that the pronounced fluctuations known to occur in population and reproductive activity may combine with small samples and irregular temporal patterns of banding and recovery to produce this situation. The data do suggest, however, that the Barn Owl is a relatively short-lived species.

Hickey's (1949, 1952:114) abridged life table for the Horned Owl, *Bubo virginianus,* is based on the recoveries of 58 individuals that were banded as nestlings in North America. The indicated first-year mortality rate is 51 per cent whereas the adult mortality rate is 23 per cent per year; the latter is confirmed by other analyses. Although the sample is small, it seems apparent that a low annual adult mortality rate and a relatively high longevity are characteristic of this species.

Apodidae

Magnusson and Svärdson (1948:132) have analyzed the data on a series of recoveries from 650 breeding Common Swifts banded in Närke Province in central Sweden from 1930 through 1947. Up through 1948, 137 of these were retrapped.[5] Applying a "recovery-efficiency" factor and considering the number of banded individuals theoretically available to attain a given age, the authors have constructed a survival series. This series is adjusted for unaccountable loss, probably partly the result of displacement, during the first year after banding. The adjusted series then indicates an adult annual mortality rate of 19 per cent, which appears not to fluctuate extensively with age. From this mortality rate it is estimated that the mean after lifetime of breeding birds, as of the date of banding, is 4.6 years. The data on swifts banded as nestlings indicate a mean longevity, as of the date of departure from the nest, of 2.4 years. The data from Weitnauer's (1947:170-173) investigation of the same species, although limited in quantity and not strictly comparable for other reasons, indicate a mean longevity similar to that obtained by Magnusson and Svärdson.

The only other extensive study on swifts is that of Arn (1942, 1945) on the Alpine Swift, *Apus melba,* in Switzerland. The mean age for a mixed sample, some recovered dead and some retrapped during the breeding season, is 4.65 years from the date of banding. This mean is certainly not comparable with that calculated by Magnusson and Svärdson (1948) but it is probable that the agreement is more than fortuitous.

Passeriformes

Although the studies on passerine species vary extensively with respect to methodology, they appear to present a reasonably consistent picture (Tables 3 and 3*a*). Annual mortality rates apparently vary from about 40 to 70 per cent.

[5] These data were misinterpreted as a single-year time-specific series by Farner (1952: 132).

There is an obvious tendency toward a constant annual adult mortality rate for several species. Several interesting studies have not been included in Tables 3 and 3*a*.

Magee (1928, 1936) has recorded data on the ages of retrapped Purple Finches which had been banded as young. Accepting the age-group composition of the retrapped sample of 136 individuals as representative of the age-group structure of the entire population, it would appear from the application of formula (4) that the mean adult annual mortality rate must be about 46 per cent, which would indicate a mean after lifetime from the banding date of about 1.7 years, presuming the mean survival within the year of death to be six months. It should be noted that von Haartman (1951:24) has recalculated Magee's data to indicate an annual mortality rate of 53 per cent and a mean longevity or after lifetime of 1.4 years. Whittle's (1929) data on this species, although more difficult to interpret, indicate a similar order of mortality rate. Possible bias in sampling by retrapping must be borne in mind in considering the results of the analyses of these data. Von Haartman (1951:24) has concluded that the data of Magee (1939) on the Evening Grosbeak indicate a mean annual mortality rate of 42 per cent and a mean after lifetime of 1.9 years from the banding date. Again the possible difficulties resulting from sampling by retrapping must be considered. Creutz (1949a:146), on the basis of investigations of a restricted population near Dresden, estimates that adult European Tree Sparrows, *Passer montanus,* survive about one year after banding. Considering this, and the data obtained on recoveries of birds banded as young, he has suggested that mean longevity for the species is about two years. It seems possible that this estimate is a bit too high.

A recalculation of the data of Hann (1948:6, 9) on 38 recoveries of Oven-birds, *Seiurus aurocapillus,* from a limited population in Michigan, suggests a mean adult annual mortality rate of 46 per cent and a mean after lifetime from the banding date of 1.7 years. Of interest also are the data obtained by Erickson (1938) on a small population of Wren-tits. These suggest (Farner, 1949:73) a mean after lifetime of 2.3 to 3.0 years as of the beginning of the first breeding season; this is unusually long for passerine species. Drost (1948:23) has tabulated observations on a small banded population (including 31 banded as young) of Yellow Wagtails, *Motacilla flava,* at Helgoland. Although Drost regards the sample as too small for calculating longevity and mortality rate, von Haartman (1951:24) suggests that they indicate an annual mortality rate of about 47 per cent. In light of the small sample and other difficulties this must be regarded as a very crude approximation.

In his monumental study of the Great Tit, Kluijver (1951:99) has estimated first-year mortality at about 87 per cent; for older birds he found the rate to be 49 per cent per year. These rates agree quite well with those of Plattner and Sutter (1946, 1947) for Switzerland (Table 3). It should be noted that the smaller quantities of data obtained by Wallace (1941) and Odum (1942:157) on the Black-capped Chickadee, *Parus atricapillus,* suggest an annual mortality rate of about 40 per cent. Kluijver's (1951:102) data on the Great Tit indicate a close conformance to a survival curve predicted on the basis of a constant adult mortality rate after the first year of life. Life expectancy once the stable mortality rate is attained is 1.5 years.

A possible variation from an age-independent random mortality pattern is suggested by the interesting data on the Pied Flycatcher, *Muscicapa hypoleuca,* that were obtained by Trettau and Merkel (1943) in Silesia. They found the breeding population to contain 39 per cent first-year birds, 32 per cent second-year, and 16 per cent third-year. Although superficially this appears to represent a case of improvement of survival with age, there are other possible explanations. It is possible that not all first-year birds breed; another factor is the greater *Ortstreue* of birds which have once bred in the locality (von Haartman, 1949:22). *Ortstreue* is more poorly developed in females. In his careful study on this species in Finland, von Haartman (1951:22) has concluded that the population dynamics are best explained by regarding the annual mortality rate as 50 per cent; he suggests that the data of Creutz (1949b) from Saxony indicate an annual mortality rate of about 51 per cent. If this is correct, the suggestion of Creutz (1949b:50) that the mean longevity is 2.0 to 2.5 years is doubtless a bit too high. Von Haartman has also studied the recovery records from Helgoland (Drost and Schilling, 1940, plus records accumulated subsequently) in which the calculated annual mortality rate is 59 per cent. Von Haartman suggests that this may be slightly high because of failure to recover older birds proportionately.

Verheyen and le Grelle (1951) have recently analyzed the available data on thrushes banded as nestlings in Belgium. It appears not possible to ascertain whether or not a date was established beyond which recoveries from further bandings were excluded in order to obtain a relatively unbiased sample. Records of recoveries less than two months after banding were excluded, however. Although these data are not strictly comparable to those on thrushes presented in Tables 3 and 3*a,* the deviations are probably not too great for approximate comparisons. In the case of the European Blackbird (276 records), 60 per cent of the recoveries were during the first year of life. The mean after lifetime as of the first July of life was 1.1 years; as of the second July apparently also about 1.1 years. Applying formulae (4) and (7) suggests an annual adult mortality rate of approximately 60 per cent which is substantially higher than that of Lack (Tables 3 and 3*a*), possibly because of failure to recover older birds proportionally. For the smaller amount (164 recoveries) of data on the Song Thrush, the corresponding mean after lifetimes were 0.8 and apparently about 1.4 years; 70 per cent of the recoveries were of first-year birds. Applying formulae (4) and (7) an adult annual mortality rate of slightly more than 50 per cent is suggested, which is in good agreement with Lack (Tables 3 and 3*a*). Verheyen and le Grelle (1951:278) appear to be able to rationalize these data with the observed productivity of these species.

Of considerable interest is a comparison of the 63 per cent annual mortality and 1.1-year longevity (Lack, 1949b:147) of the swallows with 19 per cent and 4.6 years for the swifts (Magnusson and Svärdson, 1948:136). In view of the similarities in habits, one cannot resist the temptation to speculate that the longer survival of the swifts may be associated with the remarkable ability of incubating birds and nestlings to resist, by development of a torpid condition, the starvation imposed by inclement weather (Koskimies, 1950).

SUMMARY

1. Samples of birds banded as juveniles, or at unknown ages, and subsequently recovered dead have been used extensively to obtain information on mortality rates, survival rates, mean longevity or mean after lifetime, and age-group structure of the population. Several types of bias may affect the validity of such samples. Included are (*a*) bias resulting from non-representative temporal and geographic distribution, (*b*) bias with respect to cause of death such as the disproportional numbers of young shot in certain species, and (*c*) bias resulting from loss or illegibility of older bands. These must be considered in all studies of population dynamics employing data from banded birds. Much research remains to be done with respect to methods of minimization of errors due to these factors. Encouragement should be given to programs concentrating consistently on one or a few species and to programs in which juvenal birds, in or out of the nests, are banded. Investigations should be designed to allow correlation and complementation of banding studies and other field methods. The validity of calculations from banding data should always be tested in terms of known productivity of the species.

2. Live samples obtained by trapping should be used with caution since young birds, of certain species at least, appear to be retrapped more readily than those of the older age groups.

3. In the use of birds recovered dead it is desirable for purposes of random sampling to allow a period after banding for dispersal of banded birds. For this purpose, calculations are most conveniently based on birds which survive a *selected initial date,* so designated as to allow for such dispersal and more incidentally, also, for convenience in calculation. For many species the first January 1 is suitable. Moreover, the annual mortality rate beyond the first January 1 becomes reasonably constant, regardless of age, for many species. If the sample is valid, the weighted mean may be regarded as characteristic for the population or the species which it represents.

4. Presuming the sample to be valid, the mean adult mortality rate may be calculated best by

$$M_w = \frac{\sum_{i=1}^{n} D_i}{\sum_{i=1}^{n} iD_i} . \qquad (4)$$

If the annual mortality rates for the various age groups do not vary widely from the mean mortality rate, the mean after lifetime, as of the selected initial date, may be calculated by

$$Y = \frac{1}{M} - (1 - p). \qquad (5)$$

If possible, p should be ascertained by direct observation or from the recoveries, unless there is reason to suspect a temporal bias in recovery. If it is desirable, or necessary, to assume p for the operation of a uniform mortality rate through the course of the year,

$$p = -\frac{0.4343}{\log_{10} S} - \frac{S}{M} \qquad (6)$$

and

$$Y = -\frac{0.4343}{\log_{10} S} . \qquad (7)$$

Mean after lifetime, thus calculated, usually agrees quite well with that observed from samples, if allowances are made for irregularities in the distribution of deaths through the course of the year (Table 1).

5. Mean annual mortality rates calculated according to equation (4) from valid samples taken over a number of years must be regarded only as means about which the mortality rates for individual years fluctuate, presumably in a normal-frequency distribution. The same holds for survival rates, mean after lifetime or mean longevity, and age-group structure. Consideration must be given, in the use of such calculations, to random fluctuations, cyclic fluctuations, and gradual long-term changes in populations.

6. Sufficient investigations have been accomplished to indicate order of adult mortality and survival rates as well as the order of mean after lifetime beyond designated initial dates. These data are briefly summarized in Table 4. It must be remembered that these can be regarded only as suggestions based on currently available information. It is certain that there will be modifications as more studies are completed. The adult mortality rates given in general are those which apply *after* the first 0.5 to 1.5 years, depending on the species or group concerned. The first-year mortality rates are calculated for a year beginning with fledging, leaving the colony, or some time later during the summer of hatching. Comparisons must be made with great caution. The mean after lifetime is expressed as of a designated initial date, usually 0.5 to 1.5 years after hatching. An accurate mean longevity value from the date of hatching, or even the date of fledging, would be very difficult to obtain for most species.

TABLE 4. RESUME OF INVESTIGATIONS ON MORTALITY RATES AND LONGEVITY IN BIRDS[a]

Order	Number of Species Investigated	Number of Investigations	Approximate Range of First-Year Mortality Rates	Approximate Range of Adult Annual Mortality Rates	Approximate Range of Mean After Lifetime Beyond Selected Initial Date[b]
Sphenisciformes	1	1	—	20-30	>4.5
Pelecaniformes (Phalacrocoracidae)	2	4	35-80	12-30	—
Ciconiiformes (Ardeidae)	2	4	*ca.* 60	*ca.* 30	2.5-3.0
Anseriformes (Anatidae)	5	5	50-85	40-65	0.9-2.1
Falconiformes (Accipitridae)	1	1	*ca.* 60	*ca.* 30	—
Galliformes	5	9	—	*ca.* 60-80	*ca.* 0.5-1.1
Charadriiformes					
Charadrii	5	8	—	15-50	1.4->9
Lari	4	7	40-60	18-30	2.4-5
Columbiformes (Columbidae)	1	2	*ca.* 80?	55-58	*ca.* 1
Strigiformes					
Tytonidae	3	1	50-75	28-57	—
Strigidae	1	1	*ca.* 50	*ca.* 30	—
Apodiformes (Apodidae)	1	2	—	*ca.* 19	*ca.* 5
Passeriformes	22	27	—	<40-68	1.0-2.3

[a] See Conclusion 6.
[b] See Tables 2, 3 or text.

7. There is evidence in at least two species (Starlings and Lapwings) that the higher mortality rates for certain areas, as calculated from banding data, are compensated for by higher productivity.

8. The available data appear to indicate that for several species there is a tendency towards the development of a relatively stable annual adult mortality rate. This would mean that death then is a random function, that life expectancy remains relatively constant regardless of age, and that senescence and experience have no effect, or counteracting effects, with respect to the survival curve.

9. There is a suggestion that in some species there may be an improvement in survival among the older age groups. This appears probable, for example, in cormorants and Yellow-eyed Penguins. It appears possible in Oyster-catchers and Canada Geese.

Bibliography

ADAMS, L.

1951. Confidence limits for the Peterson or Lincoln index used in animal population studies. Jour. Wildlife Mgmt., 15:13-19.

ALEXANDER, W. B.

1946. The index of heron population, 1945. Brit. Birds, 39:201-204.

ARN, H.

1942. Beringungsergebnisse der Alpensegler (*Micropus melba melba* L.). Alter und Nistplatztreue. Ornithol. Beobachter, 39:150-162.

1945. Zur Biologie des Alpenseglers, *Micropus melba melba* (L). Arch. suisses d'Ornithol., 2:137-181.

AUSTIN, O. L.

1942. The life span of the Common Tern (*Sterna hirundo*). Bird-Banding, 13:159-176.

1949. Site tenacity, a behaviour trait of the Common Tern (*Sterna hirundo* Linn.). Bird-Banding, 20:1-39.

AUSTIN, O. L., JR.

1951. The Mourning Dove on Cape Cod. Bird-Banding, 22:149-174.

BELLROSE, F. C., and E. B. CHASE

1950. Population losses in the Mallard, Black Duck, and Blue-winged Teal. Ill. Nat. Hist. Surv., Biol. Notes, 22:27 pp.

BERGMAN, G.

1946. Der Steinwälzer, *Arenaria i. interpres,* in seiner Beziehung zur Umwelt. Acta Zool. Fenn., 47:1-151.

BERGSTROM, E. A.

1952. Extreme old age in terns. Bird-Banding, 23:72-73.

BERNDT, R.

1949. Zwölf Jahre Kontrolle des Höhlenbrüterbestandes eines nordwestsächsischen Parkes. In Beiträge zur Vogelkunde (Stresemann-Festschrift). Akademische Verlagsgesellschaft, Leipzig, 1-20.

BLAKE, C. H.

1951. Wear of towhee bands. Bird-Banding, 22:179-180.

1952. A population balance for the Black-capped Chickadee. Bird-Banding, 23:165-168.

BOURLIÈRE, F.

1946. Longévité moyenne et longévité maximum chez les vertébrés. L'Année Biol., 22:249-270.

1947. Quelques remarques sur la longévité dans la nature du Freux et du Héron cendré. L'Oiseaux, 17:178-185.

BRAESTRUP, F. W.

1942. Om Svinginger i Antallet of Raeve og andre Dyr i Arktis—deres Aarsager og Virkninger. Det Grønlandske Selskabs Aarsskrift (1942):129-151.

BUMP, G., R. W. DARROW, F. C. EDMINSTER, and W. F. CRISSEY

1947. The Ruffed Grouse. New York State Conservation Department, Albany, xxxvi + 915 pp.

BURKITT, J. P.

1926. A study of the Robin by means of marked birds. Brit. Birds, 20:91-101.

1936. Young Rooks, their survivals and habits. Brit. Birds, 29:334-338.

BUSS, I. O.

1942. [Remarks on loss of bands by Ring-necked Pheasants]. Trans. Seventh N. Amer. Wildlife Conf., p. 144.

1946. Wisconsin pheasant populations. Wisconsin Conservation Department, Madison, 184 pp.

1951. The Upland Plover in southwestern Yukon Territory. Arctic, 4:204-213.

BUSS, I. O., H. MATTISON, and F. M. KOZLIK

1947. The Bobwhite Quail in Dunn County, Wisconsin. Wisconsin Conservation Department Publication 337. Reprinted from Wis. Conservation Bull., 12:8 pp.

CHAPMAN, D. G.

1951. Some properties of the hypergeometric distribution with applications to zoological sample censuses. Univ. Calif. Publ. Statistics, 1:131-160.

COLE, L. C.

1951. Population cycles and random oscillations. Jour. Wildlife Mgmt., 15:233-252.

CREUTZ, G.

1949a. Untersuchungen zur Brutbiologie des Feldsperlings (*Passer m. montanus* L.). Zool. Jahrb., Abt. Syst., Ökol., Geogr. Tiere, 78:133-172.

1949b. Die Entwicklung zweier Populationen des Treuerschnäppers, *Muscicapa h. hypoleuca* (Pall.), nach Herkunft und Alter. In Beiträge zur Vogelkunde (Stresemann-Festschrift). Akademische Verlagsgesellschaft, Leipzig, pp. 27-53.

CURRY-LINDAHL, K.

1950. Berguvens, *Bubo bubo* (L.), förekomst i Sverige jämte något om dess biologi. Vår Fågelväld, 9:113-165.

DAVIS, D. E.

1950. The growth of Starling, *Sturnus vulgaris*, populations. Auk, 67:460-465.

1951. The analysis of population by banding. Bird-Banding, 22:103-107.

1952. Definitions for the analysis of survival of nestlings. Auk, 69:316-320.

DEEVEY, E. S., JR.

1947. Life tables for natural populations of animals. Quart. Rev. Biol., 22:283-314.

DIRCKSEN, R.

1932. Die Biologie des Austernfischers, der Brandseeschwalbe und der Küstenseeschwalbe nach Beobachtungen und Untersuchungen auf Norderoog. Jour. Ornithol., 80:427-521.

DROST, R.

1948. Populationsstudien an der Englischen Schafstelze, *Motacilla flava flavissima* Blyth, auf Helgoland. Die Vogelwarte, 15:18-28.

DROST, R., and G. HARTMANN

1949. Hohes Alter einer Population des Austernfischers *Haematopus o. ostralegus* L. Die Vogelwarte, 15:102-104.

DROST, R., and L. SCHILLING

1940. Über den Zug des Trauerfliegenschnäppers, *Muscicapa hypoleuca* (Pall.). Der Vogelzug, 11:71-85.

EMLEN, J. T., JR.

1940. Sex and age ratios in survival of the California Quail. Jour. Wildlife Mgmt., 4:92-99.

ERICKSON, M. M.

1938. Territory, annual cycle, and numbers in a population of Wren-tits (*Chamaea fasciata*). Univ. Calif. Publ. Zool., 42:247-334.

ERRINGTON, P. L.

1945. Some contributions of a fifteen-year local study of the Northern Bobwhite to a knowledge of population phenomena. Ecol. Monogr., 15:1-34.

1946. Predation and vertebrate populations. Quart. Rev. Biol., 21:144-177, 221-245.

1951. Concerning fluctuations in populations of the prolific and widely distributed Muskrat. Amer. Nat., 85:273-292.

FARNER, D. S.

1945. Age groups and longevity in the American Robin. Wilson Bull., 57:56-74.

1947. [Review] Do juvenile birds survive less well than adults? Bird-Banding, 18:42.

1949. Age groups and longevity in the American Robin: comments, further discussion, and certain revisions. Wilson Bull., 61:68-81.

1952. The use of banding data in the study of certain aspects of the dynamics and structures of avian populations. Northwest Science, 26:41-50, 79-94, 119-144.

FISHER, J.

1951. The changes in the distribution of the Fulmar, *Fulmarus glacialis.* Proc. Tenth Internat. Ornithol. Cong., Uppsala, pp. 449-462.

FISHER, J., and L. S. V. VENABLES

1938. Analysis of the rate of increase of Gannets. Jour. Animal Ecol., 7:305-313.

FISHER, J., and H. G. VEVERS

1951. The present population of the North Atlantic Gannet (*Sula bassana*). Proc. Tenth Internat. Ornithol. Cong., Uppsala, pp. 463-467.

FRANZ, J.

1950. Zyklische Massenvermehrung bei Vögeln und Kleinsäugern. Die Vogelwarte, 15:141-155.

HAARTMAN, L. VON

1948. Ringmärkningen 50 år. Nordenskiöld-samfundets Tidskrift (1948): 39-52.

1949. Der Trauerfliegenschnäpper, I. Ortstreue und Rassenbildung. Acta Zool. Fenn., 56:1-104.

1951. Der Trauerfliegenschnäpper, II. Populationsprobleme. Acta Zool. Fenn., 67:1-60.

HANN, H. W.

1948. Longevity of the Oven-bird. Bird-Banding, 19:5-12.

HANSON, H. C., and R. H. SMITH

1950. Canada Geese of the Mississippi flyway with special reference to an Illinois flock. Bull. Ill. Nat. Hist. Surv., 25:67-210.

HICKEY, J. J.

1949. Survival studies of banded birds. A dissertation submitted in partial fulfillment of the requirements for the degree of doctor of philosophy in the University of Michigan, Ann Arbor.

1952. Survival studies of banded birds. U.S. Dept. Int., Fish and Wildlife Serv., Special Scient. Rept., Wildlife No. 15, 177 pp.

HOCHBAUM, H. A.

1944. The Canvasback on a prairie marsh. The American Wildlife Institute, Washington, D.C., xii + 201 pp.

HÖHN, E. O.

1948. Mortality of adult and young Mallards. Brit. Birds, 41:233-235.

HOFFMAN, E. C.

1929. Longevity of the Blue Jay. Bull. Northeast. Bird-Banding Assoc., 5:56-58.

HORNBERGER, F.

1943. Einige Ergebnisse zehnjähriger Planarbeit im "Storchforschungskreis Insterburg" der Vogelwarte Rossitten. Jour. Ornithol., 91:340-355.

JESPERSEN, P., and Å. V. TÅNING

1950. Studies in bird migration, being the collected papers of H. Chr. C. Mortensen . . . Dansk Ornithologisk Forening. Munsksgaard, Copenhagen, 272 pp.

KALELA, O.

1942. Die Ausbreitung der kulturbedingten Vogelfauna als Glied der spätquartären Faunengeschichte Europas. Ornis Fennica, 9:1-23.

1944. Ueber den 10-jährigen Massenwechsel bei pflanzenfressenden Vögeln und Säugetieren nebst einigen Gesichtspunkten zu seiner Erklärung. Ornis Fennica, 21:42-62.

1946. Zur Characteristik der neuzeitlichen Veränderungen in der Vogelfauna Mittel- und Nordeuropas. Ornis Fennica, 23:77-98.

1949. Changes in the geographic ranges in the avifauna of northern and central Europe in relation to recent changes in climate. Bird-Banding, 20:77-103.

1950. Zur säkularen Rhythmic der Arealveränderungen europäischer Vögel und Säugetiere, mit besonderer Berücksichtigung der Überwinterungsverhältnisse als Kausalfaktor. Ornis Fennica, 27:1-30.

1952. Changes in the geographic distribution of Finnish birds and mammals in relation to recent changes in climate. In The recent climatic fluctuation in Finland and its consequences, ed. by Ilmari Hustich. Fennia, 75:38-51.

KENDEIGH, S. C.

1934. The role of environment in the life of birds. Ecol. Monogr., 4:299-417.

1937. Factors affecting yearly abundance of passerine birds. Ecol. Monogr., 7:91-124.

1941. Territorial and mating behavior of the House Wren. Ill. Biol. Monogr., 18:120 pp.

KLOMP, H.

1946. Verslag van het Kievitenringstation "Reeuwijk" over de jaren 1943-1945 en gegevens over de trek van de Kievit. Limosa, 19:76-117.

1951. Over de achteruitgang van de Kievit, *Vanellus vanellus* (L.), in Nederland en gegevens over het legmechanisme en het eiproductie-vermogen. Ardea, 39:143-182.

KLUIJVER, H. N.

1933. Bijdrage tot de biologie en de ecologie van den Spreeuw (*Sturnus vulgaris* L.) gedurende zijn voortplantingstijd. Verslagen en Mededeelingen van den Plantenziektenkundigen Dienst te Wageningen, No. 69, pp. 1-145.

1935. Waarnemingen over de levenswijze van den Spreeuw (*Sturnus v. vulgaris* L.) met behulp van geringde individuen. Ardea, 24:133-166.

1951. The population ecology of the Great Tit, *Parus m. major* L. Ardea, 39:1-135.

KORTLANDT, A.

1942. Levensloop, samenstelling en structuur der Nederlandse aalscholverbevolking. Ardea, 31:175-280.

KOSKIMIES, J.

1950. The life of the Swift, *Micropus apus* (L.), in relation to the weather. Annales Academiae Scientiarum Fennicae, Ser. A, IV Biologica 15, 151 pp.

KRAAK, W. G., G. L. RINKEL, AND J. HOOGERHEIDE

1940. Oecologische bewerking van de Europese ringgegevens van de Kievit (*Vanellus vanellus* (L.)). Ardea, 29:151-175.

LACK, D.

1943a. The age of the Blackbird. Brit. Birds, 36:166-175.

1943b. The age of some more British birds. Brit. Birds, 36:193-197.

1943c. The age of some more British birds. Brit. Birds, 36:214-221.

1943d. The life of the Robin. H. F. and G. Witherby, London, 200 pp.

1946a. The balance of population in the Heron. Brit. Birds, 39:204-206.

1946b. Do juvenile birds survive less well than adults? Brit. Birds, 39:258-264.

1946c. Do juvenile birds survive less well than adults? Brit. Birds, 39:320.

1948a. Natural selection and family size in the Starling. Evolution, 2:95-110.

1948b. Notes on the ecology of the Robin. Ibis, 90:252-279.

1949a. The apparent survival-rate of ringed Herons. Brit. Birds, 42:74-79.

1949b. Vital statistics from ringed Swallows. Brit. Birds, 42:147-150.

1951. Population ecology in birds. Proc. Tenth Internat. Ornithol. Cong. Uppsala, pp. 409-448.

LACK, D., and H. ARN

1947. Die Bedeutung der Gelegegrösse beim Alpensegler. Ornithol. Beobachter, 44:188-210.

LACK, D., and A. SCHIFFERLI

1948. Die Lebensdauer des Stares. Ornithol. Beobachter, 45:107-114.

LASKEY, A. R.

1944. A study of the Cardinal in Tennessee. Wilson Bull., 56:27-44.

LAVEN, H.

1940. Beiträge zur Biologie des Sandregenpfeifers (*Charadrius hiaticula* L.). Jour. Ornithol., 88:183-287.

LEOPOLD, A. S.

1945. Sex and age ratios among Bobwhite Quail in southern Missouri. Jour. Wildlife Mgmt., 9:30-33.

LEOPOLD, A., T. M. SPERRY, W. S. FEENEY, and J. S. CATENHUSEN

1943. Population turnover on a Wisconsin pheasant refuge. Jour. Wildlife Mgmt., 7:383-394.

LIBBERT, W., H. RINGLEBEN, and E. SCHÜZ

1937. Ring-Wiederfunde deutscher Weisz-Störche *(C. c. ciconia)* aus Afrika und Asien. Der Vogelzug, 8:193-208.

LINCOLN, F. C.

1930. Calculating waterfowl abundance on the basis of banding returns. U.S. Dept. Agric. Circ. 118, 4 pp.

LINSDALE, J. M.

1949. Survival in birds banded at the Hastings Reservation. Condor, 51:88-96.

LOCKLEY, R. M.

1942. Shearwaters. Dent, London, xii + 238 pp.

LOVELL, H. B.

1948. The removal of bands by Cardinals. Bird-Banding, 19:70-71.

1951. A nine-year-old Cardinal. Bird-Banding, 22:33.

LOW, S. H.

1933. Further notes on the nesting of the Tree Swallows. Bird-Banding, 4:76-87.

1934. Nest distribution and survival ratio of Tree Swallows. Bird-Banding, 5:24-30.

1935. Notes on the survival, winter distribution, and migration speed of Eastern Mourning Doves. Bird-Banding, 6:61-65.

MAGEE, M. J.

1928. How long do Purple Finches live? Bull. Northeast. Bird-Banding Assoc., 4:132-136.

1936. The average age of the Eastern Purple Finch. Bird-Banding, 7:161-162.

1939. Notes on the sex ratio and the age of the Eastern Evening Grosbeak (*Hesperiphona vespertina vespertina*). Bird-Banding, 10:161.

MAGNUSSON, M., and G. SVÄRDSON

1948. Livslängd hos tornsvalor (*Micropus apus* L.). Vår Fågelvärld, 7:129-144.

MARSHALL, H.

1947. Longevity of the American Herring Gull. Auk, 64:188-198.

MIDDLETON, A. D.

1935. Factors controlling the population of the Partridge in Great Britain. Proc. Zool. Soc. London (1935):795-815.

NICE, M. M.

1937. Studies in the life history of the Song Sparrow, I. Trans. Linn. Soc. N.Y., 4:247 pp.

ODUM, E. P.

1942. A comparison of two chickadee seasons. Bird-Banding, 13:155-159.

PALMGREN, P.

1949. Some remarks on the short-term fluctuations in the numbers of northern birds and mammals. Oikos, 1:114-121.

PALUDAN, K.

1951. Contributions to the breeding biology of *Larus argentatus* and *Larus fuscus*. Ejnar Munksgaard, København, 142 pp.

PARKS, G. H.

1947. The Evening Grosbeaks return to Hartford. Bird-Banding, 18:57-76.

PAYNTER, R. A., JR.

1947. The fate of banded Kent Island Herring Gulls. Bird-Banding, 18:156-170.

1949. Clutch-size and the egg and chick mortality of Kent Island Herring Gulls. Ecology, 30:146-166.

PETRIDES, G. A.

1949. Viewpoints on the analysis of open season sex and age ratios. Trans. Fourteenth N. Amer. Wildlife Conf., pp. 391-410.

PLATTNER, J., and E. SUTTER

1946, 1947. Ergebnisse der Meisen- und Kleiberberingung in der Schweiz (1929-1941). Ornithol. Beobachter, 43:156-188; 44:1-35.

RICHARDSON, F.

1941. Results of the southern California quail banding program. Calif. Fish and Game, 27:234-249.

RICHDALE, L. E.

1949. A study of a group of penguins of known age. Biol. Monogr., 1:vii + 88 pp. (Published privately.)

1951. Banding and marking penguins. Bird-Banding, 22:47-54.

RUITER, C. J. S.

1941. Waarnemingen omtrent de levenswijze van de Gekraagde Roodstaart, *Phoenicurus ph. phoenicurus* (L.). Ardea, 30:175-214.

RYDZEWSKI, W.

1951. Bird-ringing schemes known to be operating at present. Proc. Tenth Internat. Ornithol. Cong., Uppsala, pp. 356-359.

SALOMONSEN, F.

1948. The distribution of birds and the recent climatic change in the North Atlantic area. Dansk Ornithol. Foren. Tidss., 42:85-99.

SCHAANNING, H. T. L.

1948. Forsatte resultator (XVII) fra den internasjonale ringmerkning vedrørende norske trekkfugler. Stavanger Museum Årbok (1947):12-25.

SCHIFFERLI, A.

1949. Schwankungen des Schleiereulenbestandes *Tyto alba* (Scopoli). Ornithol. Beobachter, 46:61-75.

SCHNEIDER, W.

1937. Beringungs-Ergebnisse an der mitteleuropäischen Schleiereule (*Tyto alba guttata* Brehm). Der Vogelzug, 8:159-170.

SCHÜZ, E., and R. BÖHRINGER

1950. Vom Zug des Weisz-Storchs in Afrika und Asien nach den Ringfunden bis 1949. Die Vogelwarte, 15:160-187.

SIIVONEN, L.

1948. Structure of short-cyclic fluctuations in numbers of mammals and birds in the northern parts of the Northern Hemisphere. Riistatieteellisiä Julkaisuja (Papers on Game Research), 1:166 pp.

SKOVGAARD, P.

1937. Storken i Danmark. Danske-Fugle, 4:67-135.

SOLOMON, M. E.

1949. The natural control of animal populations. Jour. Animal Ecol., 18:1-35.

STEWART, P. A.

1952. Dispersal, breeding behavior, and longevity of banded Barn Owls in North America. Auk, 69:227-245.

STUART, D.

1948. Vital statistics of the Mochram Cormorant. Brit. Birds, 41:194-199.

SUMNER, E. L., JR.

1935. A life history study of the California Quail, with recommendations for its conservation and management. Calif. Fish and Game, 21:167-342.

TINBERGEN, L.

1946. De sperwer als roofvijand van zangvogels. Ardea, 34:1-213.

1948. De invloed van roofdieren op de aantalssterkte van hun proeidieren. Vakblad voor Biologen, 28:217-228.

TRETTAU, W., and F. MERKEL

1943. Ergebnisse einer Planberingung des Trauerfliegenfängers (*Muscicapa hypoleuca* Pallas) in Schlesien. Der Vogelzug, 14:77-90.

VÄLIKANGAS, I., and L. SIIVONEN

1949. Die Vogelbeiringung in Finnland im Jahre 1939. Memoranda Societatis pro Fauna et Flora Fennica, 24:212-233.

VÄLIKANGAS, I., and J. KOSKIMIES

1950. Die Vogelberingung in Finnland in den Jahren 1940-47. Memoranda Societatis pro Fauna et Flora Fennica, 25:135-155.

VAN DEN AKKER, J. B., and V. T. WILSON

1949. Twenty years of bird banding at Bear River Migratory Bird Refuge, Utah. Jour. Wildlife Mgmt., 13:359-376.

VERHEYEN, R., and G. LE GRELLE

1951. Interprétation des résultats du baguage au nid de nos Grives (*Turdus*) indigènes. Le Gerfaut, 41:271-280.

1952. Interprétation des résultats de baguage relatifs au Héron cendré (*Ardea cinerea*), au Vanneau (*Vanellus vanellus*), et à la Mouette rieuse (*Larus ridibundus*). Le Gerfaut, 42:214-222.

WALLACE, G. J.

1941. Winter studies of color-banded chickadees. Bird-Banding, 12:49-67.

WEITNAUER, E.

1947. Am Neste des Mauerseglers, *Apus apus apus* (L.). Ornithol. Beobachter, 44 (Beihefte):133-182.

WHITTLE, C. L.

1929. Additional Purple Finch returning ratios. Bull. Northeast. Bird-Banding Assoc., 5:38.

WILMANN, B.

1948. Ringmerkningsresultater av Saeing (*Larus argentatus* Pont.). Stavanger Museum Årbok (1947):40-46.

1949. Ringmerkingsresultater for Svartbak (*Larus marinus* L.). Stavanger Museum Årbok (1948):123-128.

YOUNG, J. B.

1941. Unusual behavior of a banded Cardinal. Wilson Bull., 53:197-198.

chapter 13

DISEASES OF BIRDS . . . Carlton M. Herman

Although much attention has been given to the study of poultry diseases, comparatively few investigations have been made on diseases of wild birds. Most of the early reports on diseases among wild birds consisted largely of listings of organisms found. Obviously such studies contributed very little toward an understanding of disease as a factor in regulating density of populations. Only in recent years have we begun to comprehend the intimate relationship between disease and other limiting factors in the environment, such as food deficiencies, pollution, high population densities, and climatic extremes.

There have been very few comprehensive reviews of diseases of wild species and none in the English language. The most extensive reference text was the work of Olt and Strose published in Germany in 1914 and long out of date. The volume by Heelsbergen (1929), also in German, is devoted to bird diseases and includes much on wild species. The Brazilian book on bird diseases by Reis and Nobrega (1936) is a more recent and inclusive attempt but is primarily on domestic species. In North America, the publication by Biester and Schwarte (1952) on avian diseases is also mainly on domestic species. However, it is the most useful text of its kind currently available to those studying techniques and diagnosis of diseases in wild birds.

Several monographs on game and non-game birds have included from a few paragraphs to a chapter on disease. Among these might be cited studies on Bobwhite Quail, *Colinus virginianus* (Stoddard, 1931); on Bank Swallows, *Riparia riparia* (Stoner, 1936); magpies (Linsdale, 1937); Roseate Spoonbill, *Ajaia ajaja* (Allen, 1942); White-winged Dove, *Zenaida asiatica* (Arnold, 1943); Turkey, *Meleagris gallopavo* (Mosby and Handley, 1943); and Sage Grouse, *Centrocercus urophasianus* (Patterson, 1952). In such publications the space devoted to disease has been governed largely by limitations of knowledge on this subject.

ECTOPARASITES

Much more is known about the parasites of birds than other disease-causing organisms. This is undoubtedly because their presence can usually be observed

Manuscript received April 1, 1953.

without resort to microscopes or other specialized equipment and techniques. An excellent general discussion of their biology is presented in Baer's (1951) monograph on ecology of animal parasites. Boyd (1951) recently has reviewed the literature on external parasites of birds.

The most common external parasites and the ones most frequently observed by ornithologists are the so-called bird lice or feather lice (Mallophaga). These are primarily parasites of birds but a number of species also occur on mammals. They are not to be confused with sucking lice (Anoplura) which live on blood of mammals and occur only accidentally on birds. Sucking lice are of great importance as vectors of disease among mammals. Bird lice, living primarily on feather debris, do not ordinarily suck blood and are therefore not considered to be involved in the transmission of diseases. However, Wilson (1933) performed experiments which showed that a common species of bird louse of the pigeon can take blood.

The earliest extensive study on Mallophaga in North America was the work of Kellogg (1899) and his co-workers at Stanford University. Studies and publications in this field have been limited since then. Kellogg was one of the first investigators to show the connection between mallophagan distribution and phylogenetic relationship of bird hosts. Many workers since then have followed this example, the most recent being Timmermann (1952a, b) in his work on Mallophaga and gulls. This subject, as well as other relationships of fleas and Mallophaga with birds, has been interestingly presented in a recent book by Rothschild and Clay (1952). The work of Harrison (1916) has provided the chief reference on taxonomy of the Mallophaga. A recently published check-list of genera and species (Hopkins and Clay, 1952) will prove a much needed aid to anyone working with the group. One of the most active workers on Mallophaga of North American hosts currently is Emerson (1951).

Ticks, mites, and fleas are occasionally seen on birds. These groups are known to be important disease vectors in mammals but as yet very few have been proven to transmit disease among birds. Smith *et al.* (1948) showed that mites could be involved in the transmission of encephalitis from bird to bird. One species of tick has been demonstrated to be the vector of a spirochete infection of poultry in Eurasia, and this disease has recently been reported in North American turkeys by Hinshaw and McNeil (1946) and others. Some ticks require several hosts to complete their life cycle, Herman (1938a) having reported several species of Passeriformes infested with the first growth stage of the common rabbit tick. Fleas are infrequently seen on birds but are often abundant in nests. They feed primarily on the blood of nestlings. Fleas are readily collected from debris in nest boxes utilized by such species as Bluebirds, *Sialia sialis;* Tree Swallows, *Iridoprocne bicolor;* and wrens. Nests of Cliff Swallows, *Petrochelidon pyrrhonota,* phoebes, and many other species are frequently densely populated with such vermin. The most recent check-lists on fleas are those of Fox (1940), Ewing and Fox (1943), Hubbard (1947), and Holland (1949). Argasid ticks have been reviewed by Cooley and Kohls (1944), and a check-list of mites has been published by Radford (1950).

Another nest-inhabiting parasite is the maggot stage of calliphorid flies. These maggots feed on the blood of nestlings and, as reported by Neff (1945), have frequently been observed to cause extensive mortality. Mason (1944) has suggested removal of the larvae from the birds and nests as a control measure but while this procedure might be of some value in a few specific instances its application is not practical on a large scale. The taxonomy and some phases of the biology of these flies and related genera are included in a recent book by Hall (1948).

The hippoboscid flies, commonly called louse flies, constitute an interesting group of ectoparasites. Hippoboscids are broad, flat flies that live among feathers and feed on blood of the host. They move with equal facility sideways or backwards, and their flight is so rapid they seem to dart from one spot to another. They often leave the bird when it is handled and are extremely difficult to capture in the field. The flies are attracted by light and many birdbanders handling birds indoors have caught them on window panes. Equipment and methods for collection of large numbers of these flies has been described by Tarshis (1952). Hippoboscids are not readily kept alive and usually die within a few days when apart from host birds. They apparently require not only the warmth of the bird's body but a frequent blood meal. Herman (1944a) has pointed out that they produce only one offspring at a time. Dr. Bequaert (1940, 1941) of Harvard University Museum of Comparative Zoology is a leading authority on these insects and has recently prepared a monograph (1953) on them. These flies are of importance because they are known to transmit the causative agent of one type of bird malaria (*Haemoproteus*). They may also be involved in transmission of other parasitic diseases.

There are also a number of insects which act more or less as transient ectoparasites, coming to the bird only to feed on its blood. These include "no-see-ums," *Culicoides;* black flies, Simuliidae; and mosquitoes, Culicidae.

Very little is known about the biology of the *Culicoides* in relation to birds, but, as reported by Jellison and Phillip (1933), and also as observed by myself, great numbers of them engorged with blood occur in magpie nests. They are potential vectors of disease.

Black flies, several species of which are known to feed on birds, were shown by O'Roke (1934) to transmit a type of malaria (*Leucocytozoon*) in ducks with resultant high mortality in young birds. The taxonomy and distribution of simuliid flies has been reviewed by Twinn (1936) and Vargas (1945).

Mosquitoes affect the welfare of a number of birds as well as man. The value of mosquito control to human health has been brought out in Russell's

(1952) account of recent activities in malaria control. Frequently this phase of public health has conflicted with wildlife values of marsh and aquatic areas. Controversies have resulted as indicated by Cottam *et al.* (1938).

Mosquitoes serve as vectors for several diseases among birds. Malaria in man is caused by protozoa of the genus *Plasmodium*. Species of this genus also parasitize birds. Culicine mosquitoes transmit avian *Plasmodium,* but these mosquitoes are not capable of transmitting human malaria, the vectors of which are anopheline mosquitoes. Reeves (1951) and Cockburn (1952) have recently shown that birds are a reservoir of the encephalitis virus, an important mosquito-borne disease of man.

ENDOPARASITES

Among protozoan parasites of birds the most extensively studied have been those that are broadly classified as malaria producing. These include the genera *Plasmodium, Haemoproteus,* and *Leucocytozoon*. The occurrence of these parasites in North American birds has been reviewed recently by Herman (1944b). An extensive discussion of *Plasmodium* has been compiled by Hewitt (1940), and, more recently, Coatney and Roudabush (1949) brought up to date the check-list of birds parasitized by *Plasmodium*. The full effect of these protozoan parasites on birds and bird populations has not been ascertained. While a number of fatal cases have been observed in nature, the difficulty of obtaining dying or recently dead specimens still presents a major barrier in this as well as most other studies on wildlife diseases.

Herman (1938b) demonstrated that Red-winged Blackbirds, *Agelaius phoeniceus,* on Cape Cod, Massachusetts, usually do not acquire *Plasmodium* infection until after they leave the nest, but subsequent investigations by Herman *et al.* (1954) have indicated that many species of birds are infected while they are still nestlings. The greatest contributions toward knowledge on life cycles and better drug treatments for avian *Plasmodium* have arisen from laboratory investigations aimed directly at increasing our understanding of *Plasmodium* infections in man. The epizoological phases of the problem and importance of the disease in wild birds have been little studied.

The most recent check-list on *Haemoproteus* is that of Coatney (1936). This parasite appears to be even more prevalent in birds than *Plasmodium* but, perhaps because no similar parasite occurs in man, there have been few investigations on the genus. The full significance of its occurrence in birds is not well understood. It readily kills some individuals of California Quail, *Lophortyx californica,* and may persist in the blood of others that recover. Herman and Bischoff (1949) have observed that chronic infections may persist for several years.

Leucocytozoon simondi was reported by O'Roke (1934) to be the cause of large die-offs of young ducks in Michigan. Since his work, little was added to our knowledge of this disease in ducks until the outstanding investigations of Fallis *et al.* (1951) and Chernin (1952a, b). Chernin found that by exposing young domestic ducks in northern Michigan in late June and early July few infections and no deaths resulted, whereas of those exposed later in July and early August 90 to 100 per cent became infected and from 14 to 83 per cent of the infected birds succumbed. After mid-August, infections did not occur.

Clarke (1938) and Fallis (1945) have shown a relationship of *Leucocytozoon* infection to losses among grouse. Also, several workers have reported severe losses from *Leucocytozoon* infection in turkeys. The significance of *Leucocytozoon* in Passeriformes and other groups of birds is not known. The most recent check-list of this genus of parasites is that of Coatney (1937).

Trichomonas gallinae is a flagellated protozoan that lives in the throat of doves, pigeons, hawks, and other wild birds, as well as chickens and turkeys. It has been studied most extensively in North America by Stabler and a review of its occurrence has been published by Stabler and Herman (1951). Haugen (1952) reported severe losses among Mourning Doves, *Zenaidura macroura,* in Alabama. This parasite causes development of a cheesy mass in the throat which may occlude the trachea or esophagus and cause the bird to suffocate or starve. Lesions may also appear in the crop and liver, and injury may be caused to the eye. This parasite is widely reported throughout much of North America and has been suggested (Stabler and Herman, 1951) as a possible factor in the demise of the Passenger Pigeon, *Ectopistes migratorius.*

Coccidia constitute another group of parasitic protozoa very frequently found in birds. The monographic work of Becker (1934) continues to be the best reference on these forms. Boughton and Volk (1938) compiled a check-list of avian hosts of the genus *Eimeria* and a more recent list on the same genus was prepared by Hardcastle (1943). A comprehensive review of the occurrence and importance of coccidia in birds was presented by Boughton (1937).

Early workers in poultry diseases blamed English Sparrows, *Passer domesticus,* and other Passeriformes as a source of coccidial infection in poultry flocks. Boughton and others have shown that the coccidia which occur in these passeriform birds belong to the genus *Isospora* while the pathogens of domestic poultry are of the genus *Eimeria.* The most recent check-list of avian *Isospora* is that of Boughton *et al.* (1938).

In recent years, many studies have been conducted on immunity and drug treatment of avian coccidia in poultry (Brackett and Bliznick, 1950), but few investigators have attempted detailed studies on wild birds in their natural habitats. Herman *et al.* (1943) reported varying intensities of infection with *Eimeria* in California Quail sampled from a number of areas in California. Herman and Chattin (1943) reported low-grade infections in quail when diet was primarily seeds and higher intensity when diet was primarily leafy material, as during the wet season. This suggests a relationship between food habits and intensity of infection. In a symposium on coccidiosis held at the New York Academy of Sciences in 1949 a brief note on problems of control in California Quail by Herman (1949) was the only paper concerned with wild birds.

Undoubtedly more has been published on helminth parasites of birds than on any other group of disease-causing organisms in our avifauna. Most of these reports have been of a taxonomic nature and are based on examination of small samples of both parasites and hosts. The literature on this group is extensive. It is possible to list here only some of the most recent monographs and important contributions as a source for further exploration into the subject.

For information on trematodes, Dawes' (1946) text is more inclusive than any previous work although British and other European forms receive major emphasis. The taxonomy of the Cestoda is treated in the volume by Joyeux and Baer (1936). A broader text on the subject is the recent volume on the zoology of tapeworms by Wardle and McLeod (1952). On the systematics of nematodes of birds, the monograph of Cram (1927) is still the classical reference, although there have been a number of useful reviews on certain genera since that time.

Many valuable check-lists have appeared, either on particular genera or families. Among these are Cram (1936), Madsen (1945), and Read (1949) on *Capillaria* (nematodes); Madsen (1950) on *Heterakis* (nematodes); Morgan (1943) on Physalopterinae (nematodes); Hughes (1940, 1941) on *Hymenolepis* (cestodes); De Freitas (1951) on Eucotylidae (trematodes); Hughes and Schultz (1942) on *Raillietina* (cestodes); Travassos (1937) on Trichostrongylidae (nematodes); and Travassos (1944) on Dicrocoeliidae (trematodes). Also, there have been studies of parasitism in particular hosts, such as those by Gower (1939) on helminths of ducks, and Boyd (1951) on parasites of the Starling, *Sturnus vulgaris.*

An interesting theory of host-specificity was expounded by Szidat (1942) involving avian systematic relations on the basis of internal parasites. This paper is an expansion of an earlier report on trematodes by the same author (Szidat, 1940).

An important relationship of avian helminth parasites to disease in man is presented by certain schistosomes. Most surveys conducted on parasites of water-inhabiting birds indicate that schistosome blood flukes are of frequent occurrence. Some years ago, Cort (1928a, b) reported that swimmer's itch in man is caused by a developing stage of trematodes (Cercariae) in fresh-water areas. In their adult stage, most of these occur in birds as blood flukes that reach maturity in the mesenteric blood vessels. The eggs of the worm penetrate through the wall of the intestines and are discharged with the feces. Larval development takes place in a snail. The larva grows and ultimately escapes from the snail as a free-swimming organism. This stage of the parasite penetrates the skin and, in normally susceptible hosts, reaches mesenteric blood vessels to complete the life cycle. Often these free-swimming forms gain entrance to a host in which they are unable to complete their cycle and in such instances they cause a reaction in the skin. Their occurrence in man causes the widespread condition called "swimmer's itch," "cercarial dermatitis" or "schistosome dermatitis." Cort (1950) has reviewed the current status of knowledge on this disease. Penner (1950) cited marine snails on the Pacific Coast as a source of human infection, and similar records of its occurrence elsewhere have been reported. Stunkard and Hinchliffe (1952) have studied the life history of the species involved in cases of swimmers itch originating at ocean beaches in Rhode Island. Their evidence strongly suggests that migrants, particularly scaup ducks, and possibly charadriid birds, are natural hosts. It appears that snails infected in the fall start shedding the infective stage about six to eight weeks later. The snails then remain dormant over the winter and again provide infection to birds during spring migration. From this seasonal variation it was concluded that gulls (which can be infected in the laboratory) are not primarily concerned in the natural life-cycle of the parasites.

A number of additional examples have been found wherein a bird and another animal are linked in helminth parasitism. In some cases the infection is acquired through feeding or other activities of the host. These examples are as yet not completely enough understood to evaluate the parasite's importance to avian hosts involved.

Direct relationship between food habits and infection was found by Scott (1930, 1931) who indicated the close association of the White-tailed Prairie Dog, *Cynomys leucurus,* and the Ferruginous Rough-legged Hawk, *Buteo regalis,* in maintenance of the tapeworm *Cladotaenia.* The prairie dog obtains the intermediate stages of the worms by eating food contaminated by droppings of infected hawks. The birds in turn become the final host by consuming the infected prairie dog. From the evidence now available, these two species of hosts seem to be the only ones involved or susceptible.

Thomas (1949, 1950) has conducted extensive experiments on interrelations of tapeworms of fish and fish-eating birds but his material has been published only in abstract. He points out that in the Great Lakes region the heavy production of *Dibothriocephalus (= Diphyllobothrium)* tapeworms in fish and in fish-eating birds is dependent upon "size of the bird rookeries, suitable shoals for the spawning of susceptible fish, the development of mayfly and caddice fly emergents and copepods, size and availability of susceptible fish as food for the birds, the shedding of tapeworms by young birds, water temperature, and water currents, all in close proximity to the rookeries."

Macy (1934) conducted extensive studies on the common oviduct fluke, *Prosthogonimus,* of domestic fowls and showed that snails and dragonflies, consecutively, serve as intermediate hosts. It is pathogenic in chickens in the Great Lakes area, and this fluke, or related species, occurs in a wide variety of wild birds. Since this parasite is one of the worms, that, during development, inhabits the oviduct and upsets egg production, it could well be a governing factor in populations of some wild birds. Gower (1938) collected *Prosthogonimus* from a number of species of ducks, although he reported no evidence of pathology. Since then, it has been reported from a number of species of birds but with little study of possible significance.

BACTERIA AND FUNGI

Bacterial diseases in wildlife usually are not as easily studied as sickness caused by parasites. Bacteria cause avian disease in either or both of two ways: by production of toxins, or by destruction of tissues. Although bacteria are, in many cases, potentially more important as disease factors, much less is known of them. After a bird is dead, bacteria normally associated with decomposition dominate and overgrow specific pathogens so rapidly that isolation of the pathogen becomes difficult or impossible. While cases of tuberculosis, salmonellosis, or other bacterial diseases have been recognized occasionally in wild birds, most of our knowledge in this field stems from infections that have struck large numbers.

The best known bacterial disease of wild birds is botulism. This disease, often referred to in the past as alkali poisoning or western duck sickness, causes considerable losses among waterfowl as well as shorebirds and other species. The bacterial organism involved is *Clostridium botulinum,* type C, which thrives on decaying vegetable and animal matter in environments of low oxygen. During growth, it produces a toxin which, when swallowed by the birds, results in detrimental effects on the nervous system with typical paralytic symptoms known as limberneck. Unless this toxin is flushed from the body and further consumption of it prevented, the bird may die. It is estimated that millions of ducks have died of this ailment in the past few decades. The research and leadership of Kalmbach (1930), beginning in 1929, led to the clarification of the condition as a form of botulism (Giltner and Couch, 1930; and Hobmaier, 1930). Further investigations were summarized by Kalmbach and Gunderson (1934) in a classical study and review of knowledge on the malady at the time. Subsequently, there have been a number of investigations by both technical personnel and field observers. Perhaps the greatest contribution was made by a group of federal biologists in studies summarized by Sperry (1947). The earlier research on avian botulism has been reviewed by Sciple (1953). This work demonstrated the feather-edge of a body of water as an important source of infection and the possibility of controlling botulism in wild birds by manipulation of water levels. Botulism is still an important problem, particularly in western areas of the United States, and several agencies are continuing studies on the biology of *Clostridium* and on feasible methods for its control.

The other type of bacterial disease involves invasion of host tissue by bacteria. Fowl cholera is a disease of this kind which reaches epizootic proportions in wild birds. In North America it occurs chiefly in coots, gulls, and anatids, although other species may be involved to a lesser extent. Recently, two regions have been afflicted with severe outbreaks of this malady: the Texas Panhandle (Petrides and Bryant, 1951) and the San Francisco Bay area in California (Rosen and Bischoff, 1949, 1950). The disease is caused by the bacterium *Pasteurella multocida,* an organism of the same genus as those that cause tularemia and plague in man and other mammals. Symptoms of this disease, such as loss of ability to hold up the head, could easily be confused with reactions exhibited in botulism. On occasion, a greenish diarrhea may be evident in sick birds. Small hemorrhages appear on the mucous membranes, and liver pathology is likely to be evident. Generalized infection is common with a septicemia preceding death. As in botulism, large numbers of birds die within a limited area.

Fungus diseases also occur in birds. The most frequent is asperigillosis (usually caused by *Aspergillus fumigatus*) in which the fungus invades the air sacs and respiratory system. It is frequently reported from North American birds, particularly in waterfowl, gulls, and hawks. Urbain and Guillot (1938) published a complete review of this subject, including an extensive bibliography.

VIRUS DISEASES

Viruses have been less studied and are therefore less known than other disease-causing organisms. Most of the literature on this subject has been published since the middle-1930's, and most of the information has been garnered from studies on the epidemiology of human diseases.

Psittacosis (ornithosis), at first thought to be a disease primarily of psittaciform birds, has been demonstrated in many species of avian hosts, not only from the regions inhabited by parrots but from many other parts of the world. In North America, the virus has been isolated from chickens, ducks, pigeons, and gulls. In Australia and South America, where the disease is of frequent occurrence in wild birds, it is thought by some investigators to serve as a population regulator. Meyer (1948, 1952) has presented comprehensive reviews and current viewpoints on this disease.

Equine encephalomyelitis was first reported from birds in a Ring-necked Pheasant, *Phasianus colchicus,* by Tyzzer *et al.* (1938). Since then it has been reported from chickens and a number of species of wild birds in the United States. Now, birds are recognized generally as an important reservoir of the infection. Unlike psittacosis, there is little evidence that encephalitis is harmful to birds. Reeves *et al.* (1952) have pointed out that the prevalence of serum-neutralizing antibodies in the birds is a most useful index of current activity of encephalitis viruses.

Avian pox is a virus disease that is apparently confined to birds. It is frequently seen in domestic poultry or captive game birds, but is also observed in wild birds, including many species of Passeriformes. The disease may appear as wartlike lesions about the head or on the feet, or infection may occur in the throat or nasal passages. Current knowledge of this disease is reviewed by Cunningham (1952).

Newcastle disease is a recently recognized malady in birds. It was first reported from North America by Brandly *et al.* (1944) and Beach (1944) and since that time has become widespread. In some areas it is recognized as a primary problem in maintenance of domestic poultry flocks. Various reports indicate that the virus is spread chiefly by exudates, excreta, and offal of infected birds. Air-borne spread has also been demonstrated. A number of species of wild birds have been found susceptible to infection with Newcastle virus and natural infections also have occurred. The effect of this disease on wild bird populations is not known but, presumably, it could be drastic. Importations of exotic game birds and other species have been shown to be a means of introducing new strains of the virus into poultry flocks. An extensive review of Newcastle disease has been presented by Brandly (1952). Beaudette (1950) has prepared annual reviews of literature on this disease.

NUTRITION AND ENVIRONMENT

As in man and other mammals, nutrition undoubtedly plays an important part in the health of birds. Nature and man have been continually changing the habitat available to wildlife. Fire, flood, and drought cause drastic changes in the available food supply of birds. Agricultural and forestry practices as well as the industrial advances of human civilization have contributed to these changing factors.

The work of Nestler (1949), and others, serves to demonstrate the vitamin and other nutritional requirements of birds. The relationship of nutrition to disease will undoubtedly prove important in ultimate planning of control of disease losses in wildlife. The approach, in general, must be towards control of populations and environment. Some of the work of Albrecht (1944, 1949, 1951, and earlier papers) demonstrates a relationship between soil fertility and nutritional status of animals in a given area. Another indication of the effect of environment on disease has been presented by Briscoe (1952) in his observations on relationships of insects and disease to vegetation and environment.

The serious investigator in the field of avian diseases still finds the most challenging problems before him. Although many disease-causing organisms have been reported from birds, undoubtedly many more await discovery. The pathological significance of most infections has not been investigated and is not known for most of the parasites and other organisms that have been tabulated from birds. Much is yet to be learned of the effect of disease on populations, and of the relationships between disease and such factors as nutrition, quality of habitat, population density, and geographical distribution of the host animals.

Bibliography

ALBRECHT, W. A.

1944. Soil fertility and wildlife—cause and effect. Trans. Ninth N. Amer. Wildlife Conf., pp. 19-28.

1949. Nutrition via soil fertility according to the climatic pattern. British Commonwealth Scientific Official Conference Proc., Australia, 1949, pp. 384-397.

1951. Protein deficiencies via soil deficiencies. I, Ecological indications. II, Experimental evidence. Oral Surg., Oral Med., and Oral Path., 5:371-383, 483-499.

ALLEN, R. P.

1942. The Roseate Spoonbill. Nat. Audubon Soc., Research Rept. 2, 142 pp.

ARNOLD, L. W.

1943. The White-winged Dove in Arizona. Arizona Game and Fish Comm., Phoenix, 103 pp.

BAER, JEAN G.

1951. Ecology of animal parasites. University of Illinois Press, Urbana, 224 pp.

BEACH, J. R.

1944. The neutralization *in vitro* of avian pneumoencephalitis virus by Newcastle disease immune serum. Science, 100:361-362.

BEAUDETTE, F. R.

1950. Recent literature on Newcastle disease. Proc. Fifty-fourth Ann. Meet. U.S. Livestock Sanit. Assn., pp. 132-153.

BECKER, E. R.

1934. Coccidia and coccidiosis of domesticated, game, and laboratory animals and of man. Iowa State College Press, Ames, 147 pp.

BEQUAERT, J. C.

1940. Notes on Hippoboscidae. 17. The Hippoboscidae of the Antilles. Mem. Soc. Cubana Hist. Nat., 14:305-327.

1941. The Hippoboscidae of Oceania (Diptera). Occ. Pap. Bishop Mus., Honolulu., 16:247-292.

1953. The Hippoboscidae or louse-flies (Diptera) of mammals and birds. Part I. Entomologica Americana, 32:1-209; 33:211-442.

BIESTER, H. E., and L. H. SCHWARTE (Eds.)

1952. Diseases of poultry. 3rd ed. Iowa State College Press, Ames, 1245 pp.

BOUGHTON, D. C.

1937. Notes on avian coccidiosis. Auk, 54:500-509.

BOUGHTON, D. C., R. B. BOUGHTON, and J. VOLK

1938. Avian hosts of the genus *Isospora* (Coccidia). Ohio Jour. Sci., 38:149-163.

BOUGHTON, D. C., and J. J. VOLK

1938. Avian hosts of eimerian coccidia. Bird-Banding, 9:139-153.

BOYD, E. M.

1951a. The external parasites of birds: a review. Wilson Bull., 63:363-369.

1951b. A survey of parasitism of the Starling, *Sturnus vulgaris* L., in North America. Jour. Parasit., 37:56-84.

BRACKETT, S., and A. BLIZNICK

1950. The occurrence and economic importance of coccidiosis in chickens. Lederle Lab. Div., Amer. Cyanamid Co., New York, 78 pp.

BRANDLY, C. A.

1952. Newcastle disease. In Diseases of poultry, ed. by H. E. Biester and L. H. Schwarte. 3rd ed. Iowa State College Press, Ames, pp. 531-568.

BRANDLY, C. A., H. E. MOSES, and E. E. JONES

1944. Special report from the Huntington Laboratory, Jan. 20, 1944, and Interim Report No. 4 from the Huntington Laboratory to the War Dept., Mar. 27, 1944.

BRISCOE, M. S.

1952. The relation of insects and insect-borne diseases to the vegetation and environment in Liberia. Ecol., 33:187-214.

CHERNIN, E.

1952a. The epizootiology of *Leucocytozoon simondi* infections in domestic ducks in northern Michigan. Amer. Jour. Hyg., 56:39-57.

1952b. The relapse phenomenon in the *Leucocytozoon simondi* infection of the domestic duck. Amer. Jour. Hyg., 56:101-118.

CLARKE, C. H. D.

1938. Organisms of a malaria type in Ruffed Grouse, with a description of the schizogony of *Leucocytozoon bonasae.* Jour. Wildlife Mgmt., 2:146:149.

COATNEY, G. R.

1936. A check list and host index of the genus *Haemoproteus.* Jour. Parasit., 22:88-105.

1937. A catalog and host index of the genus *Leucocytozoon.* Jour. Parasit., 23:202-212.

COATNEY, G. R., and R. L. ROUDABUSH

1949. A catalog of the species of the genus *Plasmodium* and index of their hosts. In M. F. Boyd, Malariology. Vol. I. Saunders, Philadelphia, pp. 29-53.

COCKBURN, T. A.

1952. Birds and a virus. Nature Mag., 45:258-259.

COOLEY, R. A., and G. M. KOHLS

1944. The argasidae of North America, Central America and Cuba. Amer. Midl. Nat. Mon. 1, 152 pp.

CORT, W. W.

1928a. Further observations on schistosome dermatitis in the United States (Michigan). Science, 68:388.

1928b. Schistosome dermatitis in the United States (Michigan). Jour. Amer. Med. Assn., 90:1027-1029.

1950. Studies on schistosome dermatitis, XI. Status of knowledge after more than twenty years. Amer. Jour. Hyg., 52:251-307.

COTTAM, C., W. S. BOURN, F. C. BISHOPP, L. L. WILLIAMS, JR., and W. VOGT

1938. What's wrong with mosquito control? Trans. Third N. Amer. Wildlife Conf., pp. 81-98.

CRAM, E. B.

1927. Bird parasites of the nematode suborders Strongylata, Ascaridata, and Spirurata. U.S. Nat. Mus. Bull., 140:465 pp.

1936. Species of *Capillaria* parasitic in the upper digestive tract of birds. U.S.D.A. Tech. Bull., 516:27 pp.

CUNNINGHAM, C. H.

1952. Fowl pox. In Diseases of poultry, ed. by H. E. Biester and L. H. Schwarte. 3rd ed. Iowa State College Press, Ames, pp. 635-667.

DAWES, B.

1946. The Trematoda, with special reference to British and other European forms. Cambridge University Press, London, 644 pp.

EMERSON, K. C.

1951. A list of Mallophaga from gallinaceous birds of North America. Jour. Wildlife Mgmt., 15:193-195.

EWING, H. E., and I. FOX

1943. The fleas of North America. U.S.D.A. Misc. Publ., 500:142 pp.

FALLIS, A. M.

1945. Population trends and blood parasites of Ruffed Grouse in Ontario. Jour. Wildlife Mgmt., 9:203-206.

FALLIS, A. M., D. M. DAVIES, and M. A. VICKERS

1951. Life history of *Leucocytozoon simondi* Mathis and Leger in natural and experimental infections and blood changes produced in the avian host. Canad. Jour. Zool., 29:305-328.

FOX, I.

1940. Fleas of eastern United States. Iowa State College Press, Ames, 191 pp.

FREITAS, J. F. T. DE

1951. Revisao da familia Eucotylidae Skrjabin, 1924 (Trematoda). Mem. do Inst. O. Cruz, 49:33-123.

GILTNER, L. T., and J. F. COUCH

1930. Western duck sickness and botulism. Science, 72:660.

GOWER, W. C.

1938. Studies on the trematode parasites of ducks in Michigan with special reference to the Mallard. Mich. State College Agric. Exper. Station, Lansing. Mem., 3, 94 pp.

1939. Host-parasite catalogue of the helminths of ducks. Amer. Midl. Nat., 22:580-628.

HALL, D. G.

1948. The blowflies of North America. The Thomas Say Foundation, 477 pp.

HARDCASTLE, A. B.

1943. A check list and host-index of the species of the protozoan genus *Eimeria.* Proc. Helm. Soc. Wash., 10:35-69.

HARRISON, L.

1916. The genera and species of Mallophaga. Parasit., 8:338-359.

HAUGEN, A. O.

1952. Trichomoniasis in Alabama Mourning Doves. Jour. Wildlife Mgmt., 16:164-169.

HEELSBERGEN, T. VAN

1929. Handbuch der Geflugelkrankheiten und der Geflugelzucht. Enke, Stuttgart, 608 pp.

HERMAN, C. M.

1938a. Occurrence of larval and nymphal stages of the rabbit tick, *Haemaphysalis leporis-palustris,* on wild birds from Cape Cod. Bull. Brooklyn Ent. Soc., 33:133-134.

1938b. Epidemiology of malaria in Eastern Redwings, *Agelaius p. phoeniceus.* Amer. Jour. Hyg., 28:232-243.

1944a. Notes on the pupal development of *Stilbometopa impressa* (Diptera: Hippoboscidae). Jour. Parasit., 30:112-118.

1944b. The blood protozoa of North American birds. Bird-Banding, 15:89-112.

1949. Coccidiosis in native California Valley Quail and problems of control. Ann. N.Y. Acad. Sci., 52:621-623.

HERMAN, C. M., and A. I. BISCHOFF

1949. The duration of *Haemoproteus* infection in California Quail. Calif. Fish and Game, 35:293-299.

HERMAN, C. M., and J. E. CHATTIN

1943. Epidemiological studies on coccidiosis of California Quail. Calif. Fish and Game, 29:168-179.

HERMAN, C. M., J. E. CHATTIN, and R. W. SAARNI

1943. Food habits and intensity of coccidian infection in native Valley Quail in California. Jour. Parasit., 29:206-208.

HERMAN, C. M., W. C. REEVES, H. E. McCLURE, E. M. FRENCH, and W. McD. HAMMON

1954. Studies on avian malaria in vectors and hosts of encephalitis in Kern County, California, I. Infections in avian hosts. Amer. Jour. Trop. Med. and Hyg., 3:676-695.

HEWITT, R. I.

1940. Bird malaria. Johns Hopkins Press, Baltimore, 228 pp.

HINSHAW, W. R., and E. McNEIL

1946. Studies on a spirochaete found in the blood of sick turkeys. Jour. Bact., 51:38.

HOBMAIER, M.

1930. Duck disease caused by the poison of the bacillus botulinus. Calif. Fish and Game, 16:285-286.

HOLLAND, G. P.

1949. The Siphonaptera of Canada. Canad. Dept. Agric. Tech. Bull., 70:306 pp.

HOPKINS, G. H. E., and T. CLAY

1952. A check list of the genera and species of Mallophaga. Brit. Mus. (Nat. Hist.), 362 pp.

HUBBARD, C. A.

1947. Fleas of western North America. Iowa State College Press, Ames, 533 pp.

HUGHES, R. C.

1940a. The genus *Oochoristica* Luhe, 1898. Amer. Midl. Nat., 23:368-381.

1940b. The genus *Hymenolepis* Weinland, 1858. Okla. Agric. and Mech. College Agric. Exper. Station, Stillwater. Tech. Bull., 8:5-36.

1941. A key to the species of tapeworms in *Hymenolepis.* Trans. Amer. Micr. Soc., 60:378-414.

HUGHES, R. C., and R. L. SCHULTZ

1942. The genus *Raillietina* Fuhrmann, 1920. Okla. Agric. and Mech. College Agric. Exper. Station, Stillwater. Tech. Bull., 39:53 pp.

JELLISON, W. L.

1938. Birds and plague. Jour. Parasit., 24 (Dec. supple.):12.

JELLISON, W. L., and C. B. PHILLIP

1933. Faunae of nests of the Magpie and Crow in western Montana. Canad. Ent., 65:26-31.

JOYEUX, CH., and J. G. BAER

1936. Faune de France, 30, Cestodes. Federation Francaise des Societes de Sciences Naturelles, Office central de Faunistique, Paris, 613 pp.

KALMBACH, E. R.

1930. Western duck sickness produced experimentally. Science, 72:658-659.

KALMBACH, E. R., and M. F. GUNDERSON

1934. Western duck sickness: a form of botulism with bacteriological contributions. U.S.D.A. Bull., 411:82 pp.

KELLOGG, V. L.

1899. New Mallophaga, III. Occ. Pap. Calif. Acad. Sci., 6:1-52 [and earlier papers].

LINSDALE, J. M.

1937. The natural history of magpies. Pacific Coast Avifauna 25, 234 pp.

MACY, R. W.

1934. Studies on the taxonomy, morphology, and biology of *Prosthogonimus macrorchis* Macy, a common oviduct fluke of domestic fowls in North America. Univ. Minn. Agric. Exper. Station, St. Paul. Tech. Bull., 98:59 pp.

MADSEN, H.

1945. The species of *Capillaria* (Nematodes, Trichinelloidea) parasitic in the digestive tract of Danish gallinaceous and anatine game birds with a revised list of species of *Capillaria* in birds. Danish Rev. Game Biol., 1:112 pp.

1950. Studies on species of *Heterakis* (Nematodes) in birds. Danish Rev. Game Biol., 1:3-43.

MASON, E. A.

1944. Parasitism by Protocalliphora and management of cavity-nesting birds. Jour. Wildlife Mgmt., 8:232-247.

MEYER, K. F.

1948. Psittacosis. In Viral and rickettsial infections of man, ed. by T. M. Rivers. Lippincott, New York, pp. 338-346.

1952. Ornithosis and Psittacosis. In Diseases of Poultry, ed. by H. E. Biester and L. H. Schwarte. 3rd ed. Iowa State College Press, Ames, pp. 569-618.

MORGAN, B. B.

1943. The Physalopterinae (Nematoda) of Aves. Trans. Amer. Micr. Soc., 62:72-80.

MOSBY, H. S., and C. O. HANDLEY

1943. The Wild Turkey in Virginia: its status, life history and management. Va. Comm. Game and Inland Fisheries, Richmond, 281 pp.

NEFF, J. A.

1945. Maggot infestation of nestling Mourning Doves. Condor, 47:73-76.

NESTLER, R. B.

1949. Nutrition of Bobwhite Quail. Jour. Wildlife Mgmt., 13:342-358.

OLT, A., and A. STROSE

1914. Die Wildkrankheiten und ihre Bekampfung. J. Neumann, Neudamm, 633 pp.

O'ROKE, E. C.

1934. A malaria-like disease of ducks caused by *Leucocytozoon anatis* Wickware. Univ. Mich. Sch. Forest. and Conserv., Ann Arbor. Bull., 4:44 pp.

PATTERSON, R. L.

1952. The Sage Grouse in Wyoming. Wyo. Game and Fish Comm., Sage Books, Inc., Denver, 341 pp.

PENNER, L. R.

1950. *Cercaria littorinalinae* sp. nov., a dermatitis-producing schistosome larva from the marine snail, *Littorina planaxis* Philippi. Jour. Parasit., 36:466-472.

PETRIDES, G. A., and C. R. BRYANT

1951. An analysis of the 1949-50 fowl cholera epizootic in Texas Panhandle waterfowl. Trans. Sixteenth N. Amer. Wildlife Conf., pp. 193-216.

RADFORD, C. D.

1950. The mites (Acarina) parasitic on mammals, birds and reptiles. Parasit., 40:366-394.

READ, C. P.

1949. Studies on North American helminths of the genus *Capillaria* Zeder, 1800 (Nematoda), III. Capillarids from the lower digestive tract of North American birds. Jour. Parasit., 35:240-249.

REEVES, W. C.

1951. The encephalitis problem in the United States. Amer. Jour. Publ. Health, 41:678-686.

REEVES, W. C., W. McD. HAMMON, A. S. LAZARUS, B. BROOKMAN, H. E. McCLURE, and W. H. DOETSCHMAN

1952. The changing picture of encephalitis in the Yakima Valley, Washington. Jour. Inf. Dis., 90:291-301.

REIS, J., and P. NOBREGA

1936. Tratado de Doencas das aves. Inst. Biol., Sao Paulo, 468 pp.

ROSEN, M. N., and A. I. BISCHOFF

1949. The 1948-49 outbreak of fowl cholera in birds in the San Francisco Bay area and surrounding counties. Calif. Fish and Game, 35:185-192.

1950. The epidemiology of fowl cholera as it occurs in the wild. Trans. Fifteenth N. Amer. Wildlife Conf., pp. 147-153.

ROTHSCHILD, M., and T. CLAY

1952. Fleas, flukes, and cuckoos, Collins, London, 304 pp.

RUSSELL, P. F.

1952. The eradication of malaria. Sci. Amer., 186:22-25.

SCIPLE, G. W.

1953. Avian botulism: information on earlier research. U.S. Dept. Interior, Special Scientific Report Wildlife No. 23, 12 pp.

SCOTT, J. W.

1930. The development of two new *Cladotaenia* in the Ferruginous Roughleg Hawk. Jour. Parasit., 17:115.

1931. *Cladotaenia* sp. Jour. Parasit., 18:49.

SMITH, M. G., R. J. BLATTNER, F. M. HEYS, and A. MILLER

1948. Experiments on the role of the chicken mite, *Dermanyssus gallinae,* and the mosquito in the epidemiology of St. Louis encephalitis. Jour. Exper. Med., 87:119-138.

SPERRY, C. C.

1947. Botulism control by water manipulation. Trans. Twelfth N. Amer. Wildlife Conf., pp. 228-233.

STABLER, R. M., and C. M. HERMAN

1951. Upper digestive tract trichomoniasis in the Mourning Dove and other birds. Trans. Sixteenth N. Amer. Wildlife Conf., pp. 145-163.

STODDARD, H. L.

1931. The Bobwhite Quail, its habits, preservation and increase. Charles Scribner's Sons, New York, 559 pp.

STONER, D.

1936. Studies on the Bank Swallow, *Riparia riparia riparia* (Linnaeus) in the Oneida Lake Region. Roosevelt Wildlife Ann., 4:121-233.

STUNKARD, H. W., and M. C. HINCHLIFFE

1952. The morphology and life-history of *Microbilharzia variglandis* (Miller and Northrup, 1926) Stunkard and Hinchliffe, 1951, avian blood-flukes whose larvae cause "swimmer's itch" of ocean beaches. Jour. Parasit., 38:248-265.

SZIDAT, L.

1940. Uber Wirtspezifitat bei Trematoden und ihre Beziehung zur Systematik und Phylogenie der Zugehorigen Wirtstier. Third Inter. Congr. Microbiol., Rept. Proc., 1939, pp. 445-446.

1942. Ueber die Beziehungen zwischen Parasitologie und Ornithologie. Vogelzug, 13:17-35.

TARSHIS, I. B.

1952. Equipment and methods for the collection of hippoboscid flies from trapped California Valley Quail, *Lophortyx californica vallicola* (Ridgway) (Diptera). Bull. Brooklyn Ent. Soc., 47:69-78.

THOMAS, L. J.

1949. Interrelations of *Diphyllobothrium* with fish-eating birds of northern Lake Michigan. Jour. Parasit., 35 (6, Sect. 2):27.

1950. Ecological relationships of tapeworms (Diphyllobothriidae) to the infection of fish and fish-eating birds of the Great Lakes region. Jour. Parasit., 36 (6, Sect. 2):44.

TIMMERMANN, G.

1952a. The species of the genus *Quadraceps* (Mallophaga) from the Larinae, with some remarks on the systematics and the phylogeny of the gulls, Part I. Ann. and Mag. Nat. Hist., Ser. 12, 5:209-222.

1952b. The species of the genus *Quadraceps* (Mallophaga) from the Larinae, with some remarks on the systematics and the phylogeny of the gulls, Part II. Ann. and Mag. Nat. Hist., Ser. 12, 5:595-600.

TRAVASSOS, L.

1937. Revisao da familia Trichostrongylidae Leiper, 1912. Monograph do Inst. O. Cruz., 1:512 pp.

1944. Revisao de familia Dicrocoeliidae Odhner, 1910. Monograph do Inst. O. Cruz., 2:357 pp.

TWINN, C. R.

1936. The blackflies of eastern Canada (Simuliidae, Diptera). Canad. Jour. Res., 14:97-150.

TYZZER, E. E., A. W. SELLARDS, and B. L. BENNETT

1938. The occurrence in nature of "Equine encephalomyelitis" in the Ring-necked Pheasant. Science, 88:505-506.

URBAIN, A., and G. GUILLOT

1938. Les aspergillosis aviaires. Rev. Path. Comp., 38:929-955.

VARGAS, L.

1945. Simulidos del Nuevo Mundo. Inst. Salubridad y Enfer. Trop. Monograph, 1:241 pp.

WARDLE, R. A., and J. A. McLEOD

1952. The zoology of tapeworms. University of Minnesota Press, Minneapolis, 780 pp.

WILSON, F. H.

1933. A louse feeding on the blood of its host. Science, 77:490.

INDEX